PEARSON

ALWAYS LEARNING

Jane B. Reece • Martha R. Taylor
Eric J. Simon • Jean L. Dickey

Campbell Biology

Third Custom Edition for Wilbur Wright College

Taken from:
Campbell Biology: Concepts and Connections, Seventh Edition
by Jane B. Reece, Martha R. Taylor, Eric J. Simon, and Jean L. Dickey

Taken from:

Campbell Biology: Concepts and Connections, Seventh Edition
by Jane B. Reece, Martha R. Taylor, Eric J. Simon, and Jean L. Dickey
Copyright © 2012, 2009, 2006 by Pearson Education, Inc.
Published by Benjamin Cummings
San Francisco, California 94111

This special edition published in cooperation with Pearson Learning Solutions.

Pearson Learning Solutions, 501 Boylston Street, Suite 900, Boston, MA 02116
A Pearson Education Company
www.pearsoned.com

Printed in the United States of America

2 3 4 5 6 7 8 9 10 V092 16 15 14 13 12 11

000200010270763478

SD/JG

ISBN 10: 1-256-14721-4
ISBN 13: 978-1-256-14721-3

About the Authors

Jane B. Reece has worked in biology publishing since 1978, when she joined the editorial staff of Benjamin Cummings. Her education includes an A.B. in biology from Harvard University (where she was initially a philosophy major), an M.S. in microbiology from Rutgers University, and a Ph.D. in bacteriology from the University of California, Berkeley. At UC Berkeley and later as a postdoctoral fellow in genetics at Stanford University, her research focused on genetic recombination in bacteria. Dr. Reece taught biology at Middlesex County College (New Jersey) and Queensborough Community College (New York). During her 12 years as an editor at Benjamin Cummings, she played a major role in a number of successful textbooks. She is lead author of *Campbell Biology*, Ninth Edition, and coauthor of *Campbell Essential Biology*, Fourth Edition, and *Campbell Essential Biology with Physiology*, Third Edition.

Martha R. Taylor has been teaching biology for more than 35 years. She earned her B.A. in biology from Gettysburg College and her M.S. and Ph.D. in science education from Cornell University. She was assistant director of the Office of Instructional Support at Cornell for 7 years. Dr. Taylor has taught introductory biology for both majors and nonmajors at Cornell University and is currently a lecturer in the Learning Strategies Center teaching supplemental biology courses. Her experience working with students in classrooms, in laboratories, and with tutorials has increased her commitment to helping students create their own knowledge of and appreciation for biology. She has been the author of the *Student Study Guide* for all nine editions of *Campbell Biology*.

Eric J. Simon is an associate professor in the Department of Biology and Health Science at New England College, in Henniker, New Hampshire. He teaches introductory biology to science majors and nonscience majors, as well as upper-level courses in genetics, microbiology, tropical marine biology, and molecular biology.

Dr. Simon received a B.A. in biology and computer science and an M.A. in biology from Wesleyan University and a Ph.D. in biochemistry from Harvard University. His research focuses on innovative ways to use technology to improve teaching and learning in the science classroom, particularly for nonscience majors. Dr. Simon is the lead author of *Campbell Essential Biology*, Fourth Edition, and *Campbell Essential Biology with Physiology*, Third Edition.

Jean L. Dickey is a professor of biology at Clemson University. She had no idea that science was interesting until her senior year in high school, when a scheduling problem landed her in an advanced biology course. Abandoning plans to study English or foreign languages, she enrolled in Kent State University as a biology major. After receiving her B.S. in biology, she went on to earn a Ph.D. in ecology and evolution from Purdue University. Since joining the faculty at Clemson in 1984, Dr. Dickey has specialized in teaching nonscience majors, including a course designed for preservice elementary teachers and workshops for in-service teachers. She also developed an investigative laboratory curriculum for general biology. Dr. Dickey is author of *Laboratory Investigations for Biology*, Second Edition, and coauthor of *Campbell Essential Biology*, Fourth Edition, and *Campbell Essential Biology with Physiology*, Third Edition.

Neil A. Campbell (1946–2004) combined the inquiring nature of a research scientist with the soul of a caring teacher. Over his 30 years of teaching introductory biology to both science majors and nonscience majors, many thousands of students had the opportunity to learn from him and be stimulated by his enthusiasm for the study of life. While he is greatly missed by his many friends in the biology community, his coauthors remain inspired by his visionary dedication to education and are committed to searching for ever better ways to engage students in the wonders of biology.

To the Student: How to use this book

Introduce yourself to the chapter.

See where you are headed.
Look for the **Big Ideas,** which open each chapter and provide a transit map to a set of overarching concepts.

Remember the big picture.
Look for the **main headings** that organize the chapter around the big ideas.

8

The Cellular Basis of Reproduction and Inheritance

BIG IDEAS

Cell Division and Reproduction
(8.1–8.2)

Cell division underlies many of life's important processes.

The Eukaryotic Cell Cycle and Mitosis
(8.3–8.10)

Cells produce genetic duplicates through an ordered, tightly controlled series of steps.

Meiosis and Crossing Over
(8.11–8.17)

The process of meiosis produces genetically varied haploid gametes from diploid cells.

Alterations of Chromosome Number and Structure
(8.18–8.23)

Errors in cell division can produce organisms with abnormal numbers of chromosomes.

Cell Division and Reproduction

8.1 Cell division plays many important roles in the lives of organisms

The ability of organisms to reproduce their own kind is the one characteristic that best distinguishes living things from nonliving matter (see Module 1.1 to review the characteristics of life). Only amoebas produce more amoebas, only people make more people, and only maple trees produce more maple trees. These simple facts of life have been recognized for thousands of years and are summarized by the age-old saying, "Like begets like."

However, the biological concept of reproduction includes more than just the birth of new organisms. Reproduction actually occurs much more often at the cellular level. When a cell undergoes reproduction, or **cell division,** the two "daughter" cells that result are genetically identical to each other and to the original "parent" cell. (Biologists traditionally use the word *daughter* in this context; it does not imply gender.) Before the parent cell splits into two, it duplicates its **chromosomes,** the structures that contain most of the cell's DNA. Then, during the division process, one set of chromosomes is distributed to each daughter cell. As a rule, the daughter cells receive identical sets of chromosomes from the lone, original parent cell. Each offspring cell will thus be genetically identical to the other and to the original parent cell.

Sometimes, cell division results in the reproduction of a whole organism. Many single-celled organisms, such as prokaryotes or the eukaryotic yeast cell in Figure 8.1A, reproduce by dividing in half, and the offspring are genetic replicas. This is an example of **asexual reproduction,** the creation of genetically identical offspring by a single parent, without the participation of sperm and egg. Many multicellular organisms can

reproduce asexually as well. For example, some sea star species have the ability to grow new individuals from fragmented pieces (Figure 8.1B). And if you've ever grown a houseplant from a clipping, you've observed asexual reproduction in plants (Figure 8.1C). In asexual reproduction, there is one simple principle of inheritance: The lone parent and each of its offspring have identical genes.

Sexual reproduction is different; it requires fertilization of an egg by a sperm. The production of gametes—egg and sperm—involves a special type of cell division that occurs only in reproductive organs (such as testes and ovaries in humans). As you'll learn later in the chapter, a gamete has only half as many chromosomes as the parent cell that gave rise to it, and these chromosomes contain unique combinations of genes. Therefore, in sexually reproducing species, like does not precisely beget like (Figure 8.1D). Offspring produced by sexual reproduction generally resemble their parents more closely than they resemble unrelated individuals of the same species, but they are not identical to their parents or to each other. Each offspring inherits a unique combination of genes from its two

▲ Figure 8.1A A yeast cell producing a genetically identical daughter cell by asexual reproduction

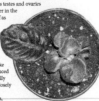

▲ Figure 8.1B A sea star reproducing asexually

▲ Figure 8.1C An African violet reproducing asexually from a cutting (the large leaf on the left)

▼ Figure 8.1D Sexual reproduction produces offspring with unique combinations of genes

126

Focus on what's important.

Use both text and figures as you study.
The **figures** illuminate the text and vice versa. Text and figures are always together—so you'll never have to turn a page to find what you need.

Understand biology one concept at a time.
Each module features a **central concept,** announced in its heading.

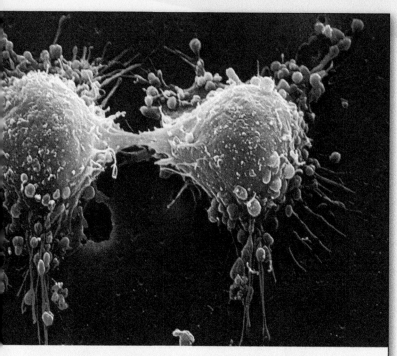

The photo above shows a cancer cell undergoing cell division, the creation of two cells from one. Cancer cells start as normal body cells that, because of genetic mutations, lose the ability to control the tempo of their own division. The result is rapid cell division that is no longer under the control of the host body—cell growth run amok! If left untreated, cancer cells may continue to divide and spread, invading other tissues and eventually killing the host. Most cancer treatments seek to prevent this outcome by disrupting one or more steps in cell division. Some anticancer drugs target dividing DNA; others disrupt cellular structures that assist in cell division. The goal of cancer treatment is to slow the spread of cancerous cells to the point that the body's immune system can overtake the growth, destroying the abnormal cells and restoring proper control of cell division.

Although cell division is harmful when it happens in a cancer cell, it is a necessary process for all forms of life. Why must cells divide? Some organisms, such as single-celled prokaryotes, reproduce themselves by splitting a single parent cell via cell division, creating two genetically identical offspring. In your body and the bodies of all other multicellular organisms, cell division allows for growth, replacement of damaged cells, and development of an embryo into an adult. Furthermore, in sexually reproducing organisms, eggs and sperm result from a particular type of cell division.

These examples illustrate the main point of this chapter: The perpetuation of life, including all aspects of reproduction and inheritance, is based on the reproduction of cells, or cell division. In this chapter, we discuss the two main types of cell division—mitosis and meiosis—and how they function within organisms.

Discover.
The ***opening essays*** introduce the chapter topic through stories that will pique your curiosity.

10.20 The AIDS virus makes DNA on an RNA template

The devastating disease **AIDS** (acquired immunodeficiency syndrome) is caused by **HIV** (human immunodeficiency virus), an RNA virus with some special properties. In outward appearance, HIV resembles the flu or mumps virus (Figure 10.20A). Its membranous envelope and glycoprotein spikes enable HIV to enter and leave a host cell much the way the mumps virus does (see Figure 10.18). Notice, however, that HIV contains two identical copies of its RNA instead of one. HIV also has a different mode of replication. HIV carries molecules of an enzyme called **reverse transcriptase**, which catalyzes reverse transcription, the synthesis of DNA on an RNA template. This unusual process which is opposite the usual DNA → RNA flow of genetic information, characterizes **retroviruses** (retro means "backward").

Figure 10.20B illustrates what happens after HIV RNA is uncoated in the cytoplasm of a host cell. ❶ Reverse transcriptase (⬤) uses the RNA as a template to make a DNA strand and then ❷ adds a second, complementary DNA strand. ❸ The

resulting viral DNA enters the cell's nucleus and inserts itself into the chromosomal DNA, becoming a provirus (analogous to a prophage). The host's RNA polymerase ❹ transcribes the proviral DNA into RNA, which can then be ❺ translated by ribosomes into viral proteins. ❻ New viruses assembled from these components leave the cell and can infect other cells.

HIV infects and kills white blood cells that play important roles in the body's immune system. The loss of such cells causes the body to become susceptible to other infections that it would normally be able to fight off. Such secondary infections cause the syndrome (a collection of symptoms) that can kill an AIDS patient. We discuss AIDS in more detail when we take up the immune system in Chapter 24.

? Why is HIV classified as a retrovirus?

If synthesizes DNA from its RNA genome. This is the reverse ("retro") of the usual DNA → RNA information flow.

Test yourself.
Get immediate feedback with a ***checkpoint question*** at the end of each module.

Never get lost.
Figures describing a process take you through a series of numbered steps keyed to explanations in the text.

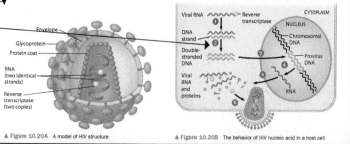

▲ **Figure 10.20A** A model of HIV structure

▲ **Figure 10.20B** The behavior of HIV nucleic acid in a host cell

Learn about biology in your world.

Make a connection.
Connection modules relate biology to your life and interests.

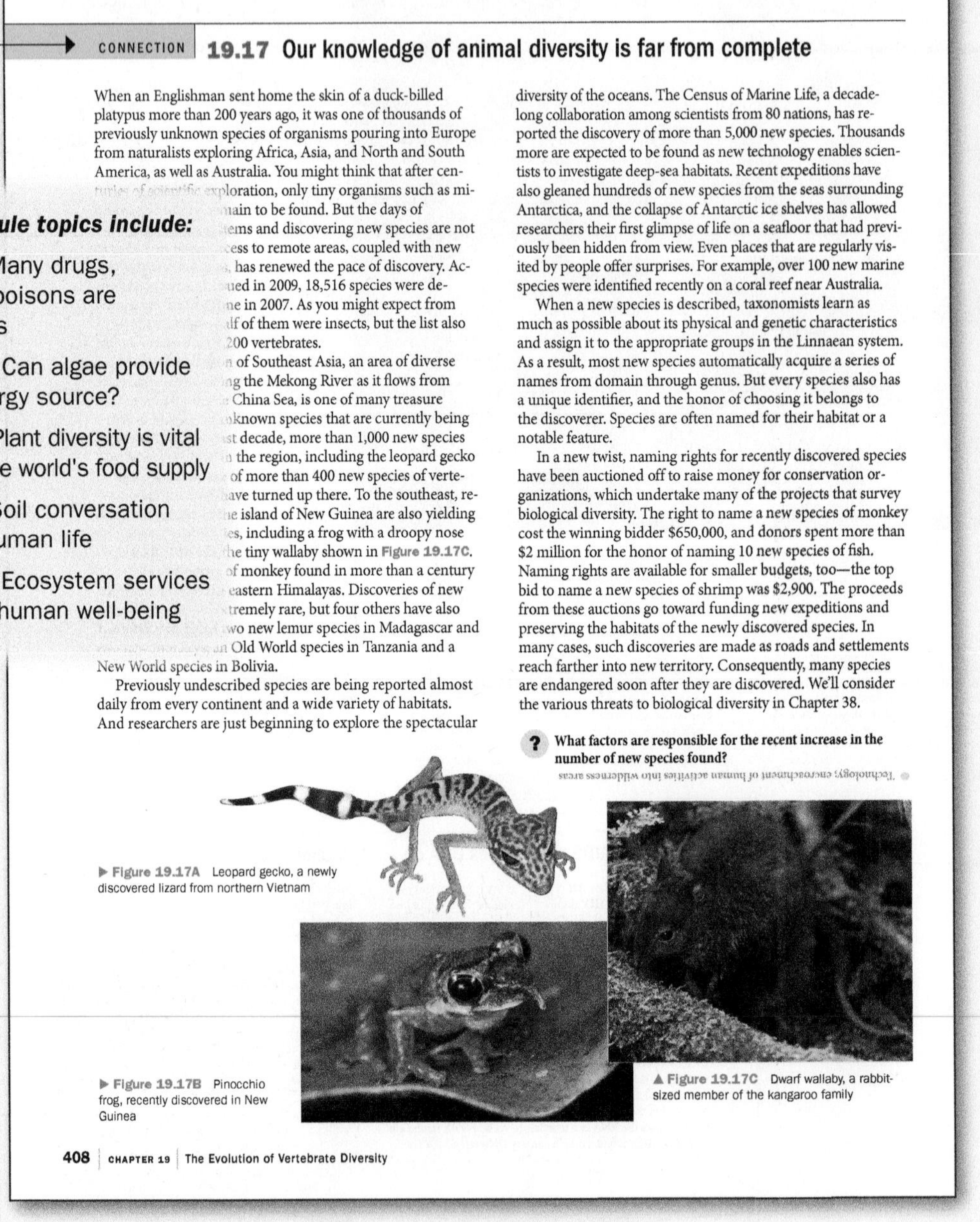

Connection Module topics include:

Module 5.16 – Many drugs, pesticides, and poisons are enzyme inhibitors

Module 16.16 – Can algae provide a renewable energy source?

Module 17.13 – Plant diversity is vital to the future of the world's food supply

Module 32.9 – Soil conversation is essential to human life

Module 37.23 – Ecosystem services are essential to human well-being

---

CONNECTION

19.17 Our knowledge of animal diversity is far from complete

When an Englishman sent home the skin of a duck-billed platypus more than 200 years ago, it was one of thousands of previously unknown species of organisms pouring into Europe from naturalists exploring Africa, Asia, and North and South America, as well as Australia. You might think that after centuries of scientific exploration, only tiny organisms such as mi-... main to be found. But the days of ...ems and discovering new species are not ...cess to remote areas, coupled with new ... has renewed the pace of discovery. Ac-...ued in 2009, 18,516 species were de-...ne in 2007. As you might expect from ...lf of them were insects, but the list also ...200 vertebrates.

...n of Southeast Asia, an area of diverse ...ng the Mekong River as it flows from ... China Sea, is one of many treasure ...known species that are currently being ...st decade, more than 1,000 new species ...n the region, including the leopard gecko ... of more than 400 new species of verte-...ave turned up there. To the southeast, re-...e island of New Guinea are also yielding ...es, including a frog with a droopy nose ...he tiny wallaby shown in **Figure 19.17C.** ... of monkey found in more than a century ... eastern Himalayas. Discoveries of new ...tremely rare, but four others have also ...wo new lemur species in Madagascar and ...an Old World species in Tanzania and a New World species in Bolivia.

Previously undescribed species are being reported almost daily from every continent and a wide variety of habitats. And researchers are just beginning to explore the spectacular diversity of the oceans. The Census of Marine Life, a decade-long collaboration among scientists from 80 nations, has reported the discovery of more than 5,000 new species. Thousands more are expected to be found as new technology enables scientists to investigate deep-sea habitats. Recent expeditions have also gleaned hundreds of new species from the seas surrounding Antarctica, and the collapse of Antarctic ice shelves has allowed researchers their first glimpse of life on a seafloor that had previously been hidden from view. Even places that are regularly visited by people offer surprises. For example, over 100 new marine species were identified recently on a coral reef near Australia.

When a new species is described, taxonomists learn as much as possible about its physical and genetic characteristics and assign it to the appropriate groups in the Linnaean system. As a result, most new species automatically acquire a series of names from domain through genus. But every species also has a unique identifier, and the honor of choosing it belongs to the discoverer. Species are often named for their habitat or a notable feature.

In a new twist, naming rights for recently discovered species have been auctioned off to raise money for conservation organizations, which undertake many of the projects that survey biological diversity. The right to name a new species of monkey cost the winning bidder $650,000, and donors spent more than $2 million for the honor of naming 10 new species of fish. Naming rights are available for smaller budgets, too—the top bid to name a new species of shrimp was $2,900. The proceeds from these auctions go toward funding new expeditions and preserving the habitats of the newly discovered species. In many cases, such discoveries are made as roads and settlements reach farther into new territory. Consequently, many species are endangered soon after they are discovered. We'll consider the various threats to biological diversity in Chapter 38.

? What factors are responsible for the recent increase in the number of new species found?

Technology; encroachment of human activities into wilderness areas

▶ Figure 19.17A Leopard gecko, a newly discovered lizard from northern Vietnam

▶ Figure 19.17B Pinocchio frog, recently discovered in New Guinea

▲ Figure 19.17C Dwarf wallaby, a rabbit-sized member of the kangaroo family

408   CHAPTER 19 | The Evolution of Vertebrate Diversity

A narrative written with you in mind.
This best-selling text has undergone an extensive revision to make biology even more approachable with ***increased use of analogies, real world examples,*** and more ***conversational language.***

Learn about the mechanisms underlying evolution.
Evolution Connection modules in every chapter relate evolution to a wide spectrum of biology topics and help explain the mechanisms underlying evolution and the evidence for it.

EVOLUTION CONNECTION

10.19 Emerging viruses threaten human health

Viruses that appear suddenly or are new to medical scientists are called **emerging viruses**. There are many familiar examples. HIV, the AIDS virus, is a classic example: This virus appeared in New York and California in the early 1980s, seemingly out of nowhere. The deadly Ebola virus, recognized initially in 1976 in central Africa, is one of several emerging viruses that cause hemorrhagic fever, an often fatal illness characterized by fever, vomiting, massive bleeding, and circulatory system collapse. A number of other dangerous new viruses cause encephalitis, an inflammation of the brain. One example is the West Nile virus, which appeared for the first time in North America in 1999 and has since spread to all 48 contiguous U.S. states. West Nile virus is spread primarily by mosquitoes, which carry the virus in blood sucked from one victim and can transfer it to another victim. Severe acute respiratory syndrome (SARS) first appeared in China in 2002. Within eight months, about 8,000 people were infected, of whom some 10% died. Researchers quickly identified the infectious agent as a previously unknown, single-stranded RNA coronavirus, so named for its crown-like "corona" of spikes.

From where and how do such viruses burst on the human scene, giv[...] re or previously unknown diseases?

▼ Figure 10.19 People in Mexico City wearing masks in an attempt to prevent spread of the 2009 H1N1 virus (shown in the inset)

Colorized TEM 8,500×

Discover how science works.
Scientific Discovery modules demonstrate the process of science, research, and discovery.

SCIENTIFIC DISCOVERY

5.7 Research on another membrane protein led to the discovery of aquaporins

Peter Agre received the 2003 Nobel Prize in Chemistry for his discovery of aquaporins. In a recent interview, Dr. Agre described his research that led to this discovery:

> I'm a blood specialist (hematologist), and my particular interest has been proteins found in the plasma membrane of red blood cells. When I joined the faculty at the John Hopkins School of Medicine, I began to study the Rh blood antigens. Rh is of medical importance because of Rh incompatibility, which occurs when Rh-negative mothers have Rh-positive babies. Membrane-spanning proteins are really messy to work with. But we worked out a method to isolate the Rh protein. Our sample seemed to consist of two proteins, but we were sure that the smaller one was just a breakdown product of the larger one. We were completely wrong.
>
> Using antibodies we made to the smaller protein, we showed it to be one of the most abundant proteins in red cell membranes—200,000 copies per cell!—and even more abundant in certain kidney cells.

We asked Dr. Agre why cells have aquaporins.

> Not all cells do. Before our discovery, however, many physiologists thought that diffusion was enough for [...] and out of *all* cells. Others

said this couldn't be enough, especially for cells whose water permeability needs to be very high or regulated. For example, our kidneys must filter and reabsorb many liters of water every day. . . . People whose kidney cells have defective aquaporin molecules need to drink 20 liters of water a day to prevent dehydration. In addition, some patients make too much aquaporin, causing them to retain too much fluid. Fluid retention in pregnant women is caused by the synthesis of too much aquaporin. Knowledge of aquaporins may in the future contribute to the solution of medical problems.

Figure 5.7 is an image taken from a simulation produced by computational biophysicists at the University of Illinois, Urbana. Their model included four aquaporin channels spanning a membrane. You can see a line of blue water molecules flipping their way single file through the gold aquaporin. The simulation of this flipping movement allowed researchers to discover how aquaporins selectively allow only water molecules to pass through them.

? Why are aquaporins important in kidney cells?

▲ Figure [...] in action

Kidney [...] a large amount of water when producing urine.

To the Student: How to use this book (continued)

Feel confident going into the test.

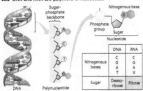

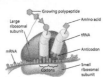

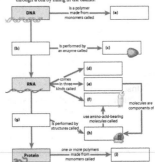

CHAPTER 10 REVIEW

For Practice Quizzes, BioFlix, MP3 Tutors, and Activities, go to www.masteringbiology.com.

Reviewing the Concepts

The Structure of the Genetic Material (10.1–10.3)

10.1 Experiments showed that DNA is the genetic material. One key experiment demonstrated that certain phages (bacterial viruses) reprogram host cells to produce more phages by injecting their DNA.

10.2 DNA and RNA are polymers of nucleotide.

10.3 DNA is a double-stranded helix. Watson and Crick worked out the three-dimensional structure of DNA: two polynucleotide strands wrapped around each other in a double helix. Hydrogen bonds between bases hold the strands together. Each base pairs with a complementary partner: A with T, G with C.

DNA Replication (10.4–10.5)

10.4 DNA replication depends on specific base pairing. DNA replication starts with the separation of DNA strands. Enzymes then use each strand as a template to assemble new nucleotides into a complementary strand.

10.5 DNA replication proceeds in two directions at many sites simultaneously. Using the enzyme DNA polymerase, the cell synthesizes one daughter strand as a continuous piece. The other strand is synthesized as a series of short pieces, which are then connected by the enzyme DNA ligase.

The Flow of Genetic Information from DNA to RNA to Protein (10.6–10.16)

10.6 The DNA genotype is expressed as proteins, which provide the molecular basis for phenotypic traits. The DNA of a gene—a linear sequence of many nucleotides—is transcribed into RNA, which is translated into a polypeptide.

10.7 Genetic information written in codons is translated into amino acid sequences. Codons are base triplets.

10.8 The genetic code dictates how codons are translated into amino acids. Nearly all organisms use an identical genetic code to convert the codons of a gene to the amino acid sequence of a polypeptide.

10.9 Transcription produces genetic messages in the form of RNA. In the nucleus, the DNA helix unzips, and RNA nucleotides line up and hydrogen-bond along one strand of the DNA, following the base-pairing rules.

10.10 Eukaryotic RNA is processed before leaving the nucleus as mRNA. Noncoding segments of RNA called introns are spliced out, and a cap and tail are added to the ends of the mRNA.

10.11 Transfer RNA molecules serve as interpreters during translation. Translation takes place in the cytoplasm. A ribosome attaches to the mRNA and translates its message into a specific polypeptide, aided by transfer RNAs (tRNAs). Each tRNA is a folded molecule bearing a base triplet called an anticodon on one end; a specific amino acid is added to the other end.

10.12 Ribosomes build polypeptides. Made of rRNA and proteins, ribosomes have binding sites for tRNAs and mRNA.

10.13 An initiation codon marks the start of an mRNA message.

10.14 Elongation adds amino acids to the polypeptide chain until a stop codon terminates translation. As the mRNA moves one codon at a time relative to the ribosome, a tRNA with a complementary anticodon pairs with each codon, adding its amino acid to the growing polypeptide chain.

10.15 Review: The flow of genetic information in the cell is DNA → RNA → protein. The sequence of codons in DNA, via the sequence of codons in mRNA, spells out the primary structure of a polypeptide.

10.16 Mutations can change the meaning of genes. Mutations are changes in the DNA nucleotide sequence, caused by errors in DNA replication or recombination, or by mutagens. Substituting, inserting, or deleting nucleotides alters a gene, with varying effects on the organism.

The Genetics of Viruses and Bacteria (10.17–10.23)

10.17 Viral DNA may become part of the host chromosome. Viruses can be regarded as genes packaged in protein. When a phage DNA enters a lytic cycle inside a bacterium, it is transcribed, and translated; the new viral DNA and protein molecules then assemble into new phages, which burst from the cell. In the lysogenic cycle, phage DNA inserts into the chromosome and is passed on to generations of daughter cells; later, it may initiate phage production.

10.18 Many viruses cause disease in animals and plants. Many viruses and most plant viruses have RNA, rather than DNA, as their genetic material. Some animal viruses steal a bit of membrane as a protective envelope. Some viruses can remain latent in the host's body for long periods.

10.19 Emerging viruses threaten human health.

10.20 The AIDS virus makes DNA on an RNA template. HIV is a retrovirus: it uses RNA as a template for making DNA, which inserts into a host chromosome.

10.21 Viroids and prions are formidable pathogens in plants and animals. Viroids are RNA molecules that can infect plants. Prions are infectious proteins that can cause brain diseases in animals.

10.22 Bacteria can transfer DNA in three ways. Bacteria can transfer genes from cell to cell by transformation, transduction, or conjugation.

10.23 Bacterial plasmids can serve as carriers for gene transfer. Plasmids are small circular DNA molecules separate from the bacterial chromosome.

Connecting the Concepts

1. Check your understanding of the flow of genetic information through a cell by filling in the blanks.

Testing Your Knowledge

Multiple Choice

2. Scientists have discovered how to put together a bacteriophage with the protein coat of phage T2 and the DNA of phage lambda. If this composite phage were allowed to infect a bacterium, the phages produced in the host cell would have _____. (Explain your answer.)
   a. the protein of T2 and the DNA of lambda
   b. the protein of lambda and the DNA of T2
   c. a mixture of the DNA and proteins of both phages
   d. the protein and DNA of T2
   e. the protein and DNA of lambda

3. A geneticist found that a particular mutation had no effect on the polypeptide encoded by a gene. This mutation probably involved
   a. deletion of one nucleotide.
   b. alteration of the start codon.
   c. insertion of one nucleotide.
   d. deletion of the entire gene.
   e. substitution of one nucleotide.

4. Which of the following correctly ranks the structures in order of size, from largest to smallest?
   a. gene-chromosome-nucleotide-codon
   b. chromosome-gene-codon-nucleotide
   c. nucleotide-chromosome-gene-codon
   d. chromosome-nucleotide-gene-codon
   e. gene-chromosome-codon-nucleotide

5. The nucleotide sequence of a DNA codon is GTA. A messenger RNA molecule with a complementary codon is transcribed from the DNA. In the process of protein synthesis, a transfer RNA pairs with the mRNA codon. What is the nucleotide sequence of the tRNA anticodon?
   a. CAT   d. CAU
   b. CUT   e. GT
   c. GUA

Describing, Comparing, and Explaining

6. Describe the process of DNA replication: the ingredients needed, the steps in the process, and the final product.

7. Describe the process by which the information in a eukaryotic gene is transcribed and translated into a protein. Correctly use these words in your description: tRNA, amino acid, start codon, transcription, RNA splicing, exons, introns, mRNA, gene, codon, RNA polymerase, ribosome, translation, anticodon, peptide bond, stop codon.

Applying the Concepts

8. A cell containing a single chromosome is placed in a medium containing radioactive phosphate so that any new DNA strands formed by DNA replication will be radioactive. The cell replicates its DNA and divides. Then the daughter cells (still in the radioactive medium) replicate their DNA and divide, and a total of four cells are present. Sketch the DNA molecules in all four cells, showing a normal (nonradioactive) DNA strand as a solid line and a radioactive DNA strand as a dashed line.

9. The base sequence of the gene coding for a short polypeptide is CTACGCTAGGCGATTGACT. What would be the base sequence of the mRNA transcribed from this gene? Using the genetic code in Figure 10.8A, give the amino acid sequence of the polypeptide translated from this mRNA. (Hint: What is the start codon?)

10. Researchers on the Human Genome Project have determined the nucleotide sequences of human genes and in many cases identified the proteins encoded by the genes. Knowledge of the nucleotide sequences of genes might be used to develop lifesaving medicines or treatments for genetic defects. In the United States, both government agencies and biotechnology companies have applied for patents on their discoveries of genes. In Britain, the courts have ruled that a naturally occurring gene cannot be patented. Do you think individuals and companies should be able to patent genes and gene products? Before answering, consider the following: What are the purposes of a patent? How might the discoverer of a gene benefit from a patent? How might the public benefit? What might be some positive and negative results of patenting genes?

Answers to all questions can be found in Appendix 4.

206 CHAPTER 10 | Molecular Biology of the Gene

Chapter 10 Review **207**

Review the main points.
The **Reviewing the Concepts** section provides helpful summary diagrams and references back to the text.

Connect the chapter's key concepts.
Connecting the Concepts activities test your ability to link topics from different modules and include concept mapping, labeling, and categorizing exercises.

Prepare for the test.
Use the questions that appear in the **Testing Your Knowledge** section to prepare for your upcoming tests.

MasteringBiology®: Study tools

www.masteringbiology.com

Study tools that you can access from anywhere.

Highlight Function
Lets you highlight what you want to remember.

Annotation Function
Allows you to take notes.

Google®-based search function.

Zoom
Lets you zoom in and out for better viewing.

Hyperlinks
Links to quizzes, tests, activities, and animations.

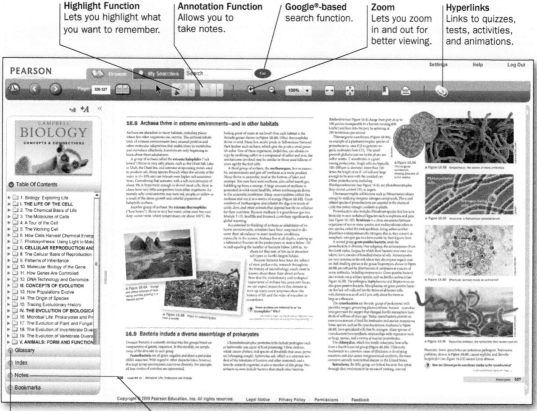

Interactive Glossary
Provides pop-up definitions and terms.

Instructor Notes
Your instructor might also share his or her notes and highlights with the class.

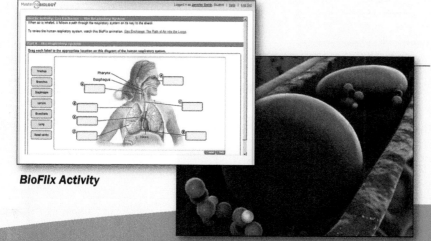

BioFlix Activity

BioFlix Animation

Access highly interactive activities with 3-D animations.
BioFlix® activities help you to visualize and learn the toughest topics in biology.

BioFlix

www.masteringbiology.com

Over 200 new MasteringBiology activities written by the author team help you arrive prepared for lectures and provide you with feedback and coaching.

Arrive prepared for lecture.

Video Tutor Sessions and MP3 Tutor Sessions Co-author Eric Simon hosts these on-the-go tutorials focused on key concepts and vocabulary.

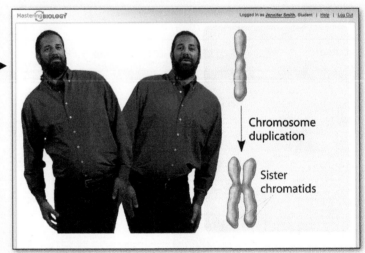

Video Tutor Session

Building Vocabulary Activities Practice the new vocabulary you are learning in class.

Learning Through Art Activities Connect the art to the concepts you are learning and enhance the text's visual approach to learning biology.

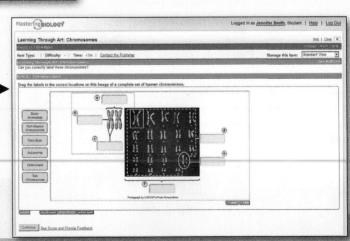

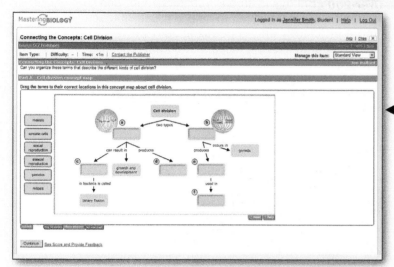

Connecting the Concepts Activities

Link the concepts you learned and see how they work together.

You Decide Activities

Explore the data behind hot topics so you can make informed decisions.

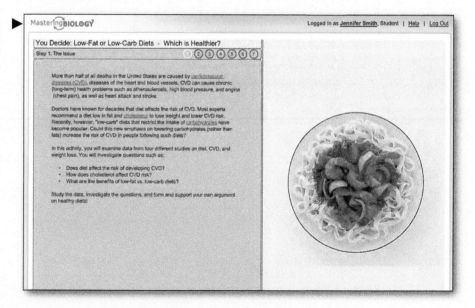

Plus, **Interpreting Data Activities** offer coaching on how to read and interpret data and graphs.

MasteringBiology®: To the Instructor

www.masteringbiology.com

MasteringBiology is an online assessment and tutorial system designed to help instructors teach more efficiently and is pedagogically proven to help students learn. It helps instructors maximize class time with customizable, easy-to-assign, and automatically graded assessments that motivate students to learn outside of class and arrive prepared for lecture.

Access students results with easy-to-interpret insights into student performance.

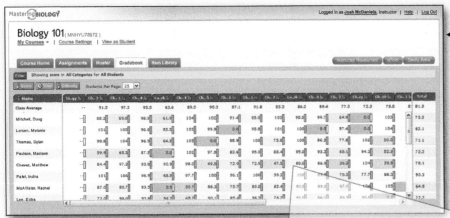

◄ **Gradebook**
Get easy-to-interpret insights into student performance using the **Gradebook**.

- Every assignment is **automatically graded.**
- At a glance, **shades of red** highlight vulnerable students and challenging assignments.

Student Performance Data ► reveals how students are doing compared to a national average and which topics they're struggling with.

Wrong answer summaries ► give unique insight into your students' misconceptions and support just-in-time teaching.

See at a glance where students are struggling and gain insight into their progress.

Get daily diagnostics.
Gradebook Diagnostics provide unique insight into class and student performance. With a single click, charts summarize the most difficult problems, vulnerable students, grade distribution, and even score improvement over the duration of the course.

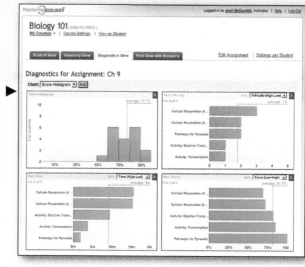

MasteringBiology® is easy for you and your students to use.

The Mastering platform is the most effective and widely-used online tutorial, homework, and assessment system for the sciences.

- Developed **by scientists** for science students and instructors
- Over **one million** active registrations
- **Data-supported** efficacy
- A proven history with over **9 years** of student use
- Active users in all **50 states** and in **30 countries**
- **99.8%** server reliability

With MasteringBiology, you can:

- **Assign** publisher-created pre-built assignments to get started quickly.
- **Easily edit** any of our questions or answers to match the precise language you use.
- **Import your own questions** and begin compiling meaningful data on student performance.
- **Easily export grades** to Microsoft® Excel or other course management systems.
- **Compare** your current class performance to that of previous classes and to the system average.
- **Communicate** with your students through announcements, email, and document posting.

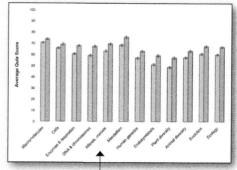

Efficacy Studies
Go to the *"Proven Results"* tab at www.masteringbiology.com to see efficacy studies.

Preface

Inspired by the thousands of students in our own classes over the years and enthusiastic feedback from the many instructors who have used our book, we are delighted to present this new, Seventh Edition. We authors have worked together closely to ensure that both the book and the supplementary material online reflect the evolving needs of today's courses and students, as well as current progress in biology. Now titled *Campbell Biology: Concepts & Connections* to honor Neil Campbell's founding role and his many contributions to biology education, this book has always had a dual purpose: to engage students from a wide variety of majors in the wonders of the living world and to show them how biology relates to their own existence and the world they inhabit. Most of these students will not become biologists themselves, but their lives will be touched by biology every day. Today, understanding the concepts of biology and their connections to our lives is more important than ever. Whether we're concerned with our own health or the health of our planet, a familiarity with biology is essential. This basic knowledge and an appreciation for how science works have become elements of good citizenship in an era when informed evaluations of health issues, environmental problems, and applications of new technology are critical.

Concepts and Connections

Concepts Biology is a vast subject that gets bigger every year, but an introductory biology course is still only one or two terms long. This book was the first introductory biology textbook to use concept modules to help students recognize and focus on the main ideas of each chapter. The heading of each module is a carefully crafted statement of a key concept. For example, "Two photosystems connected by an electron transport chain generate ATP and NADPH" announces a key concept about the light reactions of photosynthesis (Module 7.8). Such a concept heading serves as a focal point, and the module's text and illustrations converge on that concept with explanation and, often, analogies. The module text walks the student through the illustrations, just as an instructor might do in class. And in teaching a sequential process, such as the one diagrammed in Figure 7.8A, we number the steps in the text to correspond to numbered steps in the figure. The synergy between a module's verbal and graphic components transforms the concept heading into an idea with meaning to the student. The checkpoint question at the end of each module encourages students to test themselves as they proceed through a chapter. Finally, in the Chapter Review, all the concept statements are listed under the overarching section titles, explicitly reminding students of what they've just studied.

Connections Students are more motivated to study biology when they can connect it to their own lives and interests—for example, to health issues, economic problems, environmental quality, ethical controversies, and social responsibility. In this edition, blue Connection tabs mark the numerous application modules that go beyond the core biological concepts. Other connections are made in the chapter-opening essays and throughout the text. Moreover, we connect the content of each chapter to the grand unifying theme of evolution, without which the study of life has no coherence. This book remains the only non-majors biology text to connect every single chapter to evolution, with highlights featured in green-tabbed Evolution Connection modules.

New to This Edition

New Big Ideas and Chapter Transit Maps In this Seventh Edition, we take our conceptual emphasis to the next level, reframing each chapter with a smaller set of overarching concepts—"Big Ideas"—that are introduced at the beginning of the chapter. Each big idea corresponds to a major section of the chapter, and they are tied together in a "transit map" that shows the route by which the student will proceed through the chapter.

More Engaging Narrative and a New Look With the goal of making the concepts of biology more accessible and increasing the overall friendliness of the book, every chapter in this edition makes greater use of analogies, intriguing facts, examples that relate topics to the student and the real world, engaging questions, and a more conversational tone. The fresh new design used for the pages and the redesign of many figures make the book more accessible. See pages 280–281 for an example.

New Scientific Discovery Modules This edition gives greater emphasis to "how we know what we know" through a new type of module, called Scientific Discovery and marked with an orange tab. For example, the new Module 16.11 introduces Koch's postulates for identifying the cause of an infectious disease and relates how Australian microbiologist Barry Marshall used these criteria to demonstrate that most peptic ulcers are caused by a particular bacterium (a discovery that won him a Nobel Prize). Along with new Scientific Discovery modules created for this edition, we have recast Talking About Science modules and some other material from the last edition in the Scientific Discovery format to help make research advances more vivid to students. The improved introduction to the process of science in Chapter 1 will equip students to appreciate the many examples throughout the book of how scientific concepts emerge from observations and experimental evidence.

The Latest Science Biology is a dynamic field of study, and we have always taken pride in our book's currency and scientific accuracy. For this edition, as always, we have integrated the results of the latest scientific research throughout the book. We have done this with careful thought, recognizing that research advances can lead to new ways of looking at biological topics; such changes in perspective can necessitate organizational changes in our textbook to better reflect the current state of a field. You will find a unit-by-unit account of new content and organizational improvements in the "New Content" section on pp. xvi–xvii, following this Preface.

New MasteringBiology®   A specially developed version of MasteringBiology, the most widely used online tutorial and assessment program for biology, is now included with *Campbell Biology: Concepts & Connections*. The book's authors have created over 200 new Mastering activities to help students understand core concepts. An average of five author-created activities per chapter help students learn vocabulary, extend the book's emphasis on visual learning, demonstrate the connections among key concepts (helping students grasp the big ideas), and coach students on how to interpret data. Included online are 18 BioFlix® 3-D animations of difficult topics (with accompanying tutorials), new Video Tutor Sessions, MP3 Tutor Sessions, Discovery Channel™ Videos, and YouDecide and GraphIt! activities.

This Book's Flexibility

Though a biology textbook's table of contents must be linear, biology itself is more like a web of related concepts without a single starting point or prescribed path. Courses can navigate this network starting with molecules, with ecology, or somewhere in between, and most courses omit some topics. *Campbell Biology: Concepts & Connections* is uniquely suited to serve this variety of courses. The seven units of the book are largely self-contained, and in a number of the units, chapters can be assigned in a different order without much loss of coherence. The use of numbered modules makes it easy to omit modules or to relocate modules within a syllabus.

■ ■ ■

For many students, introductory biology is the only science course that they will take during their college years. Long after today's students have forgotten most of the specific content of their biology course, they will be left with general impressions and attitudes about science and scientists. We hope that this new edition of *Campbell Biology: Concepts & Connections* helps make those impressions positive and supports instructors' goals for sharing the fun of biology. In our continuing efforts to improve the book and its supporting materials, we benefit tremendously from instructor feedback, not only in formal reviews but also via informal communication. Please let us know how we are doing and how we can improve the next edition of the book.

Jane Reece, janereece@cal.berkeley.edu

Martha Taylor (Units I and III, and Chapters 1 and 20–23), mrt2@cornell.edu

Eric Simon (Units II and VI, and Chapters 24–29), esimon@nec.edu

Jean Dickey (Units IV and VII, and Chapter 30), dickeyj@clemson.edu

New Content

Below are a few highlights of new content and organizational improvements in *Campbell Biology: Concepts & Connection*, Seventh Edition.

Chapter 1, Biology: Exploring Life   The ring-tailed lemur, our cover subject for the Seventh Edition, is featured in the chapter opener and comes up again in the modules on the hierarchy of life, the interactions of organisms with their environments, and the scientific method. (Lemurs also appear in later chapters.) The opening modules of Chapter 1 have been reorganized to emphasize the common properties of living organisms and the themes that help organize the study of biology. The modules on the scientific method have been reframed to more accurately reflect the scientific process, with a focus on observations and hypotheses and a new section on the culture of science.

Unit I, The Life of the Cell   Throughout the first unit of chapters, the structure and functions of DNA have received increased coverage, as a basic understanding of nucleic acids has become more relevant to the general public. As we developed our new transit map feature, we carefully analyzed the organization of each chapter and then moved, combined, and even split some modules to improve the conceptual flow within each chapter. New subheads have been added to several modules to help students see at a glance how the material is organized. Preexisting Connection modules have been updated with new information. A new Connection module, "Many drugs, pesticides, and poisons are enzyme inhibitors," has been added to Chapter 5, and a Connection module in Chapter 6, "Interrupting cellular respiration can have both harmful and helpful effects," has been expanded. These Connection modules provide real-world examples relating to important metabolic processes. A beautiful and instructive new illustration has been added to Module 5.1 to show the various functions of membrane proteins. The illustration of phospholipids has been moved from Chapter 4 to the section on lipids in Chapter 3 so that students can more easily compare the structures of fats, fatty acids, and phospholipids (see Modules 3.8 and 3.9). The new Scientific Discovery module in Chapter 7, Module 7.14, highlights the scientists whose work contributed to the recognition and explanation of ozone depletion in the atmosphere and draws parallels with the current controversy around global climate change.

Unit II, Cellular Reproduction and Genetics   The purpose of this unit is to help students understand the relationship between DNA, chromosomes, and organisms and to help them see that genetics is not purely hypothetical but connects in many important and interesting ways to their lives, human society, and other life on Earth. In preparing this edition, we worked to clarify difficult concepts, enhancing text and illustrations and providing timely new applications of genetic

principles. A new art style helps students follow a genetic cross through multiple generations, while the text discussions linked to the figures have been revised to be both clearer and more accessible. This content is then reinforced with updated discussions of relevant topics, such as cystic fibrosis, achondroplasia, and the effect of the environment on sex determination in some species. This edition includes discussion of many recent advances in the field. Some concern our basic understanding of genetics, introducing students to some of the latest discoveries in epigenetics, microRNAs, and other mechanisms by which cells control gene expression. Other new material discusses applications, such as the 2009 epidemic of H1N1 flu, recent gene therapy trials, new applications of genetic engineering to agriculture and human health, and advances in stem cell research.

Unit III, Concepts of Evolution   Our main goal in revising this edition was to provide a coherent storyline that presents the basic principles of evolution and natural selection, the mountains of evidence that support these theories, and their relevance to all of biology—and to the lives of students. We have strengthened the conceptual organization of the unit, ensuring that the chapters and modules flow smoothly to build a clear picture of what evolution is and how it works. The particularly important Chapter 14, "The Origin of Species," includes a number of improvements. Module 14.3, the two-page introduction to reproductive barriers, has a new diagram and more effective photos. Within Module 14.4, on allopatric speciation, a new section presents evidence of this type of speciation using new research on sister species of snapping shrimp separated by the Isthmus of Panama. Module 14.8, a heavily revised module on adaptive radiation on isolated islands, now faces a Scientific Discovery module featuring the long-term research of Peter and Rosemary Grant on Galápagos Island finches.

Unit IV, The Evolution of Biological Diversity   The diversity unit surveys all life on Earth in less than a hundred pages! Consequently, descriptions and illustrations of the unifying characteristics of each major group of organisms, along with a small sample of its diversity, make up the bulk of the content. Two recurring elements are interwoven with these descriptions: evolutionary history and examples of relevance to our everyday lives and society at large. For the Seventh Edition, we have improved and updated those two elements. For instance, the evolution thread has been strengthened by changes in Chapter 16 that emphasize the evolutionary relationships between protists and multicellular eukaryotes. A new Evolution Connection in Chapter 18, Module 18.16, describes recent research on the role of homeotic genes in generating animal diversity. New Connection modules in this unit cover relevant topics such as biofilms (Module 16.5), algae as a renewable energy source (Module 16.16), the importance of plant diversity to the future of the world's food supply (Module 17.13), and exciting discoveries of new animal species (Module 19.17). In addition, Chapter 16 has been substantially reorganized to make it flow more logically, to strengthen connections among topics, and to make the terminology more manageable. The entire unit has been updated. For example, the human evolution section of Chapter 19 describes the recently reported hominin *Ardipithecus ramidus* and its significance to the evolution of our own species.

Unit V, Animals: Form and Function   This unit combines a comparative approach with an exploration of human anatomy and physiology. Most chapters begin with an overview of a general problem that animals face and a comparative discussion of how different animals address this problem, within an evolutionary context. The main part of every chapter is devoted to more detailed presentations of human body systems, frequently illuminated by discussion of the health consequences of disorders in those systems. Improvements in this edition include new descriptions and illustrations that help clarify important but difficult concepts—for example, innate versus adaptive immunity (Modules 24.1–24.15), clonal selection (Module 24.7), hormonal control of osmoregulation (Module 25.9), and the maintenance of resting potential in neurons (Module 28.3). Updates of health applications in Connection and other modules include the latest efforts to develop an AIDS vaccine (Module 24.13), advances in our understanding of autoimmune diseases (Module 24.16), sex hormone abuse by professional athletes (Module 26.10), and HPV vaccination (Module 27.7). In addition, the chapter on nutrition and digestion, Chapter 21, has an increased focus on obesity, including the chapter-opening essay and updated information on healthy eating.

Unit VI, Plants: Form and Function   To help students gain an appreciation of the importance of plants, this unit presents the anatomy and physiology of angiosperms with frequent connections to the importance of plants to society. New connections in this edition include the link between overextraction of groundwater for irrigation and the appearance of sinkholes (Module 32.9), while plant growth is related to the grafting of grapevines for wine production (Module 31.14). Throughout the unit, the text has been revised with the goal of making the material more engaging and accessible to students. There are new discussions of the Dust Bowl of the 1930s (Module 32.9), organic farming (and the multiple meanings of "organic") as one means of achieving sustainable agriculture (Module 32.10), and the challenge of feeding the world's human population (Module 32.11). These modules make the point that human society is inexorably connected to the health of plants.

Unit VII, Ecology   In this unit, students learn the fundamental principles of ecology and how these principles apply to environmental problems. For the Seventh Edition, the ecology unit has been extensively revised, with the goal of updating content to reflect current issues and research wherever possible. For example, the Deepwater Horizon oil spill is mentioned in several places, including the opening essay for Chapter 37. Global climate change is featured throughout the unit as a major ecological challenge for this generation. In addition to the four modules in Chapter 38 on climate change, the consequences of climate change are discussed elsewhere as well. New Connection modules focus on the degradation of aquatic ecosystems (Module 37.22); the necessity of ecosystem services for human well-being (Module 37.23); and the threats to biodiversity from habitat destruction, invasive species, overharvesting, and pollution (Module 38.2). Many core concept modules also include examples of current issues—for instance, plastic microbeads, deforestation in Haiti, acid rain from recent nitrogen pollution, black-footed ferrets, and ecotourism.

Acknowledgments

This Seventh Edition of *Campbell Biology: Concepts & Connections* is a result of the combined efforts of many talented and hardworking people, and the authors wish to extend heartfelt thanks to all those who contributed to this and previous editions. Our work on this edition was shaped by input from the biologists acknowledged in the Seventh Edition reviewer list on pages xix–xxi, who shared with us their experiences teaching introductory biology and provided specific suggestions for improving the book. Feedback from the authors of this edition's supplements and the unsolicited comments and suggestions we received from many biologists and biology students were also extremely helpful. In addition, this book has benefited in countless ways from the stimulating contacts we have had with the coauthors of *Campbell Biology*, Ninth Edition.

We wish to offer special thanks to the students and faculty at our teaching institutions. Marty Taylor thanks her students at Cornell University for their valuable feedback on the book. Eric Simon thanks his colleagues and friends at New England College, especially within the collegium of Natural Sciences and Mathematics, for their continued support and assistance. And Jean Dickey thanks her colleagues at Clemson University for their expertise and support.

The superb publishing team for this edition was headed up again by executive editor Chalon Bridges, with the invaluable support of editor-in-chief Beth Wilbur. We cannot thank them enough for their unstinting efforts on behalf of the book and for their commitment to excellence in biology education. We are fortunate to have had once again the contributions of executive director of development Deborah Gale and senior editorial manager Ginnie Simione Jutson. Ginnie coordinated the project on a daily basis, miraculously maintaining a calm—and calming—demeanor while solving thorny problems and soothing frayed nerves. We are similarly grateful to the members of the editorial development team—Evelyn Dahlgren, Kim Krummel, Mary Ann Murray, Debbie Hardin, and John Burner—for their steadfast commitment to quality. We thank them for their thoroughness and hard work; the book is far better than it would have been without their efforts. Thanks also to senior supplements project editor Susan Berge for her oversight of the supplements program and to editorial assistant Rachel Brickner for the efficient and enthusiastic support she provided for the entire project. We wish to express our appreciation to Linda Davis, president of Pearson Math and Science, Paul Corey, president of Pearson Benjamin Cummings, and Michael Young, editorial director, for their ongoing support.

This book and all the other components of the teaching package are both attractive and pedagogically effective in large part because of the hard work and creativity of the production professionals on our team. We wish to thank managing editor Mike Early, production project manager Lori Newman, and executive managing editor Erin Gregg. We are happy to thank copyeditor Janet Greenblatt, proofreaders Joanna Dinsmore and Pete Shanks, and indexer Lynn Armstrong. We again thank senior photo editor Donna Kalal and photo researcher Kristin Piljay for their contributions, as well as permissions editors Sue Ewing and Beth Keister. Electronic Publishing Services, Inc. was in charge of composition and rendering of new and revised illustrations. Finally, we thank manufacturing buyer Michael Penne.

Users of the Seventh Edition will enjoy the book's new look. We thank Gary Hespenheide for creating a beautiful and functional interior design, and we are again indebted to design manager Marilyn Perry. For yet another striking cover, we thank our old friend Yvo Riezebos.

The value of *Campbell Biology: Concepts & Connections* as a learning tool is greatly enhanced by the hard work and creativity of the authors of the supplements that accompany this book: Ed Zalisko (*Instructor's Guide and PowerPoint® Lecture Presentations*); Richard Liebaert (*Student Study Guide*); Kelly Hogan (*Active Learning Ideas*); Jennifer Yeh (*Test Bank, Reading Quizzes and Media Correlations*); Cindy Klevickis (*Study Area Practice Tests*); and Shannon Datwyler (*Study Card, Clicker Questions, and Quiz Shows*). In addition to Susan Berge, the editorial and production staff for the supplements program included Kim Wimpsett of Happenstance Type-O-Rama, Brady Golden, Jane Brundage, James Bruce, and John Hammett. And the superlative MasteringBiology® program for this book would not exist without Lauren Fogel, Stacy Treco, Natania Mlawer, Jonathan Ballard, Katie Foley, Kristen Sutton, Sarah Jensen, Beth Winickoff, Juliana Tringali, Sean O'Connor, Caroline Power, and David Kokorowski and his team. Thank you, one and all!

For their important roles in marketing the book, we are very grateful to marketing manager Lauren Garritson, executive marketing manager Lauren Harp, and director of marketing Christy Lawrence. We also appreciate the work of MasteringBiology® marketers Brian Buckley and Scott Dustan and the marketing communications team—Lillian Carr, Jane Campbell, Jessica Perry, and Jessica Tree. The members of the Pearson Science sales team have continued to help us connect with biology instructors and their teaching needs. We thank them for all their hard work and enthusiastic support.

Finally, we are deeply grateful to our families and friends for their support, encouragement, and patience throughout this project. Our special thanks to: Paul, Dan, Maria, Armelle, and Sean (J.B.R.); Josie, Jason, Marnie, Alice, Jack, David, Paul, and Ava (M.R.T.); Amanda, Reed, Forest, and dear friends Jamey, Nick, Jim, and Bethany (E.J.S.); and Jessie and Katherine (J.L.D.).

Jane Reece, Martha Taylor, Eric Simon, and Jean Dickey

Reviewers

Reviewers of the Seventh Edition

Caroline Ballard, *Rock Valley College*
Lisa K. Bonneau, *Metropolitan Community College, Blue River*
Delia Brownson, *University of Texas at Austin and Austin Community College*
John Campbell, *Northern Oklahoma College*
Jocelyn Cash, *Central Piedmont Community College*
Mitch Cruzan, *Portland State University*
Pat Davis, *East Central Community College*
Jean DeSaix, *University of North Carolina at Chapel Hill*
Mary Dettman, *Seminole State College of Florida*
Douglas Gayou, *University of Missouri at Columbia*
Julie Gibbs, *College of DuPage*
Eileen Gregory, *Rollins College*
Sig Harden, *Troy University Montgomery*
Brenda Hunzinger, *Lake Land College*
Mark E. Jackson, *Central Connecticut State University*
Robert Johnson, *Pierce College, Lakewood Campus*
John C. Jones, *Calhoun Community College*
Cindy Klevickis, *James Madison University*
Kurt Dubear Kroening, *University of Wisconsin, Fox Valley*
Margaret Maile Lam, *Kapiolani Community College*
MaryLynne LaMantia, *Golden West College*
Dale Lambert, *Tarrant County College, Northeast*
Liz Lawrence, *Miles Community College*
William Lemon, *Southwestern Oregon Community College*
Laurie M. Len, *El Camino College*
Caroline McNutt, *Schoolcraft College*
Jamie Moon, *University of North Florida*
Kathryn Nette, *Cuyamaca College*
James Newcomb, *New England College*
Zia Nisani, *Antelope Valley College*
Phillip Pack, *Woodbury University*
Jack Plaggemeyer, *Little Big Horn College*
Elena Pravosudova, *University of Nevada, Reno*
Kimberly Puvalowski, *Old Bridge High School*
Shanmugavel Rajendran, *Baltimore City Community College*
Luis A. Rodriguez, *San Antonio Colleges*
Connie Rye, *East Mississippi Community College*
John Richard Schrock, *Emporia State University*
Sam C. Sochet, *Thomas Edison Career and Technical Education High School*
Linda Brooke Stabler, *University of Central Oklahoma*
Megan Stringer, *Jones County Junior College*
John Tolli, *Southwestern College*
Mike Tveten, *Pima College*
Rani Vajravelu, *University of Central Florida*
Sarah VanVickle-Chavez, *Washington University*
Frederick W. Vogt, *Elgin Community College*
Dennis Walsh, *MassBay Community College*
Lisa Weasel, *Portland State University*
Jennifer Wiatrowski, *Pasco-Hernando Community College*
Robert R. Wise, *University of Wisconsin Oshkosh*
Mary E. Wisgirda, *San Jacinto College*
Tumen Wuliji, *College of Agriculture, Biotechnology and Natural Resources at University of Nevada, Reno*
Martin Zahn, *Thomas Nelson Community College*

Reviewers of Previous Editions

Michael Abbott, *Westminster College*
Tanveer Abidi, *Kean University*
Daryl Adams, *Mankato State University*
Dawn Adrian Adams, *Baylor University*
Olushola Adeyeye, *Duquesne University*
Shylaja Akkaraju, *Bronx Community College*
Felix Akojie, *Paducah Community College*
Dan Alex, *Chabot College*
John Aliff, *Georgia Perimeter College*
Sylvester Allred, *Northern Arizona University*
Jane Aloi-Horlings, *Saddleback College*
Loren Ammerman, *University of Texas at Arlington*
Dennis Anderson, *Oklahoma City Community College*
Marjay Anderson, *Howard University*
Bert Atsma, *Union County College*
Yael Avissar, *Rhode Island College*
Gail Baker, *LaGuardia Community College*
Andrei Barkovskii, *Georgia College and State University*
Mark Barnby, *Ohlone College*
Chris Barnhart, *University of San Diego*
Stephen Barnhart, *Santa Rosa Junior College*
William Barstow, *University of Georgia*
Kirk A. Bartholomew, *Central Connecticut State University*
Michael Battaglia, *Greenville Technical College*
Gail Baughman, *Mira Costa College*
Jane Beiswenger, *University of Wyoming*
Tania Beliz, *College of San Mateo*
Lisa Bellows, *North Central Texas College*
Ernest Benfield, *Virginia Polytechnic Institute*
Rudi Berkelhamer, *University of California, Irvine*
Harry Bernheim, *Tufts University*
Richard Bliss, *Yuba College*
Lawrence Blumer, *Morehouse College*
Dennis Bogyo, *Valdosta State University*
Mehdi Borhan, *Johnson County Community College*
Kathleen Bossy, *Bryant College*
William Bowen, *University of Arkansas at Little Rock*
Robert Boyd, *Auburn University*
Bradford Boyer, *State University of New York, Suffolk County Community College*
Paul Boyer, *University of Wisconsin*
William Bradshaw, *Brigham Young University*
Agnello Braganza, *Chabot College*
James Bray, *Blackburn College*
Peggy Brickman, *University of Georgia*
Chris Brinegar, *San Jose State University*
Chad Brommer, *Emory University*
Charles Brown, *Santa Rosa Junior College*
Carole Browne, *Wake Forest University*

Becky Brown-Watson, *Santa Rosa Junior College*
Michael Bucher, *College of San Mateo*
Virginia Buckner, *Johnson County Community College*
Joseph C. Bundy, Jr., *University of North Carolina at Greensboro*
Ray Burton, *Germanna Community College*
Warren Buss, *University of Northern Colorado*
Linda Butler, *University of Texas at Austin*
Jerry Button, *Portland Community College*
Carolee Caffrey, *University of California, Los Angeles*
George Cain, *University of Iowa*
Beth Campbell, *Itawamba Community College*
John Campbell, *University of Central Oklahoma*
John Capeheart, *University of Houston, Downtown*
James Cappuccino, *Rockland Community College*
M. Carabelli, *Broward Community College*
Cathryn Cates, *Tyler Junior College*
Russell Centanni, *Boise State University*
David Chambers, *Northeastern University*
Ruth Chesnut, *Eastern Illinois University*
Vic Chow, *San Francisco City College*
Van Christman, *Ricks College*
Craig Clifford, *Northeastern State University, Tahlequah*
Richard Cobb, *South Maine Community College*
Mary Colavito, *Santa Monica College*
Jennifer Cooper, *Itawamba Community College*
Bob Cowling, *Ouachita Technical College*
Don Cox, *Miami University*
Robert Creek, *Western Kentucky University*
Hillary Cressey, *George Mason University*
Norma Criley, *Illinois Wesleyan University*
Jessica Crowe, *South Georgia College*
Judy Daniels, *Monroe Community College*
Michael Davis, *Central Connecticut State University*
Lewis Deaton, *University of Louisiana*
Lawrence DeFilippi, *Lurleen B. Wallace College*
James Dekloe, *Solano Community College*
Veronique Delesalle, *Gettysburg College*
Loren Denney, *Southwest Missouri State University*
Jean DeSaix, *University of North Carolina at Chapel Hill*
Mary Dettman, *Seminole Community College*
Kathleen Diamond, *College of San Mateo*
Alfred Diboll, *Macon College*
Jean Dickey, *Clemson University*
Stephen Dina, *St. Louis University*
Robert P. Donaldson, *George Washington University*
Gary Donnermeyer, *Iowa Central Community College*
Charles Duggins, *University of South Carolina*
Susan Dunford, *University of Cincinnati*
Lee Edwards, *Greenville Technical College*
Betty Eidemiller, *Lamar University*
Jamin Eisenbach, *Eastern Michigan University*
Norman Ellstrand, *University of California, Riverside*
Thomas Emmel, *University of Florida*

Cindy Erwin, *City College of San Francisco*
Gerald Esch, *Wake Forest University*
David Essar, *Winona State University*
Cory Etchberger, *Longview Community College*
Nancy Eyster-Smith, *Bentley College*
William Ezell, *University of North Carolina at Pembroke*
Laurie Faber, *Grand Rapids Community College*
Terence Farrell, *Stetson University*
Shannon Kuchel Fehlberg, *Colorado Christian University*
Jerry Feldman, *University of California, Santa Cruz*
Eugene Fenster, *Longview Community College*
Dino Fiabane, *Community College of Philadelphia*
Kathleen Fisher, *San Diego State University*
Edward Fliss, *St. Louis Community College, Florissant Valley*
Linda Flora, *Montgomery County Community College*
Dennis Forsythe, *The Citadel Military College of South Carolina*
Robert Frankis, *College of Charleston*
James French, *Rutgers University*
Bernard Frye, *University of Texas at Arlington*
Anne Galbraith, *University of Wisconsin*
Robert Galbraith, *Crafton Hills College*
Rosa Gambier, *State University of New York, Suffolk County Community College*
George Garcia, *University of Texas at Austin*
Linda Gardner, *San Diego Mesa College*
Sandi Gardner, *Triton College*
Gail Gasparich, *Towson University*
Janet Gaston, *Troy University*
Shelley Gaudia, *Lane Community College*
Douglas Gayou, *University of Missouri*
Robert Gendron, *Indiana University of Pennsylvania*
Bagie George, *Georgia Gwinnett College*
Rebecca German, *University of Cincinnati*
Grant Gerrish, *University of Hawaii*
Frank Gilliam, *Marshall University*
Patricia Glas, *The Citadel Military College of South Carolina*
David Glenn-Lewin, *Wichita State University*
Robert Grammer, *Belmont University*
Laura Grayson-Roselli, *Burlington County College*
Peggy Green, *Broward Community College*
Miriam L. Greenberg, *Wayne State University*
Sylvia Greer, *City University of New York*
Dana Griffin, *University of Florida*
Richard Groover, *J. Sargeant Reynolds Community College*
Peggy Guthrie, *University of Central Oklahoma*
Maggie Haag, *University of Alberta*
Richard Haas, *California State University, Fresno*
Martin Hahn, *William Paterson College*
Leah Haimo, *University of California, Riverside*
James Hampton, *Salt Lake Community College*
Blanche Haning, *North Carolina State University*
Richard Hanke, *Rose State College*
Laszlo Hanzely, *Northern Illinois University*
David Harbster, *Paradise Valley Community College*
Reba Harrell, *Hinds Community College*
Jim Harris, *Utah Valley Community College*
Mary Harris, *Louisiana State University*
Chris Haynes, *Shelton State Community College*
Janet Haynes, *Long Island University*

Jean Helgeson, *Collin County Community College*
Ira Herskowitz, *University of California, San Francisco*
Paul Hertz, *Barnard College*
Margaret Hicks, *David Lipscomb University*
Jean Higgins-Fonda, *Prince George's Community College*
Phyllis Hirsch, *East Los Angeles College*
William Hixon, *St. Ambrose University*
Carl Hoagstrom, *Ohio Northern University*
Kim Hodgson, *Longwood College*
Jon Hoekstra, *Gainesville State College*
Kelly Hogan, *University of North Carolina at Chapel Hill*
John Holt, *Michigan State University*
Laura Hoopes, *Occidental College*
Lauren Howard, *Norwich University*
Robert Howe, *Suffolk University*
Michael Hudecki, *State University of New York, Buffalo*
George Hudock, *Indiana University*
Kris Hueftle, *Pensacola Junior College*
Barbara Hunnicutt, *Seminole Community College*
Catherine Hurlbut, *Florida Community College*
Charles Ide, *Tulane University*
Mark Ikeda, *San Bernardino Valley College*
Georgia Ineichen, *Hinds Community College*
Robert Iwan, *Inver Hills Community College*
Charles Jacobs, *Henry Ford Community College*
Fred James, *Presbyterian College*
Ursula Jander, *Washburn University*
Alan Jaworski, *University of Georgia*
R. Jensen, *Saint Mary's College*
Roishene Johnson, *Bossier Parish Community College*
Russell Johnson, *Ricks College*
Florence Juillerat, *Indiana University at Indianapolis*
Tracy Kahn, *University of California, Riverside*
Hinrich Kaiser, *Victor Valley College*
Klaus Kalthoff, *University of Texas at Austin*
Tom Kantz, *California State University, Sacramento*
Jennifer Katcher, *Pima Community College*
Judy Kaufman, *Monroe Community College*
Marlene Kayne, *The College of New Jersey*
Mahlon Kelly, *University of Virginia*
Kenneth Kerrick, *University of Pittsburgh at Johnstown*
Joyce Kille-Marino, *College of Charleston*
Joanne Kilpatrick, *Auburn University, Montgomery*
Stephen Kilpatrick, *University of Pittsburgh at Johnstown*
Lee Kirkpatrick, *Glendale Community College*
Peter Kish, *Southwestern Oklahoma State University*
Cindy Klevickis, *James Madison University*
Robert Koch, *California State University, Fullerton*
Eliot Krause, *Seton Hall University*
Kevin Krown, *San Diego State University*
MaryLynne LaMantia, *Golden West College*
Mary Rose Lamb, *University of Puget Sound*
Thomas Lammers, *University of Wisconsin, Oshkosh*
Carmine Lanciani, *University of Florida*
Vic Landrum, *Washburn University*
Deborah Langsam, *University of North Carolina at Charlotte*

Geneen Lannom, *University of Central Oklahoma*
Brenda Latham, *Merced College*
Steven Lebsack, *Linn-Benton Community College*
Karen Lee, *University of Pittsburgh at Johnstown*
Tom Lehman, *Morgan Community College*
Peggy Lepley, *Cincinnati State University*
Richard Liebaert, *Linn-Benton Community College*
Kevin Lien, *Portland Community College*
Harvey Liftin, *Broward Community College*
Ivo Lindauer, *University of Northern Colorado*
William Lindsay, *Monterey Peninsula College*
Kirsten Lindstrom, *Santa Rosa Junior College*
Melanie Loo, *California State University, Sacramento*
Dave Loring, *Johnson County Community College*
Eric Lovely, *Arkansas Tech University*
Paul Lurquin, *Washington State University*
James Mack, *Monmouth University*
David Magrane, *Morehead State University*
Joan Maloof, *Salisbury State University*
Joseph Marshall, *West Virginia University*
Presley Martin, *Drexel University*
William McComas, *University of Iowa*
Steven McCullagh, *Kennesaw State College*
Mitchell McGinnis, *North Seattle Community College*
James McGivern, *Gannon University*
Colleen McNamara, *Albuquerque TVI Community College*
Scott Meissner, *Cornell University*
Joseph Mendelson, *Utah State University*
Timothy Metz, *Campbell University*
Iain Miller, *University of Cincinnati*
Robert Miller, *University of Dubuque*
V. Christine Minor, *Clemson University*
Brad Mogen, *University of Wisconsin, River Falls*
James Moné, *Millersville University*
Juan Morata, *Miami Dade College*
Richard Mortensen, *Albion College*
Henry Mulcahy, *Suffolk University*
Christopher Murphy, *James Madison University*
James Newcomb, *New England College*
James Nivison, *Mid Michigan Community College*
Peter Nordloh, *Southeastern Community College*
Stephen Novak, *Boise State University*
Bette Nybakken, *Hartnell College*
Michael O'Donnell, *Trinity College*
Steven Oliver, *Worcester State College*
Karen Olmstead, *University of South Dakota*
Steven O'Neal, *Southwestern Oklahoma State University*
Lowell Orr, *Kent State University*
William Outlaw, *Florida State University*
Kevin Padian, *University of California, Berkeley*
Kay Pauling, *Foothill College*
Mark Paulissen, *Northeastern State University, Tahlequah*
Debra Pearce, *Northern Kentucky University*
David Pearson, *Bucknell University*
Patricia Pearson, *Western Kentucky University*
Kathleen Pelkki, *Saginaw Valley State University*
Andrew Penniman, *Georgia Perimeter College*
John Peters, *College of Charleston*
Gary Peterson, *South Dakota State University*
Margaret Peterson, *Concordia Lutheran College*
Russell L. Peterson, *Indiana University of Pennsylvania*
Paula Piehl, *Potomac State College*
Ben Pierce, *Baylor University*

Barbara Pleasants, *Iowa State University*
Kathryn Podwall, *Nassau Community College*
Judith Pottmeyer, *Columbia Basin College*
Donald Potts, *University of California, Santa Cruz*
Nirmala Prabhu, *Edison Community College*
James Pru, *Belleville Area College*
Rongsun Pu, *Kean University*
Charles Pumpuni, *Northern Virginia Community College*
Rebecca Pyles, *East Tennessee State University*
Bob Ratterman, *Jamestown Community College*
Jill Raymond, *Rock Valley College*
Michael Read, *Germanna Community College*
Brian Reeder, *Morehead State University*
Bruce Reid, *Kean College*
David Reid, *Blackburn College*
Stephen Reinbold, *Longview Community College*
Erin Rempala, *San Diego Mesa College*
Michael Renfroe, *James Madison University*
Tim Revell, *Mt. San Antonio College*
Douglas Reynolds, *Central Washington University*
Fred Rhoades, *Western Washington University*
John Rinehart, *Eastern Oregon University*
Laura Ritt, *Burlington County College*
Lynn Rivers, *Henry Ford Community College*
Bruce Robart, *University of Pittsburgh at Johnstown*
Jennifer Roberts, *Lewis University*
Laurel Roberts, *University of Pittsburgh*
Duane Rohlfing, *University of South Carolina*
Jeanette Rollinger, *College of the Sequoias*
Steven Roof, *Fairmont State College*
Jim Rosowski, *University of Nebraska*
Stephen Rothstein, *University of California, Santa Barbara*
Donald Roush, *University of North Alabama*
Lynette Rushton, *South Puget Sound Community College*
Connie Rye, *East Mississippi Community College*
Linda Sabatino, *State University of New York, Suffolk County Community College*
Douglas Schamel, *University of Alaska, Fairbanks*
Douglas Schelhaas, *University of Mary*
Beverly Schieltz, *Wright State University*
Fred Schindler, *Indian Hills Community College*

Robert Schoch, *Boston University*
Brian Scholtens, *College of Charleston*
Julie Schroer, *Bismarck State College*
Fayla Schwartz, *Everett Community College*
Judy Shea, *Kutztown University of Pennsylvania*
Daniela Shebitz, *Kean University*
Thomas Shellberg, *Henry Ford Community College*
Cara Shillington, *Eastern Michigan University*
Lisa Shimeld, *Crafton Hills College*
Brian Shmaefsky, *Kingwood College*
Mark Shotwell, *Slippery Rock University*
Jane Shoup, *Purdue University*
Michele Shuster, *New Mexico State University*
Linda Simpson, *University of North Carolina at Charlotte*
Gary Smith, *Tarrant County Junior College*
Marc Smith, *Sinclair Community College*
Michael Smith, *Western Kentucky University*
Phil Snider, *University of Houston*
Gary Sojka, *Bucknell University*
Ralph Sorensen, *Gettysburg College*
Ruth Sporer, *Rutgers University*
Linda Brooke Stabler, *University of Central Oklahoma*
David Stanton, *Saginaw Valley State University*
Amanda Starnes, *Emory University*
John Stolz, *Duquesne University*
Ross Strayer, *Washtenaw Community College*
Donald Streuble, *Idaho State University*
Mark Sugalski, *New England College*
Gerald Summers, *University of Missouri*
Marshall Sundberg, *Louisiana State University*
Christopher Tabit, *University of West Georgia*
David Tauck, *Santa Clara University*
Hilda Taylor, *Acadia University*
Franklin Te, *Miami Dade College*
Gene Thomas, *Solano Community College*
Kenneth Thomas, *Northern Essex Community College*
Kathy Thompson, *Louisiana State University*
Laura Thurlow, *Jackson Community College*
Anne Tokazewski, *Burlington County College*
Bruce Tomlinson, *State University of New York, Fredonia*

Nancy Tress, *University of Pittsburgh at Titusville*
Donald Trisel, *Fairmont State College*
Kimberly Turk, *Mitchell Community College*
Virginia Turner, *Harper College*
Michael Twaddle, *University of Toledo*
Rani Vajravelu, *University of Central Florida*
Leslie VanderMolen, *Humboldt State University*
Cinnamon VanPutte, *Southwestern Illinois College*
John Vaughan, *Georgetown College*
Martin Vaughan, *Indiana University*
Mark Venable, *Appalachian State University*
Ann Vernon, *St. Charles County Community College*
Rukmani Viswanath, *Laredo Community College*
Mary Beth Voltura, *State University of New York, Cortland*
Jerry Waldvogel, *Clemson University*
Robert Wallace, *Ripon College*
Patricia Walsh, *University of Delaware*
James Wee, *Loyola University*
Harrington Wells, *University of Tulsa*
Larry Williams, *University of Houston*
Ray S. Williams, *Appalachian State University*
Lura Williamson, *University of New Orleans*
Sandra Winicur, *Indiana University, South Bend*
Robert Wise, *University of Wisconsin*
Mary Wisgirda, *San Jacinto College*
Mary Jo Witz, *Monroe Community College*
Neil Woffinden, *University of Pittsburgh at Johnstown*
Michael Womack, *Macon State University*
Patrick Woolley, *East Central College*
Maury Wrightson, *Germanna Community College*
Tumen Wuliji, *Langston University*
Mark Wygoda, *McNeese State University*
Tony Yates, *Seminole State College*
William Yurkiewicz, *Millersville University of Pennsylvania*
Gregory Zagursky, *Radford University*
Martin Zahn, *Thomas Nelson Community College*
Edward J. Zalisko, *Blackburn College*
David Zeigler, *University of North Carolina at Pembroke*
Uko Zylstra, *Calvin College*

Detailed Contents

4 A Tour of the Cell 50

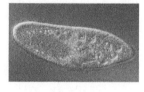
5 The Working Cell 72

6 How Cells Harvest Chemical Energy 88

Biology: *Exploring Life*

BIG IDEAS

Themes in the Study of Biology
(1.1–1.4)

Common themes help to organize the study of life.

Evolution, the Core Theme of Biology
(1.5–1.7)

Evolution accounts for the unity and diversity of life and the evolutionary adaptations of organisms to their environment.

The Process of Science
(1.8–1.9)

In studying nature, scientists make observations, form hypotheses, and test predictions with experiments.

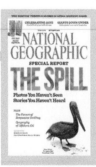

Biology and Everyday Life
(1.10–1.11)

Learning about biology helps us understand many issues involving science, technology, and society.

This young lemur spends much of its time on its mother's back. But it is also groomed and cared for by other females of the troop, a group of about 15 members led by a dominant female. About the size of large cats, these ring-tailed lemurs (scientific name, *Lemur catta*) are noted for their distinctive tails, dark eye patches and muzzle, and, as you can see on the cover of this book, entrancing eyes. They are also highly vocal primates, with 28 distinct calls, such as "predator alert," "stay out of my territory," and purrs of contentment.

About 33 species of lemurs live on the island of Madagascar, and before humans arrived 2,000 years ago, there were even more. The size of Texas, Madagascar is located about 400 km (240 miles) off the southeast coast of Africa. It is home to many plants and animals found nowhere else in the world. Its geographic history helps explain its remarkable biodiversity.

Madagascar was once part of a supercontinent that began breaking apart about 150 million years ago—before the primates (lemurs, monkeys, apes, and humans) had evolved. Apparently, 60 million years ago, ancestral lemurs floated on logs or vegetation from Africa to the island. Their new home was relatively free of predators and competitors and offered many different habitats, from tropical forests to deserts to highlands with spiny shrubs. Over millions of years, lemurs diversified on this isolated island.

The wonderful assortment of lemurs on Madagascar is the result of evolution, the process that has transformed life on Earth from its earliest beginnings to the diversity of organisms living today. In this chapter, we begin our exploration of biology—the scientific study of life, its evolution, and its amazing diversity.

Themes in the Study of Biology

1.1 All forms of life share common properties

Defining **biology** as the scientific study of life raises the obvious question: What is *life*? How would you describe what distinguishes living things from nonliving things? Even a small child realizes that a bug or a flower is alive, while a rock or water is not. They, like all of us, recognize life mainly by what living things do. **Figure 1.1** highlights seven of the properties and processes that we associate with life.

(1) *Order.* This close-up of a sunflower illustrates the highly ordered structure that typifies life. Living cells are the basis of this complex organization.

(2) *Reproduction.* Organisms reproduce their own kind. Here an emperor penguin protects its baby.

(3) *Growth and development.* Inherited information in the form of DNA controls the pattern of growth and development of all organisms, including this hatching crocodile.

(4) *Energy processing.* When this bear eats its catch, it will use the chemical energy stored in the fish to power its own activities and chemical reactions.

(5) *Response to the environment.* All organisms respond to environmental stimuli. This Venus flytrap closed its trap rapidly in response to the stimulus of a damselfly landing on it.

(6) *Regulation.* Many types of mechanisms regulate an organism's internal environment, keeping it within limits that sustain life. Pictured here is a typical lemur behavior with a regulatory function—"sunbathing"—which helps raise the animal's body temperature on cold mornings.

(7) *Evolutionary adaptation.* The leaflike appearance of this katydid camouflages it in its environment. Such adaptations evolve over many generations as individuals with traits best suited to their environment have greater reproductive success and pass their traits to offspring.

Figure 1.1 reminds us that the living world is wondrously varied. How do biologists make sense of this diversity and complexity, and how can you? Indeed, biology is a subject of enormous scope that gets bigger every year. One of the ways to help you organize all this information is to connect what you learn to a set of themes that you will encounter throughout your study of life. The next few modules introduce several of these themes: novel properties emerging at each level of biological organization, the cell as the fundamental unit of life, the correlation of structure and function, and the exchange of matter and energy as organisms interact with the environment. We then focus on the core theme of biology—evolution, the theme that makes sense of both the unity and diversity of life. And in the final two sections of the chapter, we look at the process of science and the relationship of biology to our everyday lives.

Let's begin our journey with a tour through the levels of the biological hierarchy.

? **How would you define life?**

● Life can be defined by a set of common properties such as those described in this module.

(1) Order

(2) Reproduction

(3) Growth and development

(4) Energy processing

(5) Response to the environment

(6) Regulation

(7) Evolutionary adaptation

▲ Figure 1.1   Some important properties of life

1.2 In life's hierarchy of organization, new properties emerge at each level

As Figure 1.2 illustrates, the study of life extends from the global scale of the biosphere to the microscopic scale of molecules. At the upper left we take a distant view of the **biosphere**, all of the environments on Earth that support life. These include most regions of land, bodies of water, and the lower atmosphere.

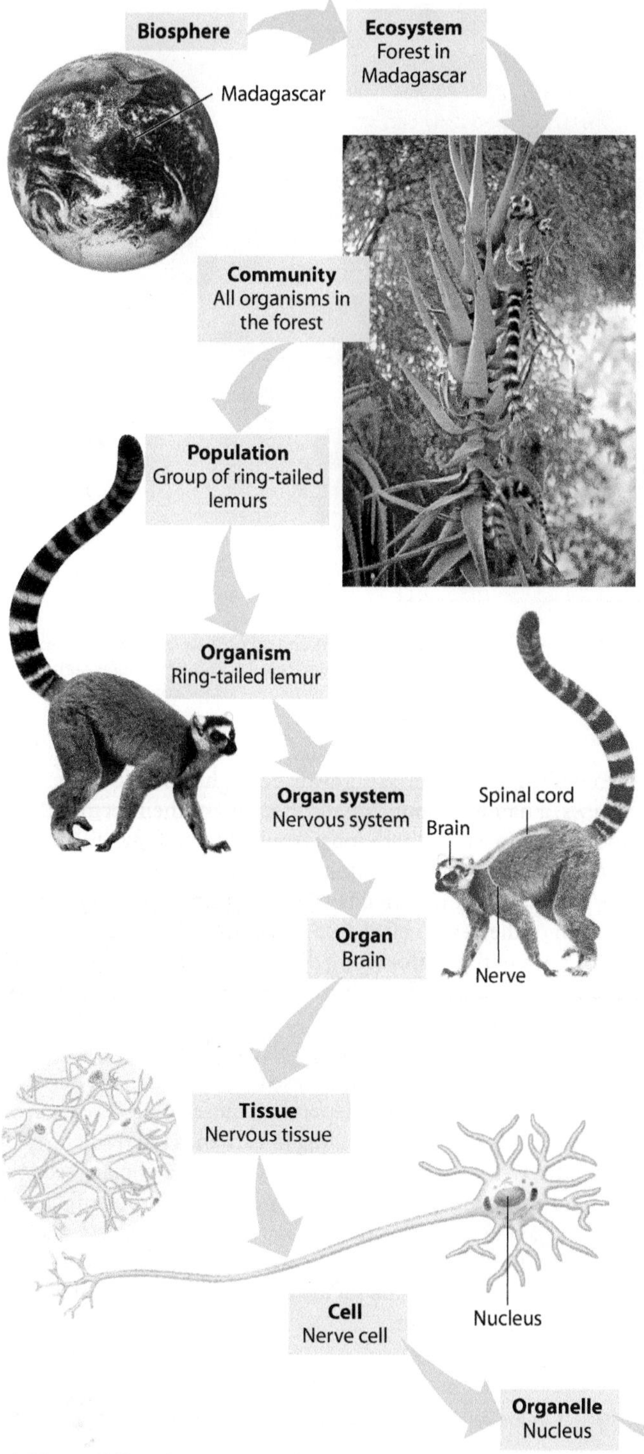

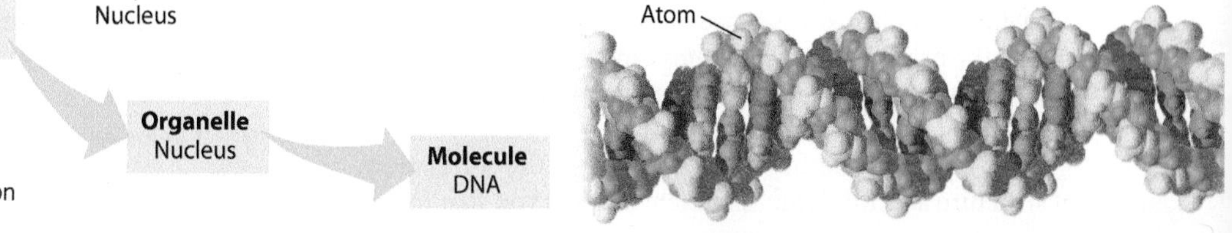

A closer look at one of these environments brings us to the level of an **ecosystem**, which consists of all the organisms living in a particular area, as well as the physical components with which the organisms interact, such as air, soil, water, and sunlight.

The entire array of organisms in an ecosystem is called a **community**. The community in this forest ecosystem in Madagascar includes the lemurs and the agave plant they are eating, as well as birds, snakes, and catlike carnivores called civets; a huge diversity of insects; many kinds of trees and other plants; fungi; and enormous numbers of microscopic protists and bacteria. Each unique form of life is called a species.

A **population** includes all the individuals of a particular species living in an area, such as all the ring-tailed lemurs in the forest community. Next in the hierarchy is the **organism**, an individual living thing.

Within a complex organism such as a lemur, life's hierarchy continues to unfold. An **organ system**, such as the circulatory system or nervous system, consists of several organs that cooperate in a specific function. For instance, the organs of the nervous system are the brain, the spinal cord, and the nerves. A lemur's nervous system controls its actions, such as climbing trees.

An **organ** is made up of several different **tissues**, each made up of a group of similar cells that perform a specific function. A **cell** is the fundamental unit of life. In the nerve cell shown here, you can see several organelles, such as the nucleus. An **organelle** is a membrane-enclosed structure that performs a specific function in a cell.

Finally, we reach the level of molecules in the hierarchy. A **molecule** is a cluster of small chemical units called atoms held together by chemical bonds. Our example in Figure 1.2 is a computer graphic of a section of DNA (deoxyribonucleic acid)—the molecule of inheritance.

Now let's work our way in the opposite direction in Figure 1.2, moving up life's hierarchy from molecules to the biosphere. It takes many molecules to build organelles, numerous organelles to make a cell, many cells to make a tissue, and so on. At each new level, there are novel properties that arise, properties that were not present at the preceding level. For example, life emerges at the level of the cell—a test tube full of organelles is not alive. Such **emergent properties** represent an important theme of biology. The familiar saying that "the whole is greater than the sum of its parts" captures this idea. The emergent properties of each level result from the specific arrangement and interactions of its parts.

? Which of these levels of biological organization includes all others in the list: cell, molecule, organ, tissue?

Organ

▲ Figure 1.2 Life's hierarchy of organization

Biosphere — Madagascar

Ecosystem — Forest in Madagascar

Community — All organisms in the forest

Population — Group of ring-tailed lemurs

Organism — Ring-tailed lemur

Organ system — Nervous system — Spinal cord, Brain, Nerve

Organ — Brain

Tissue — Nervous tissue

Cell — Nerve cell — Nucleus

Organelle — Nucleus

Molecule — DNA — Atom

1.3 Cells are the structural and functional units of life

The cell has a special place in the hierarchy of biological organization. It is the level at which the properties of life emerge—the lowest level of structure that can perform all activities required for life. A cell can regulate its internal environment, take in and use energy, respond to its environment, and develop and maintain its complex organization. The ability of cells to give rise to new cells is the basis for all reproduction and for the growth and repair of multicellular organisms.

All organisms are composed of cells. They occur singly as a great variety of unicellular (single-celled) organisms, such as amoebas and most bacteria. And cells are the subunits that make up multicellular organisms, such as lemurs and trees. Your body consists of trillions of cells of many different kinds.

All cells share many characteristics. For example, every cell is enclosed by a membrane that regulates the passage of materials between the cell and its surroundings. And every cell uses DNA as its genetic information. There are two basic types of cells. **Prokaryotic cells** were the first to evolve and were Earth's sole inhabitants for about the first 1.5 billion years of life on Earth. Fossil evidence indicates that **eukaryotic cells** evolved about 2.1 billion years ago.

Figure 1.3 shows these two types of cells as artificially colored photographs taken with an electron microscope. A prokaryotic cell is much simpler and usually much smaller than a eukaryotic cell. The cells of the microorganisms we call bacteria are prokaryotic. Plants, animals, fungi, and protists are all composed of eukaryotic cells. As you can see in Figure 1.3, a eukaryotic cell is subdivided by membranes into many functional compartments, called organelles. These include a nucleus, which houses the cell's DNA.

The properties of life emerge from the ordered arrangement and interactions of the structures of a cell. Such a combination of components forms a more complex organization that we can call a *system*. Cells are examples of biological systems, as are organisms and ecosystems. Systems and their emergent properties are not unique to life. Consider a box of bicycle parts. When all of the individual parts are properly assembled, the result is a mechanical system you can use for exercise or transportation.

The emergent properties of life, however, are particularly challenging to study because of the unrivaled complexity of biological systems. At the cutting edge of large-scale research today is an approach called **systems biology**. The goal of systems biology is to construct models for the dynamic behavior of whole systems based on studying the interactions among the parts. Biological systems can range from the functioning of the biosphere to the molecular machinery of an organelle.

Cells illustrate another theme of biology: the correlation of structure and function. Experience shows you that form

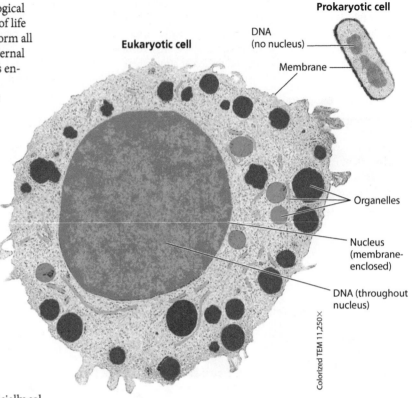

▲ **Figure 1.3** Contrasting the size and complexity of prokaryotic and eukaryotic cells (shown here approximately 11,250 times their real size)

generally fits function. A screwdriver tightens or loosens screws, a hammer pounds nails. Because of their form, these tools can't do each other's jobs. Applied to biology, this theme of form fitting function is a guide to the structure of life at all its organizational levels. For example, the long extension of the nerve cell shown in Figure 1.2 enables it to transmit impulses across long distances in the body. Often, analyzing a biological structure gives us clues about what it does and how it works.

The activities of organisms are all based on cells. For example, your every thought is based on the actions of nerve cells, and your movements depend on muscle cells. Even a global process such as the cycling of carbon is the result of cellular activities, including the photosynthesis of plant cells and the cellular respiration of nearly all cells, a process that uses oxygen to break down sugar for energy and releases carbon dioxide. In the next module, we explore these processes and how they relate to the theme of organisms interacting with their environments.

? **Why are cells considered the basic units of life?**

● They are the lowest level in the hierarchy of biological organization at which the properties of life emerge.

1.4 Organisms interact with their environment, exchanging matter and energy

An organism interacts with its environment, which includes other organisms as well as physical factors. **Figure 1.4** is a simplified diagram of such interactions taking place in a forest ecosystem in Madagascar. Plants are the *producers* that provide the food for a typical ecosystem. A tree, for example, absorbs water (H_2O) and minerals from the soil through its roots, and its leaves take in carbon dioxide (CO_2) from the air. In photosynthesis, a tree's leaves use energy from sunlight to convert CO_2 and H_2O to sugar and oxygen (O_2). The leaves release O_2 to the air, and the roots help form soil by breaking up rocks. Thus, both organism and environment are affected by the interactions between them.

The *consumers* of the ecosystem eat plants and other animals. The lemur in Figure 1.4 eats the leaves and fruits of the tamarind tree. To release the energy in food, animals (as well as plants and most other organisms) take in O_2 from the air and release CO_2. An animal's wastes return other chemicals to the environment.

Another vital part of the ecosystem includes the small animals, fungi, and bacteria in the soil that decompose wastes and the remains of dead organisms. These *decomposers* act as recyclers, changing complex matter into simpler mineral nutrients that plants can absorb and use.

The dynamics of ecosystems include two major processes—the recycling of chemical nutrients and the flow of energy. These processes are illustrated in Figure 1.4. The most basic chemicals necessary for life—carbon dioxide, oxygen, water, and various minerals—cycle within an ecosystem from the air

and soil to plants, to animals and decomposers, and back to the air and soil (blue arrows in the figure).

By contrast, an ecosystem gains and loses energy constantly. Energy flows into the ecosystem when plants and other photosynthesizers absorb light energy from the sun (yellow arrow) and convert it to the chemical energy of sugars and other complex molecules. Chemical energy (orange arrow) is then passed through a series of consumers and, eventually, decomposers, powering each organism in turn. In the process of these energy conversions between and within organisms, some energy is converted to heat, which is then lost from the system (red arrow). In contrast to chemical nutrients, which recycle within an ecosystem, energy flows through an ecosystem, entering as light and exiting as heat.

In this first section, we have touched on several themes of biology, from emergent properties in the biological hierarchy of organization, to cells as the structural and functional units of life, to the exchange of matter and energy as organisms interact with their environment. In the next section, we begin our exploration of evolution, the core theme of biology.

? **Explain how the photosynthesis of plants functions in both cycling of chemical nutrients and the flow of energy in an ecosystem.**

● Photosynthesis uses light to convert carbon dioxide and water to energy-rich food, making it the pathway by which both chemical nutrients and energy become available to most organisms.

Ecosystem

O₂ · Sunlight · **Producers (such as plants)** · CO₂ · Chemical energy (food) · **Consumers (such as animals)** · O₂ · Heat · CO₂ · Water and minerals taken up by tree roots · Cycling of chemical nutrients · Decomposers (in soil)

▲ **Figure 1.4** The cycling of nutrients and flow of energy in an ecosystem

Evolution, the Core Theme of Biology

1.5 The unity of life is based on DNA and a common genetic code

All cells have DNA, and the continuity of life depends on this universal genetic material. DNA is the chemical substance of **genes**, the units of inheritance that transmit information from parents to offspring. Genes, which are grouped into very long DNA molecules called chromosomes, also control all the activities of a cell. The molecular structure of DNA accounts for these functions. Let us explain: Each DNA molecule is made up of two long chains coiled together into what is called a double helix. The chains are made up of four kinds of chemical building blocks. **Figure 1.5** illustrates these four building blocks, called nucleotides, with different colors and letter abbreviations of their names. The right side of the figure shows a short section of a DNA double helix.

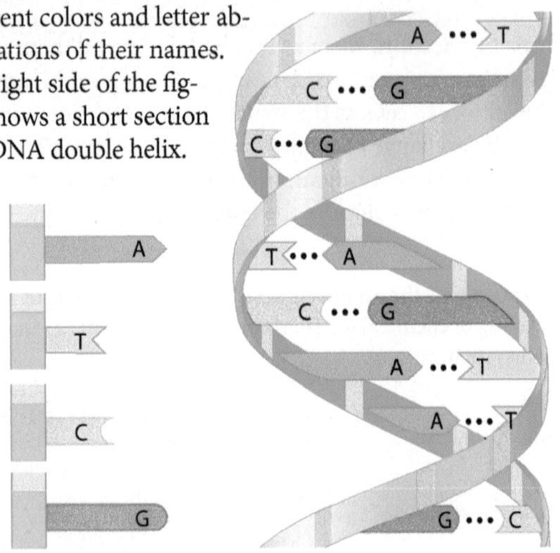

The way DNA encodes a cell's information is analogous to the way we arrange letters of the alphabet into precise sequences with specific meanings. The word *rat*, for example, conjures up an image of a rodent; *tar* and *art*, which contain the same letters, mean very different things. We can think of the four building blocks as the alphabet of inheritance. Specific sequential arrangements of these four chemical letters encode precise information in genes, which are typically hundreds or thousands of "letters" long.

The DNA of genes provides the blueprints for making proteins, and proteins serve as the tools that actually build and maintain the cell and carry out its activities. A bacterial gene may direct the cell to "Make a yellow pigment." A particular human gene may mean "Make the hormone insulin." All forms of life use essentially the same genetic code to translate the information stored in DNA into proteins. This makes it possible to engineer cells to produce proteins normally found only in some other organism. Thus, bacteria can be used to produce insulin for the treatment of diabetes by inserting a gene for human insulin into bacterial cells.

The diversity of life arises from differences in DNA sequences—in other words, from variations on the common theme of storing genetic information in DNA. Bacteria and humans are different because they have different genes. But both sets of instructions are written in the same language.

In the next module, we see how biologists attempt to organize the diversity of life.

▲ **Figure 1.5** The four building blocks of DNA (left); part of a DNA double helix (right)

 ? **What is the chemical basis for all of life's kinship?**

● DNA as the genetic material

1.6 The diversity of life can be arranged into three domains

We can think of biology's enormous scope as having two dimensions. The "vertical" dimension, which we examined in Module 1.2, is the size scale that stretches from molecules to the biosphere. But biology also has a "horizontal" dimension, spanning across the great diversity of organisms existing now and over the long history of life on Earth.

Grouping Species Diversity is a hallmark of life. Biologists have so far identified and named about 1.8 million species, and thousands more are identified each year. Estimates of the total number of species range from 10 million to over 100 million. Whatever the actual number, biologists face a major challenge in attempting to make sense of this enormous variety of life.

There seems to be a human tendency to group diverse items according to similarities. We may speak of bears or butterflies, though we recognize that each group includes many different species. We may even sort groups into broader categories, such

as mammals and insects. Taxonomy, the branch of biology that names and classifies species, arranges species into a hierarchy of broader and broader groups, from genus, family, order, class, and phylum, to kingdom.

The Three Domains of Life Until the 1990s, most biologists used a taxonomic scheme that divided all of life into five kingdoms. But new methods for assessing evolutionary relationships, such as comparison of DNA sequences, have led to an ongoing reevaluation of the number and boundaries of kingdoms. As that debate continues, however, there is consensus that life can be organized into three higher levels called **domains**. **Figure 1.6**, on the facing page, shows representatives of the three domains: Bacteria, Archaea, and Eukarya.

Domains **Bacteria** and **Archaea** both consist of prokaryotes, organisms with prokaryotic cells. Most prokaryotes are single-celled and microscopic. The photos of the prokaryotes in Figure

1.6 were made with an electron microscope, and the number along the side indicates the magnification of the image. (We will discuss microscopy in Chapter 4.) Bacteria and archaea were once combined in a single kingdom. But much evidence indicates that they represent two very distinct branches of life, each of which includes multiple kingdoms.

Bacteria are the most diverse and widespread prokaryotes. In the photo of bacteria in Figure 1.6, each of the rod-shaped structures is a bacterial cell.

Many of the prokaryotes known as archaea live in Earth's extreme environments, such as salty lakes and boiling hot springs. Each round structure in the photo of archaea in Figure 1.6 is an archaeal cell.

All the eukaryotes, organisms with eukaryotic cells, are grouped in domain **Eukarya**. As you learned in Module 1.3, eukaryotic cells have a nucleus and other internal structures called organelles.

Protists are a diverse collection of mostly single-celled organisms and some relatively simple multicellular relatives. Pictured in Figure 1.6 is an assortment of protists in a drop of pond water. Although protists were once placed in a single kingdom, it is now clear that they do not form a single natural group of species. Biologists are currently debating how to split the protists into groups that accurately reflect their evolutionary relationships.

The three remaining groups within Eukarya contain multicellular eukaryotes. These kingdoms are distinguished partly by their modes of nutrition. Kingdom Plantae consists of plants, which produce their own food by photosynthesis. The representative of kingdom Plantae in Figure 1.6 is a tropical bromeliad, a plant native to the Americas.

Kingdom Fungi, represented by the mushrooms in Figure 1.6, is a diverse group, whose members mostly decompose the remains of dead organisms and organic wastes and absorb the nutrients into their cells.

Animals obtain food by ingestion, which means they eat other organisms. Representing kingdom Animalia, the sloth in Figure 1.6 resides in the trees of Central and South American rain forests. There are actually members of two other groups in the sloth photo. The sloth is clinging to a tree (kingdom Plantae), and the greenish tinge in the animal's hair is a luxuriant growth of photosynthetic prokaryotes (domain Bacteria). This photograph exemplifies a theme reflected in our book's title: connections between living things. The sloth depends on trees for food and shelter; the tree uses nutrients from the decomposition of the sloth's feces; the prokaryotes gain access to the sunlight necessary for photosynthesis by living on the sloth; and the sloth is camouflaged from predators by its green coat.

The diversity of life and its interconnectedness are evident almost everywhere. Earlier we looked at life's unity in its shared properties, two basic types of cell structure, and common genetic code. And now we have briefly surveyed its diversity. In the next module, we explore how evolution explains both the unity and the diversity of life.

? To which of the three domains of life do we belong?

Eukarya

Domain Bacteria

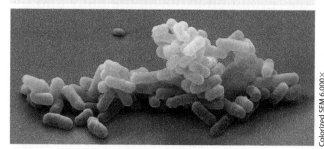

Colorized SEM 6,000×

Bacteria

Domain Archaea

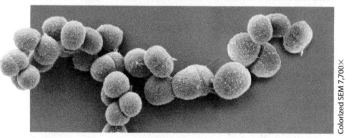

Colorized SEM 7,700×

Archaea

Domain Eukarya

LM 275×

Protists (multiple kingdoms)   Kingdom Plantae

Kingdom Fungi   Kingdom Animalia

▲ **Figure 1.6**   The three domains of life

1.7 Evolution explains the unity and diversity of life

The history of life, as documented by fossils, is a saga of a changing Earth billions of years old, inhabited by an evolving cast of living forms (Figure 1.7A). And yet, there is relatedness among these diverse forms, and patterns of ancestry can be traced through the fossil record and other evidence. Evolution accounts for life's dual nature of kinship and diversity.

In November 1859, the English naturalist Charles Darwin (Figure 1.7B) published one of the most important and influential books ever written. Entitled *On the Origin of Species by Means of Natural Selection*, Darwin's book was an immediate bestseller and soon made his name almost synonymous with the concept of evolution. Darwin stands out in history with people like Newton and Einstein, scientists who synthesized comprehensive theories with great explanatory power.

The Origin of Species articulated two main points. First, Darwin presented a large amount of evidence to support the idea of **evolution**—that species living today are descendants of ancestral species. Darwin called his evolutionary theory "descent with modification." It was an insightful phrase, as it captured both the unity of life (descent from a common ancestor) and the diversity of life (modification as species diverged from their ancestors).

Darwin's second point was to propose a mechanism for evolution, which he called **natural selection**. Darwin synthesized this idea from observations that by themselves were neither profound nor original. Others had the pieces of the puzzle, but Darwin saw how they fit together. He started with the following two observations: (1) Individuals in a population vary in their traits, many of which are passed on from parents to offspring. (2) A population can produce far more offspring than the environment can support. From these two observations, Darwin inferred that those individuals with heritable traits best suited to the environment are more likely to survive and reproduce than are less well-suited individuals. As a result of this unequal reproductive success over many generations, a higher and higher proportion of individuals will have the advantageous traits. The result of natural selection is evolutionary adaptation, the accumulation of favorable traits in a population over time.

Figure 1.7C uses a simple example to show how natural selection works. ❶ An imaginary beetle population has colonized an area where the soil has been blackened by a recent brush fire. Initially, the population varies extensively in the inherited coloration of individuals, from very light gray to charcoal. ❷ A bird eats the beetles it sees most easily, the light-colored ones. This selective predation reduces the number of light-colored beetles and favors the survival and reproductive success of the darker beetles. ❸ The surviving beetles reproduce. After several generations, the population is quite different from the original one. As a result of natural selection, the frequencies of the darker-colored beetles in the population have increased.

▲ Figure 1.7B
Charles Darwin in 1859

Darwin realized that numerous small changes in populations caused by natural selection could eventually lead to major alterations of species. He proposed that new species could evolve as a result of the gradual accumulation of changes over long periods of time. (We'll explore evolution and natural selection in more detail in Chapters 13 and 14.)

We see the exquisite results of natural selection in every kind of organism. Each species has its own set of evolutionary adaptations that have evolved over time. Consider the two very

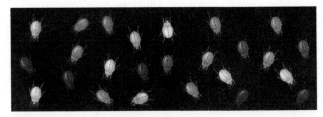

❶ Population with varied inherited traits

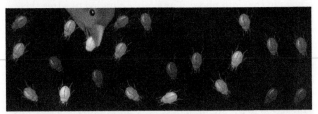

❷ Elimination of individuals with certain traits

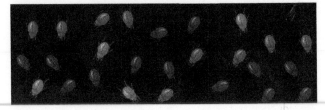

❸ Reproduction of survivors

▲ Figure 1.7C   An example of natural selection in action

▲ Figure 1.7A   Fossil of *Dimetrodon*. This 3-m-long carnivore was more closely related to mammals than to reptiles.

Ground pangolin

Killer whale

▲ Figure 1.7D Examples of adaptations to different environments

different mammals shown in **Figure 1.7D**. The ground pangolin, found in southern and eastern Africa, has a tough body armor of overlapping scales, protecting it from most predators. The pangolin uses its unusually long tongue to prod ants out of their nests. The killer whale is a mammal adapted for life at sea. It breathes air through nostrils on the top of its head and communicates with its companions by emitting clicking sounds that carry in water. Killer whales use sound echoes to detect schools of fish or other prey. The pangolin's armor and the killer whale's echolocating ability arose over many, many generations as individuals with heritable traits that made them better adapted to the environment had greater reproductive success. Evolution—descent with modification—explains both how these two mammals are related and how they differ. Evolution is the core theme that makes sense of everything we know and learn about life.

? How does natural selection adapt a population of organisms to its environment?

● On average, those individuals with heritable traits best suited to the local environment produce the greatest number of offspring. This unequal reproductive success increases the frequency of those traits in the population.

The Process of Science

1.8 Scientific inquiry is used to ask and answer questions about nature

The word *science* is derived from a Latin verb meaning "to know." Science is a way of knowing—an approach to understanding the natural world. It stems from our curiosity about ourselves and the world around us. And it involves the process of inquiry—a search for information, explanations, and answers to specific questions. Scientific inquiry involves making observations, forming hypotheses, and testing predictions.

Recorded observations and measurements are the data of science. Some data are *quantitative*, such as numerical measurements. Other data may be descriptive, or *qualitative*. For example, primatologist Alison Jolly has spent over 40 years making observations of lemur behavior during field research in Madagascar, amassing data that is mostly qualitative (Figure 1.8).

Collecting and analyzing observations can lead to conclusions based on a type of logic called **inductive reasoning**. This kind of reasoning derives generalizations from a large number of specific observations. "All organisms are made of cells" is an inductive conclusion based on the discovery of cells in every biological specimen observed over two centuries of time. Careful observations and the inductive conclusions they lead to are fundamental to understanding nature.

Observations often stimulate us to seek natural causes and explanations. Such inquiry usually involves the forming and testing of hypotheses. A **hypothesis** is a proposed explanation for a set of observations. A good hypothesis leads to predictions that scientists can test by recording additional observations or by designing experiments.

Deduction is the type of logic used to come up with ways to test hypotheses. In **deductive reasoning**, the logic flows from general premises to the specific results we should expect

if the premises are true. If all organisms are made of cells (premise 1), and humans are organisms (premise 2), then humans are composed of cells (deduction). This deduction is a prediction that can be tested by examining human tissues.

Theories in Science

How is a theory different from a hypothesis? A scientific **theory** is much broader in scope than a hypothesis. It is usually general enough to generate many new, specific hypotheses that can then be tested. And a theory is supported by a large and usually growing body of evidence. Theories that become widely adopted (such as the theory of evolution) explain a great diversity of observations and are supported by a vast accumulation of evidence.

▲ Figure 1.8 Alison Jolly with her research subjects, ring-tailed lemurs

? Contrast inductive reasoning with deductive reasoning.

● Inductive reasoning derives a generalization from many observations; deductive reasoning predicts specific outcomes from a general premise.

1.9 Scientists form and test hypotheses and share their results

Let's explore the elements of scientific inquiry with two case studies, one from everyday life and one from a research project.

A Case Study from Everyday Life   We all use hypotheses in solving everyday problems. Let's say, for example, that your flashlight fails during a campout. That's an observation. The question is obvious: Why doesn't the flashlight work? Two reasonable hypotheses based on past experience are that either the batteries in the flashlight are dead or the bulb is burned out. Each of these hypotheses leads to predictions you can test with experiments or further observations. For example, the dead-battery hypothesis predicts that replacing the batteries with new ones will fix the problem. Figure 1.9A diagrams this campground inquiry.

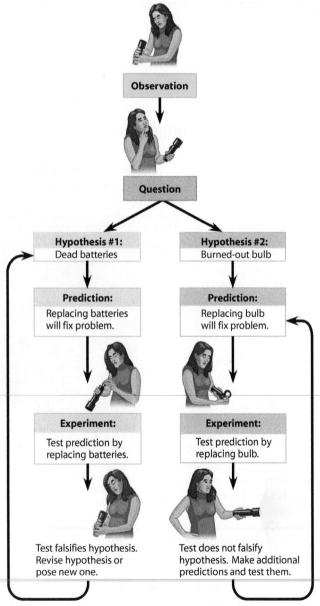

▲ Figure 1.9A   An example of hypothesis-based science

The flashlight example illustrates two important points. First, a hypothesis must be *testable*—there must be some way to check its validity. Second, a hypothesis must be *falsifiable*—there must be some observation or experiment that could show that it is not true. As shown on the left in Figure 1.9A, the hypothesis that dead batteries are the sole cause of the problem was falsified by replacing the batteries with new ones. As shown on the right, the burned-out-bulb hypothesis is the more likely explanation. Notice that testing supports a hypothesis not by proving that it is correct but by not eliminating it through falsification. Perhaps the bulb was simply loose and the new bulb was inserted correctly. Testing cannot *prove* a hypothesis beyond a shadow of doubt, because it is impossible to exhaust all alternative hypotheses. A hypothesis gains credibility by surviving multiple attempts to falsify it, while alternative hypotheses are eliminated by testing.

A Case Study from Science   To learn more about how science works, let's examine some actual scientific research.

The story begins with a set of observations and generalizations. Many poisonous animals are brightly colored, often with distinctive patterns. This so-called warning coloration apparently says "dangerous species" to potential predators. But there are also mimics. These imposters resemble poisonous species but are actually harmless. A question that follows from these observations is: What is the function of mimicry? A reasonable hypothesis is that mimicry is an evolutionary adaptation that reduces the harmless animal's risk of being eaten.

In 2001, biologists David and Karin Pfennig, along with William Harcombe, one of their undergraduate students, designed an elegant set of field experiments to test the hypothesis that mimics benefit because predators confuse them with the harmful species. A venomous snake called the eastern coral snake has warning coloration: bold, alternating rings of red, yellow, and black (Figure 1.9B, on the facing page). (A *venomous* species delivers its poison by stinging, stabbing, or biting.) Predators rarely attack these snakes. The predators do not learn this avoidance behavior by trial and error; a first encounter with a coral snake would usually be deadly. Natural selection has apparently increased the frequency of predators that inherit an instinctive avoidance of the coral snake's coloration.

The nonvenomous scarlet king snake mimics the ringed coloration of the coral snake (Figure 1.9C). Both types of snakes live in North and South Carolina, but king snakes are also found in regions that have no coral snakes.

The geographic distribution of these snakes made it possible for the researchers to test a key prediction of the mimicry hypothesis: Mimicry should help protect king snakes from predators, but only in regions where coral snakes also live. Avoiding snakes with warning coloration is an adaptation of predator populations that evolved in areas where coral snakes are present. Therefore, predators adapted to the warning coloration of coral snakes will attack king snakes less frequently than will predators in areas where coral snakes are absent.

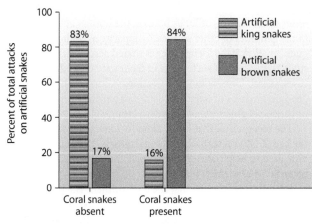

▲ Figure 1.9B Eastern coral snake (venomous)

▲ Figure 1.9C Scarlet king snake (nonvenomous)

To test this prediction, Harcombe made hundreds of artificial snakes out of wire covered with a claylike substance called plasticine. He made two versions of fake snakes: an *experimental group* with the color pattern of king snakes and a *control group* of plain brown snakes as a basis of comparison.

The researchers placed equal numbers of the two types of artificial snakes in field sites throughout North and South Carolina, including the region where coral snakes are absent. After four weeks, they retrieved the snakes and recorded how many had been attacked by looking for bite or claw marks. The most common predators were foxes, coyotes, and raccoons, but black bears also attacked some of the snakes (Figure 1.9D).

The data fit the key prediction of the mimicry hypothesis. The artificial king snakes were attacked less frequently than the artificial brown snakes only in field sites within the geographic range of the venomous coral snakes. The bar graph in Figure 1.9E summarizes the results.

This case study is an example of a **controlled experiment**, one that is designed to compare an experimental group (the artificial king snakes, in this case) with a control group (the artificial brown snakes). Ideally, the experimental and control groups differ only in the one factor the experiment is designed to test—in our example, the effect of the snakes' coloration on the behavior of predators. Without the control group, the researchers would not have been able to rule out other variables, such as the number of predators in the different test areas. The experimental design left coloration as the only factor that could account for the low predation rate on the artificial king snakes placed within the range of coral snakes.

The Culture of Science Science is a social activity, with most scientists working in teams, which often include graduate and undergraduate students. Scientists share information through publications, seminars, meetings, and personal communication. The Internet has added a new medium for this exchange of ideas and data. Scientists build on what has been learned from earlier research and often check each other's claims by attempting to confirm observations or repeat experiments.

Science seeks natural causes for natural phenomena. Thus, the scope of science is limited to the study of structures and processes that we can directly observe and measure. Science can neither support nor falsify hypotheses about supernatural forces or explanations, for such questions are outside the bounds of science.

The process of science is necessarily repetitive: In testing a hypothesis, researchers may make observations that call for rejection of the hypothesis or at least revision and further testing. This process allows biologists to circle closer and closer to their best estimation of how nature works. As in all quests, science includes elements of challenge, adventure, and luck, along with careful planning, reasoning, creativity, cooperation, competition, patience, and persistence.

? **Why is it difficult to draw a conclusion from an experiment that does not include a control group?**

● Without a control group, you don't know if the experimental outcome is due to the variable you are trying to test or to some other variable.

▲ Figure 1.9D Artificial king snake that was not attacked (above); artificial brown snake that was attacked by a bear (right)

▲ Figure 1.9E Results of mimicry experiment

Biology and Everyday Life

| ## 1.10 Biology, technology, and society are connected in important ways

Many issues facing society are related to biology (Figure 1.10). Most of these issues also involve our expanding technology. Science and technology are interdependent, but their basic goals differ. The goal of science is to understand natural phenomena. In contrast, the goal of **technology** is to apply scientific knowledge for some specific purpose. Scientists often speak of "discoveries," while engineers more often speak of "inventions." The beneficiaries of those inventions also include scientists, who use new technology in their research. And scientific discoveries often lead to the development of new technologies.

Technology depends less on the curiosity that drives basic science than on the needs and wants of people and on the social environment of the times. Debates about technology center more on "should we do it" than "can we do it." Should insurance companies have access to individuals' DNA information? Should we permit research with embryonic stem cells?

Technology has improved our standard of living in many ways, but not without adverse consequences. Technology that keeps people healthier has enabled Earth's population to grow 10-fold in the past three centuries and to more than double to 6.8 billion in just the past 40 years. The environmental effects of this growth can be devastating. Global climate change, toxic wastes, deforestation, nuclear accidents, and extinction of species are just some of the repercussions of more and more people wielding more and more technology. Science can help us identify such problems and provide insight into what course of action may prevent further damage. But solutions to these problems have as much to do with politics, economics, and cultural values as with science and technology. Now that science and technology have become such powerful aspects of society, every citizen has a responsibility to develop a reasonable amount of scientific literacy. The crucial science-technology-society relationship is a theme that adds to the significance of any biology course.

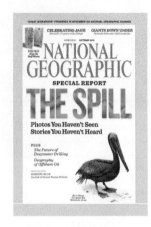

▲ Figure 1.10 Biology and technology in the news

? **How do science and technology interact?**

● *New scientific discoveries may lead to new technologies; new technologies may increase the ability of scientists to search for new knowledge.*

| ## 1.11 Evolution is connected to our everyday lives

Evolution is the core theme of biology. To emphasize the centrality of evolution to biology, we include an Evolution Connection module in each chapter in this book. But is evolution connected to your everyday life? And if so, in what ways?

Biologists now recognize that differences in DNA among individuals, populations, and species reflect the patterns of evolutionary change. The new technology of automatic DNA-sequencing machines has enabled scientists to determine the order of the billions of DNA bases in the human genome and in the genomes of other species. Comparisons of those sequences allow us to identify genes shared across many species, study the actions of such genes in other species, and, in some cases, search for new medical treatments. Identifying beneficial genes in relatives of our crop plants has permitted the breeding or genetic engineering of enhanced crops.

The recognition that DNA differs between people has led to the use of DNA tests to identify individuals. DNA profiling is now used to help convict or exonerate the accused, determine paternity, and identify remains.

Evolution teaches us that the environment is a powerful selective force for traits that best adapt populations to their environment. We are major agents of environmental change when we take drugs to combat infection or grow crops in pesticide-dependent monocultures or alter Earth's habitats. We have seen the effects of such environmental changes in antibiotic-resistant bacteria, pesticide-resistant pests, endangered species, and increasing rates of extinction.

How can evolutionary theory help? It can help us be more judicious in our use of antibiotics and pesticides and help us develop strategies for conservation efforts. It can help us create flu vaccines and HIV drugs by tracking the rapid evolution of these viruses. It can identify new sources of drugs. For example, by tracing the evolutionary history of the endangered Pacific Yew tree, once the only source of the cancer drug Taxol, scientists have discovered similar compounds in more common trees.

We hope this book will help you develop an appreciation for evolution and biology and help you apply your new knowledge to evaluating issues ranging from your personal health to the well-being of the whole world. Biology offers us a deeper understanding of ourselves and our planet and a chance to more fully appreciate life in all of its diversity.

? **How might an understanding of evolution contribute to the development of new drugs?**

● *As one example, we can find organisms that share our genes and similar cellular processes and test the actions of potential drugs in these organisms.*

For Practice Quizzes, BioFlix, MP3 Tutors, and Activities, go to www.masteringbiology.com.

Reviewing the Concepts

Themes in the Study of Biology (1.1–1.4)

1.1 All forms of life share common properties. Biology is the scientific study of life. Properties of life include order, reproduction, growth and development, energy processing, response to the environment, regulation, and evolutionary adaptation.

1.2 In life's hierarchy of organization, new properties emerge at each level. Biological organization unfolds as follows: biosphere > ecosystem > community > population > organism > organ system > organ > tissue > cell > organelle > molecule. Emergent properties result from the interactions among component parts.

1.3 Cells are the structural and functional units of life. Eukaryotic cells contain membrane-enclosed organelles, including a nucleus containing DNA. Prokaryotic cells are smaller and lack such organelles. Structure is related to function at all levels of biological organization. Systems biology models the complex interactions of biological systems, such as the molecular interactions within a cell.

1.4 Organisms interact with their environment, exchanging matter and energy. Ecosystems are characterized by the cycling of chemical nutrients from the atmosphere and soil through producers, consumers, decomposers, and back to the environment. Energy flows one way through an ecosystem—entering as sunlight, converted to chemical energy by producers, passed on to consumers, and exiting as heat.

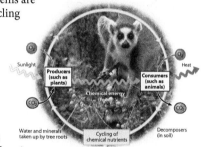

Evolution, the Core Theme of Biology (1.5–1.7)

1.5 The unity of life is based on DNA and a common genetic code. DNA is responsible for heredity and for programming the activities of a cell. A species' genes are coded in the sequences of the four building blocks making up DNA's double helix.

1.6 The diversity of life can be arranged into three domains. Taxonomy names species and classifies them into a system of broader groups. Domains Bacteria and Archaea consist of prokaryotes. The eukaryotic domain, Eukarya, includes various protists and the kingdoms Fungi, Plantae, and Animalia.

1.7 Evolution explains the unity and diversity of life. Darwin synthesized the theory of evolution by natural selection.

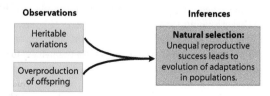

The Process of Science (1.8–1.9)

1.8 Scientific inquiry is used to ask and answer questions about nature. Scientists use inductive reasoning to draw general conclusions from many observations. They form hypotheses and use deductive reasoning to make predictions. Data may be qualitative or quantitative. A scientific theory is broad in scope, generates new hypotheses, and is supported by a large body of evidence.

1.9 Scientists form and test hypotheses and share their results. Predictions can be tested with experiments, and results can either falsify or support the hypothesis. In a controlled experiment, the use of control and experimental groups helps to demonstrate the effect of a single variable. Science is a social process: scientists share information and review each other's results.

Biology and Everyday Life (1.10–1.11)

1.10 Biology, technology, and society are connected in important ways. Technological advances stem from scientific research, and research benefits from new technologies.

1.11 Evolution is connected to our everyday lives. Evolutionary theory is useful in medicine, agriculture, forensics, and conservation. Human-caused environmental changes are powerful selective forces that affect the evolution of many species.

Connecting the Concepts

1. Biology can be described as having both a vertical scale and a horizontal scale. Explain what that means.

2. Complete the following map organizing some of biology's major concepts.

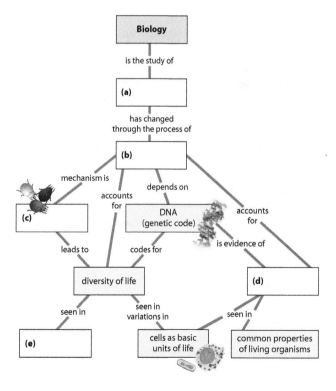

Testing Your Knowledge

Multiple Choice

3. Which of the following best describes the logic of the scientific process?
   a. If I generate a testable hypothesis, tests and observations will support it.
   b. If my prediction is correct, it will lead to a testable hypothesis.
   c. If my observations are accurate, they will not falsify my hypothesis.
   d. If my hypothesis is correct, I can make predictions and my results will not falsify my hypothesis.
   e. If my predictions are good and my tests are right, they will prove my hypothesis.

4. Single-celled amoebas and bacteria are grouped into different domains because
   a. amoebas eat bacteria.
   b. bacteria are not made of cells.
   c. bacterial cells lack a membrane-enclosed nucleus.
   d. bacteria decompose amoebas.
   e. amoebas are motile; bacteria are not.

5. A biologist studying interactions among the protists in an ecosystem could *not* be working at which level in life's hierarchy? (*Choose carefully and explain your answer.*)
   a. the population level
   b. the molecular level
   c. the community level
   d. the organism level
   e. the organ level

6. Which of the following questions is outside the realm of science?
   a. Which organisms play the most important role in energy input to a forest?
   b. What percentage of music majors take a biology course?
   c. What is the physical nature of the universe?
   d. What is the influence of the supernatural on current events?
   e. What is the dominance hierarchy in a troop of ring-tailed lemurs?

7. Which of the following statements best distinguishes hypotheses from theories in science?
   a. Theories are hypotheses that have been proved.
   b. Hypotheses are tentative guesses; theories are correct answers to questions about nature.
   c. Hypotheses usually are narrow in scope; theories have broad explanatory power.
   d. Hypotheses and theories are different terms for essentially the same thing in science.
   e. Theories cannot be falsified; hypotheses can be falsified.

8. Which of the following best demonstrates the unity among all living organisms?
   a. descent with modification
   b. related DNA sequences and common genetic code
   c. emergent properties
   d. natural selection
   e. the three domains

9. The core idea that makes sense of all of biology is
   a. the process of science.
   b. the correlation of function with structure.
   c. systems biology.
   d. evolution.
   e. the emergence of life at the level of the cell.

Describing, Comparing, and Explaining

10. In an ecosystem, how is the movement of energy similar to that of chemical nutrients, and how is it different?

11. Explain the role of heritable variations in Darwin's theory of natural selection.

12. Explain what is meant by this statement: The scientific process is not a rigid method.

13. Contrast technology with science. Give an example of each to illustrate the difference.

14. Explain what is meant by this statement: Natural selection is an editing mechanism rather than a creative process.

Applying the Concepts

15. The graph below shows the results of an experiment in which mice learned to run through a maze.

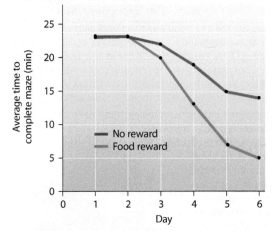

   a. State the hypothesis and prediction that you think this experiment tested.
   b. Which was the control group and which the experimental? Why was a control group needed?
   c. List some variables that must have been controlled so as not to affect the results.
   d. Do the data support the hypothesis? Explain.

16. In an experiment similar to the mimicry experiment described in Module 1.9, a researcher counted more predator attacks on artificial king snakes in areas with coral snakes than in areas outside the range of coral snakes. From those numbers, the researcher concluded that the mimicry hypothesis is false. Do you think this conclusion is justified? Why or why not?

17. The fruits of wild species of tomato are tiny compared to the giant beefsteak tomatoes available today. This difference in fruit size is almost entirely due to the larger number of cells in the domesticated fruits. Plant biologists have recently discovered genes that are responsible for controlling cell division in tomatoes. Why would such a discovery be important to producers of other kinds of fruits and vegetables? To the study of human development and disease? To our basic understanding of biology?

18. The news media and popular magazines frequently report stories that are connected to biology. In the next 24 hours, record the ones you hear or read about in three different sources and briefly describe the biological connections in each story.

Answers to all questions can be found in Appendix 4.

The Life of the Cell

The Chemical Basis of Life

BIG IDEAS

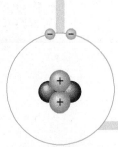

Elements, Atoms, and Compounds
(2.1–2.4)

Living organisms are made of atoms of certain elements, mostly combined into compounds.

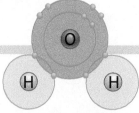

Chemical Bonds
(2.5–2.9)

The structure of an atom determines what types of bonds it can form with other atoms.

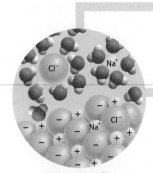

Water's Life-Supporting Properties
(2.10–2.16)

The unique properties of water derive from the polarity of water molecules.

Biology is about life, but it is also about chemistry. Chemicals are the very stuff making up our bodies, those of other organisms, and the physical environment around us. Your cells, tissues, and organs are all made of chemical compounds. And the activities of your body—from reading these words to running a race—are all based on chemical reactions. So understanding and appreciating life begins with a basic understanding of chemistry: the elements that make up living matter and the ways in which the atoms of those elements interact.

Life's chemistry is tied to water. The chemical reactions of your body take place in cells whose water content ranges from 70% to 95%. As you can see in this satellite photograph of our planet, three-quarters of Earth's surface is covered by water. Life began in water and evolved there for 3 billion years before spreading onto land. And modern life, even land-dwelling life, is still dependent on water. All living organisms require water more than any other substance. What properties of the simple water molecule make it so indispensable to life on Earth? You'll find out in this chapter.

This chapter will also make connections to the themes introduced in Chapter 1. One of these themes is the organization of life into a hierarchy of structural levels, with new properties emerging at each successive level. Emergent properties are apparent even at the lowest levels of biological organization— the ordering of atoms into molecules and the interactions of those molecules. The intricate structures and complex functions of all living organisms arise from these interactions. We begin our story of biology with the basic concepts of chemistry that will apply throughout our study of life.

Elements, Atoms, and Compounds

2.1 Organisms are composed of elements, in combinations called compounds

Living organisms and everything around them are composed of **matter**, which is defined as anything that occupies space and has mass. (In everyday language, we can think of mass as an object's weight.) Matter is found on Earth in three physical states: solid, liquid, and gas.

Types of matter as diverse as rocks, water, air, and biology students are all composed of chemical elements. An **element** is a substance that cannot be broken down to other substances by ordinary chemical means. Today, chemists recognize 92 elements that occur in nature; gold, copper, carbon, and oxygen are some examples. Chemists have also made a few dozen synthetic elements. Each element has a symbol, the first letter or two of its English, Latin, or German name. For instance, the symbol for sodium, Na, is from the Latin word *natrium*; the symbol O comes from the English word *oxygen*.

A **compound** is a substance consisting of two or more different elements combined in a fixed ratio. Compounds are much more common than pure elements. In fact, few elements exist in a pure state in nature.

Many compounds consist of only two elements; for instance, table salt (sodium chloride, NaCl) has equal parts of the elements sodium (Na) and chlorine (Cl). Pure sodium is a metal and pure chlorine is a poisonous gas. Chemically combined, however, they form an edible compound (**Figure 2.1**). The elements hydrogen (H) and oxygen (O) exist as gases. Combined in a ratio of 2:1, they form the most abundant compound on Earth—water (H_2O). These are simple examples of organized matter having emergent properties: A compound has characteristics different from those of its elements.

Most of the compounds in living organisms contain at least three or four elements. Sugar, for example, is formed of carbon (C), hydrogen, and oxygen. Proteins are compounds containing carbon, hydrogen, oxygen, nitrogen (N), and a small amount of sulfur (S). Different arrangements of the atoms of these elements give rise to the unique properties of each compound.

About 25 elements are essential to life. As you can see in Table 2.1, four of these—oxygen, carbon, hydrogen, and nitrogen—make up about 96% of the weight of the human body, as well as that of most other living organisms. These four

TABLE 2.1 | ELEMENTS IN THE HUMAN BODY

Element	Symbol	Percentage of Body Weight (Including Water)	
Oxygen	O	65.0%	⎫
Carbon	C	18.5%	⎬ 96.3%
Hydrogen	H	9.5%	
Nitrogen	N	3.3%	⎭
Calcium	Ca	1.5%	⎫
Phosphorus	P	1.0%	
Potassium	K	0.4%	
Sulfur	S	0.3%	⎬ 3.7%
Sodium	Na	0.2%	
Chlorine	Cl	0.2%	
Magnesium	Mg	0.1%	⎭

Trace elements, less than 0.01% of human body weight: Boron (B), chromium (Cr), cobalt (Co), copper (Cu), fluorine (F), iodine (I), iron (Fe), manganese (Mn), molybdenum (Mo), selenium (Se), silicon (Si), tin (Sn), vanadium (V), zinc (Zn)

elements are the main ingredients of biological molecules such as proteins, sugars, and fats. Calcium (Ca), phosphorus (P), potassium (K), sulfur, sodium, chlorine, and magnesium (Mg) account for most of the remaining 4% of the human body. These elements are involved in such important functions as bone formation (calcium and phosphorus) and nerve signaling (potassium, sodium, calcium, and chlorine).

The **trace elements** listed at the bottom of the table are essential, but only in minute quantities. We explore the importance of trace elements to your health next.

 Explain how table salt illustrates the theme of emergent properties.

● The elements that make up the edible crystals of table salt, sodium and chlorine, are in pure form a metal and a poisonous gas.

Sodium   Chlorine   Sodium chloride

▲ **Figure 2.1** The emergent properties of the edible compound sodium chloride

2.2 Trace elements are common additives to food and water

Some trace elements, such as iron (Fe), are needed by all forms of life. Iron makes up only about 0.004% of your body weight but is vital for energy processing and for transporting oxygen in your blood. Other trace elements, such as iodine (I), are required only by certain species. You need to ingest only a tiny amount of iodine each day, about 0.15 milligram (mg). Iodine is an essential ingredient of a hormone produced by the thyroid gland, which is located in the neck. An iodine deficiency in the diet causes the thyroid gland to grow to abnormal size, a condition called goiter (Figure 2.2A). Iodine deficiency is also linked to mental retardation. Adding iodine to table salt has reduced the incidence of iodine deficiency in many countries. Unfortunately, iodized salt is not available everywhere, and an estimated 2 billion people

▲ Figure 2.2A   Goiter, a symptom of iodine deficiency, in a Burmese woman

worldwide have insufficient iodine intake. Seafood, kelp, strawberries, and dark, leafy greens are good natural sources. Thus, deficiencies are often found in inland regions, especially in areas where the soil is lacking in iodine. Although most common in developing nations, iodine deficiencies may also result from excessive consumption of highly processed foods (which often use non-iodized salt) and low-salt diets intended to lower the risk of cardiovascular disease.

Iodine is just one example of a trace element added to food or water to improve health. For more than 50 years, the American Dental Association has supported fluoridation of community drinking water as a public health measure. Fluoride is a form of fluorine (F), an element in Earth's crust that is found in small amounts in all water sources. In many areas, fluoride is added during the municipal water treatment process to raise levels to a concentration that can reduce tooth decay. If you mostly drink bottled water, your fluoride intake may be reduced, although some bottled water now contains added fluoride. Fluoride is also frequently added to dental products, such as toothpaste and mouthwash (Figure 2.2B).

Chemicals are added to food to help preserve it, make it more nutritious, or simply make it look better. Look at the nutrition facts label from the side of the cereal box in Figure 2.2C to see a familiar example of how foods are fortified with mineral elements. Iron, for example, is a trace element commonly added to foods. (You can actually see that iron has been added to a fortified cereal by crushing the cereal and then stirring a magnet through it.) Also note that the nutrition facts label lists numerous vitamins that are added to improve the nutritional value of the cereal. For instance, the cereal in this example supplies 10% of the

◀ Figure 2.2B
Mouthwash and toothpaste with added fluoride

recommended daily value for vitamin A. Vitamins consist of more than one element and are examples of compounds.

In the next module, we explore the structure of an atom and how this structure determines the chemical properties of elements.

? **In addition to iron, what other trace elements are found in the cereal in Figure 2.2C? Does Total provide the "total" amount needed of these elements?**

● Zinc and copper: Total provides 100% of the zinc but only 4% of the copper needed in a day.

▲ Figure 2.2C   Nutrition facts from a fortified cereal

Nutrition Facts
Serving Size ¾ cup (30g)
Servings Per Container about 17

Amount Per Serving	Whole Grain Total	with ½ cup skim milk
Calories	100	140
Calories from Fat	5	10
		% Daily Value**
Total Fat 0.5g*	1%	1%
Saturated Fat 0g	0%	0%
Trans Fat 0g		
Polyunsaturated Fat 0g		
Monounsaturated Fat 0g		
Cholesterol 0mg	0%	1%
Sodium 190mg	8%	11%
Potassium 90mg	3%	8%
Total Carbohydrate 23g	8%	10%
Dietary Fiber 3g	10%	10%
Sugars 5g		
Other Carbohydrate 15g		
Protein 2g		
Vitamin A	10%	15%
Vitamin C	100%	100%
Calcium	100%	110%
Iron	100%	100%
Vitamin D	10%	25%
Vitamin E	100%	100%
Thiamin	100%	100%
Riboflavin	100%	110%
Niacin	100%	100%
Vitamin B$_6$	100%	100%
Folic Acid	100%	100%
Vitamin B$_{12}$	100%	110%
Pantothenic Acid	100%	100%
Phosphorus	8%	20%
Magnesium	6%	10%
Zinc	100%	100%
Copper	4%	4%

* Amount in cereal. A serving of cereal plus skim milk provides 1g total fat, less than 5mg cholesterol, 260mg sodium, 290mg potassium, 29g total carbohydrate (11g sugars) and 7g protein.
** Percent Daily Values are based on a 2,000 calorie diet. Your daily values may be higher or lower depending on your calorie needs:

		Calories	2,000	2,500
Total Fat	Less than		65g	80g
Sat Fat	Less than		20g	25g
Cholesterol	Less than		300mg	300mg
Sodium	Less than		2,400mg	2,400mg
Potassium			3,500mg	3,500mg
Total Carbohydrate			300g	375g
Dietary Fiber			25g	30g

2.3 Atoms consist of protons, neutrons, and electrons

Each element consists of one kind of atom, which is different from the atoms of other elements. An **atom**, named from a Greek word meaning "indivisible," is the smallest unit of matter that still retains the properties of an element. Atoms are so small that it would take about a million of them to stretch across the period printed at the end of this sentence.

Subatomic Particles   Physicists have split the atom into more than a hundred types of subatomic particles. However, only three kinds of particles are relevant here. A **proton** is a subatomic particle with a single positive electrical charge ($+$). An **electron** is a subatomic particle with a single negative charge ($-$). A **neutron**, as its name implies, is electrically neutral (has no charge).

Figure 2.3A shows two very simple models of an atom of the element helium (He), the "lighter-than-air" gas that makes balloons rise. Notice that two protons (⊕) and two neutrons (●) are tightly packed in the atom's central core, or **nucleus**. Two electrons (⊖) move around the nucleus at nearly the speed of light. The attraction between the negatively charged electrons and the positively charged protons holds the electrons near the nucleus. The left-hand model shows the number of electrons in the atom. The right-hand model, slightly more realistic, shows a spherical cloud of negative charge created by the rapidly moving electrons. Neither model is drawn to scale. In real atoms, the electrons are very much smaller than the protons and neutrons, and the electron cloud is much bigger compared to the nucleus. Imagine that this atom was the size of a baseball stadium: The nucleus would be the size of a fly in center field, and the electrons would be like two tiny gnats buzzing around the stadium.

Atomic Number and Atomic Mass   All atoms of a particular element have the same unique number of protons. This number is the element's **atomic number**. Thus, an atom of helium, with 2 protons, has an atomic number of 2. Carbon, with 6 protons, has an atomic number of 6 (Figure 2.3B). Note that in these atoms, the atomic number is also the number of

TABLE 2.3 | ISOTOPES OF CARBON

	Carbon-12		Carbon-13		Carbon-14	
Protons	6	} Mass number 12	6	} Mass number 13	6	} Mass number 14
Neutrons	6		7		8	
Electrons	6		6		6	

electrons. Unless otherwise indicated, an atom has an equal number of protons and electrons, and thus its net electrical charge is 0 (zero).

An atom's **mass number** is the sum of the number of protons and neutrons in its nucleus. For helium, the mass number is 4; for carbon, it is 12 (Figures 2.3A and 2.3B). The mass of a proton and the mass of a neutron are almost identical and are expressed in a unit of measurement called the dalton. Protons and neutrons each have masses close to 1 dalton. An electron has only about 1/2,000 the mass of a proton, so it contributes very little to an atom's mass. Thus, an atom's **atomic mass** (or weight) is approximately equal to its mass number—the sum of its protons and neutrons.

Isotopes   All atoms of an element have the same atomic number, but some atoms of that element may differ in mass number. The different **isotopes** of an element have the same number of protons and behave identically in chemical reactions, but they have different numbers of neutrons. Table 2.3 shows the numbers of subatomic particles in the three isotopes of carbon. Carbon-12 (also written ^{12}C), with 6 neutrons, accounts for about 99% of the carbon in nature. Most of the remaining 1% consists of carbon-13 (^{13}C), with 7 neutrons. A third isotope, carbon-14 (^{14}C), with 8 neutrons, occurs in minute quantities. Notice that all three isotopes have 6 protons—otherwise, they would not be carbon.

Both ^{12}C and ^{13}C are stable isotopes, meaning their nuclei remain intact more or less forever. The isotope ^{14}C, on the other hand, is unstable, or radioactive. A **radioactive isotope** is one in which the nucleus decays spontaneously, giving off particles and energy. Radiation from decaying isotopes can damage cellular molecules and thus can pose serious risks to living organisms. But radioactive isotopes can be helpful, as in their use in dating fossils (see Module 15.5). They are also used in biological research and medicine, as we see next.

? A nitrogen atom has 7 protons, and its most common isotope has 7 neutrons. A radioactive isotope of nitrogen has 9 neutrons. What is the atomic number and mass number of this radioactive nitrogen?

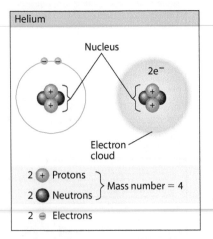

▲ **Figure 2.3A**   Two models of a helium atom

Helium

Nucleus

$2e^-$

Electron cloud

2 ⊕ Protons
2 ● Neutrons } Mass number = 4
2 ⊖ Electrons

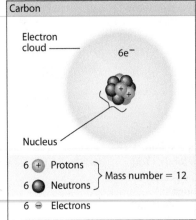

▲ **Figure 2.3B**   Model of a carbon atom

Carbon

Electron cloud

$6e^-$

Nucleus

6 ⊕ Protons
6 ● Neutrons } Mass number = 12
6 ⊖ Electrons

| ## 2.4 Radioactive isotopes can help or harm us

Living cells cannot distinguish between isotopes of the same element. Consequently, organisms take up and use compounds containing radioactive isotopes in the usual way. Because radioactivity is easily detected by instruments, radioactive isotopes are useful as tracers—biological spies, in effect—for monitoring the fate of atoms in living organisms.

Basic Research   Biologists often use radioactive tracers to follow molecules as they undergo chemical changes in an organism. For example, researchers have used carbon dioxide (CO_2) containing the radioactive isotope ^{14}C to study photosynthesis. Using sunlight to power the conversion, plants take in CO_2 from the air and use it to make sugar molecules. Radioactively labeled CO_2 has enabled researchers to trace the sequence of molecules made by plants in the chemical route from CO_2 to sugar.

Medical Diagnosis and Treatment   Radioactive isotopes may also be used to tag chemicals that accumulate in specific areas of the body, such as phosphorus in bones. After injection of such a tracer, a special camera produces an image of where the radiation collects. In most diagnostic uses, the patient receives only a tiny amount of an isotope.

Sometimes radioactive isotopes are used for treatment. As you learned in Module 2.2, the body uses iodine to make a thyroid hormone. Because radioactive iodine accumulates in the thyroid, it can be used to kill cancer cells there.

Substances that the body metabolizes such as glucose or oxygen, may also be labeled with a radioactive isotope. **Figure 2.4A** shows a patient being examined by a PET (positron-emission tomography) scanner, which can produce three-dimensional images of areas of the body with high metabolic activity. PET is useful for diagnosing certain heart disorders and cancers and for basic research on the brain (see Module 28.17).

The early detection of Alzheimer's disease may be a new use for such techniques. This devastating illness gradually destroys a person's memory and ability to think. As the disease progresses, the brain becomes riddled with deposits (plaques) of a protein

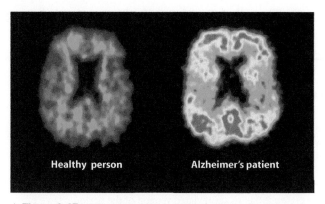
▲ **Figure 2.4B**   PET images of brains of a healthy person (left) and a person with Alzheimer's disease (right). Red and yellow colors indicate high levels of PIB bound to beta-amyloid plaques.

called beta-amyloid. Researchers have identified a protein molecule called PIB that binds to beta-amyloid. PIB contains a radioactive isotope that can be detected on a PET scan. **Figure 2.4B** shows PET images of the brains of a healthy person (left) and a person with Alzheimer's (right) injected with PIB. Notice that the brain of the Alzheimer's patient has high levels of PIB (red and yellow areas), whereas the unaffected person's brain has lower levels (blue). New therapies are focused on limiting the production of beta-amyloid or clearing it from the brain. A diagnostic test using PIB would allow researchers to monitor the effectiveness of new drugs in people living with the disease.

Dangers   Although radioactive isotopes have many beneficial uses, uncontrolled exposure to them can harm living organisms by damaging molecules, especially DNA. The particles and energy thrown off by radioactive atoms can break chemical bonds and also cause abnormal bonds to form. The explosion of a nuclear reactor at Chernobyl, Ukraine, in 1986 released large amounts of radioactive isotopes into the environment, which drifted over large areas of Russia, Belarus, and Europe. A few dozen people died from acute radiation poisoning, and over 100,000 people were evacuated from the immediate area. Increased rates of thyroid cancer in children exposed to the radiation have been reported, and many thousands may be at increased risk of future cancers.

Natural sources of radiation can also pose a threat. Radon, a radioactive gas, may be a cause of lung cancer. Radon can contaminate buildings in regions where underlying rocks naturally contain uranium, a radioactive element. Homeowners can buy a radon detector or hire a company to test their home to ensure that radon levels are safe. If levels are found to be unsafe, technology exists to remove radon from homes.

? **Why are radioactive isotopes useful as tracers in research on the chemistry of life?**

● Organisms incorporate radioactive isotopes of an element into their molecules, and researchers can use special scanning devices to detect the presence of these isotopes in biological pathways or locations in the body.

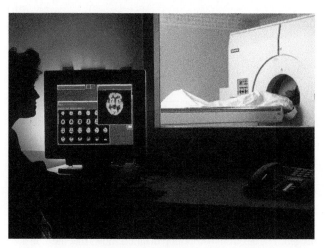

▲ **Figure 2.4A**   Technician monitoring the output of a PET scanner

Chemical Bonds

2.5 The distribution of electrons determines an atom's chemical properties

To understand how atoms interact with each other—the main subject of this section—we need to explore atomic structure further. Of the three subatomic particles—protons, neutrons, and electrons—only electrons are directly involved in the chemical activity of an atom. Electrons vary in the amount of energy they possess. The farther an electron is from the positively charged nucleus, the greater its energy. Electrons move around the nucleus only at certain energy levels, called **electron shells**. Depending on an element's atomic number, an atom may have one, two, or more electron shells surrounding the nucleus.

Figure 2.5 is an abbreviated version of the periodic table of the elements (see Appendix 2). It shows the distribution of electrons for the first 18 elements, arranged in rows according to the number of electron shells (one, two, or three). Within each shell, electrons travel in different *orbitals*, which are discrete volumes of space in which electrons are most likely to be found.

Each orbital can hold a maximum of 2 electrons. The first electron shell has only one orbital and can hold only 2 electrons. Thus, hydrogen and helium are the only elements in the first row. For the second and third rows, the outer shell has four orbitals and can hold up to 8 electrons (four pairs). Note that the number of electrons increases by one as you read from left to right across each row in the table and that the electrons don't pair up until all orbitals have at least one electron.

It is the number of electrons in the outermost shell, called the valence shell, that determines the chemical properties of an atom. Atoms whose outer shells are not full (have unpaired electrons) tend to interact with other atoms—that is, to participate in chemical reactions.

Look at the electron shells of the atoms of the four elements that are the main components of biological molecules (highlighted in green in Figure 2.5). Because their outer shells are incomplete all these atoms react readily with other atoms. The hydrogen atom has only 1 electron in its single electron shell, which can accommodate 2 electrons. Atoms of carbon, nitrogen, and oxygen also are reactive because their valence shells, which can hold 8 electrons, are also incomplete. In contrast, the helium atom has a first-level shell that is full with 2 electrons. Neon and argon also have full outer electron shells. As a result, these elements are chemically inert (unreactive).

How do chemical interactions between atoms enable them to fill their outer electron shells? When two atoms with incomplete outer shells react, each atom will share, donate, or receive electrons, so that both partners end up with completed outer shells. These interactions usually result in atoms staying close together, held by attractions known as **chemical bonds.** In the next two modules, we look at two important types of chemical bonds.

? **How many electrons and electron shells does a sodium atom have? How many electrons are in its valence shell?**

● 11 electrons; 3 electron shells; 1 electron in the outer shell

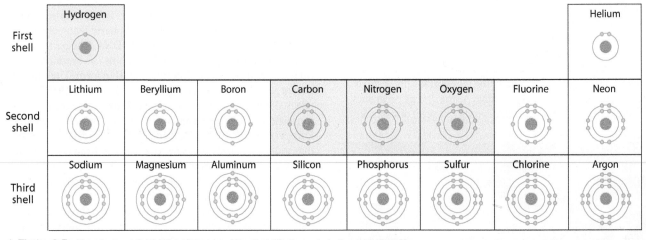

▲ Figure 2.5   The electron distribution diagrams of the first 18 elements in the periodic table

2.6 Covalent bonds join atoms into molecules through electron sharing

The strongest kind of chemical bond is the **covalent bond**, in which two atoms *share* one or more pairs of outer-shell electrons. Two or more atoms held together by covalent bonds form a **molecule**. For example, a covalent bond connects two hydrogen atoms in a molecule of the gas H_2.

Table 2.6, on the next page, shows four ways to represent this molecule. The symbol H_2, called the molecular formula, tells you that a hydrogen molecule consists of two atoms of hydrogen. The electron distribution diagram shows that the atoms share two electrons; as a result, both atoms fill their outer (and

TABLE 2.6 | ALTERNATIVE WAYS TO REPRESENT FOUR COMMON MOLECULES

Molecular Formula	Electron Distribution Diagram	Structural Formula	Space-Filling Model
H_2 Hydrogen	(H) (H)	H—H Single bond	
O_2 Oxygen	(O) (O)	O=O Double bond	
H_2O Water	(O) (H) (H)	H O H	
CH_4 Methane	(H) (H) (C) (H) (H)	H | H—C—H | H	

only) shells. The third column shows a structural formula. The line between the hydrogen atoms represents the single covalent bond formed by the sharing of a pair of electrons (1 electron from each atom). A space-filling model, shown in the fourth column, uses color-coded balls to symbolize atoms and comes closest to showing a molecule's shape.

How many covalent bonds can an atom form? It depends on the number of additional electrons needed to fill its outer, or valence, shell. This number is called the *valence*, or bonding capacity, of an atom. Looking back at the electron distribution diagrams in Figure 2.5, we see that H can form one bond; O can form two; N, three; and C, four.

In an oxygen molecule (O_2), shown next in Table 2.6, the two oxygen atoms share two pairs of electrons, forming a double bond. A double bond is indicated by a pair of lines.

H_2 and O_2 are molecules composed of only one element. The third example in the table is a compound. Water (H_2O) is a molecule in which two hydrogen atoms are joined to oxygen by single bonds. And as shown at the bottom of Table 2.6, it takes four hydrogen atoms, each with a valence of 1, to satisfy carbon's valence of 4. This compound, methane (CH_4), is a major component of natural gas.

Atoms in a molecule are in a constant tug-of-war for the shared electrons of their covalent bonds. An atom's

attraction for shared electrons is called its **electronegativity**. The more electronegative an atom, the more strongly it pulls shared electrons toward its nucleus. In molecules of only one element, such as O_2 and H_2, the two identical atoms exert an equal pull on the electrons. The bonds in such molecules are said to be **nonpolar covalent bonds** because the electrons are shared equally between the atoms. Compounds such as methane also have nonpolar bonds, because the atoms of carbon and hydrogen are not substantially different in electronegativity.

In contrast to O_2, H_2, and CH_4, water is composed of atoms with different electronegativities. Oxygen is one of the most electronegative of the elements. (Nitrogen is also highly electronegative.) As indicated by the arrows in Figure 2.6, oxygen attracts the shared electrons in H_2O much more strongly than does hydrogen, so that the electrons spend more time near the oxygen atom than near the hydrogen atoms. This unequal sharing of electrons produces a **polar covalent bond**. In a polar covalent bond, the pulling of shared, negatively charged electrons closer to the more electronegative atom makes that atom partially negative and the other atom partially positive. Thus, in H_2O, the oxygen atom actually has a slight negative charge and each hydrogen atom a slight positive charge. Because of its polar covalent bonds and the wide V shape of the molecule, water is a **polar molecule**—that is, it has an unequal distribution of charges. It is slightly negative at the oxygen end of the molecule (point of the V) and slightly positive at each of the two hydrogen ends.

In some cases, two atoms are so unequal in their attraction for electrons that the more electronegative atom strips an electron completely away from its partner, as we see next.

? **What is chemically nonsensical about this structure?**

$$H—C=C—H$$

● Each carbon atom has only three covalent bonds instead of the four required by its valence.

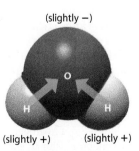

(slightly −)

(slightly +)   (slightly +)

▲ **Figure 2.6**   A water molecule, with polar covalent bonds

2.7 Ionic bonds are attractions between ions of opposite charge

Table salt is an example of how the transfer of electrons can bond atoms together. **Figure 2.7A** shows how a sodium atom and a chlorine atom can form the compound sodium chloride (NaCl). Notice that sodium has only 1 electron in its outer shell, whereas chlorine has 7. When these atoms interact, the sodium atom donates its single outer electron to chlorine. Sodium now has only two shells, the outer shell having a full set of 8 electrons. When chlorine accepts sodium's electron, its own outer shell is now full with 8 electrons.

Remember that electrons are negatively charged particles. The transfer of an electron between the two atoms moves one unit of negative charge from one atom to the other. As you can see on the right in Figure 2.7A, sodium, with 11 protons but now only 10 electrons, has a net electrical charge of 1+. Chlorine, having gained an extra electron, now has 18 electrons but only 17 protons, giving it a net electrical charge of 1−. In each case, an atom has become what is called an ion. An **ion** is an atom or molecule with an electrical charge resulting from a gain or loss of one or more electrons. (As shown in the figure, the ion formed from chlorine is called a chloride ion.) Two ions with opposite charges attract each other. When the attraction holds them together, it is called

an **ionic bond**. The resulting compound, in this case NaCl, is electrically neutral.

Sodium chloride is a familiar type of **salt**, a synonym for an ionic compound. Salts often exist as crystals in nature. **Figure 2.7B** shows the ions Na⁺ and Cl⁻ in a crystal of sodium chloride. An NaCl crystal can be of any size (there is no fixed number of ions), but sodium and chloride ions are always present in a 1:1 ratio. The ratio of ions can differ in the various kinds of salts.

The environment affects the strength of ionic bonds. In a dry salt crystal, the bonds are so strong that it takes a hammer and chisel to break enough of them to crack the crystal. If the same salt crystal is placed in water, however, the ionic bonds break when the ions interact with water molecules and the salt dissolves, as we'll discuss in Module 2.13. Most drugs are manufactured as salts because they are quite stable when dry but can dissolve easily in water.

? Explain what holds together the atoms in a crystal of table salt (NaCl).

Opposite charges attract. The positively charged sodium ions (Na⁺) and the negatively charged chloride ions (Cl⁻) are held together by ionic bonds, attractions between oppositely charged ions.

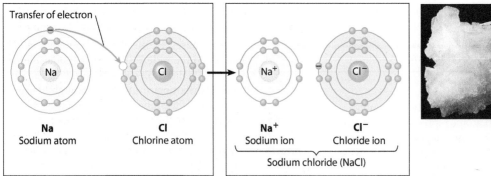

▲ **Figure 2.7A** Formation of an ionic bond, producing sodium chloride

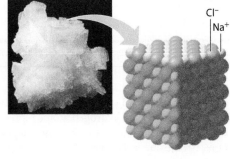

▲ **Figure 2.7B** A crystal of sodium chloride

2.8 Hydrogen bonds are weak bonds important in the chemistry of life

In living organisms, most of the strong chemical bonds are covalent, linking atoms to form a cell's molecules. But crucial to the functioning of a cell are weaker bonds within and between molecules, such as the ionic bonds we just discussed. Most large molecules are held in their three-dimensional shape by weak bonds. In addition, molecules in a cell may be held together briefly by weak bonds, respond to one another in some way, and then separate.

As you saw in Module 2.6, a hydrogen atom that has formed a polar covalent bond with an electronegative atom (such as oxygen or nitrogen) has a partial positive charge.

This partial positive charge allows it to be attracted to a nearby partially negative atom (often an oxygen or nitrogen) of another molecule. These weak but important bonds are best illustrated with water molecules, as shown in **Figure 2.8**. The charged regions on each water molecule are electrically attracted to oppositely charged regions on neighboring molecules. Because the positively charged region in this special type of bond is always a hydrogen atom, the bond is called a **hydrogen bond**. As Figure 2.8 shows, the negative (oxygen) pole of a water molecule can form hydrogen bonds (dotted lines) to two hydrogen atoms. And each hydrogen atom of

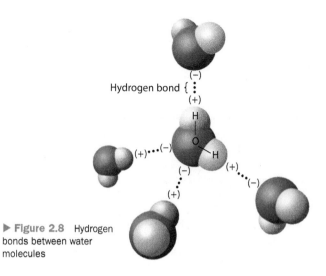

▶ Figure 2.8 Hydrogen bonds between water molecules

a water molecule can form a hydrogen bond with a nearby partial negative oxygen atom of another water molecule. Thus, each H_2O molecule can hydrogen-bond to as many as four partners.

You will learn in Chapter 3 how hydrogen bonds help to create a protein's shape (and thus its function) and hold the two strands of a DNA molecule together. Later in this chapter, we explore how water's polarity and hydrogen bonds give it unique, life-supporting properties. But first we discuss how the making and breaking of bonds change the composition of matter.

? **What enables neighboring water molecules to hydrogen-bond to one another?**

● The molecules are polar, with the negative (oxygen end) of one molecule attracted to a positive end (hydrogen end) of its neighbor.

2.9 Chemical reactions make and break chemical bonds

The basic chemistry of life has an overarching theme: The structure of atoms and molecules determines the way they behave. As we have seen, the chemical behavior of an atom is determined by the number and arrangement of its subatomic particles, particularly its electrons. Other properties emerge when atoms combine to form molecules and when molecules interact. Water is a good example, because its emergent properties sustain all life on Earth.

Hydrogen and oxygen gases can react to form water:

$$2\,H_2 + O_2 \longrightarrow 2\,H_2O$$

This is a **chemical reaction**, the breaking and making of chemical bonds, leading to changes in the composition of matter. In this case, two molecules of hydrogen (2 H_2) react with one molecule of oxygen (O_2) to produce two molecules of water (2 H_2O). The arrow indicates the conversion of the starting materials, called the **reactants**, to the **product**, the material resulting from the chemical reaction. Notice that the same *numbers* of hydrogen and oxygen atoms appear on the left and right sides of the arrow, although they are grouped differently. Chemical reactions do not create or destroy matter; they only rearrange it in various ways. As

shown in **Figure 2.9**, the covalent bonds (represented here as white "sticks" between atoms) holding hydrogen atoms together in H_2 and holding oxygen atoms together in O_2 are broken, and new bonds are formed to yield the H_2O product molecules.

Organisms cannot make water from H_2 and O_2, but they do carry out a great number of chemical reactions that rearrange matter in significant ways. Let's examine a chemical reaction that is essential to life on Earth: photosynthesis. The raw materials of photosynthesis are carbon dioxide (CO_2), which is taken from the air, and water (H_2O), which plants absorb from the soil. Within green plant cells, sunlight powers the conversion of these reactants to the sugar product glucose ($C_6H_{12}O_6$) and oxygen (O_2), a by-product that the plant releases into the air. The following chemical shorthand summarizes the process:

$$6\,CO_2 + 6\,H_2O \longrightarrow C_6H_{12}O_6 + 6\,O_2$$

Although photosynthesis is actually a sequence of many chemical reactions, we see that we end up with the same number and kinds of atoms we started with. Matter has simply been rearranged, with an input of energy provided by sunlight.

The chemistry of life is dynamic. Living cells routinely carry out thousands of chemical reactions. These reactions take place in the watery environment of a cell, and we look at the life-supporting properties of water next.

? **Fill in the blanks with the correct numbers in the following chemical process:**

$$C_6H_{12}O_6 + \underline{}O_2 \longrightarrow \underline{}CO_2 + \underline{}H_2O$$

What process do you think this reaction represents? (*Hint:* Think about how your cells use these reactants to produce energy.)

● $C_6H_{12}O_6 + 6\,O_2 \longrightarrow 6\,CO_2 + 6\,H_2O$; the breakdown of sugar in the presence of oxygen to carbon dioxide and water, with the release of energy that the cell can use

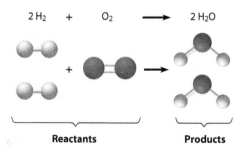

$$2\,H_2 \quad + \quad O_2 \quad \longrightarrow \quad 2\,H_2O$$

Reactants   Products

▲ Figure 2.9 Breaking and making of bonds in a chemical reaction

Water's Life-Supporting Properties

2.10 Hydrogen bonds make liquid water cohesive

We can trace water's life-supporting properties to the structure and interactions of its molecules—their polarity and resulting hydrogen bonding between molecules (review Figure 2.8).

Hydrogen bonds between molecules of liquid water last for only a few trillionths of a second, yet at any instant, many molecules are hydrogen-bonded to others. This tendency of molecules of the same kind to stick together, called **cohesion**, is much stronger for water than for most other liquids. The cohesion of water is important in the living world. Trees, for example, depend on cohesion to help transport water and nutrients from their roots to their leaves. The evaporation of water from a leaf exerts a pulling force on water within the veins of the leaf. Because of cohesion, the force is relayed all the way down to the roots. **Adhesion**, the clinging of one substance to another, also plays a role. The adhesion of water to the cell walls of a plant's thin veins helps counter the downward pull of gravity.

Related to cohesion is **surface tension**, a measure of how difficult it is to stretch or break the surface of a liquid.

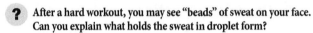
◀ **Figure 2.10** Surface tension allows a water strider to walk on water.

Hydrogen bonds give water unusually high surface tension, making it behave as though it were coated with an invisible film. You can observe the surface tension of water by slightly overfilling a glass; the water will stand above the rim. The water strider in **Figure 2.10** takes advantage of the high surface tension of water to "stride" across ponds without breaking the surface.

? After a hard workout, you may see "beads" of sweat on your face. Can you explain what holds the sweat in droplet form?

● The cohesion of water molecules and its high surface tension hold water in droplets. The adhesion of water to your skin helps hold the beads in place.

2.11 Water's hydrogen bonds moderate temperature

If you have ever burned your finger on a metal pot while waiting for the water in it to boil, you know that water heats up much more slowly than metal. In fact, because of hydrogen bonding, water has a stronger resistance to temperature change than most other substances.

Temperature and heat are related but different. A swimmer crossing San Francisco Bay has a higher temperature than the water, but the bay contains far more heat because of its immense volume. **Heat** is the amount of energy associated with the movement of atoms and molecules in a body of matter. **Temperature** measures the intensity of heat—that is, the *average* speed of molecules rather than the *total* amount of heat energy in a body of matter.

Heat must be absorbed in order to break hydrogen bonds, and heat is released when hydrogen bonds form. To raise the temperature of water, heat energy must first disrupt hydrogen bonds before water molecules can move faster. Thus, water absorbs a large amount of heat while warming up only a few degrees. Conversely, when water cools, more hydrogen bonds form, and a considerable amount of heat is released.

Earth's giant water supply moderates temperatures, helping to keep them within limits that permit life. Oceans, lakes, and rivers store a huge amount of heat from the sun during warm periods. Heat given off from gradually cooling water warms the air. That's why coastal areas generally have milder climates than inland regions. Water's resistance to temperature change also stabilizes ocean temperatures, creating a favorable environment for marine life. Since water accounts

◀ **Figure 2.11** Evaporative cooling occurs as sweat dries.

for approximately 66% of your body weight, it also helps moderate your temperature.

When a substance evaporates (changes physical state from a liquid to a gas), the surface of the liquid that remains behind cools down. This **evaporative cooling** occurs because the molecules with the greatest energy (the "hottest" ones) leave. It's as if the 10 fastest runners on the track team left school, lowering the average speed of the remaining team. Evaporative cooling helps prevent some land-dwelling organisms from overheating. Evaporation from a plant's leaves keeps them from becoming too warm in the sun, just as sweating helps dissipate our excess body heat (**Figure 2.11**). On a much larger scale, the evaporation of surface waters cools tropical seas.

? Explain the popular adage "It's not the heat, it's the humidity."

● High humidity hampers cooling by slowing the evaporation of sweat.

2.12 Ice is less dense than liquid water

Water exists on Earth in the form of a gas (water vapor), liquid, and solid. Unlike most substances, water is less dense as a solid than as a liquid. And as you might guess, this unusual property is due to hydrogen bonds.

As water freezes, each molecule forms stable hydrogen bonds with its neighbors, holding them at "arm's length" and creating a three-dimensional crystal. In Figure 2.12, compare the spaciously arranged molecules in the ice crystal with the more tightly packed molecules in the liquid water. The ice crystal has fewer molecules than an equal volume of liquid water. Therefore, ice is less dense and floats on top of liquid water.

If ice sank, then eventually ponds, lakes, and even oceans would freeze solid. Instead, when a deep body of water cools, the floating ice insulates the water below from colder air above. This "blanket" prevents the water below from freezing and allows fish and many other aquatic forms of life to survive under the frozen surface.

In the Arctic, this frozen surface serves as the winter hunting ground for polar bears (Figure 2.12). The shrinking of this ice cover as a result of global warming may doom these bears.

? **Explain how the freezing of water can crack boulders.**

● Water in the crevices of a boulder expands as it freezes because the water molecules become spaced farther apart in forming ice crystals, cracking the rock.

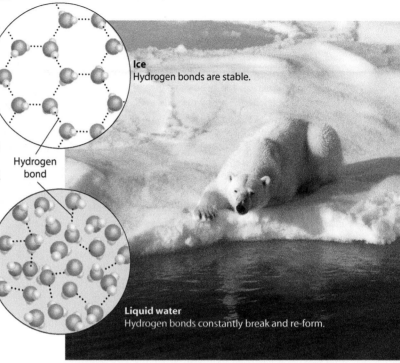

Ice
Hydrogen bonds are stable.

Hydrogen bond

Liquid water
Hydrogen bonds constantly break and re-form.

▲ **Figure 2.12** Hydrogen bonds between water molecules in ice and water

2.13 Water is the solvent of life

If you add a teaspoon of table salt to a glass of water, the salt will dissolve and eventually become evenly mixed with the water, forming a solution. A **solution** is a liquid consisting of a uniform mixture of two or more substances. The dissolving agent (in this case, water) is the **solvent**, and a substance that is dissolved (salt) is a **solute**. An **aqueous solution** (from the Latin *aqua*, water) is one in which water is the solvent.

Water's versatility as a solvent results from the polarity of its molecules. **Figure 2.13** shows how a teaspoon of salt dissolves in water. At the surface of each grain, or crystal, the sodium and chloride ions are exposed to water. These ions and the water molecules are attracted to each other due to their opposite charges. The oxygen ends (red) of the water molecules have a partial negative charge and cling to the positive sodium ions (Na⁺). The hydrogens of the water molecules, with their partial positive charge, are attracted to the negative chloride ions (Cl⁻). Working inward from the surface of each salt crystal, water molecules eventually surround and separate all the ions. Water dissolves other ionic compounds as well. Seawater, for instance, contains a great variety of dissolved ions, as do your cells.

A compound doesn't need to be ionic to dissolve in water. A spoonful of sugar will also dissolve in a glass of water. Polar molecules such as sugar dissolve as water molecules surround them and form hydrogen bonds with their polar regions. Even large molecules, such as proteins, can dissolve if they have ionic or polar regions on their surface. As the solvent inside all cells, in blood, and in plant sap, water dissolves an enormous variety of solutes necessary for life.

? **Why are blood and most other biological fluids classified as aqueous solutions?**

● The solvent is water.

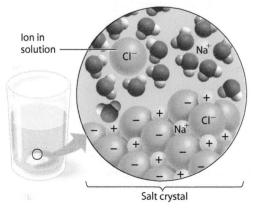

Ion in solution

Salt crystal

▲ **Figure 2.13** A crystal of salt (NaCl) dissolving in water

2.14 The chemistry of life is sensitive to acidic and basic conditions

In aqueous solutions, a very small percentage of the water molecules actually break apart (dissociate) into ions. The ions formed are called hydrogen ions (H^+) and hydroxide ions (OH^-). Hydrogen and hydroxide ions are very reactive. The proper balance of these ions is critical for the chemical processes that occur within an organism.

Some chemical compounds contribute additional H^+ to an aqueous solution, whereas others remove H^+ from it. A compound that donates hydrogen ions to solutions is called an **acid**. One example of a strong acid is hydrochloric acid (HCl), the acid in the gastric juice in your stomach. In solution, HCl dissociates completely into H^+ and Cl^-. An acidic solution has a higher concentration of H^+ than OH^-.

A **base** is a compound that accepts hydrogen ions and removes them from solution. Some bases, such as sodium hydroxide (NaOH), do this by donating OH^-; the OH^- combines with H^+ to form H_2O, thus reducing the H^+ concentration. Sodium hydroxide, also called lye, is a common ingredient in oven cleaners. The more basic a solution, the higher its OH^- concentration and the lower its H^+ concentration. Basic solutions are also called alkaline solutions.

We use the **pH scale** to describe how acidic or basic a solution is (pH stands for potential of hydrogen). As shown in **Figure 2.14**, the scale ranges from 0 (most acidic) to 14 (most basic). Each pH unit represents a 10-fold change in the concentration of H^+ in a solution. For example, lemon juice at pH 2 has 10 times more H^+ than an equal amount of a cola at pH 3 and 100 times more H^+ than tomato juice at pH 4.

Pure water and aqueous solutions that are neither acidic nor basic are said to be neutral; they have a pH of 7. They do contain some hydrogen and hydroxide ions, but the concentrations of the two kinds of ions are equal. The pH of the solution inside most living cells is close to 7. Even a slight change in pH can be harmful because the proteins and other complex molecules in cells are extremely sensitive to the concentrations of H^+ and OH^-.

The pH of human blood plasma (the fluid portion of the blood) is very close to 7.4. A person cannot survive for more than a few minutes if the blood pH drops to 7.0 or rises to 7.8. If you add a small amount of a strong acid to a liter of pure water, the pH drops from 7.0 to 2.0. If the same amount of acid is added to a liter of blood, however, the pH decrease is only from 7.4 to 7.3. How can the acid have so much less effect on the pH of blood? Biological fluids contain **buffers**, substances that minimize changes in pH. They do so by accepting H^+ when it is in excess and donating H^+ when it is depleted. There are several types of buffers that contribute to the pH stability in blood and many other internal solutions.

In the next module, we explore how changes in acidity can have environmental consequences.

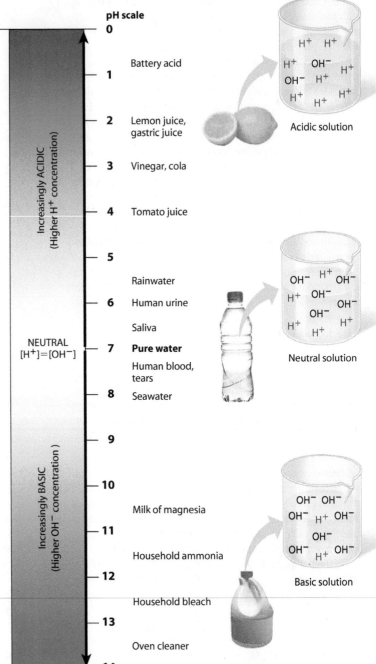

pH scale

0	
1	Battery acid
2	Lemon juice, gastric juice
3	Vinegar, cola
4	Tomato juice
5	
6	Rainwater / Human urine / Saliva
7	**Pure water** / Human blood, tears
8	Seawater
9	
10	
11	Milk of magnesia
12	Household ammonia
13	Household bleach
14	Oven cleaner

Increasingly ACIDIC (Higher H^+ concentration)

NEUTRAL [H^+]=[OH^-]

Increasingly BASIC (Higher OH^- concentration)

Acidic solution

Neutral solution

Basic solution

▲ **Figure 2.14** The pH scale reflects the relative concentrations of H^+ and OH^-.

> **?** Compared to a basic solution at pH 9, the same volume of an acidic solution at pH 4 has _____ times more hydrogen ions (H^+).

● 100,000

2.15 Acid precipitation and ocean acidification threaten the environment

Considering the dependence of all life on water, contamination of rivers, lakes, seas, and precipitation poses serious environmental problems. The burning of fossil fuels (coal, oil, and gas), which releases air-polluting compounds and large amounts of CO_2 into the atmosphere, is among the many threats to water quality posed by human activities. Chemical reactions of these compounds with water increase acidity and alter the delicate balance of conditions for life on Earth.

Sulfur oxides and nitrogen oxides released by burning fossil fuels react with water in the air to form strong acids, which fall to Earth with rain or snow. **Acid precipitation** refers to rain, snow, or fog with a pH lower than 5.2 (the pH of uncontaminated rain is 5.6). Acid precipitation has damaged life in lakes and streams and adversely affected plants through changes in soil chemistry. In the United States, amendments made in 1990 to the Clean Air Act have reduced acid precipitation and improved the health of most North American lakes and forests.

Carbon dioxide is the main product of fossil fuel combustion, and its steadily increasing release into the atmosphere is linked to global climate change (see Module 38.6). About 25% of human-generated CO_2 is absorbed by the oceans. An increase in CO_2 absorption is expected to change ocean chemistry and harm marine life and ecosystems.

In **ocean acidification**, CO_2 dissolving in seawater lowers ocean pH. That's because CO_2 reacts with water to produce carbonic acid (H_2CO_3). The change in acidity decreases the concentration of carbonate ions, which are required by corals and other organisms to produce their skeletons or shells, a

▲ **Figure 2.15** Coral reefs are threatened by ocean acidification.

process called calcification. Coral reef ecosystems act as havens for a great diversity of organisms (Figure 2.15). Other calcifying organisms are important food sources for salmon, herring, and other ocean fishes. Decreased calcification is likely to affect marine food webs and may substantially alter the productivity and biodiversity of Earth's oceans.

? **What is the relationship between fossil fuel consumption and coral reefs?**

● Some of the increased CO_2 released by burning fossil fuels dissolves in and lowers the pH of the oceans. A lower pH reduces levels of carbonate ions, which then lowers the rate of calcification by coral animals.

2.16 The search for extraterrestrial life centers on the search for water

When astrobiologists search for signs of extraterrestrial life on distant planets, they look for evidence of water. Why? As we've seen in this chapter, the emergent properties of water (its cohesion, ability to moderate temperature and insulate, and versatility as a solvent) support life on Earth in many ways. Is it possible that some form of life has evolved on other planets that have water in their environment?

Researchers with the National Aeronautics and Space Administration (NASA) have found evidence that water was once abundant on Mars. In January 2004, NASA succeeded in landing two golf-cart-sized rovers, named *Spirit* and *Opportunity*, on Mars. These robotic geologists, using sophisticated instruments to determine the composition of rocks, detected a mineral that is formed only in the presence of water. And pictures sent back from the rovers and various orbiting Mars spacecraft have revealed physical evidence of past water.

In 2008, an analysis of Martian soil by the *Phoenix Mars Lander* provided evidence that components of the soil had at one time been dissolved in water. Figure 2.16 shows a robotic arm of *Phoenix* that has gathered samples and scraped trenches that exposed ice just below the surface on Mars.

▶ **Figure 2.16** Robotic arm of the *Phoenix Mars Lander* probing for evidence of water

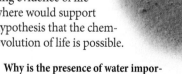

No evidence for life on Mars has yet been found. But is it possible that life is not unique to planet Earth? Chapter 15 presents evidence that life could originate in the environment of early Earth. Finding evidence of life elsewhere would support the hypothesis that the chemical evolution of life is possible.

? **Why is the presence of water important in the search for extraterrestrial life?**

● Water plays important roles in life as we know it, from moderating temperatures on the planet to functioning as the solvent of life.

Reviewing the Concepts

Elements, Atoms, and Compounds (2.1–2.4)

2.1 Organisms are composed of elements, in combinations called compounds. Oxygen, carbon, hydrogen, and nitrogen make up about 96% of living matter.

2.2 Trace elements are common additives to food and water.

2.3 Atoms consist of protons, neutrons, and electrons.

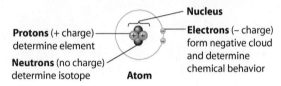

2.4 Radioactive isotopes can help or harm us. Radioactive isotopes are valuable in basic research and medicine.

Chemical Bonds (2.5–2.9)

2.5 The distribution of electrons determines an atom's chemical properties. An atom whose outer electron shell is not full tends to interact with other atoms and share, gain, or lose electrons, resulting in attractions called chemical bonds.

2.6 Covalent bonds join atoms into molecules through electron sharing. In a nonpolar covalent bond, electrons are shared equally. In polar covalent bonds, such as those found in water, electrons are pulled closer to the more electronegative atom.

2.7 Ionic bonds are attractions between ions of opposite charge. Electron gain and loss create charged atoms, called ions.

2.8 Hydrogen bonds are weak bonds important in the chemistry of life. The slightly positively charged H atoms in one polar molecule may be attracted to the partial negative charge of an O or N atom in a neighboring molecule.

2.9 Chemical reactions make and break chemical bonds. The composition of matter is changed as bonds are broken and formed to convert reactants to products.

Water's Life-Supporting Properties (2.10–2.16)

2.10 Hydrogen bonds make water molecules cohesive. Cohesion creates surface tension and allows water to move from plant roots to leaves.

2.11 Water's hydrogen bonds moderate temperature. Heat is absorbed when hydrogen bonds break and released when hydrogen bonds form. This helps keep temperatures relatively steady. As the most energetic water molecules evaporate, the surface of a substance cools.

2.12 Ice is less dense than liquid water. Floating ice protects lakes and oceans from freezing solid.

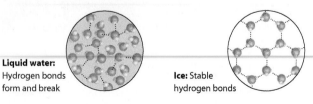

Liquid water: Hydrogen bonds form and break

Ice: Stable hydrogen bonds

2.13 Water is the solvent of life. Polar or charged solutes dissolve when water molecules surround them, forming aqueous solutions.

2.14 The chemistry of life is sensitive to acidic and basic conditions. A compound that releases H^+ in solution is an acid, and one that accepts H^+ is a base. The pH scale ranges from 0 (most acidic) to 14 (most basic). The pH of most cells is close to 7 (neutral) and kept that way by buffers.

2.15 Acid precipitation and ocean acidification threaten the environment. The burning of fossil fuels increases the amount of CO_2 in the atmosphere and dissolved in the oceans. The acidification of the ocean threatens coral reefs and other marine organisms.

2.16 The search for extraterrestrial life centers on the search for water. The emergent properties of water support life on Earth and may contribute to the potential for life to have evolved on other planets.

Connecting the Concepts

1. Fill in the blanks in this concept map to help you tie together the key concepts concerning elements, atoms, and molecules.

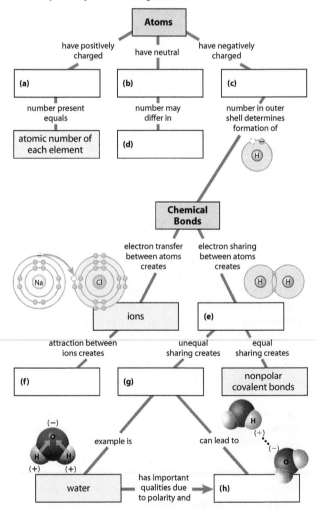

2. Create a concept map to organize your understanding of the life-supporting properties of water. A sample map is in the answer section, but the value of this exercise is in the thinking and integrating you must do to create your own map.

Testing Your Knowledge

Multiple Choice

3. Changing the _____ would change it into an atom of a different element.
   a. number of electrons surrounding the nucleus of an atom
   b. number of bonds formed by an atom
   c. number of protons in the nucleus of an atom
   d. electrical charge of an atom
   e. number of neutrons in the nucleus of an atom

4. Your body contains the smallest amount of which of the following elements?
   a. nitrogen   c. carbon   e. hydrogen
   b. phosphorus   d. oxygen

5. A solution at pH 6 contains _____ than the same amount of a solution at pH 8.
   a. 2 times more H^+
   b. 4 times more H^+
   c. 100 times more H^+
   d. 4 times less H^+
   e. 100 times less H^+

6. Most of the unique properties of water result from the fact that water molecules
   a. are very small.
   b. are held together by covalent bonds.
   c. easily separate from one another.
   d. are constantly in motion.
   e. are polar and form hydrogen bonds.

7. A sulfur atom has 6 electrons in its outer shell. As a result, it forms _____ covalent bonds with other atoms. (*Explain your answer.*)
   a. two   c. four   e. eight
   b. three   d. six

8. What does the word *trace* mean when you're talking about a trace element?
   a. The element is required in very small amounts.
   b. The element can be used as a label to trace atoms through an organism's body.
   c. The element is very rare on Earth.
   d. The element enhances health but is not essential for the organism's long-term survival.
   e. The element passes rapidly through the organism.

9. A can of cola consists mostly of sugar dissolved in water, with some carbon dioxide gas that makes it fizzy and makes the pH less than 7. In chemical terms, you could say that cola is an aqueous solution where water is the _____, sugar is a _____, and carbon dioxide makes the solution _____.
   a. solvent … solute … basic
   b. solute … solvent … basic
   c. solvent … solute … acidic
   d. solute … solvent … acidic
   e. not enough information to say

10. Radioactive isotopes can be used in medical studies because
    a. they allow researchers to time how long processes take.
    b. they are more reactive than nonradioactive isotopes.
    c. the cell does not recognize the extra protons in the nucleus, so isotopes are readily used in cellular processes.
    d. their location or quantity can be determined because of their radioactivity.
    e. their extra neutrons produce different colors that can be traced through the body.

True/False (Change false statements to make them true.)

11. Table salt, water, and carbon are compounds.

12. The smallest unit of an element is a molecule.

13. A bathtub full of lukewarm water may hold more heat than a teakettle full of boiling water.

14. If the atoms in a molecule share electrons equally, the molecule is said to be nonpolar.

15. Ice floats because water molecules in ice are more tightly packed than in liquid water.

16. Atoms in a water molecule are held together by the sharing of electrons.

17. Most acid precipitation results from the presence of pollutants from aerosol cans and air conditioners.

18. An atom that has gained or lost electrons is called an ion.

Describing, Comparing, and Explaining

19. Make a sketch that shows how water molecules hydrogen-bond with one another. Why do water molecules form hydrogen bonds? What unique properties of water result from water's tendency to form hydrogen bonds?

20. Describe two ways in which the water in your body helps stabilize your body temperature.

21. Compare covalent and ionic bonds.

22. What is an acid? A base? How is the acidity of a solution described?

Applying the Concepts

23. The diagram below shows the arrangement of electrons around the nucleus of a fluorine atom (left) and a potassium atom (right). What kind of bond do you think would form between these two atoms?

Fluorine atom   Potassium atom

24. Look back at the abbreviated periodic table of the elements in Figure 2.5. If two or more elements are in the same row, what do they have in common? If two elements are in the same column, what do they have in common?

25. This chapter explains how the emergent properties of water contribute to the suitability of the environment for life. Until fairly recently, scientists assumed that other physical requirements for life included a moderate range of temperature, pH, and atmospheric pressure, as well as low levels of toxic chemicals. That view has changed with the discovery of organisms known as extremophiles, which have been found flourishing in hot, acidic sulfur springs, around hydrothermal vents deep in the ocean, and in soils with high levels of toxic metals. Why would astrobiologists be interested in studying extremophiles? What does the existence of life in such extreme environments say about the possibility of life on other planets?

Answers to all questions can be found in Appendix 4.

CHAPTER

3

The Molecules of Cells

BIG IDEAS

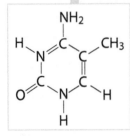

Introduction to Organic Compounds
(3.1–3.3)

Carbon-containing compounds are the chemical building blocks of life.

Carbohydrates
(3.4–3.7)

Carbohydrates serve as a cell's fuel and building material.

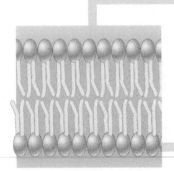

Lipids
(3.8–3.10)

Lipids are hydrophobic molecules with diverse functions.

Proteins
(3.11–3.13)

Proteins are essential to the structures and functions of life.

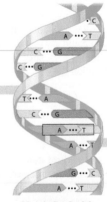

Nucleic Acids
(3.14–3.16)

Nucleic acids store, transmit, and help express hereditary information.

Is a big glass of milk a way to a healthy diet—or an upset stomach? Quite often, the answer is the latter. Most of the world's adult populations cannot easily digest milk-based foods. Such people suffer from lactose intolerance, the inability to properly break down lactose, the main sugar found in milk. Almost all infants are able to drink breast milk or other dairy products, benefiting from the proteins, fats, and sugars in this nutritious food. But as they grow older, many people find that drinking milk comes with a heavy dose of digestive discomfort.

The brightly colored ribbon model pictured above shows the three-dimensional structure of a large biological molecule called a protein. This protein is lactase, the enzyme that speeds the digestion of lactose into smaller sugars that can be absorbed by cells in the intestine. In most human populations, the production

of this enzyme begins to decline after the age of 2. In the United States, as many as 80% of African Americans and Native Americans and 90% of Asian Americans are lactase-deficient once they reach their teenage years. Americans of northern European descent make up one of the few groups in which lactase production continues into adulthood. As a result, only about 10% of people in this group are lactose intolerant.

In people who easily digest milk, lactose (a sugar) is broken down by lactase (a protein), which is coded for by a gene made of DNA (a nucleic acid). Such molecular interactions, repeated in countless variations, drive all biological processes. In this chapter, we explore the structure and function of sugars, proteins, fats, and nucleic acids—the biological molecules that are essential to life. We begin with a look at carbon, the versatile atom at the center of life's molecules.

Introduction to Organic Compounds

3.1 Life's molecular diversity is based on the properties of carbon

When it comes to making molecules, carbon usually takes center stage. Almost all the molecules a cell makes are composed of carbon atoms bonded to one another and to atoms of other elements. Carbon is unparalleled in its ability to form large and complex molecules, which build the structures and carry out the functions required for life.

Carbon-based molecules are called **organic compounds**. Why are carbon atoms the lead players in the chemistry of life? As we discussed in Chapter 2, the number of electrons in the outermost shell of its atoms determines an element's chemical properties. A carbon atom has 4 electrons in a valence shell that holds 8. Carbon completes its outer shell by sharing electrons with other atoms in four covalent bonds (see Module 2.6). Thus, each carbon atom is a connecting point from which a molecule can branch in up to four directions.

Figure 3.1A illustrates three representations of methane (CH_4), one of the simplest organic molecules. The structural formula shows that covalent bonds link four hydrogen atoms to the carbon atom. Each of the four lines in the formula represents a pair of shared electrons. The two models help you see that methane is three-dimensional, with the space-filling model on the right better portraying its overall shape. The ball-and-stick model shows that carbon's four bonds (the gray "sticks") angle out toward the corners of an imaginary tetrahedron (an object with four triangular sides). The red lines trace this shape, which occurs wherever a carbon atom participates in four single bonds. Different bond angles and shapes occur when carbon atoms form double bonds. Large organic molecules can have very elaborate shapes. And as we will see many times, a molecule's shape often determines its function.

Compounds composed of only carbon and hydrogen are called **hydrocarbons**. Methane and propane are examples of hydrocarbon fuels. As components of fats, longer hydrocarbons provide fuel to your body cells. Figure 3.1B illustrates some of the variety of hydrocarbon structures. The chain of carbon atoms in an organic molecule is called a **carbon skeleton** (shaded in gray in the figure). Carbon skeletons can vary in length and can be unbranched or branched. Carbon skeletons may also include double bonds, which can vary in number and location. Some carbon skeletons are arranged in rings.

The two compounds in the second row of Figure 3.1B, butane and isobutane, have the same molecular formula,

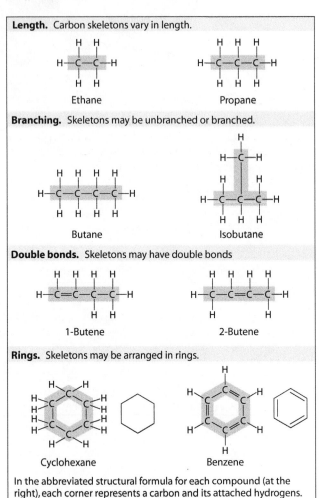

Length. Carbon skeletons vary in length.

Ethane   Propane

Branching. Skeletons may be unbranched or branched.

Butane   Isobutane

Double bonds. Skeletons may have double bonds

1-Butene   2-Butene

Rings. Skeletons may be arranged in rings.

Cyclohexane   Benzene

In the abbreviated structural formula for each compound (at the right), each corner represents a carbon and its attached hydrogens.

▲ Figure 3.1B Four ways that carbon skeletons can vary

C_4H_{10}, but differ in the bonding pattern of their carbon skeleton. The two molecules in the third row also have the same numbers of atoms, but they have different three-dimensional shapes because of the location of the double bond. Compounds with the same formula but different structural arrangements are called **isomers**. Isomers can also result from different spatial arrangements of the four partners bonded to a carbon atom. This type of isomer is important in the pharmaceutical industry, because the two isomers of a drug may not be equally effective or may have different (and sometimes harmful) effects. The different shapes of isomers result in unique properties and add greatly to the diversity of organic molecules.

> **?** One isomer of methamphetamine is the addictive illegal drug known as "crank." The other is a medicine for sinus congestion. How can you explain the differing effects of the two isomers?

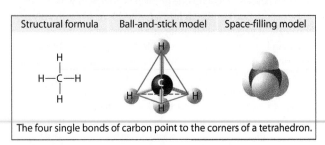

Structural formula	Ball-and-stick model	Space-filling model

The four single bonds of carbon point to the corners of a tetrahedron.

▲ Figure 3.1A Three representations of methane (CH_4)

● Isomers have different structures, or shapes, and the shape of a molecule usually helps determine the way it functions in the body.

3.2 A few chemical groups are key to the functioning of biological molecules

The unique properties of an organic compound depend not only on the size and shape of its carbon skeleton but also on the groups of atoms that are attached to that skeleton.

Table 3.2 illustrates six chemical groups important in the chemistry of life. The first five are called **functional groups**. They affect a molecule's function by participating in chemical reactions in characteristic ways. These groups are polar, because oxygen or nitrogen atoms exert a strong pull on shared electrons. This polarity tends to make compounds containing these groups **hydrophilic** (water-loving) and therefore soluble in water—a necessary condition for their roles in water-based life. The sixth group, a methyl group, is nonpolar and not reactive, but it affects molecular shape and thus function.

A **hydroxyl group** consists of a hydrogen atom bonded to an oxygen atom, which in turn is bonded to the carbon skeleton. Ethanol, shown in the table, and other organic compounds containing hydroxyl groups are called alcohols.

In a **carbonyl group**, a carbon atom is linked by a double bond to an oxygen atom. If the carbonyl group is at the end of a carbon skeleton, the compound is called an aldehyde; if it is within the chain, the compound is called a ketone. Sugars contain a carbonyl group and several hydroxyl groups.

A **carboxyl group** consists of a carbon double-bonded to an oxygen atom and also bonded to a hydroxyl group. The carboxyl group acts as an acid by contributing an H^+ to a solution (see Module 2.14) and thus becoming ionized. Compounds with carboxyl groups are called carboxylic acids. Acetic acid, shown in the table, gives vinegar its sour taste.

An **amino group** has a nitrogen bonded to two hydrogens and the carbon skeleton. It acts as a base by picking up an H^+ from a solution. Organic compounds with an amino group are called amines. The building blocks of proteins are called amino acids because they contain an amino and a carboxyl group.

A **phosphate group** consists of a phophorus atom bonded to four oxygen atoms. It is usually ionized and attached to the carbon skeleton by one of its oxygen atoms. This structure is abbreviated as ⓟ in this text. Compounds with phosphate groups are called organic phosphates and are often involved in energy transfers, as is the energy-rich compound ATP, shown in the table.

A **methyl group** consists of a carbon bonded to three hydrogens. Compounds with methyl groups are called methylated compounds. The addition of a methyl group to the component of DNA shown in the table affects the expression of genes.

Figure 3.2 shows how a small difference in chemical groups can lead to a big difference in body form and behavior. The male and female sex hormones shown here differ only in the groups highlighted with colored boxes. These subtle differences result in the different actions of these molecules, which help produce the contrasting features of males and females in lions and other vertebrates. Keeping in mind this basic scheme—carbon skeletons with chemical groups—we are now ready to see how our cells make large molecules out of smaller ones.

? Identify the chemical groups that do *not* contain carbon.

⦁ The hydroxyl, amino, and phosphate groups

TABLE 3.2	IMPORTANT CHEMICAL GROUPS OF ORGANIC COMPOUNDS

Chemical Group	Examples
Hydroxyl group —OH	Alcohol
Carbonyl group $\diagdown C=O$	Aldehyde · Ketone
Carboxyl group —COOH	Carboxylic acid · Ionized
Amino group —NH₂	Amine · Ionized
Phosphate group —OPO₃²⁻	Adenosine—O—P—O—P—O—P—O⁻ Organic phosphate
Methyl group —CH₃	Methylated compound

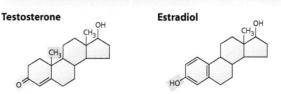

Testosterone   **Estradiol**

▲ Figure 3.2 Differences in the chemical groups of sex hormones

3.3 Cells make a huge number of large molecules from a limited set of small molecules

Given the rich complexity of life on Earth, we might expect there to be an enormous diversity of types of molecules. Remarkably, however, the important molecules of all living things—from bacteria to elephants—fall into just four main classes: carbohydrates, lipids, proteins, and nucleic acids. On a molecular scale, molecules of three of these classes—carbohydrates, proteins, and nucleic acids—may be gigantic; in fact, biologists call them **macromolecules**. For example, a protein may consist of thousands of atoms. How does a cell make such a huge molecule?

Cells make most of their macromolecules by joining smaller molecules into chains called **polymers** (from the Greek *polys*, many, and *meros*, part). A polymer is a large molecule consisting of many identical or similar building blocks strung together, much as a train consists of a chain of cars. The building blocks of polymers are called **monomers**.

Making Polymers   Cells link monomers together to form polymers by a **dehydration reaction**, a reaction that removes a molecule of water. As you can see in **Figure 3.3A**, an unlinked monomer has a hydrogen atom (—H) at one end and a hydroxyl group (—OH) at the other. For each monomer added to a chain, a water molecule (H_2O) is released. Notice in Figure 3.3A that one monomer (the one at the right end of the short polymer in this example) loses a hydroxyl group and the other monomer loses a hydrogen atom to form H_2O. As this occurs, a new covalent bond forms, linking the two monomers. Dehydration reactions are the same regardless of the specific monomers and the type of polymer the cell is producing.

Breaking Polymers   Cells not only make macromolecules but also have to break them down. For example, most of the organic molecules in your food are in the form of polymers that are much too large to enter your cells. You must digest these polymers to make their monomers available to your cells. This digestion process is called **hydrolysis**. Essentially the reverse of a dehydration reaction, hydrolysis means to break (*lyse*) with water (*hydro-*). As **Figure 3.3B** shows, the bond between monomers is broken by the addition of a water molecule, with the hydroxyl group from the water attaching to one monomer and a hydrogen attaching to the adjacent monomer.

The lactose-intolerant individuals you learned about in the chapter introduction are unable to hydrolyze such a bond in the sugar lactose because they lack the enzyme lactase. Both dehydration reactions and hydrolysis require the help of enzymes to make and break bonds. **Enzymes** are specialized macromolecules that speed up chemical reactions in cells.

The Diversity of Polymers   The diversity of macromolecules in the living world is vast. Remarkably, a cell makes all its thousands of different macromolecules from a small list of ingredients—about 40 to 50 common components and a few others that are rare. Proteins, for example, are built from only

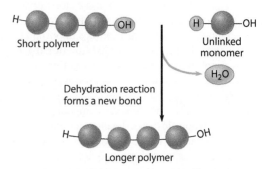

▲ **Figure 3.3A**   Dehydration reaction building a polymer chain

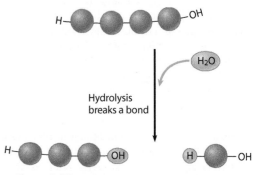

▲ **Figure 3.3B**   Hydrolysis breaking down a polymer

20 kinds of amino acids. Your DNA is built from just four kinds of monomers called nucleotides. The key to the great diversity of polymers is arrangement—variation in the sequence in which monomers are strung together.

The variety in polymers accounts for the uniqueness of each organism. The monomers themselves, however, are essentially universal. Your proteins and those of a tree or an ant are assembled from the same 20 amino acids. Life has a simple yet elegant molecular logic: Small molecules common to all organisms are ordered into large molecules, which vary from species to species and even from individual to individual in the same species.

In the remainder of the chapter, we explore each of the four classes of large biological molecules. Like water and simple organic molecules, large biological molecules have unique emergent properties arising from the orderly arrangement of their atoms. As you will see, for these molecules of life, structure and function are inseparable.

?   **Suppose you eat some cheese. What reactions must occur for the protein of the cheese to be broken down into its amino acid monomers and then for these monomers to be converted to proteins in your body?**

● In digestion, the proteins are broken down into amino acids by hydrolysis. New proteins are formed in your body cells from these monomers in dehydration reactions.

Carbohydrates

3.4 Monosaccharides are the simplest carbohydrates

The name **carbohydrate** refers to a class of molecules ranging from the small sugar molecules dissolved in soft drinks to large polysaccharides, such as the starch molecules we consume in pasta and potatoes.

The carbohydrate monomers (single-unit sugars) are **monosaccharides** (from the Greek *monos*, single, and *sacchar*, sugar). The honey shown in Figure 3.4A consists mainly of monosaccharides called glucose and fructose. These and other single-unit sugars can be hooked together by dehydration reactions to form more complex sugars and polysaccharides.

Monosaccharides generally have molecular formulas that are some multiple of CH_2O. For example, the formula for glucose, a common monosaccharide of central importance in the chemistry of life, is $C_6H_{12}O_6$. Figure 3.4B illustrates the molecular structure of glucose, with its carbons numbered 1 to 6. This structure also shows the two trademarks of a sugar: a number of hydroxyl groups (—OH) and a carbonyl group ($>C=O$, highlighted in blue). The hydroxyl groups make a sugar an alcohol, and the carbonyl group, depending on its location, makes it either an aldose (an aldehyde sugar) or a ketose (a ketone sugar). As you see in Figure 3.4B, glucose is an aldose and fructose is a ketose. (Note that most names for sugars end in *-ose*. Also, as you saw with the enzyme lactase that digests lactose, the names for most enzymes end in *-ase*.)

If you count the numbers of different atoms in the fructose molecule in Figure 3.4B, you will find that its molecular formula is $C_6H_{12}O_6$, identical to that of glucose. Thus, glucose and fructose are isomers; they differ only in the arrangement of their atoms (in this case, the positions of the carbonyl groups). Seemingly minor differences like this give isomers different properties, such as how they react with other molecules. These differences also make fructose taste considerably sweeter than glucose.

The carbon skeletons of both glucose and fructose are six carbon atoms long. Other monosaccharides may have three to seven carbons. Five-carbon sugars, called pentoses, and six-carbon sugars, called hexoses, are among the most common.

It is convenient to draw sugars as if their carbon skeletons were linear, but in aqueous solutions, many monosaccharides form rings, as shown for glucose in Figure 3.4C. To form the glucose ring, carbon 1 bonds to the oxygen attached to carbon 5. As shown in the middle representation, the ring diagram of glucose and other sugars may be abbreviated by not showing the carbon atoms at the corners of the ring. Also, the bonds in the ring are often drawn with varied thickness, indicating that the ring is a relatively flat structure with attached atoms extending above and below it. The simplified ring symbol on the right is often used in this book to represent glucose.

Monosaccharides, particularly glucose, are the main fuel molecules for cellular work. Because cells release energy from glucose when they break it down, an aqueous solution of glucose (often called dextrose) may be injected into the bloodstream of sick or injured patients; the glucose provides an immediate energy source to tissues in need of repair. Cells also use the carbon skeletons of monosaccharides as raw material for making other kinds of organic molecules, such as amino acids and fatty acids. Sugars not used in these ways may be incorporated into disaccharides and polysaccharides, as we see next.

? Write the formula for a monosaccharide that has three carbons.

$C_3H_6O_3$

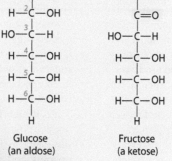

◀ Figure 3.4B   Structures of glucose and fructose

Glucose
(an aldose)

Fructose
(a ketose)

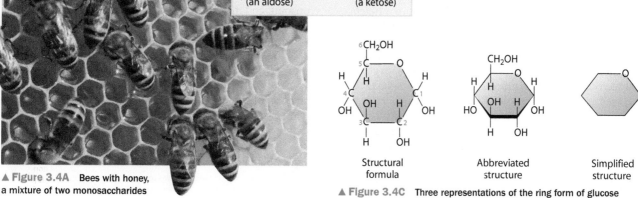

▲ Figure 3.4A   Bees with honey, a mixture of two monosaccharides

Structural formula

Abbreviated structure

Simplified structure

▲ Figure 3.4C   Three representations of the ring form of glucose

3.5 Two monosaccharides are linked to form a disaccharide

Cells construct a **disaccharide** from two monosaccharide monomers by a dehydration reaction. **Figure 3.5** shows how maltose, also called malt sugar, is formed from two glucose monomers. One monomer gives up a hydroxyl group and the other gives up a hydrogen atom from a hydroxyl group. As H_2O is released, an oxygen atom is left, linking the two monomers. Maltose, which is common in germinating seeds, is used in making beer, malted milk shakes, and malted milk candy.

The most common disaccharide is sucrose, which is made of a glucose monomer linked to a fructose monomer. Transported in plant sap, sucrose provides a source of energy and raw materials to all the parts of the plant. We extract it from the stems of sugarcane or the roots of sugar beets to use as table sugar.

> ❓ Lactose, as you read in the chapter introduction, is the disaccharide sugar in milk. It is formed from glucose and galactose. The formula for both these monosaccharides is $C_6H_{12}O_6$. What is the formula for lactose?
>
> $C_{12}H_{22}O_{11}$

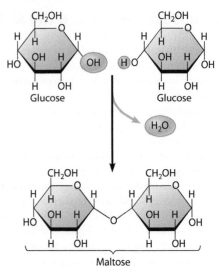

▲ **Figure 3.5** Disaccharide formation by a dehydration reaction

---

CONNECTION ## 3.6 What is high-fructose corn syrup, and is it to blame for obesity?

▲ **Figure 3.6** High-fructose corn syrup (HFCS), a main ingredient of soft drinks and processed foods

If you want to sweeten your coffee or tea, you probably reach for sugar—the disaccharide sucrose. But if you drink sodas or fruit drinks, you're probably consuming the monosaccharides of sucrose in the form of high-fructose corn syrup. In fact, if you look at the label of almost any processed food, you will see high-fructose corn syrup listed as one of the ingredients (**Figure 3.6**). And you have probably heard reports linking high-fructose corn syrup to the "obesity epidemic."

What is high-fructose corn syrup (HFCS)? Let's start with the corn syrup part. The main carbohydrate in corn is starch, a polysaccharide. Industrial processing hydrolyzes starch into its component monomers, glucose, producing corn syrup. Glucose, however, does not taste as sweet to us as sucrose. Fructose, on the other hand, tastes much sweeter than both glucose and sucrose. When a new process was developed in the 1970s that used an enzyme to rearrange the atoms of glucose into the sweeter isomer, fructose (see Figure 3.4B), the high-fructose corn syrup industry was born. (High-fructose corn syrup is a bit of a misnomer, however, because the fructose is combined with regular corn syrup to produce a mixture of about 55% fructose and 45% glucose, not much different from the proportions in sucrose.)

This clear, goopy liquid is cheaper than sucrose and easier to mix into drinks and processed food. And it contains the same monosaccharides as sucrose, the disaccharide it is replacing. So is there a problem with HFCS? Some point to circumstantial evidence. From 1980 to 2000, the incidence of obesity doubled in the United States. In that same time period, the consumption of HFCS more than tripled, whereas the consumption of refined cane and beet sugar decreased 21%. Overall, the combined per capita consumption of HFCS and refined sugars increased 25% in that period. A 2001–2004 national health survey showed the average intake of added sugars and sweeteners was 22.2 teaspoons a day, with soft drinks and other beverages sweetened with HFCS the number one source.

So, is high-fructose corn syrup to blame for increases in obesity, type 2 diabetes, high blood pressure, and other chronic diseases associated with increased weight? Scientific studies are ongoing, and the jury is still out. There is consensus, however, that overconsumption of sugar or HFCS along with dietary fat and decreased physical activity contribute to weight gain. In addition, high sugar consumption also tends to replace eating more varied and nutritious foods. Sugars have been described as "empty calories" because they contain only negligible amounts of other nutrients. For good health, you require proteins, fats, vitamins, and minerals, as well as complex carbohydrates, the topic of the next module.

> ❓ How is high-fructose corn syrup made from corn?
>
> Corn starch is hydrolyzed to glucose; then enzymes convert glucose to fructose. This fructose is combined with corn syrup to produce HFCS.

3.7 Polysaccharides are long chains of sugar units

Polysaccharides are macromolecules, polymers of hundreds to thousands of monosaccharides linked together by dehydration reactions. Polysaccharides may function as storage molecules or as structural compounds. Figure 3.7 illustrates three common types of polysaccharides: starch, glycogen, and cellulose.

Starch, a storage polysaccharide in plants, consists entirely of glucose monomers. Starch molecules coil into a helical shape and may be unbranched (as shown in the figure) or branched. Starch granules serve as carbohydrate "banks" from which plant cells can withdraw glucose for energy or building materials. Humans and most other animals have enzymes that can hydrolyze plant starch to glucose. Potatoes and grains, such as wheat, corn, and rice, are the major sources of starch in the human diet.

Animals store glucose in a different form of polysaccharide, called **glycogen**. Glycogen is more highly branched than starch, as shown in the figure. Most of your glycogen is stored as granules in your liver and muscle cells, which hydrolyze the glycogen to release glucose when it is needed.

Cellulose, the most abundant organic compound on Earth, is a major component of the tough walls that enclose plant cells. Cellulose is also a polymer of glucose, but its monomers are linked together in a different orientation. (Carefully compare the oxygen "bridges" highlighted in yellow between glucose monomers in starch, glycogen, and cellulose in the figure.) Arranged parallel to each other, cellulose molecules are joined by hydrogen bonds, forming cable-like microfibrils. Layers of microfibrils combine with other polymers, producing strong support for trees and structures we build with lumber.

Animals do not have enzymes that can hydrolyze the glucose linkages in cellulose. Therefore, cellulose is not a nutrient for humans, although it does contribute to digestive system health. The cellulose that passes unchanged through your digestive tract is referred to as "insoluble fiber." Fresh fruits, vegetables, and grains are rich in fiber.

Some microorganisms do have enzymes that can hydrolyze cellulose. Cows and termites house such microorganisms in their digestive tracts and are thus able to derive energy from cellulose. Decomposing fungi also digest cellulose, helping to recycle its chemical elements within ecosystems.

Another structural polysaccharide, **chitin**, is used by insects and crustaceans to build their exoskeleton, the hard case enclosing the animal. Chitin is also found in the cell walls of fungi. Humans use chitin to make a strong and flexible surgical thread that decomposes after a wound or incision heals.

Almost all carbohydrates are hydrophilic owing to the many hydroxyl groups attached to their sugar monomers (see Figure 3.4B). Thus, cotton bath towels, which are mostly cellulose, are quite water absorbent due to the water-loving nature of cellulose. Next we look at a class of macromolecules that are not hydrophilic.

? **Compare and contrast starch and cellulose, two plant polysaccharides.**

Both are polymers of glucose, but the bonds between glucose monomers have different shapes. Starch functions mainly for sugar storage. Cellulose is a structural polysaccharide that is the main material of plant cell walls.

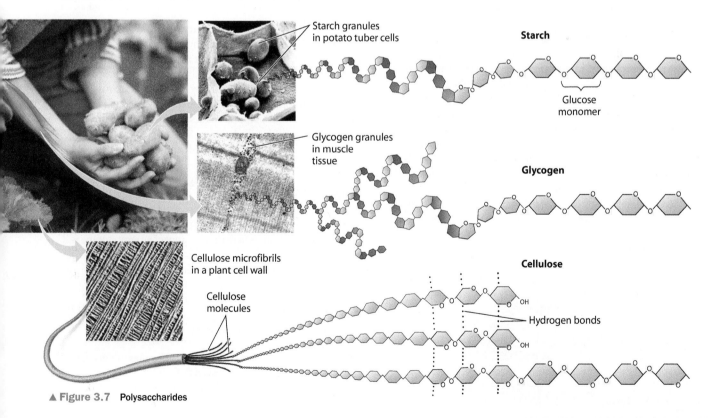

Figure 3.7 Polysaccharides

Starch granules in potato tuber cells

Starch

Glucose monomer

Glycogen granules in muscle tissue

Glycogen

Cellulose microfibrils in a plant cell wall

Cellulose molecules

Cellulose

OH

Hydrogen bonds

OH

Lipids

3.8 Fats are lipids that are mostly energy-storage molecules

Lipids are diverse compounds that are grouped together because they share one trait: They do not mix well with water. Lipids consist mainly of carbon and hydrogen atoms linked by nonpolar covalent bonds. In contrast to carbohydrates and most other biological molecules, lipids are **hydrophobic** (water-fearing). You can see this chemical behavior in an unshaken bottle of salad dressing: The oil (a type of lipid) separates from the vinegar (which is mostly water). The oils that ducks spread on their feathers make the feathers repel water (Figure 3.8A), which helps such waterfowl stay afloat.

Lipids also differ from carbohydrates, proteins, and nucleic acids in that they are neither huge macromolecules nor polymers built from similar monomers. You will see that lipids vary a great deal in structure and function. In this and the next two modules, we will consider three types of lipids: fats, phospholipids, and steroids.

A **fat** is a large lipid made from two kinds of smaller molecules: glycerol and fatty acids. Shown at the top in Figure 3.8B, glycerol is an alcohol with three carbons, each bearing a hydroxyl group (—OH). A fatty acid consists of a carboxyl group (the functional group that gives these molecules the name fatty *acid*, —COOH) and a hydrocarbon chain, usually 16 or 18 carbon atoms in length. The nonpolar hydrocarbon chains are the reason fats are hydrophobic.

Figure 3.8B shows how one fatty acid molecule can link to a glycerol molecule by a dehydration reaction. Linking three fatty acids to glycerol produces a fat, as illustrated in Figure 3.8C. A synonym for fat is *triglyceride*, a term you may see on food labels or on medical tests for fat in the blood.

Some fatty acids contain one or more double bonds, which cause kinks (or bends) in the carbon chain. See the third fatty acid in Figure 3.8C. Such an **unsaturated fatty acid** has one fewer hydrogen atom on each carbon of the double bond. Fatty acids with no double bonds in their hydrocarbon chain have the maximum number of hydrogen atoms (are "saturated" with hydrogens) and are called **saturated fatty acids**. The kinks in unsaturated fatty acids prevent fats containing them from packing tightly together and solidifying at room temperature. Corn oil, olive oil, and other vegetable oils are called unsaturated fats.

Most animal fats are saturated. Their unkinked fatty acid chains pack closely together, making butter and beef fat solid at room temperature. When you see "hydrogenated vegetable oils" on a margarine label, it means that

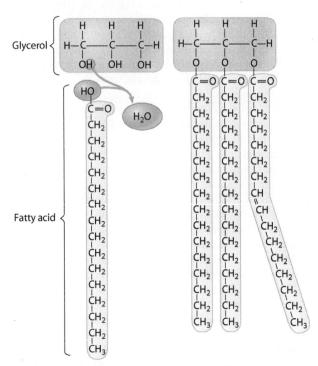

▲ Figure 3.8B A dehydration reaction linking a fatty acid molecule to a glycerol molecule

▲ Figure 3.8C A fat molecule (triglyceride) consisting of three fatty acids linked to glycerol

unsaturated fats have been converted to saturated fats by adding hydrogen. Unfortunately, hydrogenation also creates **trans fats**, a form of fat that recent research associates with health risks. Diets rich in saturated fats and trans fats may contribute to cardiovascular disease by promoting atherosclerosis. In this condition, lipid-containing deposits called plaques build up within the walls of blood vessels, reducing blood flow. Unsaturated fatty acids called omega-3 fatty acids are found in certain nuts, plant oils, and fatty fish and appear to protect against cardiovascular disease.

The main function of fats is long-term energy storage. A gram of fat stores more than twice as much energy as a gram of polysaccharide. For immobile plants, the bulky energy storage form of starch is not a problem. (Vegetable oils are generally obtained from seeds, where more compact energy storage is a benefit.) A mobile animal, such as a duck or a human, can get around much more easily carrying its energy stores in the form of fat. Of course, the downside of this energy-packed storage form is that it takes more effort for a person to "burn off" excess fat. In addition to storing energy, fatty tissue cushions vital organs and insulates the body.

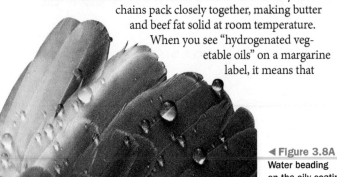

◀ Figure 3.8A Water beading on the oily coating of feathers

? How do you think the structure of a monounsaturated fat differs from a polyunsaturated fat?

● A monounsaturated fat has a fatty acid with a single double bond in its carbon chain. A polyunsaturated fat has a fatty acid with several double bonds.

3.9 Phospholipids and steroids are important lipids with a variety of functions

Cells could not exist without **phospholipids**, the major component of cell membranes. Phospholipids are structurally similar to fats, but they contain only two fatty acids attached to glycerol instead of three. As shown in **Figure 3.9A**, a negatively charged phosphate group (shown as a yellow circle in the figure and linked to another small molecule) is attached to glycerol's third carbon. (Note that glycerol is shown in orange.) The structure of phospholipids provides a classic example of how form fits function. The hydrophilic and hydrophobic ends of multiple

molecules assemble in a bilayer of phospholipids to form a membrane (**Figure 3.9B**). The hydrophobic tails of the fatty acids cluster in the center, and the hydrophilic phosphate heads face the watery environment on either side of the membrane. Each gray-headed, yellow-tailed structure in the membrane shown here represents a phospholipid; this symbol is used throughout in this book. We will explore the structure and function of biological membranes further in Chapter 4.

Steroids are lipids in which the carbon skeleton contains four fused rings, as shown in the structural formula of cholesterol in **Figure 3.9C**. (The diagram omits the carbons making up the rings and most of the chain and also their attached hydrogens.) **Cholesterol** is a common component in animal cell membranes, and animal cells also use it as a starting material for making other steroids, including sex hormones. Different steroids vary in the chemical groups attached to the rings, as you saw in Figure 3.2. Too much cholesterol in the blood may contribute to atherosclerosis.

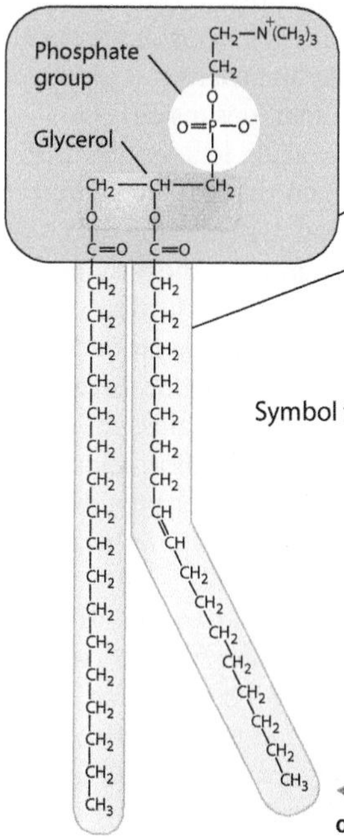

? Compare the structure of a phospholipid with that of a fat (triglyceride).

A phospholipid has two fatty acids and a phosphate group attached to glycerol. Three fatty acids are attached to the glycerol of a fat molecule.

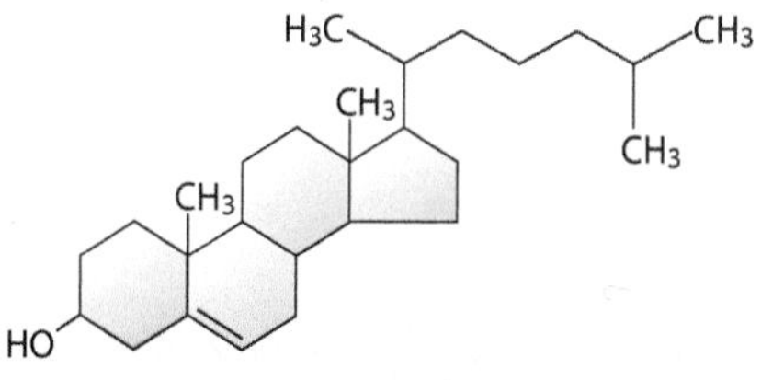

◀ **Figure 3.9A** Chemical structure of a phospholipid molecule

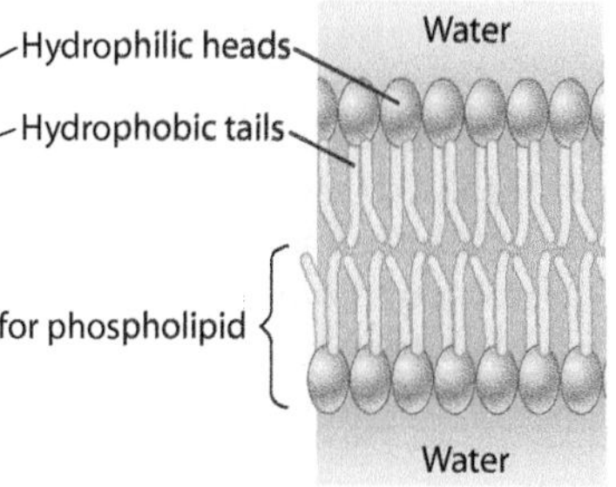

▲ **Figure 3.9B** Section of a phospholipid membrane

Phosphate group

Glycerol

Hydrophilic heads
Hydrophobic tails
Symbol for phospholipid
Water
Water

▲ **Figure 3.9C** Cholesterol, a steroid

3.10 Anabolic steroids pose health risks

Anabolic steroids are synthetic variants of the male hormone testosterone. Testosterone causes a general buildup of muscle and bone mass in males during puberty and maintains masculine traits throughout life. Because anabolic steroids structurally resemble testosterone, they also mimic some of its effects. (The word *anabolic* comes from *anabolism*, the building of substances by the body.)

As prescription drugs, anabolic steroids are used to treat general anemia and diseases that destroy body muscle. However, some athletes use these drugs to build up their muscles quickly and enhance their performance. But at what cost? Steroid abuse may cause violent mood swings ("roid rage"), depression, liver damage or cancer, and high cholesterol levels and blood pressure. Use of these drugs often makes the body reduce its output of natural male sex hormones, which can cause shrunken testicles, reduced sex drive, infertility, and breast enlargement in men. Use in women has been linked to menstrual cycle disruption and development of masculine characteristics. A serious effect in teens is that bones may

stop growing, stunting growth.

Despite the risks, some athletes continue to use steroids, and unscrupulous chemists, trainers, and coaches try to find ways to avoid their detection. Meanwhile, the U.S. Congress, professional sports authorities, and high school and college athletic programs ban the use of anabolic steroids, implement drug testing, and penalize violators in an effort to keep the competition fair and protect the health of athletes.

? How are dietary fats and anabolic steroids similar?

Both fats and steroids are lipids, grouped together because they are hydrophobic molecules.

Proteins

3.11 Proteins are made from amino acids linked by peptide bonds

Nearly every dynamic function in your body depends on proteins. You have tens of thousands of different proteins, each with a specific structure and function. Of all of life's molecules, proteins are structurally the most elaborate and diverse. A **protein** is a polymer of amino acids. Protein diversity is based on differing arrangements of a common set of just 20 amino acid monomers.

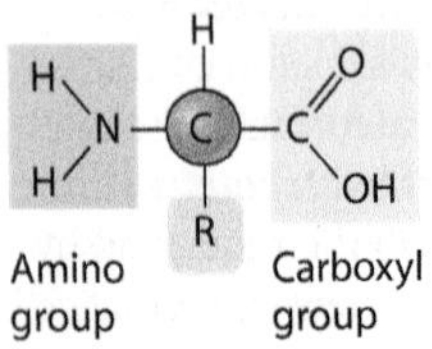

Amino acids all have an amino group and a carboxyl group (which makes it an acid, hence the name amino *acid*). As you can see in the general structure shown in **Figure 3.11A**, both of these functional groups are covalently bonded to a central carbon atom, called the alpha carbon. Also bonded to the alpha carbon is a hydrogen atom and a chemical group symbolized by the letter R. The R group, also called the side chain, differs with each amino acid. In the simplest amino acid (glycine), the R group is just a hydrogen atom. In all others, such as those shown in **Figure 3.11B**, the R group consists of one or more carbon atoms with various chemical groups attached. The composition and structure of the R group determines the specific properties of each of the 20 amino acids that are found in proteins (see Appendix 3).

Amino group   Carboxyl group

▲ Figure 3.11A
General structure of an amino acid

The amino acids in Figure 3.11B represent two main types, hydrophobic and hydrophilic. Leucine (abbreviated Leu) is an example of an amino acid in which the R group is nonpolar and hydrophobic. Serine (Ser), with a hydroxyl group in its R group, is an example of an amino acid with a polar, hydrophilic R group. Aspartic acid (Asp) is acidic and negatively charged at the pH of a cell. (Indeed, all the amino and carboxyl groups of amino acids are usually ionized at cellular pH, as shown in Table 3.2.) Other amino acids have basic R groups and are positively charged. Amino acids with polar and charged R groups help proteins dissolve in the aqueous solutions inside cells.

Now that we have examined amino acids, let's see how they are linked to form polymers. Can you guess? Cells join amino acids together in a dehydration reaction that links the carboxyl group of one amino acid to the amino group of the next amino acid as a water molecule is removed (**Figure 3.11C**). The resulting covalent linkage is called a **peptide bond**. The product of the reaction shown in the figure is called a *di*peptide, because it was made from *two* amino acids. Additional amino acids can be added by the same process to form a chain of amino acids, a **polypeptide**. To release amino acids from the polypeptide by hydrolysis, a molecule of H_2O must be added back to break each peptide bond.

How is it possible to make thousands of different kinds of proteins from just 20 amino acids? The answer has to do with sequence. You know that thousands of English words can be made by varying the sequence of letters and word length. Although the protein "alphabet" is slightly smaller (just 20 "letters," rather than 26), the "words" are much longer. Most polypeptides are at least 100 amino acids in length; some are 1,000 or more. Each polypeptide has a unique sequence of amino acids. But a long polypeptide chain of specific sequence is not the same as a protein, any more than a long strand of yarn is the same as a sweater that can be knit from that yarn. A functioning protein is one or more polypeptide chains precisely coiled, twisted, and folded into a unique three-dimensional shape.

? **In what way is the production of a dipeptide similar to the production of a disaccharide?**

In both cases, the monomers are joined by a dehydration reaction.

Hydrophobic	Hydrophilic	
Leucine (Leu)	Serine (Ser)	Aspartic acid (Asp)

▲ Figure 3.11B   Examples of amino acids with hydrophobic and hydrophilic R groups

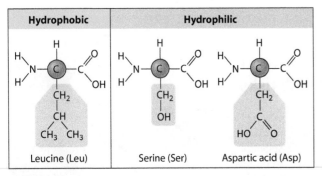

Carboxyl group   Amino group

Dehydration reaction

Peptide bond

Amino acid   +   Amino acid   →   Dipeptide

H_2O

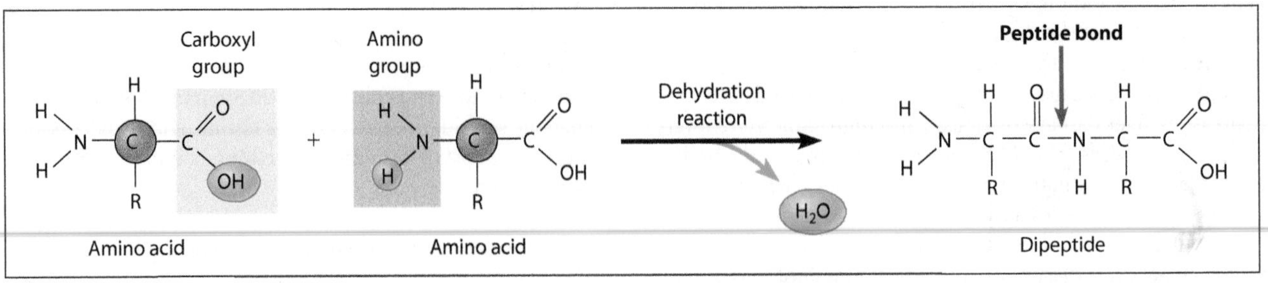

▲ Figure 3.11C   Peptide bond formation

3.12 A protein's specific shape determines its function

What do the tens of thousands of different proteins in your body do? Probably their most important role is as *enzymes*, the chemical catalysts that speed and regulate virtually all chemical reactions in cells. Lactase, which you read about in the chapter introduction, is just one of thousands of different enzymes that may be produced by cells.

In **Figure 3.12A**, you can see examples of two other types of proteins.

Structural proteins are found in hair and the fibers that make up connective tissues such as tendons and ligaments. Muscle cells are packed with *contractile proteins*.

Other types of proteins include *defensive proteins*, such as the antibodies of the immune system, and *signal proteins*, such as many of the hormones and other chemical messengers that help coordinate body activities by facilitating communication between cells. *Receptor proteins* may be built into cell membranes and transmit signals into cells. Hemoglobin in red blood cells is a *transport protein* that delivers O₂ to working muscles and tissues throughout the body. Other transport proteins move sugar molecules into cells for energy. Some proteins are *storage proteins*, such as ovalbumin, the protein of egg white, which serves as a source of amino acids for developing embryos. Milk proteins provide amino acids for baby mammals, and plant seeds contain storage proteins that nourish developing plant embryos.

The functions of all these different types of proteins depend on their specific shape. **Figure 3.12B** shows a ribbon model of lysozyme, an enzyme found in your sweat, tears, and saliva. Lysozyme consists of one long polypeptide, represented by the purple ribbon. Lysozyme's general shape is called globular. This overall shape is more apparent in **Figure 3.12C**, a space-filling model of lysozyme. In that model, the colors represent the different atoms of carbon, oxygen, nitrogen, and hydrogen. The barely visible yellow balls are sulfur atoms that form the stabilizing bonds shown as yellow lines in the ribbon model. Most enzymes and other proteins are globular. Structural proteins, such as those making up hair, tendons, and ligaments, are typically long and thin and are called fibrous proteins.

Descriptions such as globular and fibrous refer to a protein's general shape. Each protein also has a much more specific shape. The coils and twists of lysozyme's polypeptide ribbon appear haphazard, but they represent the molecule's specific, three-dimensional shape, and this shape is what determines its specific function. Nearly all proteins must recognize and bind to some other molecule to function. Lysozyme, for example, can destroy bacterial cells, but first it must bind to specific molecules on the bacterial cell surface. Lysozyme's specific shape enables it to recognize and attach to its molecular target, which fits into the groove you see on the right in the figures.

The dependence of protein function on a protein's specific shape becomes clear when proteins are altered. In a process called **denaturation**, polypeptide chains unravel, losing their specific shape and, as a result, their function. Changes in salt concentration and pH can denature many proteins, as can excessive heat. For example, visualize what happens when you fry an egg. Heat quickly denatures the clear proteins surrounding the yolk, making them solid, white, and opaque. One of the reasons why extremely high fevers are so dangerous is that some proteins in the body become denatured and cannot function.

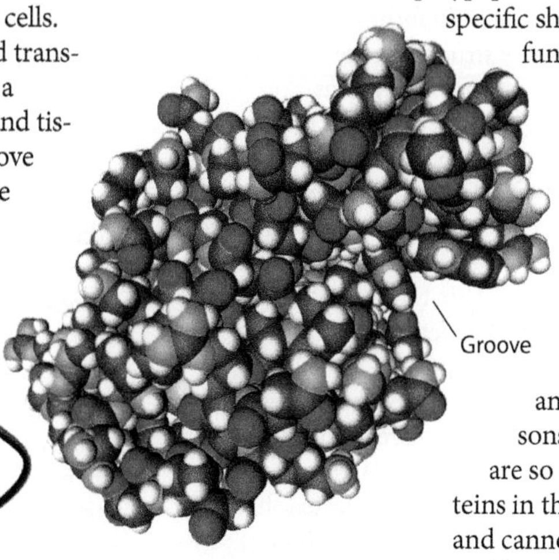

Given the proper cellular environment, a newly synthesized polypeptide chain spontaneously folds into its functional shape. We examine the four levels of a protein's structure next.

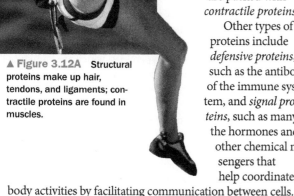

▲ **Figure 3.12A** Structural proteins make up hair, tendons, and ligaments; contractile proteins are found in muscles.

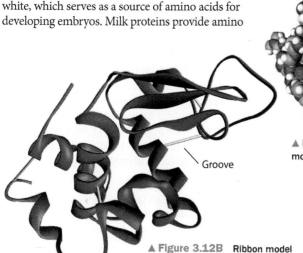

▲ **Figure 3.12B** Ribbon model of the protein lysozyme

Groove

▲ **Figure 3.12C** Space-filling model of the protein lysozyme

Groove

? Why does a denatured protein no longer function normally?

● The function of each protein is a consequence of its specific shape, which is lost when a protein denatures.

3.13 A protein's shape depends on four levels of structure

Primary Structure The **primary structure** of a protein is its unique sequence of amino acids. As an example, let's consider transthyretin, an important transport protein found in your blood. Its specific shape enables it to transport vitamin A and one of the thyroid hormones throughout your body. A complete molecule of transthyretin has four identical polypeptide chains, each made up of 127 amino acids. **Figure 3.13A**, on the next page, shows part of one of these chains unraveled for a closer look at its primary structure. The three-letter abbreviations represent the specific amino acids that make up the chain.

In order for transthyretin or any other protein to perform its specific function, it must have the correct amino acids arranged in a precise order. The primary structure of a protein is determined by inherited genetic information. Even a slight change in primary structure may affect a protein's overall shape and thus its ability to function. For instance, a single amino acid change in hemoglobin, the oxygen-carrying blood protein, causes sickle-cell disease, a serious blood disorder.

Secondary Structure In the second level of protein structure, parts of the polypeptide coil or fold into local patterns called **secondary structure**. Coiling of a polypeptide chain results in a secondary structure called an alpha helix; a certain kind of folding leads to a secondary structure called a beta pleated sheet. Both of these patterns are maintained by regularly spaced hydrogen bonds between hydrogen atoms and oxygen atoms along the backbone of the polypeptide chain.

Each hydrogen bond is represented in **Figure 3.13B** by a row of dots. Because the R groups of the amino acids are not involved in forming these secondary structures, they are omitted from the diagrams.

Transthyretin has only one alpha helix region (see **Figure 3.13C**). In contrast, some fibrous proteins, such as the structural protein of hair, have the alpha helix structure over most of their length.

Beta pleated sheets make up the core of many globular proteins, as is the case for transthyretin. Pleated sheets also dominate some fibrous proteins, including the silk protein of a spider's web, shown to the left. The combined strength of so many hydrogen bonds makes each silk fiber stronger than a steel strand of the same weight. Potential uses of spider silk proteins include surgical thread, fishing line, and bulletproof vests.

Tertiary Structure The term **tertiary structure** refers to the overall three-dimensional shape of a polypeptide, which, as we've said, determines the function of a protein. As shown in Figure 3.13C, a transthyretin polypeptide has a globular shape, which results from the compact arrangement of its alpha helix region and beta pleated sheet regions.

Here the R groups of the amino acids making up the polypeptide get involved in creating a protein's shape. Tertiary structure results from interactions between these R groups. For example, transthyretin and other proteins found in aqueous solutions are folded so that the hydrophobic R groups are on the inside of the molecule and the hydrophilic R groups on the outside, exposed to water. In addition to the clustering of hydrophobic groups, hydrogen bonding between polar side chains and ionic bonding of some of the charged (ionized) R groups help maintain the tertiary structure. A protein's shape may be reinforced further by covalent bonds called disulfide bridges. You saw disulfide bridges as the yellow lines in the ribbon model of lysozyme in Figure 3.12B.

Quaternary Structure Many proteins consist of two or more polypeptide chains aggregated into one functional macromolecule. Such proteins have a **quaternary structure**, resulting from the association of these polypeptides, which are known as "subunits." **Figure 3.13D** shows a complete transthyretin molecule with its four identical globular subunits.

Another example of a protein with quaternary structure is collagen, shown to the right. Collagen is a fibrous protein with three helical polypeptides intertwined into a larger triple helix. This arrangement gives the long fibers great strength, suited to their function as the girders of connective tissue in skin, bone, tendons, and ligaments. Collagen accounts for 40% of the protein in your body.

Many other proteins have subunits that are different from one another. For example, the oxygen-transporting molecule hemoglobin has four polypeptides of two distinct types (see Figure 22.11). Each polypeptide has a nonprotein attachment, called a heme, with an iron atom that binds oxygen.

What happens if a protein folds incorrectly? Many diseases, such as Alzheimer's and Parkinson's, involve an accumulation of misfolded proteins. Prions are infectious misshapen proteins that are associated with serious degenerative brain diseases such as mad cow disease (see Module 10.21). Such diseases reinforce the theme that structure fits function: A protein's unique three-dimensional shape determines its proper functioning.

Polypeptide chain

Collagen

? If a genetic mutation changes the primary structure of a protein, how might this destroy the protein's function?

● Primary structure, the amino acid sequence, affects the secondary structure, which affects the tertiary structure, which affects the quaternary structure (if any). Thus, primary structure determines the shape of a protein, and the function of a protein depends on its shape. A shape change could eliminate function.

Four Levels of Protein Structure

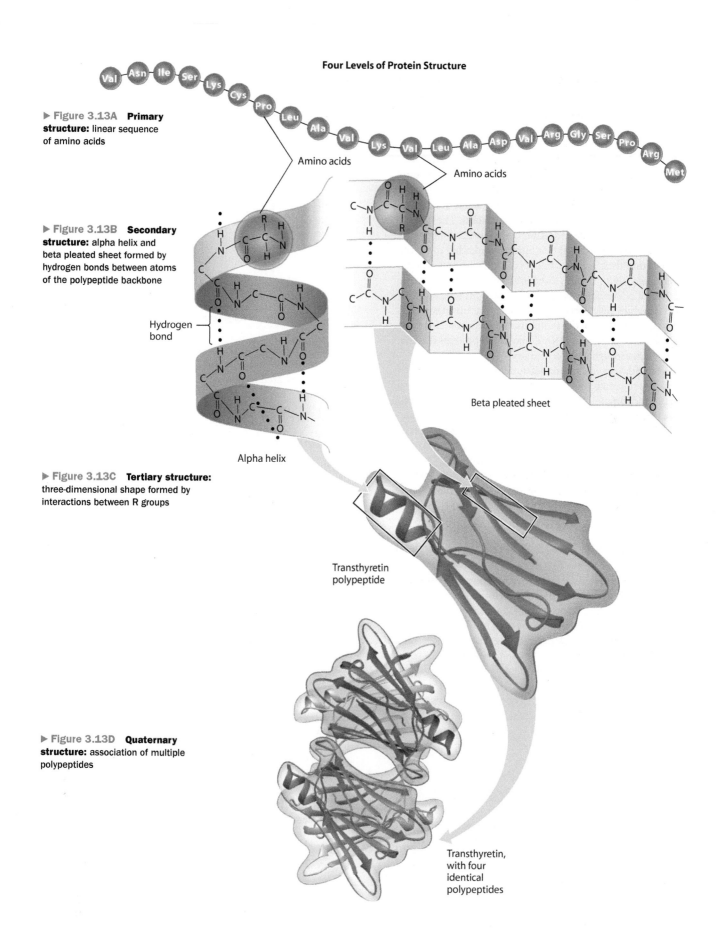

► Figure 3.13A **Primary structure:** linear sequence of amino acids

Amino acids

Amino acids

► Figure 3.13B **Secondary structure:** alpha helix and beta pleated sheet formed by hydrogen bonds between atoms of the polypeptide backbone

Hydrogen bond

Beta pleated sheet

Alpha helix

► Figure 3.13C **Tertiary structure:** three-dimensional shape formed by interactions between R groups

Transthyretin polypeptide

► Figure 3.13D **Quaternary structure:** association of multiple polypeptides

Transthyretin, with four identical polypeptides

Nucleic Acids

3.14 DNA and RNA are the two types of nucleic acids

As we just saw, the primary structure of a polypeptide determines the shape of a protein. But what determines the primary structure? The amino acid sequence of a polypeptide is programmed by a discrete unit of inheritance known as a **gene**. Genes consist of **DNA (deoxyribonucleic acid)**, one of the two types of polymers called **nucleic acids**. The name *nucleic* comes from their location in the nuclei of eukaryotic cells. The genetic material that humans and other organisms inherit from their parents consists of DNA. Unique among molecules, DNA provides directions for its own replication. Thus, as a cell divides, its genetic instructions are passed to each daughter cell. These instructions program all of a cell's activities by directing the synthesis of proteins.

The genes present in DNA do not build proteins directly. They work through an intermediary—the second type of nucleic acid, known as **ribonucleic acid (RNA)**. Figure 3.14 illustrates the main roles of these two types of nucleic acids in the production of proteins. In the nucleus of a eukaryotic cell, a gene directs the synthesis of an RNA molecule. We say that DNA is transcribed into RNA. The RNA molecule moves out of the nucleus and interacts with the protein-building machinery of the cell. There, the gene's instructions, written in "nucleic acid language," are translated into "protein language," the amino acid sequence of a polypeptide. (In prokaryotic cells,

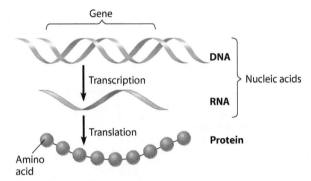
▲ Figure 3.14   The flow of genetic information in the building of a protein

which lack nuclei, both transcription and translation take place within the cytoplasm of the cell.)

Recent research has found previously unknown types of RNA molecules that play many other roles in the cell. We return to the functions of DNA and RNA later in the book.

?   **How are the two types of nucleic acids functionally related?**

● The hereditary material of DNA contains the instructions for the primary structure of polypeptides. RNA is the intermediary that conveys those instructions to the protein-making machinery that assembles amino acids in the designated order.

3.15 Nucleic acids are polymers of nucleotides

The monomers that make up nucleic acids are **nucleotides**. As indicated in **Figure 3.15A**, each nucleotide contains three parts. At the center of a nucleotide is a five-carbon sugar (blue); the sugar in DNA is deoxyribose (shown in Figure 3.15A), whereas RNA has a slightly different sugar called ribose. Linked to one side of the sugar in both types of nucleotides is a negatively charged phosphate group (yellow). Linked to the sugar's other side is a nitrogenous base (green), a molecular structure containing nitrogen and carbon. (The nitrogen atoms tend to take up H$^+$ in aqueous solutions, which explains why it is called

a nitrogenous *base*.) Each DNA nucleotide has one of four different nitrogenous bases: adenine (A), thymine (T), cytosine (C), and guanine (G). Thus, all genetic information is written in a four-letter alphabet. RNA nucleotides also contain the bases A, C, and G; but the base uracil (U) is found instead of thymine.

Like polysaccharides and polypeptides, a nucleic acid polymer—a polynucleotide— is built from its monomers by dehydration reactions. In this process, the sugar of one nucleotide bonds to the phosphate group of the next monomer. The result is a repeating sugar-phosphate backbone in the polymer, as represented by the blue and yellow ribbon in **Figure 3.15B**. (Note that the nitrogenous bases are not part of the backbone.)

RNA usually consists of a single polynucleotide strand, but DNA is a

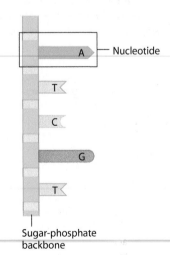
▲ Figure 3.15B   Part of a polynucleotide

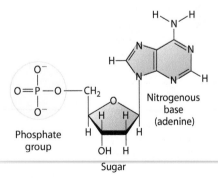
▲ Figure 3.15A   A nucleotide, consisting of a phosphate group, a sugar, and a nitrogenous base

double helix, in which two polynucleotides wrap around each other **(Figure 3.15C)**. The nitrogenous bases protrude from the two sugar-phosphate backbones and pair in the center of the helix. As shown by their diagrammatic shapes in the figure, A always pairs with T, and C always pairs with G. The two DNA chains are held together by hydrogen bonds (indicated by the dotted lines) between their paired bases. These bonds are individually weak, but collectively they zip the two strands together into a very stable double helix. Most DNA molecules have thousands or even millions of base pairs.

Because of the base-pairing rules, the two strands of the double helix are said to be *complementary*, each a predictable counterpart of the other. Thus, if a stretch of nucleotides on one strand has the base sequence –AGCACT–, then the same stretch on the other strand must be –TCGTGA–. Complementary base pairing is the key to how a cell makes two identical copies of each of its

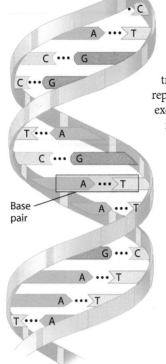

Base pair

▲ **Figure 3.15C**   DNA double helix

DNA molecules every time it divides. Thus, the structure of DNA accounts for its function of transmitting genetic information whenever a cell reproduces. The same base-pairing rules (with the exception that U nucleotides of RNA pair with A nucleotides of DNA) also account for the precise transcription of information from DNA to RNA. The details of gene transcription and translation are covered in detail in Chapter 10.

An organism's genes determine the proteins and thus the structures and functions of its body. Let's return to the subject of the chapter introduction—lactose intolerance—to conclude our study of biological molecules. In the next chapter, we move up in the biological hierarchy to the level of the cell.

? **What roles do complementary base pairing play in the functioning of nucleic acids?**

Complementary base pairing makes possible the precise replication of DNA, ensuring that genetic information is faithfully transmitted every time a cell divides. It also ensures that RNA molecules carry accurate instructions for the synthesis of proteins.

3.16 Lactose tolerance is a recent event in human evolution

As you'll recall from the chapter introduction, the majority of people stop producing the enzyme lactase in early childhood and thus do not easily digest the milk sugar lactose. Researchers were curious about the genetic and evolutionary basis for the regional distribution of lactose tolerance and intolerance. In 2002, a group of scientists completed a study of the genes of 196 lactose-intolerant adults of African, Asian, and European descent. They determined that lactose intolerance is actually the human norm. It is "lactose tolerance" that represents a relatively recent mutation in the human genome.

The ability to make lactase into adulthood is concentrated in people of northern European descent, and the researchers speculated that lactose tolerance became widespread among this group because it offered a survival advantage. In northern Europe's relatively cold climate, only one harvest a year is possible. Therefore, animals were a main source of food for early humans in that region. Cattle were first domesticated in northern Europe about 9,000 years ago **(Figure 3.16)**. With milk and other dairy products at hand year-round, natural selection would have favored anyone with a mutation that kept the lactase gene switched on.

Researchers wondered whether the lactose tolerance mutation found in Europeans might be present in other cultures who kept dairy herds. Indeed, a 2006 study compared the genetic makeup and lactose tolerance of 43 ethnic groups in East Africa. The researchers identified three mutations, all different from each other and from the European mutation, that keep the lactase gene permanently turned on. The mutations appear to have occurred beginning around 7,000 years ago, around the

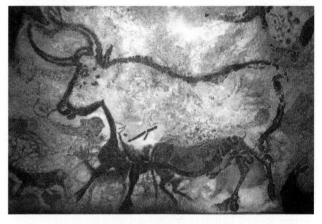

▲ **Figure 3.16**   A prehistoric European cave painting of cattle

time that archaeological evidence shows the domestication of cattle in these African regions.

Mutations that conferred a selective advantage, such as surviving cold winters or withstanding drought by drinking milk, spread rapidly in these early pastoral peoples. Their evolutionary and cultural history is thus recorded in their genes and in their continuing ability to digest milk.

? **Explain how lactose tolerance involves three of the four major classes of biological macromolecules.**

Lactose, milk sugar, is a carbohydrate that is hydrolyzed by the enzyme lactase, a protein. The ability to make this enzyme and the regulation of when it is made is coded for in DNA, a nucleic acid.

For Practice Quizzes, BioFlix, MP3 Tutors, and Activities, go to www.masteringbiology.com.

Reviewing the Concepts

Introduction to Organic Compounds (3.1–3.3)

3.1 Life's molecular diversity is based on the properties of carbon. Carbon's ability to bond with four other atoms is the basis for building large and diverse organic compounds. Hydrocarbons are composed of only carbon and hydrogen. Isomers have the same molecular formula but different structures.

3.2 A few chemical groups are key to the functioning of biological molecules. Hydrophilic functional groups give organic molecules specific chemical properties.

3.3 Cells make a huge number of large molecules from a limited set of small molecules.

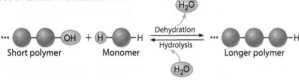

Carbohydrates (3.4–3.7)

3.4 Monosaccharides are the simplest carbohydrates. A monosaccharide has a formula that is a multiple of CH_2O and contains hydroxyl groups and a carbonyl group.

3.5 Two monosaccharides are linked to form a disaccharide.

3.6 What is high-fructose corn syrup, and is it to blame for obesity? HFCS, a mixture of glucose and fructose derived from corn, is commonly added to drinks and processed foods.

3.7 Polysaccharides are long chains of sugar units. Starch and glycogen are storage polysaccharides; cellulose is structural, found in plant cell walls. Chitin is a component of insect exoskeletons and fungal cell walls.

Lipids (3.8–3.10)

3.8 Fats are lipids that are mostly energy-storage molecules. Lipids are diverse, hydrophobic compounds composed largely of carbon and hydrogen. Fats (triglycerides) consist of glycerol linked to three fatty acids. Saturated fatty acids are found in animal fats; unsaturated fatty acids are typical of plant oils.

3.9 Phospholipids and steroids are important lipids with a variety of functions. Phospholipids are components of cell membranes. Steroids include cholesterol and some hormones.

3.10 Anabolic steroids pose health risks.

Proteins (3.11–3.13)

3.11 Proteins are made from amino acids linked by peptide bonds. Protein diversity is based on different sequences of amino acids, monomers that contain an amino group, a carboxyl group, an H, and an R group, all attached to a central carbon. The R groups distinguish 20 amino acids, each with specific properties.

3.12 A protein's specific shape determines its function. Proteins are involved in almost all of a cell's activities; as enzymes, they regulate chemical reactions.

3.13 A protein's shape depends on four levels of structure. A protein's primary structure is the sequence of amino acids in its polypeptide chain. Its secondary structure is the coiling or folding of the chain, stabilized by hydrogen bonds. Tertiary structure is the overall three-dimensional shape of a polypeptide, resulting from interactions among R groups. Proteins made of more than one polypeptide have quaternary structure.

Nucleic Acids (3.14–3.16)

3.14 DNA and RNA are the two types of nucleic acids. DNA and RNA serve as the blueprints for proteins and thus control the life of a cell.

3.15 Nucleic acids are polymers of nucleotides. Nucleotides are composed of a sugar, a phosphate group, and a nitrogenous base. DNA is a double helix; RNA is a single polynucleotide chain.

3.16 Lactose tolerance is a recent event in human evolution. Mutations in DNA have led to lactose tolerance in several human groups whose ancestors raised dairy cattle.

Connecting the Concepts

1. The diversity of life is staggering. Yet the molecular logic of life is simple and elegant: Small molecules common to all organisms are ordered into unique macromolecules. Explain why carbon is central to this diversity of organic molecules. How do carbon skeletons, chemical groups, monomers, and polymers relate to this molecular logic of life?

2. Complete the table to help review the structures and functions of the four classes of organic molecules.

Classes of Molecules and Their Components	Functions	Examples
Carbohydrates (Monosaccharides)	Energy for cell, raw material	a. _____
	b. _____	Starch, glycogen
	Plant cell support	c. _____
Lipids (don't form polymers) (Components of a fat molecule: Glycerol, Fatty acid)	Energy storage	d. _____
	e. _____	Phospholipids
	Hormones	f. _____
Proteins (g. _____ h. _____; i. _____; Amino acid)	j. _____	Lactase
	k. _____	Hair, tendons
	l. _____	Muscles
	Transport	m. _____
	Communication	Signal proteins
	n. _____	Antibodies
	Storage	Egg albumin
	Receive signals	Receptor protein
Nucleic Acids (o. _____; p. _____; Nucleotide q. _____)	Heredity	r. _____
	s. _____	DNA and RNA

Testing Your Knowledge

Multiple Choice

3. A glucose molecule is to starch as (*Explain your answer.*)
   a. a steroid is to a lipid.
   b. a protein is to an amino acid.
   c. a nucleic acid is to a polypeptide.
   d. a nucleotide is to a nucleic acid.
   e. an amino acid is to a nucleic acid.

4. What makes a fatty acid an acid?
   a. It does not dissolve in water.
   b. It is capable of bonding with other molecules to form a fat.
   c. It has a carboxyl group that donates an H$^+$ to a solution.
   d. It contains only two oxygen atoms.
   e. It is a polymer made of many smaller subunits.

5. Where in the tertiary structure of a water-soluble protein would you most likely find an amino acid with a hydrophobic R group?
   a. at both ends of the polypeptide chain
   b. on the outside, next to the water
   c. covalently bonded to another R group
   d. on the inside, away from water
   e. hydrogen-bonded to nearby amino acids

6. Cows can derive nutrients from cellulose because
   a. they produce enzymes that recognize the shape of the glucose-glucose bonds and hydrolyze them.
   b. they rechew their cud to break down cellulose fibers.
   c. one of their stomachs contains prokaryotes that can hydrolyze the bonds of cellulose.
   d. their intestinal tract contains termites, which produce enzymes to hydrolyze cellulose.
   e. they convert cellulose to starch and can digest starch.

7. A shortage of phosphorus in the soil would make it especially difficult for a plant to manufacture
   a. DNA.
   b. proteins.
   c. cellulose.
   d. fatty acids.
   e. sucrose.

8. Lipids differ from other large biological molecules in that they
   a. are much larger.
   b. are not polymers.
   c. do not have specific shapes.
   d. are nonpolar and therefore hydrophilic.
   e. contain nitrogen atoms.

9. Of the following functional groups, which is/are polar, tending to make organic compounds hydrophilic?
   a. carbonyl
   b. amino
   c. hydroxyl
   d. carboxyl
   e. all of the above

10. Unsaturated fats
    a. are more common in animals than in plants.
    b. have fewer fatty acid molecules per fat molecule.
    c. are associated with greater health risks than are saturated fats.
    d. have double bonds in their fatty acid chains.
    e. are usually solid at room temperature.

Describing, Comparing, and Explaining

11. List three different kinds of lipids and describe their functions.

12. Explain why heat, pH changes, and other environmental changes can interfere with a protein's function.

13. How can a cell make many different kinds of protein out of only 20 amino acids? Of the myriad possibilities, how does the cell "know" which proteins to make?

14. Briefly describe the various functions performed by proteins in a cell.

15. Explain how DNA controls the functions of a cell.

16. Sucrose is broken down in your intestine to the monosaccharides glucose and fructose, which are then absorbed into your blood. What is the name of this type of reaction? Using this diagram of sucrose, show how this would occur.

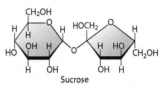

Sucrose

17. Circle and name the functional groups in this organic molecule. What type of compound is this? For which class of macromolecules is it a monomer?

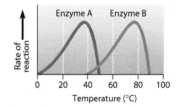

Applying the Concepts

18. Enzymes usually function best at an optimal pH and temperature. The following graph shows the effectiveness of two enzymes at various temperatures.

a. At which temperature does enzyme A perform best? Enzyme B?
b. One of these enzymes is found in humans and the other in thermophilic (heat-loving) bacteria. Which enzyme would you predict comes from which organism?
c. From what you know about enzyme structure, explain why the rate of the reaction catalyzed by enzyme A slows down at temperatures above 40°C (140°F).

19. Some scientists hypothesize that life elsewhere in the universe might be based on the element silicon rather than on carbon. Look at the electron shell diagrams in Figure 2.6. What properties does silicon share with carbon that would make silicon-based life more likely than, for example, neon-based or sulfur-based life?

Answers to all questions can be found in Appendix 4.

A Tour of the Cell

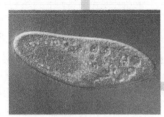

Introduction to the Cell
(4.1–4.4)

Microscopes reveal the structures of cells—the fundamental units of life.

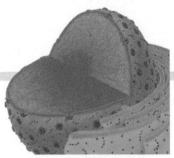

The Nucleus and Ribosomes
(4.5–4.6)

A cell's genetic instructions are housed in the nucleus and carried out by ribosomes.

The Endomembrane System
(4.7–4.12)

The endomembrane system participates in the manufacture, distribution, and breakdown of materials.

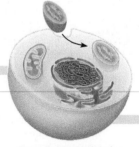

Energy-Converting Organelles
(4.13–4.15)

Mitochondria in all cells and chloroplasts in plant cells function in energy processing.

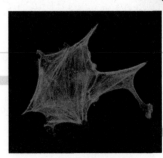

The Cytoskeleton and Cell Surfaces
(4.16–4.22)

The cytoskeleton and extracellular components provide support, motility, and functional connections.

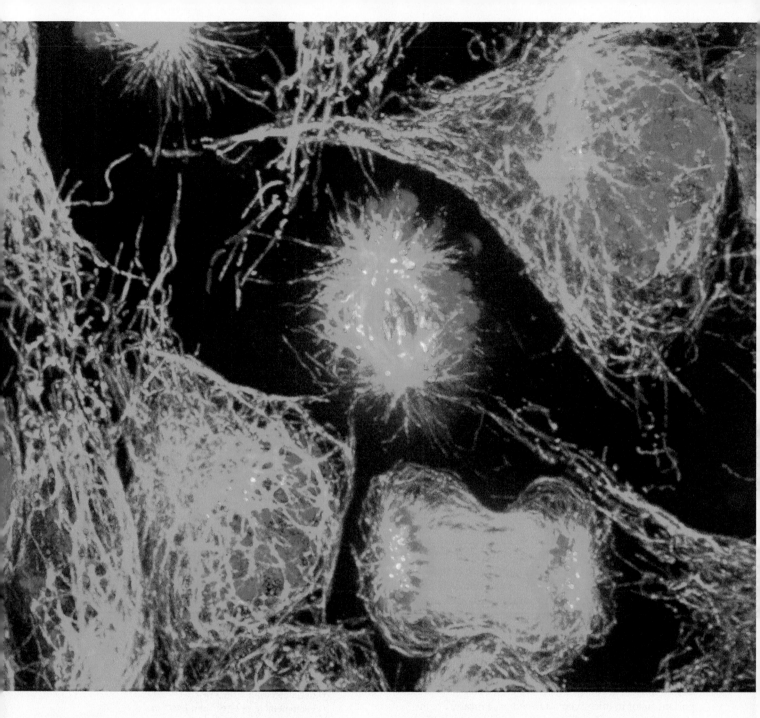

In the previous two chapters, we explored the chemistry of life, from atoms to large biological molecules. In this chapter, we make the crucial leap to the next level of biological organization, the cell—the level at which life emerges. The cell is the simplest collection of matter that can be alive. But cells are anything but simple, as we're sure you'll agree after reading this chapter.

In 1665, Robert Hooke used a crude microscope to examine a piece of cork. Hooke compared the structures he saw to "little rooms"—*cellulae* in Latin—and the term *cells* stuck. Hooke's contemporary, Antoni van Leeuwenhoek, working with more refined lenses, examined numerous subjects, from blood and sperm to pond water. His reports to the Royal Society of London included drawings and enthusiastic descriptions of his discoveries.

Since the days of Hooke and Leeuwenhoek, improved microscopes have vastly expanded our view of the cell.

This micrograph (photo taken through a microscope) shows beautiful but deadly cancer cells in the midst of dividing. Part of their beauty comes from the fluorescently colored stains attached to certain parts of the cells. In this chapter, micrographs are often paired with drawings that help emphasize specific details.

But neither drawings nor micrographs allow you to see the dynamic nature of living cells. For that you need to look through a microscope or view videos in lectures or on websites, such as the one associated with this book. As you study the images in this chapter, keep in mind that cellular parts are not static; they are constantly moving and interacting.

This chapter focuses on cellular structures and functions. As you learn about the parts, however, remember that the phenomenon we call life emerges from the arrangement and interactions of the many components of a cell.

Introduction to the Cell

4.1 Microscopes reveal the world of the cell

Our understanding of nature often goes hand in hand with the invention and refinement of instruments that extend human senses. Before microscopes were first used in the 17th century, no one knew that living organisms were composed of cells. The first microscopes were light microscopes, like the ones you may use in a biology laboratory. In a **light microscope (LM)**, visible light is passed through a specimen, such as a microorganism or a thin slice of animal or plant tissue, and then through glass lenses. The lenses bend the light in such a way that the image of the specimen is magnified as it is projected into your eye or a camera.

Magnification is the increase in the apparent size of an object. Figure 4.1A shows a single-celled protist called *Paramecium*. The notation "LM230×" printed along the right edge of this **micrograph** tells you that the photograph was taken through a light microscope and that this image is 230 times the actual size of the organism.

The actual size of this *Paramecium* is about 0.33 millimeter (mm) in length. Figure 4.1B shows the size range of cells compared with objects both larger and smaller. The most common units of length that biologists use are listed at the bottom of the figure. Notice that the scale along the left side of the figure is logarithmic to accommodate the range of sizes shown. Starting at the top of the scale with 10 meters (m) and going down, each reference measurement marks a 10-fold decrease in length. Most cells are between 1 and 100 micrometers (μm) in diameter (yellow region of the figure) and are therefore visible only with a microscope. Certain bacteria are as small as 0.2 μm in diameter and can barely be seen with a light microscope, whereas bird eggs are large enough to be seen with the unaided eye. A single nerve cell running from the base of your spinal cord to your big toe may be 1 m in length, although it is so thin you would still need a microscope to see it.

Light microscopes can effectively magnify objects about 1,000 times. Greater magnification does not show more details clearly; indeed, the image becomes blurry. Thus, another important factor in microscopy is *resolution*, a measure of the clarity of an image. Resolution is the ability of an optical

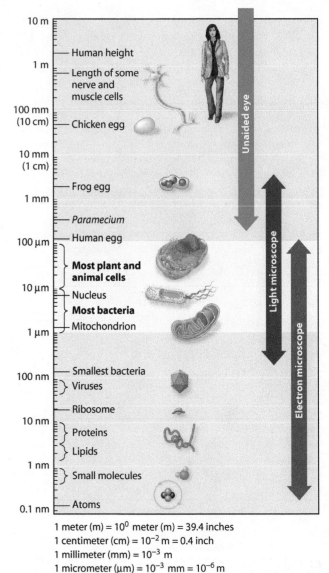

1 meter (m) = 10^0 meter (m) = 39.4 inches
1 centimeter (cm) = 10^{-2} m = 0.4 inch
1 millimeter (mm) = 10^{-3} m
1 micrometer (μm) = 10^{-3} mm = 10^{-6} m
1 nanometer (nm) = 10^{-3} μm = 10^{-9} m

▲ **Figure 4.1B** The size range of cells and related objects

instrument to show two nearby objects as separate. For example, what looks to your unaided eye like a single star in the sky may be resolved as twin stars with a telescope. Just as the resolution of the human eye is limited, the light microscope cannot resolve detail finer than about 0.2 μm, about the size of the smallest bacterium. No matter how many times its image of such a bacterium is magnified, the light microscope cannot show the details of this small cell's structure.

From the time that Hooke discovered cells in 1665 until the middle of the 20th century, biologists had only light microscopes for viewing cells. With these microscopes and various staining techniques to increase contrast and highlight

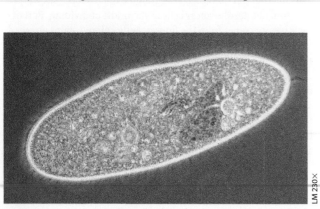

LM 230×

▲ **Figure 4.1A**   Light micrograph of a protist, *Paramecium* parts of the sample, these early biologists discovered a great deal—microorganisms, animal and plant cells, and even some of the structures within cells. By the mid-1800s, these discoveries led to the **cell theory**, which states that all living things are composed of cells and that all cells come from other cells.

Our knowledge of cell structure took a giant leap forward as biologists began using the electron microscope in the 1950s. Instead of using light, an **electron microscope (EM)** focuses a beam of electrons through a specimen or onto its surface. Electron microscopes can distinguish biological structures as small as about 2 nanometers (nm), a 100-fold improvement over the light microscope. This high resolution has enabled biologists to explore cell ultrastructure, the complex internal anatomy of a cell.

Figures 4.1C and **4.1D** show images produced by two kinds of electron microscopes. Biologists use the **scanning electron microscope (SEM)** to study the detailed architecture of cell surfaces. The SEM uses an electron beam to scan the surface of a cell or other sample, which is usually coated with a thin film of gold. The beam excites electrons on the surface, and these electrons are then detected by a device that translates their pattern into an image projected onto a video screen. The scanning electron micrograph in Figure 4.1C highlights the numerous

cilia on *Paramecium*, projections it uses for movement. Notice the indentation, called the oral groove, through which food enters the cell. As you can see, the SEM produces images that look three-dimensional.

The **transmission electron microscope (TEM)** is used to study the details of internal cell structure. The TEM aims an electron beam through a very thin section of a specimen, just as a light microscope aims a beam of light through a specimen. The section is stained with atoms of heavy metals, which attach to certain cellular structures more than others. Electrons are scattered by these more dense parts, and the image is created by the pattern of transmitted electrons. Instead of using glass lenses, the TEM uses electromagnets as lenses to bend the paths of the electrons, magnifying and focusing an image onto a viewing screen or photographic film. The transmission electron micrograph in Figure 4.1D shows internal details of a protist called *Toxoplasma*. SEMs and TEMs are initially black and white but are often artificially colorized, as they are in these figures, to highlight or clarify structural features.

Electron microscopes have truly revolutionized the study of cells and their structures. Nonetheless, they have not replaced the light microscope. One problem is that electron microscopes cannot be used to study living specimens because the methods used to prepare the specimen kill the cells. For a biologist studying a living process, such as the movement of *Paramecium*, a light microscope equipped with a video camera is more suitable than either an SEM or a TEM.

There are different types of light microscopy. **Figure 4.1E** shows *Paramecium* as seen using differential interference contrast microscopy. This optical technique amplifies differences in density so that the structures in living cells appear almost three-dimensional. Other techniques use fluorescent stains that selectively bind to various cellular molecules (see the chapter introduction). In the last decade or two, light microscopy has seen significant and exciting technical advances that have increased magnification, resolution, and contrast. You will see many beautiful and illuminating examples of microscopy in this textbook.

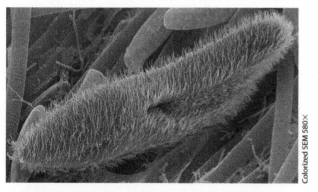

Colorized SEM 580×

▲ **Figure 4.1C** Scanning electron micrograph of *Paramecium*

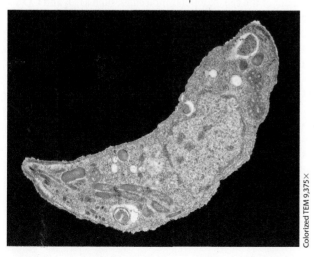

Colorized TEM 9,375×

▲ **Figure 4.1D** Transmission electron micrograph of *Toxoplasma*

> **?** Which type of microscope would you use to study (a) the changes in shape of a living human white blood cell; (b) the finest details of surface texture of a human hair; (c) the detailed structure of an organelle in a liver cell?

(a) Light microscope; (b) scanning electron microscope; (c) transmission electron microscope

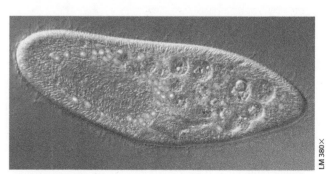

LM 380×

▲ **Figure 4.1E** Differential interference contrast micrograph of *Paramecium*

4.2 The small size of cells relates to the need to exchange materials across the plasma membrane

As you saw in Figure 4.1B, most cells are microscopic—unable to be seen without a microscope. Are there advantages to being so small? The logistics of carrying out a cell's functions appear to set both lower and upper limits on cell size. At minimum, a cell must be large enough to house enough DNA, protein molecules, and structures to survive and reproduce. But why aren't most cells as large as chicken eggs? The maximum size of a cell is influenced by geometry—the need to have a surface area large enough to service the volume of a cell. Active cells have a huge amount of traffic across their outer surface. A chicken's egg cell isn't very active, but once a chick embryo starts to develop, the egg is divided into many microscopic cells, each bounded by a membrane that allows the essential flow of oxygen, nutrients, and wastes across its surface.

Surface-to-Volume Ratio   Large cells have more surface area than small cells, but they have much less surface area relative to their volume than small cells. **Figure 4.2A** illustrates this relationship by comparing one large cube to 27 small ones. Using arbitrary units of measurement, the total volume is the same in both cases: 27 units³ (height × width × length). The total surface areas, however, are quite different. A cube has six sides; thus, its surface area is six times the area of each side (height × width). The surface area of the large cube is 54 units², while the total surface area of all 27 cubes is 162 units² (27 × 6 × 1 × 1), three times greater than the surface area of the large cube. Thus, we see that the smaller cubes have a much greater surface-to-volume ratio than the large cube. How about those neurons that extend from the base of your spine to your toes? Very thin, elongated shapes also provide a large surface area relative to a cell's volume.

The Plasma Membrane   So what is a cell's surface like? And how does it control the traffic of molecules across it? The **plasma membrane** forms a flexible boundary between the living cell and its surroundings. For a structure that separates life from nonlife, this membrane is amazingly thin. It would take a stack

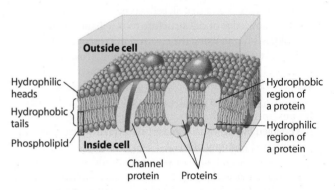

▲ **Figure 4.2B**   A plasma membrane: a phospholipid bilayer with associated proteins

of more than 8,000 of them to equal the thickness of this page. And, as you have come to expect with all things biological, the structure of the plasma membrane correlates with its function.

As you learned in Module 3.9, the structure of phospholipid molecules is well suited to their role as the main components of biological membranes. Composed of two distinct regions—a head with a negatively charged phosphate group and two nonpolar fatty acid tails, phospholipids form a two-layer sheet called a phospholipid bilayer. As you can see in **Figure 4.2B**, the phospholipids' hydrophilic (water-loving) heads face outward, exposed to the aqueous solutions on both sides of a membrane. Their hydrophobic (water-fearing) tails point inward, mingling together and shielded from water. Embedded in this lipid bilayer are diverse proteins, floating like icebergs in a phospholipid sea. The regions of the proteins within the center of the membrane are hydrophobic; the exterior sections exposed to water are hydrophilic.

Now let's see how the properties of the phospholipid bilayer and the proteins embedded in it relate to the plasma membrane's job as a traffic cop, regulating the flow of material into and out of the cell. Nonpolar molecules, such as O_2 and CO_2, can easily move across the membrane's hydrophobic interior. Some of the membrane's proteins form channels (tunnels) that shield ions and polar molecules as they pass through the hydrophobic center of the membrane. Still other proteins serve as pumps, using energy to actively transport molecules into or out of the cell.

We will return to a more detailed look at the structure and function of biological membranes in Chapter 5. In the next module, we consider other features common to all cells and take a closer look at the prokaryotic cells of domains Bacteria and Archaea.

? **To convince yourself that a small cell has more surface area relative to volume than a large cell, compare the surface-to-volume ratios of the large cube and one of the small cubes in Figure 4.2A.**

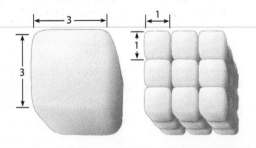

Total volume	27 units³	27 units³
Total surface area	54 units²	162 units²
Surface-to-volume ratio	2	6

▲ **Figure 4.2A**   Effect of cell size on surface area

● Large cube: 54/27 = 2; small cube: 6/1 = 6 (surface area is 1 × 1 × 6 sides = 6 units²; volume is 1 × 1 × 1 unit³)

4.3 Prokaryotic cells are structurally simpler than eukaryotic cells

Two kinds of cells, which differ in size and structure, have evolved over time. Bacteria and archaea consist of **prokaryotic cells**, whereas all other forms of life (protists, fungi, plants, and animals) are composed of **eukaryotic cells**. Eukaryotic cells are distinguished by having a membrane-enclosed nucleus, which houses most of their DNA. The word *eukaryote* means "true nucleus" (from the Greek *eu*, true, and *karyon*, kernel, referring to the nucleus). The word *prokaryote* means "before nucleus" (from the Greek *pro*, before), reflecting the fact that prokaryotic cells evolved before eukaryotic cells. They are also, as you shall see, structurally much simpler than eukaryotic cells while sharing some common characteristics.

All cells have several basic features in common. In addition to being bounded by a plasma membrane, all cells have one or more **chromosomes** carrying genes made of DNA. And all cells contain **ribosomes**, tiny structures that make proteins according to instructions from the genes. The interior of both types of cell is called the **cytoplasm**. However, in eukaryotic cells, this term refers only to the region between the nucleus and the plasma membrane. The cytoplasm of a eukaryotic cell contains many membrane-enclosed organelles that perform specific functions.

The cutaway diagram in **Figure 4.3** reveals the structure of a generalized prokaryotic cell. Notice that the DNA is coiled into a region called the **nucleoid** (nucleus-like), but in contrast to the nucleus of eukaryotic cells, no membrane surrounds the DNA. The ribosomes of prokaryotes (shown here in brown) are smaller and differ somewhat from those of eukaryotes. These molecular differences are the basis for the action of some antibiotics, such as tetracycline and streptomycin, which target

prokaryotic ribosomes. Thus, protein synthesis can be blocked for the bacterium that's invaded you, but not for you, the eukaryote who is taking the drug.

Outside the plasma membrane (shown here in gray) of most prokaryotes is a fairly rigid, chemically complex cell wall (orange). The wall protects the cell and helps maintain its shape. Some antibiotics, such as penicillin, prevent the formation of these protective walls. Again, since your cells don't have such walls, these antibiotics can kill invading bacteria without harming your cells. Certain prokaryotes have a sticky outer coat called a capsule (yellow) around the cell wall, helping to glue the cells to surfaces, such as sticks and rocks in fast-flowing streams or tissues within the human body. In addition to capsules, some prokaryotes have surface projections. Short projections help attach prokaryotes to each other or their substrate. Longer projections called **flagella** (singular, *flagellum*) propel a prokaryotic cell through its liquid environment.

It takes an electron microscope to see the details of any cell, and this is especially true of prokaryotic cells (Figure 4.3, right side). Most prokaryotic cells are about one-tenth the size of a typical eukaryotic cell (see Figure 1.3). Prokaryotes will be described in more detail in Chapter 16. Eukaryotic cells are the main focus of this chapter, so we turn to these next.

? List three features that are common to prokaryotic and eukaryotic cells. List three features that differ.

● Both types of cells have plasma membranes, chromosomes containing DNA, and ribosomes. Prokaryotic cells are smaller, do not have a nucleus that houses their DNA or other membrane-enclosed organelles, and have smaller, somewhat different ribosomes.

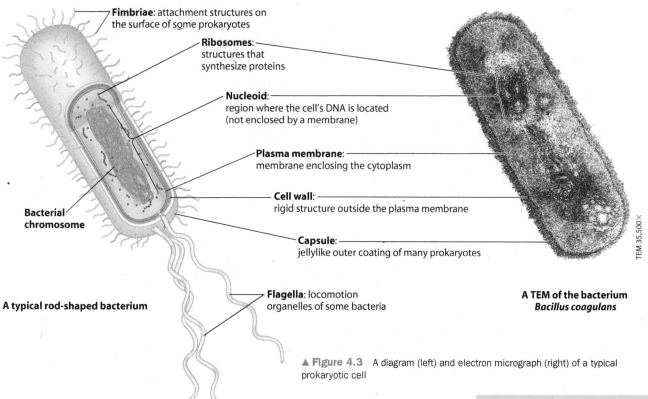

Fimbriae: attachment structures on the surface of some prokaryotes

Ribosomes: structures that synthesize proteins

Nucleoid: region where the cell's DNA is located (not enclosed by a membrane)

Plasma membrane: membrane enclosing the cytoplasm

Cell wall: rigid structure outside the plasma membrane

Capsule: jellylike outer coating of many prokaryotes

Bacterial chromosome

Flagella: locomotion organelles of some bacteria

A typical rod-shaped bacterium

TEM 35,500×

A TEM of the bacterium *Bacillus coagulans*

▲ **Figure 4.3** A diagram (left) and electron micrograph (right) of a typical prokaryotic cell

4.4 Eukaryotic cells are partitioned into functional compartments

All eukaryotic cells—whether from animals, plants, protists, or fungi—are fundamentally similar to one another and profoundly different from prokaryotic cells. Let's look at an animal cell and a plant cell as representatives of the eukaryotes.

Figure 4.4A is a diagram of an idealized animal cell. No cell would look exactly like this. We color-code the various organelles and other structures in the diagrams for easier identification. And recall from the chapter introduction that in living cells many of these structures are moving and interacting.

The nucleus is the most obvious difference between a prokaryotic and eukaryotic cell. A eukaryotic cell also contains various other **organelles** ("little organs"), which perform specific functions in the cell. Just as the cell itself is wrapped in a membrane made of phospholipids and proteins that perform various functions, each organelle is bounded by a membrane with a lipid and protein composition that suits its function.

The organelles and other structures of eukaryotic cells can be organized into four basic functional groups as follows: (1) The nucleus and ribosomes carry out the genetic control of the cell. (2) Organelles involved in the manufacture, distribution, and breakdown of molecules include the endoplasmic reticulum, Golgi apparatus, lysosomes, vacuoles, and peroxisomes. (3) Mitochondria in all cells and chloroplasts in plant cells function in energy processing. (4) Structural support, movement, and communication between cells are the functions of the cytoskeleton, plasma membrane, and plant cell wall. These cellular components are identified in the figures on these two pages and will be examined in greater detail in the remaining modules of this chapter.

In essence, the internal membranes of a eukaryotic cell partition it into compartments. Many of the chemical activities of cells—activities known collectively as **cellular metabolism**—occur within organelles. In fact, many enzymatic proteins essential for metabolic processes are built into the membranes of organelles. The fluid-filled spaces within organelles are important as sites where specific chemical conditions are maintained. These conditions vary from one organelle to another and favor the metabolic processes occurring in each kind of organelle.

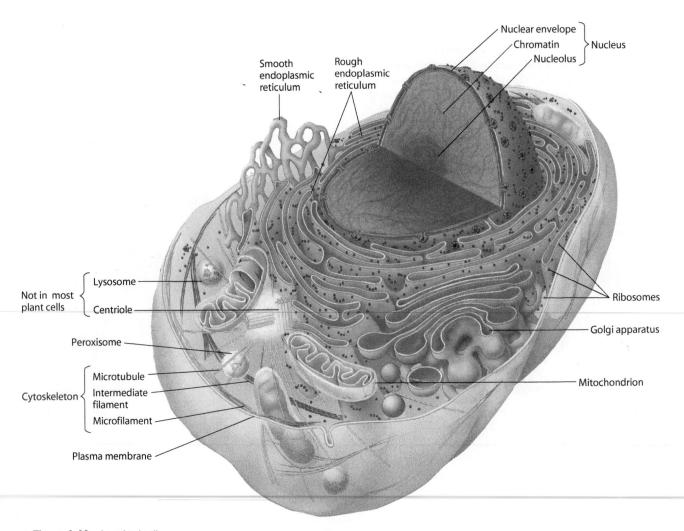

▲ Figure 4.4A   An animal cell

For example, while a part of the endoplasmic reticulum is engaged in making steroid hormones, neighboring peroxisomes may be detoxifying harmful compounds and making hydrogen peroxide (H_2O_2) as a poisonous by-product of their activities. But because the H_2O_2 is confined within peroxisomes, where it is quickly converted to H_2O by resident enzymes, the rest of the cell is protected from destruction.

Almost all of the organelles and other structures of animal cells are also present in plant cells. As you can see in Figure 4.4A, however, there are a few exceptions: Lysosomes and centrioles are not found in plant cells. Also, although some animal cells have flagella or cilia (not shown in Figure 4.4A), among plants, only the sperm cells of a few species have flagella. (As you will learn in Chapter 16, the flagella of prokaryotic cells differ in both structure and function from eukaryotic flagella.)

A plant cell (Figure 4.4B) also has some structures that an animal cell lacks. For example, a plant cell has a rigid, rather thick cell wall (as do the cells of fungi and many protists). Cell walls protect cells and help maintain their shape. Chemically different from prokaryotic cell walls, plant cell walls contain the polysaccharide cellulose. Plasmodesmata (singular, plasmodesma) are cytoplasmic channels through cell walls that connect adjacent cells. An important organelle found in plant cells is the chloroplast, where photosynthesis occurs. (Chloroplasts are also found in algae and some other protists.) Unique to plant cells is a large central vacuole, a compartment that stores water and a variety of chemicals.

Although we have emphasized organelles, eukaryotic cells contain nonmembranous structures as well. The cytoskeleton is composed of different types of protein fibers that extend throughout the cell. These networks provide for support and movement. As you can see by the many brown dots in both figures, ribosomes occur throughout the cytoplasm, as they do in prokaryotic cells. In addition, eukaryotic cells have many ribosomes attached to parts of the endoplasmic reticulum (making it appear "rough") and to the outer membrane of the nucleus.

Let's begin our in-depth tour of the eukaryotic cell, starting with the nucleus.

? Which of the following cellular structures differs from the others in the list: mitochondrion, chloroplast, ribosome, lysosome, vacuole? How does it differ?

● Ribosome, because it is the only structure in the list that is not bounded by a membrane.

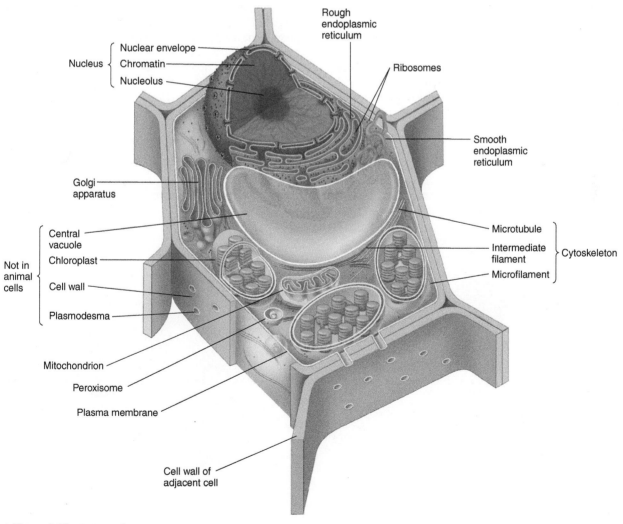

▲ Figure 4.4B A plant cell

The Nucleus and Ribosomes

4.5 The nucleus is the cell's genetic control center

You just saw a preview of the many intricate structures that can be found in a eukaryotic cell. A cell must build and maintain these structures and process energy for the work of transport, import, export, movement, and communication. But who is in charge of this bustling factory? Who stores the master plans, gives the orders, changes course in response to environmental input, and, when called upon, makes another factory just like itself? The cell's nucleus is this command center.

The **nucleus** contains most of the cell's DNA—its master plans—and controls the cell's activities by directing protein synthesis. The DNA is associated with many proteins in the structures called chromosomes. The proteins help organize and coil the long DNA molecule. Indeed, the DNA of the 46 chromosomes in one of your cells laid end to end would stretch to a length of over 2 m, but it must coil up to fit into a nucleus only 5 μm in diameter. When a cell is not dividing, this complex of proteins and DNA, called **chromatin**, appears as a diffuse mass, as shown in the TEM (left) and diagram (right) of a nucleus in Figure 4.5.

As a cell prepares to divide, the DNA is copied so that each daughter cell can later receive an identical set of genetic instructions. Just prior to cell division, the thin chromatin fibers coil up further, becoming thick enough to be visible with a light microscope as the familiar separate structures you would probably recognize as chromosomes.

Enclosing the nucleus is a double membrane called the **nuclear envelope**. Each of the membranes is a separate phospholipid bilayer with associated proteins. Similar in function to the plasma membrane, the nuclear envelope controls the flow of materials into and out of the nucleus. As you can see in the diagram in Figure 4.5, the nuclear envelope is perforated with protein-lined pores that regulate the movement of large molecules and also connects with the cell's network of membranes called the endoplasmic reticulum.

The **nucleolus**, a prominent structure in the nucleus, is the site where a special type of RNA called *ribosomal RNA* (rRNA) is synthesized according to instructions in the DNA. Proteins brought in through the nuclear pores from the cytoplasm are assembled with this rRNA to form the subunits of ribosomes. These subunits then exit through the pores to the cytoplasm, where they will join to form functional ribosomes.

The nucleus directs protein synthesis by making another type of RNA, *messenger RNA* (mRNA). Essentially, mRNA is a transcription of protein-synthesizing instructions written in a gene's DNA (see Figure 3.14). The mRNA moves through the pores in the nuclear envelope to the cytoplasm. There it is translated by ribosomes into the amino acid sequences of proteins. Let's look at ribosomes next.

? **What are the main functions of the nucleus?**

● To house and copy DNA and pass it on to daughter cells in cell division; to build ribosomal subunits; to transcribe DNA instructions into RNA and thereby control the cell's functions

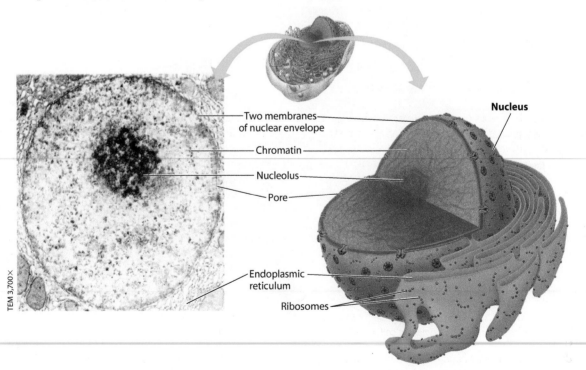

▲ **Figure 4.5** Transmission electron micrograph (left) and diagram (right) of the nucleus

4.6 Ribosomes make proteins for use in the cell and for export

If the nucleus is the command center, then ribosomes are the machines on which those commands are carried out. Ribosomes are the cellular components that use instructions sent from the nucleus to carry out protein synthesis. Cells that make a lot of proteins have a large number of ribosomes. For example, a human pancreas cell producing digestive enzymes may contain a few million ribosomes. What other structure would you expect to be prominent in cells that are active in protein synthesis? As you just learned, nucleoli assemble the subunits of ribosomes out of ribosomal RNA and protein.

As shown in the colorized TEM in **Figure 4.6**, ribosomes are found in two locations in the cell. *Free ribosomes* are suspended in the fluid of the cytoplasm, while *bound ribosomes* are attached to the outside of the endoplasmic reticulum or nuclear envelope. Free and bound ribosomes are structurally identical, and ribosomes can alternate between the two locations.

Most of the proteins made on free ribosomes function within the cytoplasm; examples are enzymes that catalyze the first steps of sugar breakdown. In Module 4.8, you will see how bound ribosomes make proteins that will be inserted into membranes, packaged in certain organelles, or exported from the cell.

At the bottom right in Figure 4.6, you see how ribosomes interact with messenger RNA (carrying the instructions from a gene) to build a protein. The nucleotide sequence of an mRNA molecule is translated into the amino acid sequence of a polypeptide. Protein synthesis is explored in more detail in

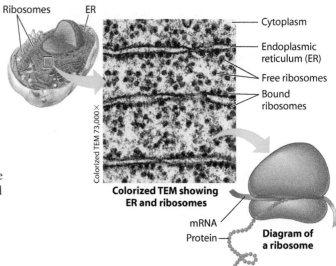

Colorized TEM showing ER and ribosomes

Diagram of a ribosome

▲ Figure 4.6 The locations and structure of ribosomes

Chapter 10. Next let's look at more of the manufacturing equipment of the cell.

? **What role do ribosomes play in carrying out the genetic instructions of a cell?**

● Ribosomes synthesize proteins according to the instructions carried by messenger RNA from the DNA in the nucleus.

The Endomembrane System

4.7 Overview: Many cell organelles are connected through the endomembrane system

Ribosomes may be a cell's protein-making machines, but running a factory as complex as a cell requires infrastructure and many different departments that perform separate but related functions. Internal membranes, a distinguishing feature of eukaryotic cells, are involved in most of a cell's functions. Many of the membranes of the eukaryotic cell are part of an **endomembrane system**. Some of these membranes are physically connected and some are related by the transfer of membrane segments by tiny **vesicles**, sacs made of membrane.

The endomembrane system includes the nuclear envelope, endoplasmic reticulum, Golgi apparatus, lysosomes, vacuoles, and the plasma membrane. (The plasma membrane is not exactly an *endo*membrane in physical location, but it is related to the other membranes by the transfer of vesicles). Many of these organelles work together in the synthesis, distribution, storage, and export of molecules. We focus on these interrelated membranes in Modules 4.8–4.11.

The extensive network of flattened sacs and tubules called the **endoplasmic reticulum (ER)** is a prime example of the direct interrelatedness of parts of the endomembrane system. (The term *endoplasmic* means "within the cytoplasm," and *reticulum* is Latin for "little net.") As shown in Figure 4.5 on the facing page, membranes of the ER are continuous with the nuclear envelope. As we discuss next, there are two regions of ER—smooth ER and rough ER—that differ both in structure and in function. The membranes that form them, however, are connected.

The tubules and sacs of the ER enclose an interior space that is separate from the cytoplasmic fluid. Dividing the cell into separate functional compartments is an important aspect of the endomembrane system.

? **Which structure includes all others in the list: rough ER, smooth ER, endomembrane system, nuclear envelope?**

● Endomembrane system

4.8 The endoplasmic reticulum is a biosynthetic factory

One of the major manufacturing sites in a cell is the endoplasmic reticulum. The diagram in **Figure 4.8A** shows a cutaway view of the interconnecting membranes of the smooth and rough ER. These two types of ER can be distinguished in the electron micrograph. **Smooth endoplasmic reticulum** is called *smooth* because it lacks attached ribosomes. **Rough endoplasmic reticulum** has ribosomes that stud the outer surface of the membrane; thus, it appears *rough* in the electron micrograph.

Smooth ER The smooth ER of various cell types functions in a variety of metabolic processes. Enzymes of the smooth ER are important in the synthesis of lipids, including oils, phospholipids, and steroids. In vertebrates, for example, cells of the ovaries and testes synthesize the steroid sex hormones. These cells are rich in smooth ER, a structural feature that fits their function by providing ample machinery for steroid synthesis.

Our liver cells also have large amounts of smooth ER, with other important functions. Certain enzymes in the smooth ER of liver cells help process drugs, alcohol, and other potentially harmful substances. The sedative phenobarbital and other barbiturates are examples of drugs detoxified by these enzymes. As liver cells are exposed to such chemicals, the amount of smooth ER and its detoxifying enzymes increases, thereby increasing the rate of detoxification and thus the body's tolerance to the drugs. The result is a need for higher and higher doses of a drug to achieve a particular effect, such as sedation. Also, because detoxifying enzymes often cannot distinguish among related chemicals, the growth of smooth ER in response to one drug can increase tolerance to other drugs. Barbiturate abuse, for example, can decrease the effectiveness of certain antibiotics and other useful drugs.

Smooth ER has yet another function, the storage of calcium ions. In muscle cells, for example, a specialized smooth ER membrane pumps calcium ions into the interior of the ER. When a nerve signal stimulates a muscle cell, calcium ions rush from the smooth ER into the cytoplasmic fluid and trigger contraction of the cell.

Rough ER One of the functions of rough ER is to make more membrane. Phospholipids made by enzymes of the rough ER are inserted into the ER membrane. Thus, the ER membrane grows, and portions of it are transferred to other components of the endomembrane system as vesicles.

The bound ribosomes attached to rough ER produce proteins that will be inserted into the growing ER membrane, transported to other organelles, or secreted by the cell. An example of a secretory protein is insulin, a hormone secreted by specialized cells in the pancreas. Type 1 diabetes results when these cells are destroyed and a lack of insulin disrupts glucose metabolism in the body.

Figure 4.8B follows the synthesis, modification, and packaging of a secretory protein. ❶ As the polypeptide is synthesized by a bound ribosome following the instructions of an mRNA, it

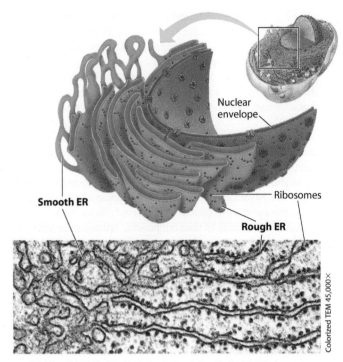

Smooth ER

Rough ER

Nuclear envelope

Ribosomes

▲ **Figure 4.8A** Smooth and rough endoplasmic reticulum

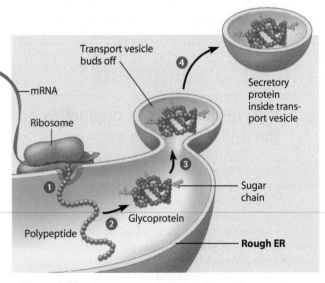

mRNA

Ribosome

Polypeptide

Transport vesicle buds off

Secretory protein inside transport vesicle

Sugar chain

Glycoprotein

Rough ER

▲ **Figure 4.8B** Synthesis and packaging of a secretory protein by the rough ER

is threaded into the cavity of the rough ER. As it enters, the new protein folds into its three-dimensional shape. ❷ Short chains of sugars are often linked to the polypeptide, making the molecule a **glycoprotein** (*glyco* means "sugar"). ❸ When the molecule is ready for export from the ER, it is packaged in a **transport vesicle**, a vesicle that moves from one part of the cell to another. ❹ This vesicle buds off from the ER membrane.

Colorized TEM 45,000×

The vesicle now carries the protein to the Golgi apparatus (described in the next module) for further processing. From there, a transport vesicle containing the finished molecule makes its way to the plasma membrane and releases its contents from the cell.

4.9 The Golgi apparatus finishes, sorts, and ships cell products

After leaving the ER, many transport vesicles travel to the **Golgi apparatus**. Using a light microscope and a staining technique he developed, Italian scientist Camillo Golgi discovered this membranous organelle in 1898. The electron microscope confirmed his discovery more than 50 years later, revealing a stack of flattened sacs, looking much like a pile of pita bread. A cell may contain many, even hundreds, of these stacks. The number of Golgi stacks correlates with how active the cell is in secreting proteins—a multistep process that, as we have just seen, is initiated in the rough ER.

The Golgi apparatus serves as a molecular warehouse and finishing factory for products manufactured by the ER. You can follow this process in Figure 4.9. Note that the flattened Golgi sacs are not connected, as are ER sacs. ❶ One side of a Golgi stack serves as a receiving dock for transport vesicles produced by the ER. ❷ A vesicle fuses with a Golgi sac, adding its membrane and contents to the receiving side. ❸ Products of the ER are modified during their transit through the Golgi. ❹ The other side of the Golgi, the shipping side, gives rise to vesicles, which bud off and travel to other sites.

How might ER products be processed during their transit through the Golgi? Various Golgi enzymes modify the carbohydrate portions of the glycoproteins made in the ER, removing some sugars and substituting others. Molecular identification tags, such as phosphate groups, may be added that help the Golgi sort molecules into different batches for different destinations.

Until recently, the Golgi was viewed as a static structure, with products in various stages of processing moved from sac to sac by transport vesicles. Recent research has given rise to a new *maturation model* in which entire sacs "mature" as they move from the receiving to the shipping side, carrying and modifying their cargo as they go. The shipping side of the Golgi stack serves as a depot from which finished secretory products, packaged in transport vesicles, move to the plasma membrane for export from the cell. Alternatively, finished products may become part of the plasma membrane itself or part of another organelle, such as a lysosome, which we discuss next.

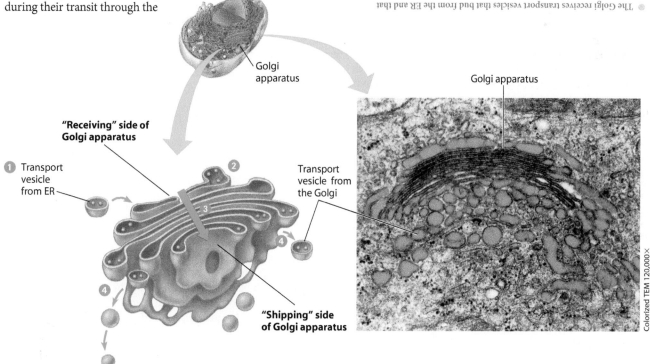

Golgi apparatus

Golgi apparatus

"Receiving" side of Golgi apparatus

❶ Transport vesicle from ER

❷

Transport vesicle from the Golgi

❸

❹

❹

"Shipping" side of Golgi apparatus

Colorized TEM 120,000×

▲ **Figure 4.9** The Golgi apparatus

4.10 Lysosomes are digestive compartments within a cell

A **lysosome** is a membranous sac of digestive enzymes. The name *lysosome* is derived from two Greek words meaning "breakdown body." The enzymes and membranes of lysosomes are made by rough ER and processed in the Golgi apparatus. Illustrating a main theme of eukaryotic cell structure—compartmentalization—a lysosome provides an acidic environment for its enzymes, while safely isolating them from the rest of the cell.

Lysosomes have several types of digestive functions. Many protists engulf food particles into membranous sacs called food vacuoles. As Figure 4.10A shows, lysosomes fuse with food vacuoles and digest the food. The nutrients are then released into the cell fluid. Our white blood cells engulf and destroy bacteria using lysosomal enzymes. Lysosomes also serve as recycling centers for animal cells. Damaged organelles or small amounts of cell fluid become surrounded by a membrane. A lysosome fuses with such a vesicle (Figure 4.10B) and dismantles its contents, making organic molecules available for reuse. With the help of lysosomes, a cell continually renews itself.

The cells of people with inherited lysosomal storage diseases lack one or more lysosomal enzymes. The lysosomes become engorged with undigested material, eventually interfering with cellular function. In Tay-Sachs disease, for example, a lipid-digesting enzyme is missing, and brain cells become impaired by an accumulation of lipids. Lysosomal storage diseases are often fatal in early childhood.

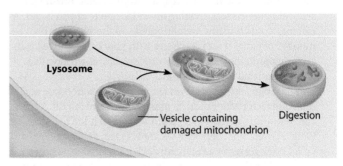

▲ **Figure 4.10A** Lysosome fusing with a food vacuole and digesting food

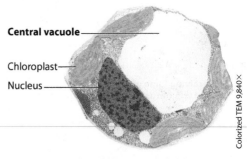

▲ **Figure 4.10B** Lysosome fusing with a vesicle containing a damaged organelle and digesting and recycling its contents

? **How is a lysosome like a recycling center?**

 It breaks down damaged organelles and recycles their molecules.

4.11 Vacuoles function in the general maintenance of the cell

Vacuoles are large vesicles that have a variety of functions. In Figure 4.10A, you saw how a food vacuole forms as a cell ingests food. Figure 4.11A shows two contractile vacuoles in the protist *Paramecium*, looking somewhat like wheel hubs with radiating spokes. The "spokes" collect water from the cell, and the hub expels it to the outside. Freshwater protists constantly take in water from their environment. Without a way to get rid of the excess water, the cell would swell and burst.

In plants, some vacuoles have a digestive function similar to that of lysosomes in animal cells. Vacuoles in flower petals contain pigments that attract pollinating insects. Vacuoles may also contain poisons or unpalatable compounds that protect the plant against herbivores; examples include

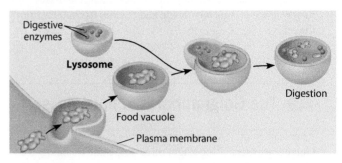

▲ **Figure 4.11B** Central vacuole in a plant cell

nicotine, caffeine, and various chemicals we use as pharmaceutical drugs. Figure 4.11B shows a plant cell's large **central vacuole**, which helps the cell grow in size by absorbing water and enlarging. It also stockpiles vital chemicals and acts as a trash can, safely storing toxic waste products.

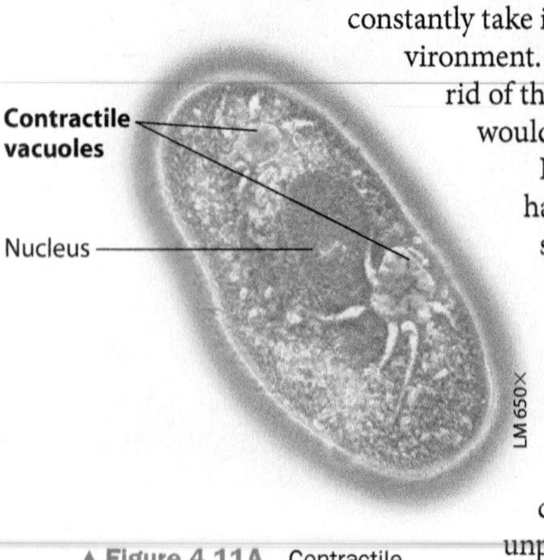

? **Is a food vacuole part of the endomembrane system?**

 Yes; it forms by pinching in from the plasma membrane, which is part of the endomembrane system.

▲ **Figure 4.11A** Contractile vacuoles in *Paramecium*, a single-celled organism

4.12 A review of the structures involved in manufacturing and breakdown

Figure 4.12 summarizes the relationships within the endomembrane system. You can see the direct *structural* connections between the nuclear envelope, rough ER, and smooth ER. The red arrows show the *functional* connections, as membranes and proteins produced by the ER travel in transport vesicles to the Golgi and on to other destinations. Some vesicles develop into lysosomes or vacuoles. Others transport products to the outside of the cell. When these vesicles fuse with the plasma membrane, their contents are secreted from the cell and their membrane is added to the plasma membrane.

Peroxisomes (see Figures 4.4A and B) are metabolic compartments that do not originate from the endomembrane system. In fact, how they are related to other organelles is still unknown. Some peroxisomes break down fatty acids to be used as cellular fuel. In your liver, peroxisomes detoxify harmful compounds, including alcohol. In these processes, enzymes transfer hydrogen from various compounds to oxygen, producing hydrogen peroxide (H_2O_2). Other enzymes in the peroxisome quickly convert this toxic product to water—another example of the importance of a cell's compartmental structure.

A cell requires a continuous supply of energy to perform the work of life. Next we consider two organelles that act as cellular power stations—mitochondria and chloroplasts.

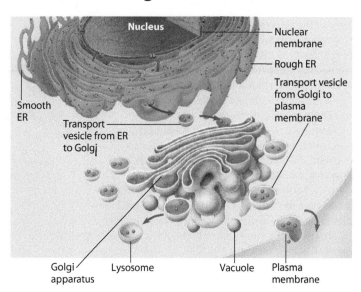

▲ Figure 4.12 Connections among the organelles of the endomembrane system

? How do transport vesicles help tie together the endomembrane system?

● Transport vesicles move membranes and substances they enclose between components of the endomembrane system.

Energy-Converting Organelles

4.13 Mitochondria harvest chemical energy from food

Mitochondria (singular, *mitochondrion*) are organelles that carry out cellular respiration in nearly all eukaryotic cells, converting the chemical energy of foods such as sugars to the chemical energy of the molecule called ATP (adenosine triphosphate). ATP is the main energy source for cellular work.

As you have come to expect, a mitochondrion's structure suits its function. It is enclosed by two membranes, each a phospholipid bilayer with a unique collection of embedded proteins (Figure 4.13). The mitochondrion has two internal compartments. The first is the intermembrane space, the narrow region between the inner and outer membranes. The inner membrane encloses the second compartment, the **mitochondrial matrix**, which contains mitochondrial DNA and ribosomes, as well as many enzymes that catalyze some of the reactions of cellular respiration. The inner membrane is highly folded and contains many embedded protein molecules that function in ATP synthesis. The folds, called **cristae**, increase the membrane's surface area, enhancing the mitochondrion's ability to produce ATP. We discuss the role of mitochondria in cellular respiration in more detail in Chapter 6.

? What is cellular respiration?

● A process that converts the chemical energy of sugars and other food molecules to the chemical energy of ATP.

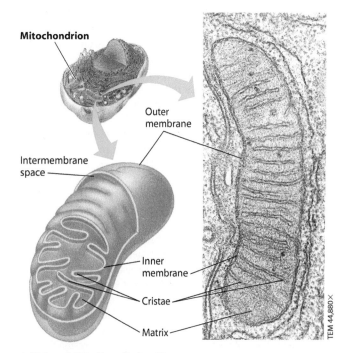

▲ Figure 4.13 The mitochondrion

4.14 Chloroplasts convert solar energy to chemical energy

Most of the living world runs on the energy provided by photosynthesis, the conversion of light energy from the sun to the chemical energy of sugar molecules. **Chloroplasts** are the photosynthesizing organelles of all photosynthetic eukaryotes. The chloroplast's solar power system is much more efficient than anything yet produced by human ingenuity.

Befitting an organelle that carries out complex, multistep processes, internal membranes partition the chloroplast into compartments (Figure 4.14). The chloroplast is enclosed by an inner and outer membrane separated by a thin intermembrane space. The compartment inside the inner membrane holds a thick fluid called **stroma**, which contains chloroplast DNA and ribosomes as well as many enzymes. A network of interconnected sacs called **thylakoids** is inside the chloroplast. The compartment inside these sacs is called the thylakoid space. In some regions, thylakoids are stacked like poker chips; each stack is called a **granum** (plural, *grana*). The grana are the chloroplast's solar power packs—the sites where the green chlorophyll molecules embedded in thylakoid membranes trap solar energy. In Chapter 7, you will learn how this compartmental organization enables the chloroplast to convert solar energy to chemical energy. In the next module, we explore the surprising origin of mitochondria and chloroplasts.

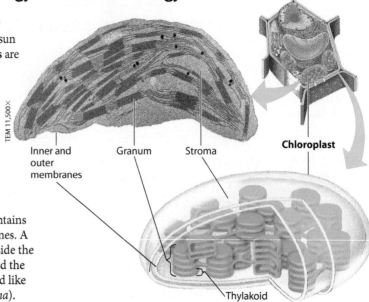

TEM 11,500×

Inner and outer membranes

Granum

Stroma

Chloroplast

Thylakoid

▲ Figure 4.14   The chloroplast

? Which membrane in a chloroplast appears to be the most extensive? Why might this be so?

● The thylakoid membranes are most extensive, providing a large area of membrane that contains chlorophyll for photosynthesis.

EVOLUTION CONNECTION

4.15 Mitochondria and chloroplasts evolved by endosymbiosis

Does it seem odd to you that mitochondria and chloroplasts contain DNA and ribosomes? Indeed, they have a single circular DNA molecule, similar in structure to the chromosome of prokaryotes. And their ribosomes are more similar to prokaryotic ribosomes than to eukaryotic ribosomes. Another interesting observation is that mitochondria and chloroplasts reproduce by a splitting process that is similar to that of certain prokaryotes.

The widely accepted **endosymbiont theory** states that mitochondria and chloroplasts were formerly small prokaryotes that began living within larger cells. The term *endosymbiont* refers to a cell that lives within another cell, called the host cell. These small prokaryotes may have gained entry to the larger cell as undigested prey or internal parasites (Figure 4.15).

By whatever means the relationship began, we can hypothesize how the symbiosis could have become beneficial. In a world that was becoming increasingly aerobic from the oxygen-generating photosynthesis of prokaryotes, a host would have benefited from an endosymbiont that was able to use oxygen to release large amounts of energy from organic molecules by cellular respiration. And a host cell could derive nourishment from a photosynthetic endosymbiont. Over time, the host and endosymbionts would have become increasingly interdependent, eventually becoming a single organism.

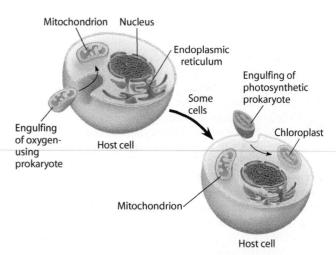

Mitochondrion

Nucleus

Endoplasmic reticulum

Engulfing of photosynthetic prokaryote

Some cells

Chloroplast

Engulfing of oxygen-using prokaryote

Host cell

Mitochondrion

Host cell

▲ Figure 4.15   Endosymbiotic origin of mitochondria and chloroplasts

? All eukaryotes have mitochondria, but not all eukaryotes have chloroplasts. Can you propose an evolutionary explanation for this observation?

● The first endosymbiotic event would have given rise to eukaryotic cells containing mitochondria. At least one of these cells may have then taken up a photosynthetic prokaryote, giving rise to eukaryotic cells that contain chloroplasts in addition to mitochondria.

The Cytoskeleton and Cell Surfaces

4.16 The cell's internal skeleton helps organize its structure and activities

Biologists once thought that organelles floated freely in the cell. But improvements in both light microscopy and electron microscopy have allowed scientists to uncover a network of protein fibers, collectively called the **cytoskeleton**, extending throughout the cytoplasm of a cell. These fibers function like a skeleton in providing for both structural support and cell motility. Cell motility includes both the internal movement of cell parts and the locomotion of a cell. These movements generally require the interaction of the cytoskeleton with proteins called motor proteins.

Three main kinds of fibers make up the cytoskeleton: microfilaments, the thinnest fiber; microtubules, the thickest; and intermediate filaments, in between in thickness. **Figure 4.16** shows three micrographs of cells of the same type, each stained with a different fluorescent dye that selectively highlights one of these types of fibers.

Microfilaments, also called actin filaments, are solid rods composed mainly of globular proteins called actin, arranged in a twisted double chain (bottom left of Figure 4.16). Microfilaments form a three-dimensional network just inside the plasma membrane that helps support the cell's shape. This is especially important for animal cells, which lack cell walls.

Microfilaments are also involved in cell movements. As we will see in Chapter 30, actin filaments and thicker filaments made of the motor protein myosin interact to cause contraction of muscle cells. Localized contractions brought about by actin and myosin are involved in the amoeboid (crawling) movement of the protist *Amoeba* and some of our white blood cells.

Intermediate filaments may be made of various fibrous proteins that supercoil into thicker cables. Intermediate filaments serve mainly to reinforce cell shape and to anchor certain organelles. The nucleus is held in place by a cage of intermediate filaments. While microfilaments may be disassembled and reassembled elsewhere, intermediate filaments are often more permanent fixtures in the cell. The outer layer of your skin consists of dead skin cells full of intermediate filaments made of keratin proteins.

Microtubules are straight, hollow tubes composed of globular proteins called tubulins. As indicated in the bottom right of Figure 4.16, microtubules elongate by the addition of tubulin proteins, which consist of two subunits. Microtubules are readily disassembled in a reverse manner, and the tubulin proteins can be reused elsewhere in the cell. In many animal cells, microtubules grow out from a "microtubule-organizing center" near the nucleus. Within this region is a pair of **centrioles** (see Figure 4.4A). We will return to centrioles when we discuss cell division in Chapter 8.

Microtubules shape and support the cell and also act as tracks along which organelles equipped with motor proteins move. For example, a lysosome might "walk" along a microtubule to reach a food vacuole. Microtubules also guide the movement of chromosomes when cells divide, and as we see next, they are the main components of cilia and flagella—the locomotive appendages of cells.

? **Which component of the cytoskeleton is most important in (a) holding the nucleus in place within the cell; (b) guiding transport vesicles from the Golgi to the plasma membrane; (c) contracting muscle cells?**

● (a) Intermediate filaments; (b) microtubules; (c) microfilaments

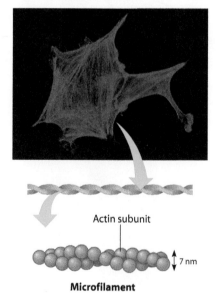
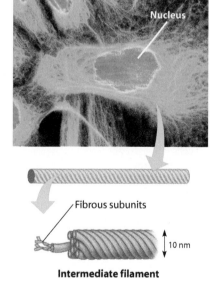
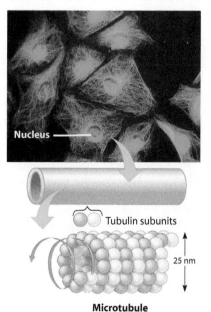

Actin subunit — 7 nm — **Microfilament**

Fibrous subunits — 10 nm — **Intermediate filament**

Tubulin subunits — 25 nm — **Microtubule**

Nucleus

▲ Figure 4.16 Three types of fibers of the cytoskeleton: microfilaments are stained red (left), intermediate filaments yellow-green (center), and microtubules green (right)

4.17 Cilia and flagella move when microtubules bend

The role of the cytoskeleton in movement is clearly seen in the motile appendages that protrude from certain cells. The short, numerous appendages that propel protists such as *Paramecium* (see Figure 4.1C) are called **cilia** (singular, *cilium*). Other protists may move using flagella, which are longer than cilia and usually limited to one or a few per cell.

Some cells of multicellular organisms also have cilia or flagella. For example, Figure 4.17A shows cilia on cells lining the human windpipe. In this case, the cilia sweep mucus containing trapped debris out of your lungs. (This cleaning function is impaired by cigarette smoke, which paralyzes the cilia.) Most animals and some plants have flagellated sperm. A flagellum, shown in Figure 4.17B, propels the cell by an undulating whiplike motion. In contrast, cilia work more like the coordinated oars of a rowing team.

Though different in length and beating pattern, cilia and flagella have a common structure and mechanism of movement (Figure 4.17C). Both are composed of microtubules wrapped in an extension of the plasma membrane. In nearly all eukaryotic cilia and flagella, a ring of nine microtubule doublets surrounds a central pair of microtubules. This arrangement is called the 9 + 2 pattern. The microtubule assembly extends into an anchoring structure called a basal body (not shown in the figure), which consists of a ring of nine microtubule triplets. Basal bodies are very similar in structure to centrioles, which are found in the microtubule-organizing center of animal cells.

How does this microtubule assembly produce the bending movement of cilia and flagella? Bending involves large motor proteins called dyneins (red in the figure) that are attached along each outer microtubule doublet. A dynein protein has

two "feet" that "walk" along an adjacent doublet, one foot maintaining contact while the other releases and reattaches one step farther along its neighboring microtubule. The outer doublets and two central microtubules are held together by flexible cross-linking proteins and radial spokes (purple in the diagram). If the doublets were not held in place, the walking action would make them slide past each other. Instead, the movements of the dynein feet cause the microtubules—and consequently the cilium or flagellum—to bend.

A cilium may also serve as a signal-receiving "antenna" for the cell. Cilia with this function are generally nonmotile (they lack the central pair of microtubules) and there is only one per cell. In fact, in vertebrate animals, it appears that almost all cells have what is called a *primary cilium*. Although the primary cilium was discovered over a century ago, its importance to embryonic development, sensory reception, and cell function is only now being recognized. Defective primary cilia have been linked to polycystic kidney disease and other human disorders.

? **Compare and contrast cilia and flagella.**

● Both cilia and flagella have the same 9 + 2 pattern of microtubules and mechanism for bending. Cilia are shorter, are more numerous, and beat in a coordinated oar-like pattern. The longer flagella, which are limited to one or a few per cell, undulate like a whip.

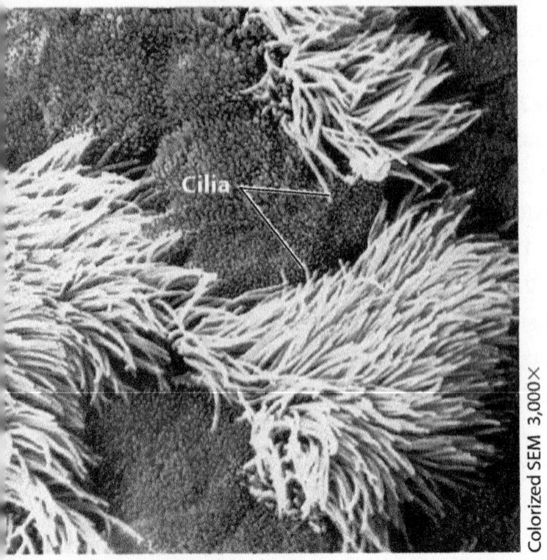

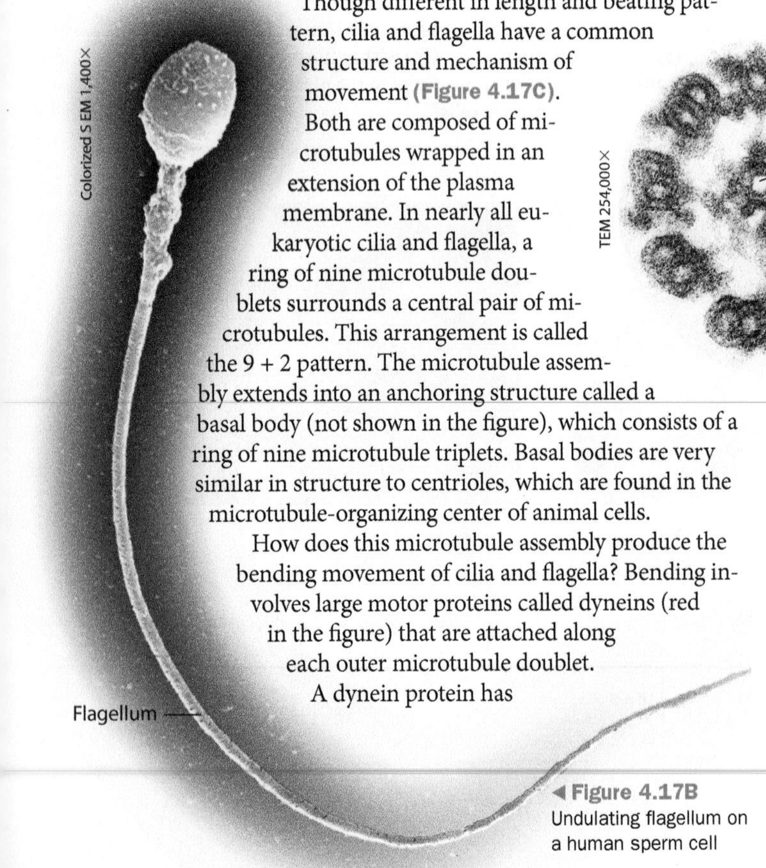

▲ **Figure 4.17A**   Cilia on cells lining the respiratory tract

Colorized SEM 3,000×

Colorized S EM 1,400×

Flagellum

◀ **Figure 4.17B**
Undulating flagellum on a human sperm cell

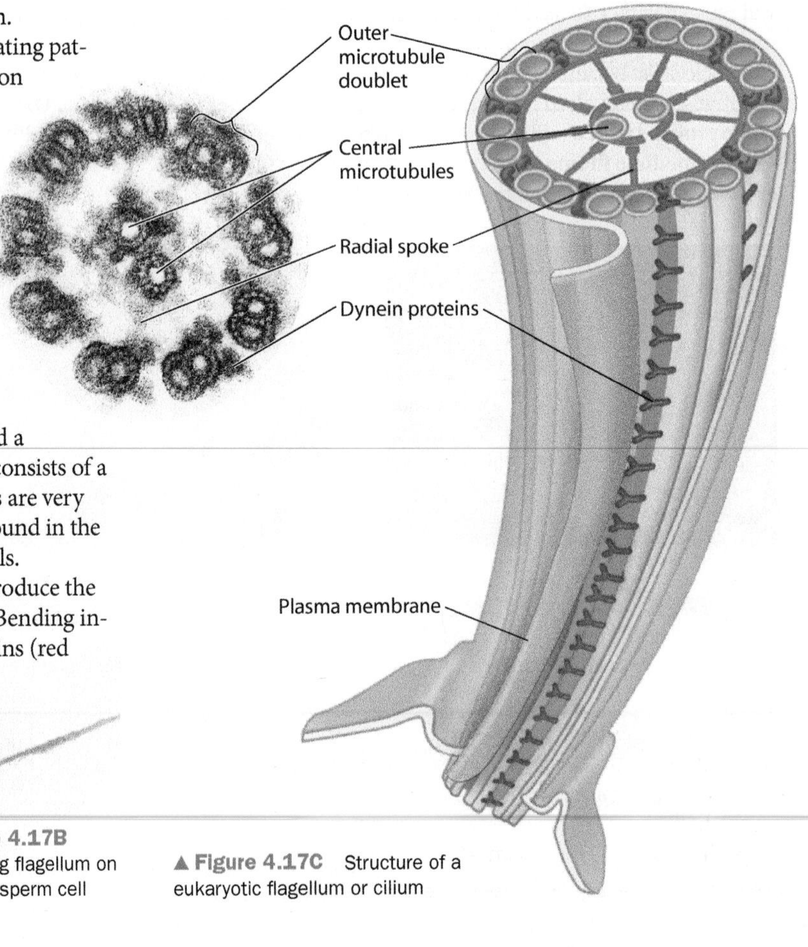

TEM 254,000×

Outer microtubule doublet

Central microtubules

Radial spoke

Dynein proteins

Plasma membrane

▲ **Figure 4.17C**   Structure of a eukaryotic flagellum or cilium

Human sperm quality varies among men and in different geographic areas. In developed countries over the last 50 years, there has been an apparent decline in sperm quality—lower sperm counts, higher proportions of malformed sperm, and reduced motility. Various environmental factors are being studied as possible causes. One hypothesis links this trend to an increase in hormonally active chemicals in the environment.

One common group of chemicals that may be implicated is phthalates. These chemicals are used in cosmetics and are found in many types of plastics, including those used in medical tubing and, until banned by a U.S. congressional act that took effect in 2009, children's toys. Research has indicated that phthalates interfere with sex hormones and adversely affect sperm quality in rodents. Critics of these studies have claimed that the environmental exposures of people are beneath the levels causing effects in rodents. Several new studies, however, have indicated that normal levels of human exposure to these chemicals may result in impaired sperm quality.

Results of a five-year study of 463 men who had come to a hospital for infertility treatment found that the men with higher concentrations of breakdown products of phthalates in their urine had lower sperm counts and motility. But does a statistical correlation indicate cause and effect? Research

continues on the potential reproductive health risks of hormone-disrupting chemicals in the environment.

Other problems with sperm motility are clearly genetic. Primary ciliary dyskinesia (PCD), also known as immotile cilia syndrome, is a fairly rare disease characterized by recurrent infections of the respiratory tract and immotile sperm. Compare the cross section of the flagellum of a sperm of a male with PCD in Figure 4.18 with the TEM in Figure 4.17C. Do you notice the absence of the dynein proteins? How does that explain the seemingly unrelated symptoms of PCD? If microtubules cannot bend (see Module 4.17), then cilia cannot help cleanse the respiratory tract and sperm cannot swim.

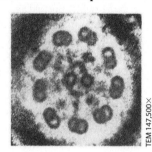

TEM 147,500×

▲ **Figure 4.18** Cross section of immotile sperm flagellum

? **Why does a lack of dynein proteins affect the action of both cilia and flagella?**

● Both cilia and flagella have the same arrangement of microtubule doublets with attached dynein motor proteins that cause them to bend.

4.19 The extracellular matrix of animal cells functions in support and regulation

The plasma membrane is usually regarded as the boundary of the living cell, but most cells synthesize and secrete materials that remain outside the plasma membrane. These extracellular structures are essential to many cell functions.

Animal cells produce an elaborate **extracellular matrix (ECM)** (Figure 4.19). This layer helps hold cells together in tissues and protects and supports the plasma membrane. The main components of the ECM are glycoproteins, proteins bonded with carbohydrates. The most abundant glycoprotein is collagen, which forms strong fibers outside the cell. In fact, collagen accounts for about 40% of the protein in your body. The collagen fibers are embedded in a network woven from other types of glycoproteins. Large complexes form when hundreds of small glycoproteins connect to a central long polysaccharide molecule (green in the figure). The ECM may attach to the cell through other glycoproteins that then bind to membrane proteins called integrins. **Integrins** span the membrane, attaching on the other side to proteins connected to microfilaments of the cytoskeleton.

As their name implies, integrins have the function of integration: They transmit signals between the ECM and the cytoskeleton. Thus, the cytoskeleton can influence the organization of the ECM and vice versa. For example, research shows that the ECM can regulate a cell's behavior, directing the path along which embryonic cells move and even influencing the activity of genes through the signals it relays. Genetic changes

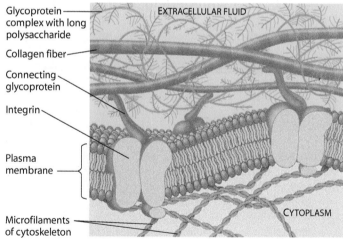

Glycoprotein complex with long polysaccharide
EXTRACELLULAR FLUID
Collagen fiber
Connecting glycoprotein
Integrin
Plasma membrane
Microfilaments of cytoskeleton
CYTOPLASM

▲ **Figure 4.19** The extracellular matrix (ECM) of an animal cell

in cancer cells may result in a change in the composition of the ECM they produce, causing such cells to lose their connections and spread to other tissues.

? **Referring to Figure 4.19, describe the structures that provide support to the plasma membrane.**

● The membrane is attached through membrane proteins (integrins) to the microfilaments in the cytoskeleton and the glycoproteins and collagen fibers of the ECM.

4.20 Three types of cell junctions are found in animal tissues

Neighboring cells in animal tissues often adhere, interact, and communicate through specialized junctions between them. Figure 4.20 uses cells lining the digestive tract to illustrate three types of cell junctions. (The projections at the top of the cells increase the surface area for absorption of nutrients.)

At *tight junctions*, the plasma membranes of neighboring cells are tightly pressed against each other and knit together by proteins. Forming continuous seals around cells, tight junctions prevent leakage of fluid across a layer of cells. The green arrows in the figure show how tight junctions prevent the contents of the digestive tract from leaking into surrounding tissues.

Anchoring junctions function like rivets, fastening cells together into strong sheets. Intermediate filaments made of sturdy keratin proteins anchor these junctions in the cytoplasm. Anchoring junctions are common in tissues subject to stretching or mechanical stress, such as skin and heart muscle.

Gap junctions, also called communicating junctions, are channels that allow small molecules to flow through protein-lined pores between cells. The flow of ions through gap junctions in the cells of heart muscle coordinates their contraction. Gap junctions are common in embryos, where communication between cells is essential for development.

? **A muscle tear injury would probably involve the rupture of which type of cell junction?**

● Anchoring junction

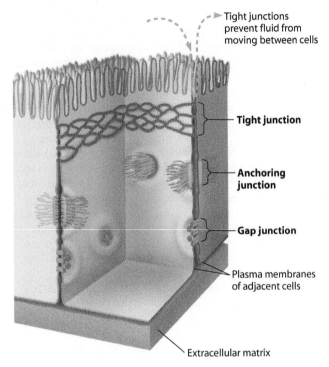

▲ Figure 4.20 Three types of cell junctions in animal tissues

4.21 Cell walls enclose and support plant cells

The **cell wall** is one feature that distinguishes plant cells from animal cells. This rigid extracellular structure not only protects the cells but provides the skeletal support that keeps plants upright on land. Plant cell walls consist of fibers of cellulose (see Figure 3.7) embedded in a matrix of other polysaccharides and proteins. This fibers-in-a-matrix construction resembles that of fiberglass, a manufactured product also noted for its strength.

Figure 4.21 shows the layered structure of plant cell walls. Cells initially lay down a relatively thin and flexible primary wall, which allows the growing cell to continue to enlarge. Some cells then add a secondary wall deposited in laminated layers. Wood consists mainly of secondary walls, which are strengthened with rigid molecules called lignin. Between adjacent cells is a layer of sticky polysaccharides called pectins (shown here in dark brown), which glue the cells together. (Pectin is used to thicken jams and jellies.)

Despite their thickness, plant cell walls do not totally isolate the cells from each other. To function in a coordinated way as part of a tissue, the cells must have cell junctions, structures that connect them to one another. Figure 4.21 shows the numerous channels between adjacent plant cells, called **plasmodesmata** (singular, *plasmodesma*). Notice that the plasma membrane and the cytoplasm of the cells extend through the plasmodesmata, so that water and other small

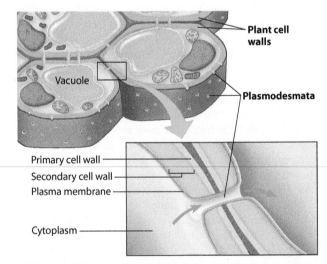

▲ Figure 4.21 Plant cell walls and plasmodesmata

molecules can readily pass from cell to cell. Through plasmodesmata, the cells of a plant tissue share water, nourishment, and chemical messages.

? **Which animal cell junction is analogous to a plasmodesma?**

● A gap junction

4.22 Review: Eukaryotic cell structures can be grouped on the basis of four main functions

Congratulations, you have completed the grand tour of the cell. In the process, you have been introduced to many important cell structures. To provide a framework for this information and reinforce the theme that structure is correlated with function, we have grouped the eukaryotic cell organelles into four categories by general function, as reviewed in Table 4.22.

The first category is genetic control. Here we include the nucleus that houses a cell's genetic instructions and the ribosomes that produce the proteins coded for in those instructions. The second category includes organelles of the endomembrane system that are involved in the manufacture, distribution, and breakdown of materials. (Vacuoles have other functions as well.) The third category includes the two energy-processing organelles. The fourth category is structural support, movement, and intercellular communication. These functions are related because there must be rigid support against which force can be applied for movement to occur. In addition, a supporting structure that forms the cell's outer boundary is necessarily involved in communication with neighboring cells.

TABLE 4.22	EUKARYOTIC CELL STRUCTURES AND FUNCTIONS
1. Genetic Control	
Nucleus	DNA replication, RNA synthesis; assembly of ribosomal subunits (in nucleoli)
Ribosomes	Polypeptide (protein) synthesis
2. Manufacturing, Distribution, and Breakdown	
Rough ER	Synthesis of membrane lipids and proteins, secretory proteins, and hydrolytic enzymes; formation of transport vesicles
Smooth ER	Lipid synthesis; detoxification in liver cells; calcium ion storage
Golgi apparatus	Modification and sorting of macromolecules; formation of lysosomes and transport vesicles
Lysosomes (in animal cells and some protists)	Digestion of ingested food, bacteria, and a cell's damaged organelles and macromolecules for recycling
Vacuoles	Digestion (food vacuole); storage of chemicals and cell enlargement (central vacuole); water balance (contractile vacuole)
Peroxisomes (not part of endomembrane system)	Diverse metabolic processes, with breakdown of toxic hydrogen peroxide by-product
3. Energy Processing	
Mitochondria	Conversion of chemical energy in food to chemical energy of ATP
Chloroplasts (in plants and some protists)	Conversion of light energy to chemical energy of sugars
4. Structural Support, Movement, and Communication Between Cells	
Cytoskeleton (microfilaments, intermediate filaments, and microtubules)	Maintenance of cell shape; anchorage for organelles; movement of organelles within cells; cell movement (crawling, muscle contraction, bending of cilia and flagella)
Extracellular matrix (in animals)	Support; regulation of cellular activities
Cell junctions	Communication between cells; binding of cells in tissues
Cell walls (in plants, fungi, and some protists)	Support and protection; binding of cells in tissues

Within most of these categories, a structural similarity underlies the general function of each component. Manufacturing depends heavily on a network of structurally and functionally connected membranes. All the organelles involved in the breakdown or recycling of materials are membranous sacs, inside of which enzymatic digestion can safely occur. In the energy-processing category, expanses of metabolically active membranes and intermembrane compartments within the organelles enable chloroplasts and mitochondria to perform the complex energy conversions that power the cell. Even in the diverse fourth category, there is a common structural theme in the various protein fibers of these cellular systems.

We can summarize further by emphasizing that these cellular structures form an integrated team—with the property of life emerging at the level of the cell from the coordinated functions of the team members. And finally we note that the overall structure of a cell is closely related to its specific function. Thus, cells that produce proteins for export contain a large quantity of ribosomes and rough ER, while muscle cells are packed with microfilaments, myosin motor proteins, and mitochondria.

All organisms share the fundamental feature of consisting of cells, each enclosed by a membrane that maintains internal conditions different from the surroundings and each carrying out metabolism, which involves the interconversion of different forms of energy and of chemical compounds. We expand on the subjects of membranes and metabolism in Chapter 5.

 How do mitochondria, smooth ER, and the cytoskeleton all contribute to the contraction of a muscle cell?

● Mitochondria supply energy in the form of ATP. The smooth ER helps regulate contraction by the uptake and release of calcium ions. Microfilaments function in the actual contractile apparatus.

Reviewing the Concepts

Introduction to the Cell (4.1–4.4)

4.1 Microscopes reveal the world of the cell. The light microscope can magnify up to 1,000 times. The greater magnification and resolution of the scanning and transmission electron microscopes reveal the ultrastructure of cells.

4.2 The small size of cells relates to the need to exchange materials across the plasma membrane. The microscopic size of most cells provides a large surface-to-volume ratio. The plasma membrane is a phospholipid bilayer with embedded proteins.

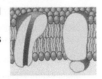

4.3 Prokaryotic cells are structurally simpler than eukaryotic cells. All cells have a plasma membrane, DNA, ribosomes, and cytoplasm. Prokaryotic cells are smaller than eukaryotic cells and lack a membrane-enclosed nucleus.

4.4 Eukaryotic cells are partitioned into functional compartments. Membranes form the boundaries of organelles, compartmentalizing a cell's activities.

The Nucleus and Ribosomes (4.5–4.6)

4.5 The nucleus is the cell's genetic control center. The nucleus houses the cell's DNA and directs protein synthesis by making messenger RNA. The nucleolus makes the subunits of ribosomes.

4.6 Ribosomes make proteins for use in the cell and for export. Composed of ribosomal RNA and proteins, ribosomes synthesize proteins according to directions from DNA.

The Endomembrane System (4.7–4.12)

4.7 Overview: Many cell organelles are connected through the endomembrane system.

4.8 The endoplasmic reticulum is a biosynthetic factory. The ER is a membranous network of tubes and sacs. Smooth ER synthesizes lipids and processes toxins. Rough ER manufactures membranes, and ribosomes on its surface produce membrane and secretory proteins.

4.9 The Golgi apparatus finishes, sorts, and ships cell products. The Golgi apparatus consists of stacks of sacs that modify ER products and then ship them to other organelles or to the cell surface.

4.10 Lysosomes are digestive compartments within a cell. Lysosomes house enzymes that function in digestion and recycling within the cell.

4.11 Vacuoles function in the general maintenance of the cell. Some protists have contractile vacuoles. Plant cells contain a large central vacuole that stores molecules and wastes and facilitates growth.

4.12 A review of the structures involved in manufacturing and breakdown. The organelles of the endomembrane system are interconnected structurally and functionally.

Energy-Converting Organelles (4.13–4.15)

4.13 Mitochondria harvest chemical energy from food.

4.14 Chloroplasts convert solar energy to chemical energy.

4.15 Mitochondria and chloroplasts evolved by endosymbiosis. These organelles originated from prokaryotic cells that became residents in a host cell.

The Cytoskeleton and Cell Surfaces (4.16–4.22)

4.16 The cell's internal skeleton helps organize its structure and activities. The cytoskeleton is a network of protein fibers. Microfilaments of actin enable cells to change shape and move. Intermediate filaments reinforce the cell and anchor certain organelles. Microtubules give the cell rigidity and act as tracks for organelle movement.

4.17 Cilia and flagella move when microtubules bend. Eukaryotic cilia and flagella are locomotor appendages made of microtubules in a 9 + 2 arrangement.

4.18 Problems with sperm motility may be environmental or genetic. Environmental chemicals or genetic disorders may interfere with movement of sperm and cilia.

4.19 The extracellular matrix of animal cells functions in support and regulation. The ECM consists mainly of glycoproteins, which bind tissue cells together, support the membrane, and communicate with the cytoskeleton.

4.20 Three types of cell junctions are found in animal tissues. Tight junctions bind cells to form leakproof sheets. Anchoring junctions rivet cells into strong tissues. Gap junctions allow substances to flow from cell to cell.

4.21 Cell walls enclose and support plant cells. Plant cell walls are made largely of cellulose. Plasmodesmata are connecting channels between cells.

4.22 Review: Eukaryotic cell structures can be grouped on the basis of four main functions. These functions are (1) genetic control; (2) manufacturing, distribution, and breakdown; (3) energy processing; and (4) structural support, movement, and communication between cells.

Connecting the Concepts

1. Label the structures in this diagram of an animal cell. Review the functions of each of these organelles.

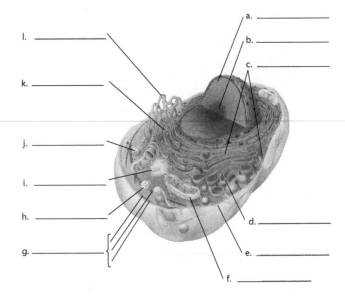

a. _____
b. _____
c. _____
d. _____
e. _____
f. _____
g. _____
h. _____
i. _____
j. _____
k. _____
l. _____

2. List some structures found in animal cells but not in plant cells.

3. List some structures found in plant cells but not in animal cells.

Testing Your Knowledge

Multiple Choice

4. The ultrastructure of a chloroplast is best studied using a
   a. light microscope.
   b. telescope.
   c. scanning electron microscope.
   d. transmission electron microscope.
   e. light microscope and fluorescent dyes.

5. The cells of an ant and a horse are, on average, the same small size; a horse just has more of them. What is the main advantage of small cell size?
   a. Small cells are less likely to burst than large cells.
   b. A small cell has a larger plasma membrane surface area than does a large cell.
   c. Small cells can better take up sufficient nutrients and oxygen to service their cell volume.
   d. It takes less energy to make an organism out of small cells.
   e. Small cells require less oxygen than do large cells.

6. Which of the following clues would tell you whether a cell is prokaryotic or eukaryotic?
   a. the presence or absence of a rigid cell wall
   b. whether or not the cell is partitioned by internal membranes
   c. the presence or absence of ribosomes
   d. whether or not the cell carries out cellular metabolism
   e. whether or not the cell contains DNA

7. Which statement correctly describes bound ribosomes?
   a. Bound ribosomes are enclosed in a membrane.
   b. Bound and free ribosomes are structurally different.
   c. Bound ribosomes are most commonly found on the surface of the plasma membrane.
   d. Bound ribosomes generally synthesize membrane proteins and secretory proteins.
   e. Bound ribosomes produce the subunits of microtubules, microfilaments, and intermediate filaments.

Choose from the following cells for questions 8–12:
   a. muscle cell in thigh of long-distance runner
   b. pancreatic cell that secretes digestive enzymes
   c. ovarian cell that produces the steroid hormone estrogen
   d. cell in tissue layer lining digestive tract
   e. white blood cell that engulfs bacteria

8. In which cell would you find the most lysosomes?

9. In which cell would you find the most mitochondria?

10. In which cell would you find the most smooth ER?

11. In which cell would you find the most rough ER?

12. In which cell would you find the most tight junctions?

13. A type of cell called a lymphocyte makes proteins that are exported from the cell. Which of the following traces the path of a protein from the site where its polypeptides are made to its export?
    a. chloroplast . . . Golgi . . . lysosomes . . . plasma membrane
    b. Golgi . . . rough ER . . . smooth ER . . . transport vesicle
    c. rough ER . . . Golgi . . . transport vesicle . . . plasma membrane
    d. smooth ER . . . Golgi . . . lysosome . . . plasma membrane
    e. nucleus . . . rough ER . . . Golgi . . . plasma membrane

14. Which of the following structures is *not* directly involved in cell support or movement?
    a. microfilament
    b. flagellum
    c. microtubule
    d. gap junction
    e. cell wall

Describing, Comparing, and Explaining

15. What four cellular components are shared by prokaryotic and eukaryotic cells?

16. Briefly describe the three kinds of junctions that can connect animal cells, and compare their functions.

17. What general function do the chloroplast and mitochondrion have in common? How are their functions different?

18. In what ways do the internal membranes of a eukaryotic cell contribute to the functioning of the cell?

19. Describe two different ways in which the motion of cilia can function in organisms.

20. Explain how a protein inside the ER can be exported from the cell without ever crossing a membrane.

21. Is this statement true or false? "Animal cells have mitochondria; plant cells have chloroplasts." Explain your answer.

22. Describe the structure of the plasma membrane of an animal cell. What would be found directly inside and outside the membrane?

Applying the Concepts

23. Imagine a spherical cell with a radius of 10 μm. What is the cell's surface area in μm²? Its volume, in μm³? What is the ratio of surface area to volume for this cell? Now do the same calculations for a second cell, this one with a radius of 20 μm. Compare the surface-to-volume ratios of the two cells. How is this comparison significant to the functioning of cells? (*Note*: For a sphere of radius *r*, surface area $= 4\pi r^2$ and volume $= \pi r^3$. Remember that the value of π is 3.14.)

24. Cilia are found on cells in almost every organ of the human body, and the malfunction of cilia is involved in several human disorders. During embryological development, for example, cilia generate a leftward flow of fluid that initiates the left-right organization of the body organs. Some individuals with primary ciliary dyskinesia (see Module 4.18) exhibit *situs inversus*, in which internal organs such as the heart are on the wrong side of the body. Explain why this reversed arrangement may be a symptom of PCD.

25. The cells of plant seeds store oils in the form of droplets enclosed by membranes. Unlike typical biological membranes, this oil droplet membrane consists of a single layer of phospholipids rather than a bilayer. Draw a model for a membrane around such an oil droplet. Explain why this arrangement is more stable than a bilayer of phospholipids.

26. Doctors at a California university removed a man's spleen, standard treatment for a type of leukemia, and the disease did not recur. Researchers kept the spleen cells alive in a nutrient medium. They found that some of the cells produced a blood protein that showed promise as a treatment for cancer and AIDS. The researchers patented the cells. The patient sued, claiming a share in profits from any products derived from his cells. The California Supreme Court ruled against the patient, stating that his suit "threatens to destroy the economic incentive to conduct important medical research." The U.S. Supreme Court agreed. Do you think the patient was treated fairly? Is there anything else you would like to know about this case that might help you decide?

Answers to all questions can be found in Appendix 4.

5

The Working Cell

BIG IDEAS

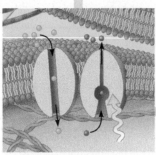

Membrane Structure and Function
(5.1–5.9)

The phospholipid and protein structure of cell membranes enables their many important functions.

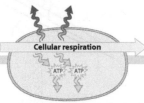

Energy and the Cell
(5.10–5.12)

A cell's metabolic reactions transform energy, producing ATP, which drives cellular work.

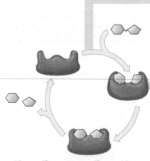

How Enzymes Function
(5.13–5.16)

Enzymes speed up a cell's chemical reactions and provide precise control of metabolism.

Would you believe that this squid's glowing blue lights are a form of camouflage? Ocean predators often hunt by looking up, searching for a silhouette of their prey above them. But can an animal hide its silhouette in the open ocean? The answer is yes, if it turns on the lights. The firefly squid (*Watasenia scintillans*) shown here has light-producing organs called photophores, which emit a soft glow that matches the light filtering down from above. This counter-illumination masks the squid's silhouette. It turns out that many marine invertebrates and fishes hide from predators by producing such light, a process called bioluminescence.

You may be familiar with bioluminescence if you've seen fireflies. While such light production is fairly rare for land animals, it is quite common in the ocean. An estimated 90% of deep-sea marine life bioluminesce. For example, some microorganisms light up when attacked, drawing the attention of larger predators that may feed on their attackers. Some squids expel a cloud of glowing material instead of ink to confuse predators. And a deep-sea anglerfish uses a glowing glob of bacteria on a lure hanging above its huge mouth to attract both mates and prey.

The light these organisms produce comes from a chemical reaction that converts chemical energy to visible light. Bioluminescence is just one example of the multitude of energy conversions that a cell can perform. Many of a cell's reactions take place in organelles, such as those in the light-producing cells of a squid. And the enzymes that control these reactions are often embedded in the membranes of the organelle. Indeed, everything that happens when a squid turns on the lights to hide has some relation to the topics of this chapter: how working cells use membranes, energy, and enzymes.

Membrane Structure and Function

5.1 Membranes are fluid mosaics of lipids and proteins with many functions

The plasma membrane is the edge of life, the boundary that encloses a living cell. In eukaryotic cells, internal membranes partition the cell into specialized compartments. Recall from Modules 4.2 and 4.19 that membranes are composed of a bilayer of phospholipids with embedded and attached proteins. Biologists describe such a structure as a **fluid mosaic**.

In the cell, a membrane remains about as "fluid" as salad oil, with most of its components able to drift about like partygoers moving through a crowded room. Double bonds in the unsaturated fatty acid tails of some phospholipids produce kinks that prevent phospholipids from packing too tightly (see Module 3.8). In animal cell membranes, the steroid cholesterol helps stabilize the membrane at warm temperatures but also helps keep the membrane fluid at lower temperatures.

A membrane is a "mosaic" in having diverse protein molecules embedded in its fluid framework. The word *mosaic* can also refer to the varied functions of these proteins. Different types of cells have different membrane proteins, and the various membranes within a cell each contain a unique collection of proteins.

Figure 5.1, which diagrams the plasma membranes of two adjacent cells, illustrates six major functions performed by membrane proteins, represented by the purple oval structures. Some proteins help maintain cell shape and coordinate changes inside and outside the cell through their attachment to the cytoskeleton and extracellular matrix (ECM). Other proteins

function as receptors for chemical messengers (signaling molecules) from other cells. The binding of a signaling molecule triggers a change in the protein, which relays the message into the cell, activating molecules that perform specific functions. This message-transfer process, called signal transduction, will be described in more detail in Module 11.10.

Some membrane proteins are enzymes, which may be grouped in a membrane to carry out sequential steps of a metabolic pathway. Membrane glycoproteins may be involved in cell-cell recognition. Their attached carbohydrates function as identification tags that are recognized by membrane proteins of other cells. This recognition allows cells in an embryo to sort into tissues and enables cells of the immune system to recognize and reject foreign cells, such as infectious bacteria. Membrane proteins also participate in the intercellular junctions that attach adjacent cells (see Module 4.20).

A final critical function is in transport of substances across the membrane. Membranes exhibit **selective permeability**; that is, they allow some substances to cross more easily than others. Many essential ions and molecules, such as glucose, require transport proteins to enter or leave the cell.

? **Review the six different types of functions that proteins in a plasma membrane can perform.**

● Attachment to the cytoskeleton and ECM, signal transduction, enzymatic activity, cell-cell recognition, intercellular joining, and transport

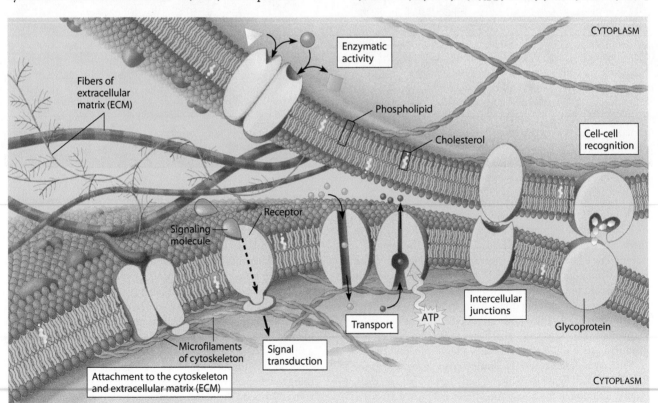

▲ Figure 5.1 Some functions of membrane proteins

5.2 Membranes form spontaneously, a critical step in the origin of life

Phospholipids, the key ingredients of biological membranes, were probably among the first organic molecules that formed from chemical reactions on early Earth (see Module 15.2). These lipids could spontaneously self-assemble into simple membranes, as we can demonstrate in a test tube. When a mixture of phospholipids and water is shaken, the phospholipids organize into bilayers surrounding water-filled bubbles (Figure 5.2). This

assembly requires neither genes nor other information beyond the properties of the phospholipids themselves.

The formation of membrane-enclosed collections of molecules was probably a critical step in the evolution of the first cells. A membrane can enclose a solution that is different in composition from its surroundings. A plasma membrane that allows cells to regulate their chemical exchanges with the environment is a basic requirement for life. Indeed, all cells are enclosed by a plasma membrane that is similar in structure and function—illustrating the evolutionary unity of life.

▲ **Figure 5.2** Artificial membrane-bounded sacs

? This is a diagram of a section of one of the membrane sacs shown in Figure 5.2. Describe its structure.

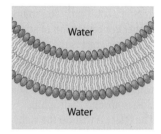

● The phospholipids form a bilayer. The hydrophobic fatty acid tails cluster in the center, and the hydrophilic phosphate heads face the water on both sides.

5.3 Passive transport is diffusion across a membrane with no energy investment

Molecules vibrate and move randomly as a result of a type of energy called thermal motion (heat). One result of this motion is **diffusion**, the tendency for particles of any kind to spread out evenly in an available space. How might diffusion affect the movement of substances into or out of a cell?

The figures to the right will help you to visualize diffusion across a membrane. **Figure 5.3A** shows a solution of green dye separated from pure water by a membrane. Assume that this membrane has microscopic pores through which dye molecules can move. Thus, we say it is permeable to the dye. Although each molecule moves randomly, there will be a *net* movement from the side of the membrane where dye molecules are more concentrated to the side where they are less concentrated. Put another way, the dye diffuses down its **concentration gradient**. Eventually, the solutions on both sides will have equal concentrations of dye. At this dynamic equilibrium, molecules still move back and forth, but there is no *net* change in concentration on either side of the membrane.

Figure 5.3B illustrates the important point that two or more substances diffuse independently of each other; that is, each diffuses down its own concentration gradient.

Because a cell does not have to do work when molecules diffuse across its membrane, such movement across a membrane is called **passive transport**. Much of the traffic across cell membranes occurs by diffusion. For example, diffusion down concentration gradients is the sole means by which oxygen (O_2), essential for metabolism, enters your cells and carbon dioxide (CO_2), a metabolic waste, passes out of them.

Both O_2 and CO_2 are small, nonpolar molecules that diffuse easily across the phospholipid bilayer of a membrane. But can ions and polar molecules also diffuse across the

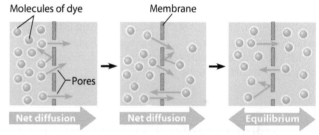

▲ **Figure 5.3A** Passive transport of one type of molecule

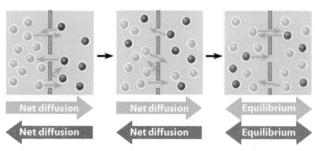

▲ **Figure 5.3B** Passive transport of two types of molecules

hydrophobic interior of a membrane? They can if they are moving down their concentration gradients and if they have transport proteins to help them cross.

? Why is diffusion across a membrane called passive transport?

● The cell does not expend energy to transport substances that are diffusing down their concentration gradients.

5.4 Osmosis is the diffusion of water across a membrane

One of the most important substances that crosses membranes by passive transport is water. In the next module, we consider the critical balance of water between a cell and its environment. But first let's explore a physical model of the diffusion of water across a selectively permeable membrane, a process called **osmosis**. Remember that a selectively permeable membrane allows some substances to cross more easily than others.

The top of **Figure 5.4** shows what happens if a membrane permeable to water but not to a solute (such as glucose) separates two solutions with different concentrations of solute. (A solute is a substance that dissolves in a liquid solvent, producing a solution.) The solution on the right side initially has a higher concentration of solute than that on the left. As you can see, water crosses the membrane until the solute concentrations are equal on both sides.

In the close-up view at the bottom of Figure 5.4, you can see what happens at the molecular level. Polar water molecules cluster around hydrophilic (water-loving) solute molecules. The effect is that on the right side, there are fewer water molecules available to cross the membrane. The less concentrated solution on the left, with fewer solute molecules, has more water molecules *free* to move. There is a net movement of water down its own concentration gradient, from the solution with more free water molecules (and lower solute concentration) to that with fewer free water molecules (and higher solute concentration). The result of this water movement is the difference in water levels you see at the top right of Figure 5.4.

Let's now apply to living cells what we have learned about osmosis in artificial systems.

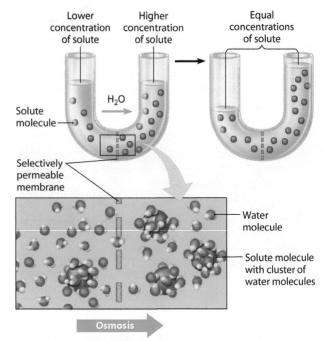

▲ **Figure 5.4** Osmosis, the diffusion of water across a membrane

? Indicate the direction of net water movement between two solutions—a 0.5% sucrose solution and a 2% sucrose solution—separated by a membrane not permeable to sucrose.

From the 0.5% sucrose solution (lower solute concentration) to the 2% sucrose solution (higher solute concentration).

5.5 Water balance between cells and their surroundings is crucial to organisms

Biologists use a special vocabulary to describe the relationship between a cell and its surroundings with regard to the movement of water. The term **tonicity** refers to the ability of a surrounding solution to cause a cell to gain or lose water. The tonicity of a solution mainly depends on its concentration of solutes that cannot cross the plasma membrane relative to the concentration of solutes inside the cell.

Figure 5.5, on the facing page, illustrates how the principles of osmosis and tonicity apply to cells. The effects of placing an animal cell in solutions of various tonicities are shown in the top row of the illustration; the effects of the same solutions on a plant cell are shown in the bottom row.

As shown in the top center of the figure, when an animal cell is immersed in a solution that is **isotonic** to the cell (*iso*, same, and *tonos*, tension), the cell's volume remains constant. The solute concentration of a cell and its isotonic environment are essentially equal, and the cell gains water at the same rate that it loses it. In your body, red blood cells are transported in the isotonic plasma of the blood. Intravenous (IV) fluids administered in hospitals must also be isotonic to blood cells. The body cells of most animals are bathed in an extracellular fluid

that is isotonic to the cells. And seawater is isotonic to the cells of many marine animals, such as sea stars and crabs.

The upper left of the figure shows what happens when an animal cell is placed in a **hypotonic** solution (*hypo*, below), a solution with a solute concentration lower than that of the cell. (Can you figure out in which direction osmosis will occur? Where are there more free water molecules available to move?) The cell gains water, swells, and may burst (lyse) like an overfilled balloon. The upper right shows the opposite case—an animal cell placed in a **hypertonic** solution (*hyper*, above), a solution with a higher solute concentration. The cell shrivels and can die from water loss.

For an animal to survive in a hypotonic or hypertonic environment, it must have a way to prevent excessive uptake or excessive loss of water. The control of water balance is called **osmoregulation**. For example, a freshwater fish, which lives in a hypotonic environment, has kidneys and gills that work constantly to prevent an excessive buildup of water in the body. (We will discuss osmoregulation further in Module 25.4.)

Water balance issues are somewhat different for the cells of plants, prokaryotes, and fungi because of their cell walls.

As shown in the bottom center of Figure 5.5, a plant cell immersed in an isotonic solution is flaccid (limp). In contrast, a plant cell is turgid (very firm), which is the healthy state for most plant cells, in a hypotonic environment (bottom left). To become turgid, a plant cell needs a net inflow of water. Although the somewhat elastic cell wall expands a bit, the pressure it exerts prevents the cell from taking in too much water and bursting, as an animal cell would in a hypotonic environment. Plants that are not woody, such as most houseplants, depend on their turgid cells for mechanical support.

In a hypertonic environment (bottom right), a plant cell is no better off than an animal cell. As a plant cell loses water, it shrivels, and its plasma membrane pulls away from the cell wall. This process, called plasmolysis, causes the plant to wilt and can be lethal to the cell and the plant. The walled cells of bacteria and fungi also plasmolyze in hypertonic environments. Thus, meats and other foods can be preserved with concentrated salt solutions because the cells of food-spoiling bacteria or fungi become plasmolyzed and eventually die.

Hypotonic solution	Isotonic solution	Hypertonic solution

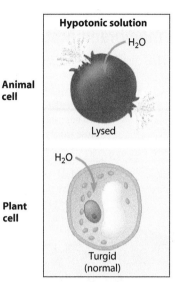
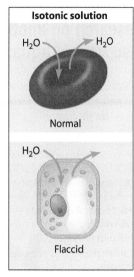
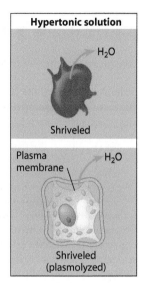

Animal cell — Lysed / Normal / Shriveled

Plant cell — Turgid (normal) / Flaccid / Shriveled (plasmolyzed)

▲ **Figure 5.5** How animal and plant cells react to changes in tonicity. (Deepening shades of blue reflect increasing concentrations of solutes in the surrounding solutions.)

In the next module, we explore how water and other polar solutes move across cell membranes.

? Explain the function of the contractile vacuoles in the freshwater *Paramecium* shown in Figure 4.11A in terms of what you have just learned about water balance in cells.

● The pond water in which *Paramecium* lives is hypotonic to the cell. The contractile vacuoles expel the water that constantly enters the cell by osmosis.

5.6 Transport proteins can facilitate diffusion across membranes

Recall that nonpolar, hydrophobic molecules can dissolve in the lipid bilayer of a membrane and cross it with ease. Polar or charged substances, meanwhile, can move across a membrane with the help of specific transport proteins in a process called **facilitated diffusion**. Without the transport protein, the substance cannot cross the membrane or it diffuses across it too slowly to be useful to the cell. Facilitated diffusion is a type of passive transport because it does not require energy. As in all passive transport, the driving force is the concentration gradient.

Figure 5.6 shows a common type of transport protein, which provides a hydrophilic channel that some molecules or ions use as a tunnel through the membrane. Another type of transport protein binds its passenger, changes shape, and releases its passenger on the other side. In both cases, the transport protein is specific for the substance it helps move across the membrane. The greater the number of transport proteins for a particular solute in a membrane, the faster the solute's rate of diffusion across the membrane.

Substances that use facilitated diffusion for crossing cell membranes include a number of sugars, amino acids, ions—and even water. The water molecule is very small, but because it is polar (see Module 2.6), its diffusion through a membrane's hydrophobic interior is relatively slow. The very rapid

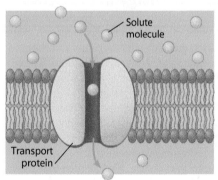

◀ **Figure 5.6** Transport protein providing a channel for the diffusion of a specific solute across a membrane

Solute molecule

Transport protein

diffusion of water into and out of certain cells, such as plant cells, kidney cells, and red blood cells, is made possible by a protein channel called an **aquaporin**. A single aquaporin allows the entry or exit of up to 3 billion water molecules per second—a tremendous increase in water transport over simple diffusion.

? How do transport proteins contribute to a membrane's selective permeability?

● Because they are specific for the solutes they transport, the numbers and kinds of transport proteins affect a membrane's permeability to various solutes.

5.7 Research on another membrane protein led to the discovery of aquaporins

Peter Agre received the 2003 Nobel Prize in Chemistry for his discovery of aquaporins. In a recent interview, Dr. Agre described his research that led to this discovery:

I'm a blood specialist (hematologist), and my particular interest has been proteins found in the plasma membrane of red blood cells. When I joined the faculty at the John Hopkins School of Medicine, I began to study the Rh blood antigens. Rh is of medical importance because of Rh incompatibility, which occurs when Rh-negative mothers have Rh-positive babies. Membrane-spanning proteins are really messy to work with. But we worked out a method to isolate the Rh protein. Our sample seemed to consist of two proteins, but we were sure that the smaller one was just a breakdown product of the larger one. We were completely wrong.

Using antibodies we made to the smaller protein, we showed it to be one of the most abundant proteins in red cell membranes—200,000 copies per cell!—and even more abundant in certain kidney cells.

We asked Dr. Agre why cells have aquaporins.

Not all cells do. Before our discovery, however, many physiologists thought that diffusion was enough for getting water into and out of *all* cells. Others said this couldn't be enough, especially for cells whose water permeability needs to be very high or regulated. For example, our kidneys must filter and reabsorb many liters of water every day. . . . People whose kidney cells have defective aquaporin molecules need to drink 20 liters of water a day to prevent dehydration. In addition, some patients make too much aquaporin, causing them to retain too much fluid. Fluid retention in pregnant women is caused by the synthesis of too much aquaporin. Knowledge of aquaporins may in the future contribute to the solution of medical problems.

Figure 5.7 is an image taken from a simulation produced by computational biophysicists at the University of Illinois, Urbana. Their model included four aquaporin channels spanning a membrane. You can see a line of blue water molecules flipping their way single file through the gold aquaporin. The simulation of this flipping movement allowed researchers to discover how aquaporins selectively allow only water molecules to pass through them.

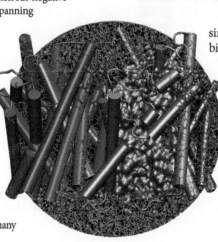

▲ **Figure 5.7** Aquaporin in action

? Why are aquaporins important in kidney cells?

● Kidney cells must reabsorb a large amount of water when producing urine.

5.8 Cells expend energy in the active transport of a solute

In **active transport**, a cell must expend energy to move a solute *against* its concentration gradient—that is, across a membrane toward the side where the solute is more concentrated. The energy molecule ATP (described in more detail in Module 5.12) supplies the energy for most active transport.

Figure 5.8 shows a simple model of an active transport system that pumps a solute out of the cell against its concentration gradient. ❶ The process begins when solute molecules on the cytoplasmic side of the plasma membrane attach to specific binding sites on the transport protein. ❷ ATP then transfers a phosphate group to the transport protein, ❸ causing the protein to change shape in such a way that the solute is released on the other side of the membrane. ❹ The phosphate group detaches, and the transport protein returns to its original shape.

Active transport allows a cell to maintain internal concentrations of small molecules and ions that are different from concentrations in its surroundings. For example, the inside of an animal cell has a higher concentration of potassium ions (K^+) and a lower concentration of sodium ions (Na^+) than the solution outside the cell. The generation of nerve signals depends on these concentration differences, which a transport protein called the sodium-potassium pump helps maintain by shuttling Na^+ and K^+ against their concentration gradients.

? Cells actively transport Ca^{2+} out of the cell. Is calcium more concentrated inside or outside of the cell? Explain.

● Outside: Active transport moves calcium against its concentration gradient.

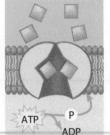
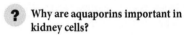
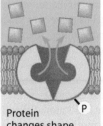

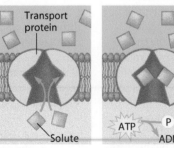

❶ Solute binding ❷ Phosphate attaching ❸ Transport ❹ Protein reversion

Transport protein

Solute

ATP ADP

Protein changes shape. P

Phosphate detaches. P

▲ **Figure 5.8** Active transport of a solute across a membrane

5.9 Exocytosis and endocytosis transport large molecules across membranes

So far, we've focused on how water and small solutes enter and leave cells. The story is different for large molecules.

A cell uses the process of **exocytosis** (from the Greek *exo*, outside, and *kytos*, cell) to export bulky materials such as proteins or polysaccharides. As you saw in Figure 4.12, a transport vesicle filled with macromolecules buds from the Golgi apparatus and moves to the plasma membrane. Once there, the vesicle fuses with the plasma membrane, and the vesicle's contents spill out of the cell when the vesicle membrane becomes part of the plasma membrane. When we weep, for instance, cells in our tear glands use exocytosis to export a salty solution containing proteins. In another example, certain cells in the pancreas manufacture the hormone insulin and secrete it into the bloodstream by exocytosis.

Endocytosis (*endo*, inside) is a transport process that is the opposite of exocytosis. In endocytosis, a cell takes in large molecules. A depression in the plasma membrane pinches in and forms a vesicle enclosing material that had been outside the cell.

Figure 5.9 shows three kinds of endocytosis. The top diagram illustrates **phagocytosis**, or "cellular eating." A cell engulfs a particle by wrapping extensions called pseudopodia around it and packaging it within a membrane-enclosed sac large enough to be called a vacuole. As described in Module 4.10, the vacuole then fuses with a lysosome, whose hydrolytic enzymes digest the contents of the vacuole. The micrograph on the top right shows an amoeba taking in a food particle via phagocytosis.

The center diagram shows **pinocytosis**, or "cellular drinking." The cell "gulps" droplets of fluid into tiny vesicles. Pinocytosis is not specific; it takes in any and all solutes dissolved in the droplets. The micrograph in the middle shows pinocytosis vesicles forming (arrows) in a cell lining a small blood vessel.

In contrast to pinocytosis, **receptor-mediated endocytosis** is highly selective. Receptor proteins for specific molecules are embedded in regions of the membrane that are lined by a layer of coat proteins. The bottom diagram shows that the plasma membrane has indented to form a coated pit, whose receptor proteins have picked up particular molecules from the surroundings. The coated pit then pinches closed to form a vesicle that carries the molecules into the cytoplasm. The micrograph shows material bound to receptor proteins inside a coated pit.

Your cells use receptor-mediated endocytosis to take in cholesterol from the blood for synthesis of membranes and as a precursor for other steroids. Cholesterol circulates in the blood in particles called low-density lipoproteins (LDLs). LDLs bind to receptor proteins and then enter cells by endocytosis. In humans with the inherited disease familial hypercholesterolemia, LDL receptor proteins are defective and cholesterol accumulates to high levels in the blood, leading to atherosclerosis (see Modules 9.11 and 23.6).

? As a cell grows, its plasma membrane expands. Does this involve endocytosis or exocytosis? Explain.

● Exocytosis: When a transport vesicle fuses with the plasma membrane, its contents are released and the vesicle membrane adds to the plasma membrane.

Phagocytosis

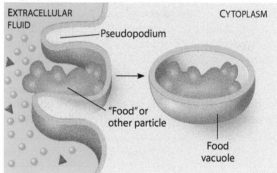

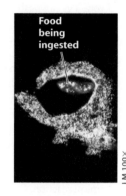

Pinocytosis

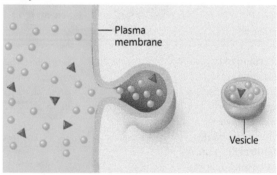

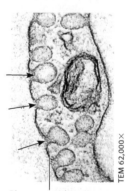

Receptor-mediated endocytosis

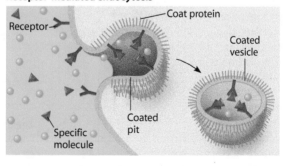

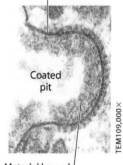

▲ **Figure 5.9** Three kinds of endocytosis

Energy and the Cell

5.10 Cells transform energy as they perform work

The title of this chapter is "The Working Cell." But just what type of work does a cell do? You just learned that a cell actively transports substances across membranes. The cell also builds those membranes and the proteins embedded in them. A cell is a miniature chemical factory in which thousands of reactions occur within a microscopic space. Some of these reactions release energy; others require energy. To understand how the cell works, you must have a basic knowledge of energy.

Forms of Energy We can define **energy** as the capacity to cause change or to perform work. There are two basic forms of energy: kinetic energy and potential energy. **Kinetic energy** is the energy of motion. Moving objects can perform work by transferring motion to other matter. For example, the movement of your legs can push bicycle pedals, turning the wheels and moving you and your bike up a hill. **Heat**, or thermal energy, is a type of kinetic energy associated with the random movement of atoms or molecules. Light, also a type of kinetic energy, can be harnessed to power photosynthesis.

Potential energy, the second main form of energy, is energy that matter possesses as a result of its location or structure. Water behind a dam and you on your bicycle at the top of a hill possess potential energy. Molecules possess potential energy because of the arrangement of electrons in the bonds between their atoms. **Chemical energy** is the potential energy available for release in a chemical reaction. Chemical energy is the most important type of energy for living organisms; it is the energy that can be transformed to power the work of the cell.

Energy Transformations **Thermodynamics** is the study of energy transformations that occur in a collection of matter. Scientists use the word *system* for the matter under study and refer to the rest of the universe—everything outside the system—as the *surroundings*. A system can be an electric power plant, a single cell, or the entire planet. An organism is an open system; that is, it exchanges both energy and matter with its surroundings.

The **first law of thermodynamics**, also known as the law of energy conservation, states that the energy in the universe is constant. Energy can be transferred and transformed, but it cannot be created or destroyed. A power plant does not create energy; it merely converts it from one form (such as the energy stored in coal) to the more convenient form of electricity. A plant cell converts light energy to chemical energy; it, too, is an energy transformer, not an energy producer.

If energy cannot be destroyed, then why can't organisms simply recycle their energy? It turns out that during every transfer or transformation, some energy becomes unusable—unavailable to do work. In most energy transformations, some energy is converted to heat, a disordered form of energy. Scientists use a quantity called **entropy** as a measure of disorder, or randomness. The more randomly arranged a collection of matter is, the greater its entropy. According to the **second law of thermodynamics**, energy conversions increase the entropy (disorder) of the universe.

Figure 5.10 compares a car and a cell to show how energy can be transformed and how entropy increases as a result. Automobile engines and living cells use the same basic process to make the chemical energy of their fuel available for work. The engine mixes oxygen with gasoline in an explosive chemical reaction that pushes the pistons, which eventually move the wheels. The waste products emitted from the exhaust pipe are mostly carbon dioxide and water, energy-poor, simple molecules. Only about 25% of the chemical energy stored in gasoline is converted to the kinetic energy of the car's movement; the rest is lost as heat.

Cells also use oxygen in reactions that release energy from fuel molecules. In the process called **cellular respiration**, the

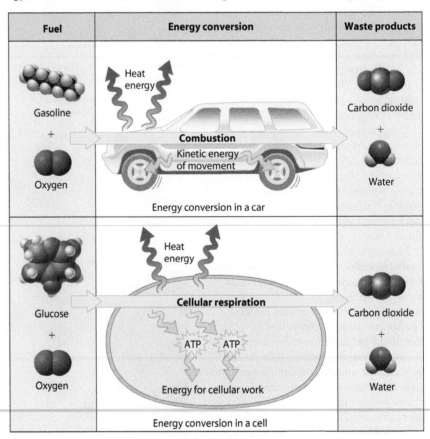

Fuel	Energy conversion	Waste products
Gasoline + Oxygen	Heat energy · **Combustion** · Kinetic energy of movement · Energy conversion in a car	Carbon dioxide + Water
Glucose + Oxygen	Heat energy · **Cellular respiration** · ATP ATP · Energy for cellular work · Energy conversion in a cell	Carbon dioxide + Water

▲ Figure 5.10 Energy transformations (with an increase in entropy) in a car and a cell

chemical energy stored in organic molecules is converted to a form that the cell can use to perform work. Just like for the car, the waste products are mostly carbon dioxide and water. Cells are more efficient than car engines, however, converting about 34% of the chemical energy in their fuel to energy for cellular work. The other 66% generates heat, which explains why vigorous exercise makes you so warm.

According to the second law of thermodynamics, energy transformations result in the universe becoming more disordered. How, then, can we account for biological order? A cell creates intricate structures from less organized materials. Although this increase in order corresponds to a decrease in

entropy, it is accomplished at the expense of ordered forms of matter and energy taken in from the surroundings. As shown in Figure 5.10, cells extract the chemical energy of glucose and return disordered heat and lower-energy carbon dioxide and water to the surroundings. In a thermodynamic sense, a cell is an island of low entropy in an increasingly random universe.

? **How does the second law of thermodynamics explain the diffusion of a solute across a membrane?**

 Diffusion across a membrane results in equal concentrations of solute, which is a more disordered arrangement (higher entropy) than a high concentration on one side and a low concentration on the other.

5.11 Chemical reactions either release or store energy

Chemical reactions are of two types: Either they release energy or they require an input of energy and store energy.

An **exergonic reaction** is a chemical reaction that releases energy (*exergonic* means "energy outward"). As shown in Figure 5.11A, an exergonic reaction begins with reactants whose covalent bonds contain more energy than those in the products. The reaction releases to the surroundings an amount of energy equal to the difference in potential energy between the reactants and the products.

As an example of an exergonic reaction, consider what happens when wood burns. One of the major components of wood is cellulose, a large energy-rich carbohydrate composed of many glucose monomers. The burning of wood releases the energy of glucose as heat and light. Carbon dioxide and water are the products of the reaction.

As you learned in Module 5.10, cells release energy from fuel molecules in the process called cellular respiration. Burning and cellular respiration are alike in being exergonic. They differ in that burning is essentially a one-step process that releases all of a substance's energy at once. Cellular respiration, on the other hand, involves many steps, each a separate chemical reaction; you can think of it as a "slow burn." Some of the energy released from glucose by cellular respiration escapes as heat, but a substantial amount is converted to the chemical energy of ATP. Cells use ATP as an immediate source of energy.

The other type of chemical reaction requires a net input of energy. **Endergonic reactions** yield products that are rich in potential energy (*endergonic* means "energy inward"). As shown in Figure 5.11B, an endergonic reaction starts out with reactant molecules that contain relatively little potential energy. Energy is absorbed from the surroundings as the reaction occurs, so the products of an endergonic reaction contain more chemical energy than the reactants did. And as the graph shows, the amount of additional energy stored in the products equals the difference in potential energy between the reactants and the products.

Photosynthesis, the process by which plant cells make sugar, is an example of an endergonic process. Photosynthesis starts with energy-poor reactants (carbon dioxide and water molecules) and, using energy absorbed from sunlight, produces energy-rich sugar molecules.

Every working cell in every organism carries out thousands of exergonic and endergonic reactions. The total of an organism's

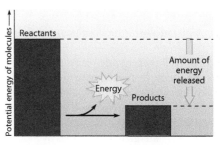

◀ **Figure 5.11A**
Exergonic reaction, energy released

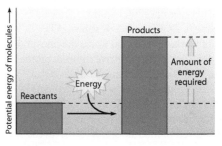

◀ **Figure 5.11B**
Endergonic reaction, energy required

chemical reactions is called **metabolism** (from the Greek *metabole*, change). We can picture a cell's metabolism as a road map of thousands of chemical reactions arranged as intersecting metabolic pathways. A **metabolic pathway** is a series of chemical reactions that either builds a complex molecule or breaks down a complex molecule into simpler compounds. The "slow burn" of cellular respiration is an example of a metabolic pathway in which a sequence of reactions slowly releases the potential energy stored in sugar.

All of an organism's activities require energy, which is obtained from sugar and other molecules by the exergonic reactions of cellular respiration. Cells then use that energy in endergonic reactions to make molecules and do the work of the cell. **Energy coupling**—the use of energy released from exergonic reactions to drive essential endergonic reactions—is a crucial ability of all cells. ATP molecules are the key to energy coupling. In the next module, we explore the structure and function of ATP.

? **Cellular respiration is an exergonic process. Remembering that energy must be conserved, what becomes of the energy extracted from food during cellular respiration?**

 Some of it is stored in ATP molecules; the rest is released as heat.

5.12 ATP drives cellular work by coupling exergonic and endergonic reactions

ATP powers nearly all forms of cellular work. The structure of ATP, or adenosine triphosphate, is shown below in **Figure 5.12A**. The adenosine part of ATP consists of adenine, a nitrogenous base (see Module 3.15), and ribose, a five-carbon sugar. The triphosphate part is a chain of three phosphate groups (each symbolized by P). All three phosphate groups are negatively charged (see Table 3.2). These like charges are crowded together, and their mutual repulsion makes the triphosphate chain of ATP the chemical equivalent of a compressed spring.

As a result, the bonds connecting the phosphate groups are unstable and can readily be broken by hydrolysis, the addition of water. Notice in Figure 5.12A that when the bond to the third group breaks, a phosphate group leaves ATP—which becomes ADP (adenosine diphosphate)—and energy is released.

Thus, the hydrolysis of ATP is exergonic—it releases energy. How does the cell couple this reaction to an endergonic one? It usually does so by transferring a phosphate group from ATP to some other molecule. This phosphate transfer is called **phosphorylation**, and most cellular work depends on ATP energizing molecules by phosphorylating them.

There are three main types of cellular work: chemical, mechanical, and transport. As **Figure 5.12B** shows, ATP drives all three types of work. In chemical work, the phosphorylation of reactants provides energy to drive the endergonic synthesis of products. In an example of mechanical work, the transfer of phosphate groups to special motor proteins in muscle cells causes the proteins to change shape and pull on protein filaments, in turn causing the cells to contract. In transport work, as discussed in Module 5.8, ATP drives the active transport of solutes across a membrane against their concentration gradient by phosphorylating transport proteins.

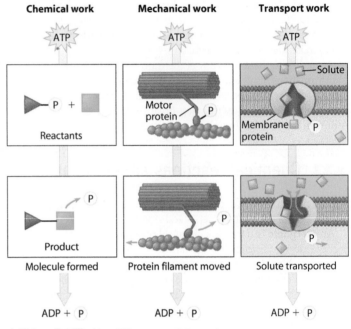

▲ **Figure 5.12B** How ATP powers cellular work

Work can be sustained because ATP is a renewable resource that cells regenerate. **Figure 5.12C**, below, shows the ATP cycle. Each side of this cycle illustrates energy coupling. Energy released in exergonic reactions, such as the breakdown of glucose during cellular respiration, is used to regenerate ATP from ADP. In this endergonic (energy-storing) process, a phosphate group is bonded to ADP. The hydrolysis of ATP releases energy that drives endergonic reactions. A cell at work uses ATP continuously, and the ATP cycle runs at an astonishing pace. In fact, a working muscle cell may consume and regenerate 10 million ATP molecules each second.

But even with a constant supply of energy, few metabolic reactions would occur without the assistance of enzymes. We explore these biological catalysts next.

? Explain how ATP transfers energy from exergonic to endergonic processes in the cell.

● Exergonic processes phosphorylate ADP to form ATP. ATP transfers energy to endergonic processes by phosphorylating other molecules.

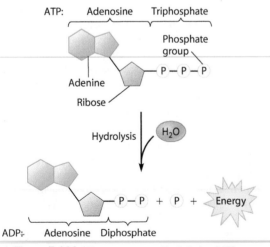

▲ **Figure 5.12A** The structure and hydrolysis of ATP. The reaction of ATP and water yields ADP, a phosphate group, and energy.

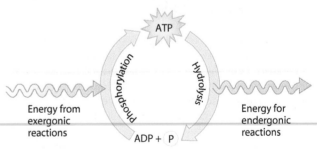

▲ **Figure 5.12C** The ATP cycle

How Enzymes Function

5.13 Enzymes speed up the cell's chemical reactions by lowering energy barriers

Your room gets messier; water flows downhill; sugar crystals dissolve in your coffee. Ordered structures tend toward disorder, and high-energy systems tend to change toward a more stable state of low energy. Proteins, DNA, carbohydrates, lipids—most of the complex molecules of your cells are rich in potential energy. Why don't these high-energy, ordered molecules spontaneously break down into less ordered, lower-energy molecules? They remain intact for the same reason that wood doesn't normally burst into flames or the gas in an automobile's gas tank doesn't spontaneously explode.

There is an energy barrier that must be overcome before a chemical reaction can begin. Energy must be absorbed to contort or weaken bonds in reactant molecules so that they can break and new bonds can form. We call this the **activation energy** (abbreviated E_A for energy of activation). We can think of E_A as the amount of energy needed for reactant molecules to move "uphill" to a higher-energy, unstable state so that the "downhill" part of a reaction can begin.

The energy barrier of E_A protects the highly ordered molecules of your cells from spontaneously breaking down. But now we have a dilemma. Life depends on countless chemical reactions that constantly change a cell's molecular makeup. Most of the essential reactions of metabolism must occur quickly and precisely for a cell to survive. How can the specific reactions that a cell requires get over that energy barrier?

One way to speed reactions is to add heat. Heat speeds up molecules and agitates atoms so that bonds break more easily and reactions can proceed. Certainly, adding a match to kindling will start a fire, and the firing of a spark plug ignites gasoline in an engine. But heating a cell would speed up all chemical reactions, not just the necessary ones, and too much heat would kill the cell.

The answer to our dilemma lies in **enzymes**—molecules that function as biological catalysts, increasing the rate of a reaction without being consumed by the reaction. Almost all enzymes are proteins, although some RNA molecules can also function as enzymes. An enzyme speeds up a reaction by lowering the E_A needed for a reaction to begin. Figure 5.13 compares a reaction without (left) and with (right) an enzyme. Notice how much easier it is for the reactant to get over the activation energy barrier when an enzyme is involved. In the next module, we explore how the structure of an enzyme enables it to lower the activation energy, allowing a reaction to proceed.

? The graph below illustrates the course of a reaction with and without an enzyme. Which curve represents the enzyme-catalyzed reaction? What energy changes are represented by the lines labeled a, b, and c?

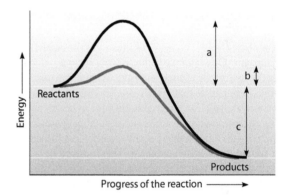

● The red (lower) curve is the enzyme-catalyzed reaction. Line a is E_A without enzyme; b is E_A with enzyme; c is the change in energy between reactants and products, which is the same for both the catalyzed and uncatalyzed reactions.

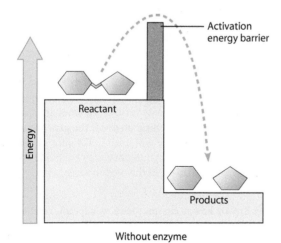

Without enzyme

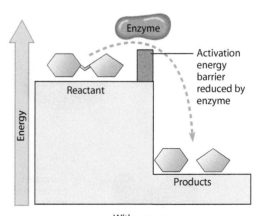

With enzyme

▲ **Figure 5.13** The effect of an enzyme in lowering E_A

5.14 A specific enzyme catalyzes each cellular reaction

You just learned that an enzyme catalyzes a reaction by lowering the E_A barrier. How does it do that? With the aid of an enzyme, the bonds in a reactant are contorted into the higher-energy, unstable state from which the reaction can proceed. Without an enzyme, the energy of activation might never be reached. For example, a solution of sucrose (table sugar) can sit for years at room temperature with no appreciable hydrolysis into its components glucose and fructose. But if we add a small amount of an enzyme to the solution, all the sucrose will be hydrolyzed within seconds.

An enzyme is very selective in the reaction it catalyzes. As a protein, an enzyme has a unique three-dimensional shape, and that shape determines the enzyme's specificity. The specific reactant that an enzyme acts on is called the enzyme's **substrate**. A substrate fits into a region of the enzyme called an **active site**. An active site is typically a pocket or groove on the surface of the enzyme formed by only a few of the enzyme's amino acids. The rest of the protein maintains the shape of the active site. Enzymes are specific because their active sites fit only specific substrate molecules.

The Catalytic Cycle Figure 5.14 illustrates the catalytic cycle of an enzyme. Our example is the enzyme sucrase, which catalyzes the hydrolysis of sucrose to glucose and fructose. (Most enzymes have names that end in -ase, and many are named for their substrate.) ❶ The enzyme starts with an empty active site. ❷ Sucrose enters the active site, attaching by weak bonds. The active site changes shape slightly, embracing the substrate more snugly, like a firm handshake. This **induced fit** may contort substrate bonds or place chemical groups of the amino acids making up the active site in position to catalyze the reaction. (In reactions involving two or more reactants, the active

site holds the substrates in the proper orientation for a reaction to occur.) ❸ The strained bond of sucrose reacts with water, and the substrate is converted (hydrolyzed) to the products glucose and fructose. ❹ The enzyme releases the products and emerges unchanged from the reaction. Its active site is now available for another substrate molecule, and another round of the cycle can begin. A single enzyme molecule may act on thousands or even millions of substrate molecules per second.

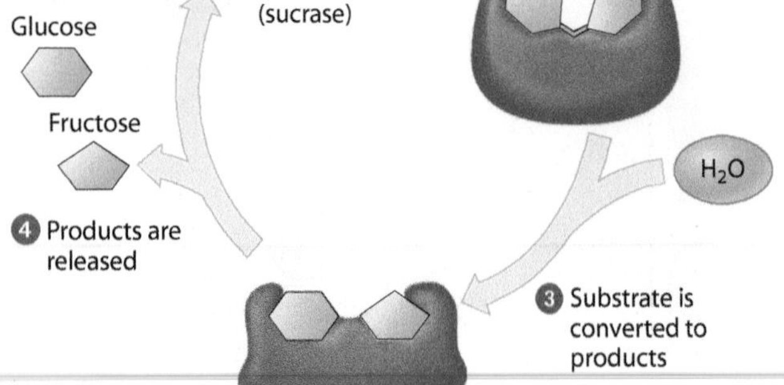

Optimal Conditions for Enzymes As with all proteins, an enzyme's shape is central to its function, and this three-dimensional shape is affected by the environment. For every enzyme, there are optimal conditions under which it is most effective. Temperature, for instance, affects molecular motion, and an enzyme's optimal temperature produces the highest rate of contact between reactant molecules and the enzyme's active site. Higher temperatures denature the enzyme, altering its specific shape and destroying its function. Most human enzymes work best at 35–40°C (95–104°F), close to our normal body temperature of 37°C. Prokaryotes that live in hot springs, however, contain enzymes with optimal temperatures of 70°C (158°F) or higher. You will learn in Module 12.12 how the enzymes of these bacteria are used in a technique that rapidly replicates DNA sequences from small samples.

The optimal pH for most enzymes is near neutrality, in the range of 6–8. There are exceptions, however. Pepsin, a digestive enzyme in the stomach, works best at pH 2. Such an environment would denature most enzymes, but the structure of pepsin is most stable and active in the acidic environment of the stomach.

Cofactors Many enzymes require nonprotein helpers called **cofactors**, which bind to the active site and function in catalysis. The cofactors of some enzymes are inorganic, such as the ions of zinc, iron, and copper. If the cofactor is an organic molecule, it is called a **coenzyme**. Most vitamins are important in nutrition because they function as coenzymes or raw materials from which coenzymes are made. For example, folic acid is a coenzyme for a number of enzymes involved in the synthesis of nucleic acids. And in Chapter 6, you will learn about the roles of riboflavin and niacin as coenzymes of important enzymes involved in cellular respiration.

Chemical chaos would result if all of a cell's metabolic pathways were operating simultaneously. A cell must tightly control when and where its various enzymes are active. It does this either by switching on or off the genes that encode specific enzymes (as you will learn in Chapter 11) or by regulating the activity of enzymes once they are made. We explore this second mechanism in the next module.

? Explain how an enzyme speeds up a specific reaction.

● An enzyme lowers the activation energy needed for a reaction when its specific substrate enters its active site. With an induced fit, the enzyme strains bonds that need to break or positions substrates in an orientation that aids the conversion of reactants to products.

❶ Enzyme available with empty active site

Active site

Substrate (sucrose)

Enzyme (sucrase)

❷ Substrate binds to enzyme with induced fit

Glucose

Fructose

H_2O

❹ Products are released

❸ Substrate is converted to products

▲ **Figure 5.14** The catalytic cycle of an enzyme

5.15 Enzyme inhibitors can regulate enzyme activity in a cell

A chemical that interferes with an enzyme's activity is called an inhibitor. Scientists have learned a great deal about enzyme function by studying the effects of these chemicals. Some inhibitors resemble the enzyme's normal substrate and compete for entry into the active site. As shown in the lower left of Figure 5.15A, such a **competitive inhibitor** reduces an enzyme's productivity by blocking substrate molecules from entering the active site. Competitive inhibition can be overcome by increasing the concentration of the substrate, making it more likely that a substrate molecule rather than an inhibitor will be nearby when an active site becomes vacant.

In contrast, a **noncompetitive inhibitor** does not enter the active site. Instead, it binds to the enzyme somewhere else, a place called an allosteric site, and its binding changes the shape of the enzyme so that the active site no longer fits the substrate (lower right of Figure 5.15A).

Although enzyme inhibition sounds harmful, cells use inhibitors as important regulators of cellular metabolism. Many of a cell's chemical reactions are organized into metabolic pathways in which a molecule is altered in a series of steps, each catalyzed by a specific enzyme, to form a final product. If a cell is producing more of that product than it needs, the product may act as an inhibitor of one of the enzymes early in the pathway. Figure 5.15B illustrates this sort of inhibition, called **feedback inhibition**. Because only weak interactions bind inhibitor and enzyme, this inhibition is reversible. When the product is used up by the cell, the enzyme is no longer inhibited and the pathway functions again.

In the next module, we explore some uses that people make of enzyme inhibitors.

? Explain an advantage of feedback inhibition to a cell.

● It prevents the cell from wasting valuable resources by synthesizing more of a particular product than is needed.

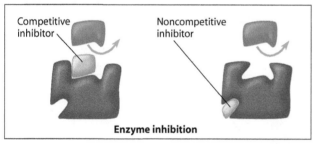

▲ Figure 5.15A How inhibitors interfere with substrate binding

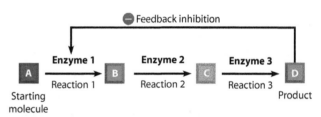

▲ Figure 5.15B Feedback inhibition of a biosynthetic pathway in which product D acts as an inhibitor of enzyme 1

5.16 Many drugs, pesticides, and poisons are enzyme inhibitors

Many beneficial drugs act as enzyme inhibitors. Ibuprofen (Figure 5.16) is a common drug that inhibits an enzyme involved in the production of prostaglandins—messenger molecules that increase the sensation of pain and inflammation. Other drugs that function as enzyme inhibitors include some blood pressure medicines and antidepressants. Many antibiotics work by inhibiting enzymes of disease-causing bacteria. Penicillin, for example, blocks the active site of an enzyme that many bacteria use in making cell walls. Protease inhibitors are HIV drugs that target a key viral enzyme. And many cancer drugs are inhibitors of enzymes that promote cell division.

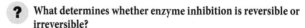

▲ Figure 5.16
Ibuprofen, an enzyme inhibitor

Humans have developed enzyme inhibitors as pesticides, and occasionally as deadly poisons for use in warfare. Poisons often attach to an enzyme by covalent bonds, making the inhibition irreversible. Poisons called nerve gases bind in the active site of an enzyme vital to the transmission of nerve impulses. The inhibition of this enzyme leads to rapid paralysis of vital functions and death. Pesticides such as malathion and parathion are toxic to insects (and dangerous to the people who apply them) because they also irreversibly inhibit this enzyme. Interestingly, some drugs reversibly inhibit this same enzyme and are used in anesthesia and treatment of certain diseases.

? What determines whether enzyme inhibition is reversible or irreversible?

● If the inhibitor binds to the enzyme with covalent bonds, the inhibition is usually irreversible. When weak chemical interactions bind inhibitor and enzyme, the inhibition is reversible.

For Practice Quizzes, BioFlix, MP3 Tutors, and Activities, go to www.masteringbiology.com.

Reviewing the Concepts

Membrane Structure and Function (5.1–5.9)

5.1 Membranes are fluid mosaics of lipids and proteins with many functions. The proteins embedded in a membrane's phospholipid bilayer perform various functions.

5.2 Membranes form spontaneously, a critical step in the origin of life.

5.3 Passive transport is diffusion across a membrane with no energy investment. Solutes diffuse across membranes down their concentration gradients.

5.4 Osmosis is the diffusion of water across a membrane.

5.5 Water balance between cells and their surroundings is crucial to organisms. Cells shrink in a hypertonic solution and swell in a hypotonic solution. In isotonic solutions, animal cells are normal, but plant cells are flaccid.

5.6 Transport proteins can facilitate diffusion across membranes.

5.7 Research on another membrane protein led to the discovery of aquaporins. Aquaporins are water channels in cells with high water transport needs.

5.8 Cells expend energy in the active transport of a solute.

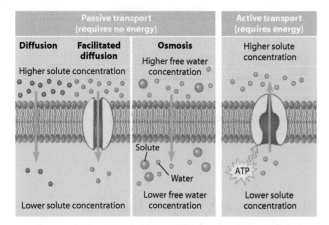

5.9 Exocytosis and endocytosis transport large molecules across membranes. A vesicle may fuse with the membrane and expel its contents (exocytosis), or the membrane may fold inward, enclosing material from the outside (endocytosis).

Energy and the Cell (5.10–5.12)

5.10 Cells transform energy as they perform work. Kinetic energy is the energy of motion. Potential energy is energy stored in the location or structure of matter. Chemical energy is potential energy available for release in a chemical reaction. According to the laws of thermodynamics, energy can change form but cannot be created or destroyed, and energy transformations increase disorder, or entropy, with some energy being lost as heat.

5.11 Chemical reactions either release or store energy. Exergonic reactions release energy. Endergonic reactions require energy and yield products rich in potential energy. Metabolism encompasses all of a cell's chemical reactions.

5.12 ATP drives cellular work by coupling exergonic and endergonic reactions. The transfer of a phosphate group from ATP is involved in chemical, mechanical, and transport work.

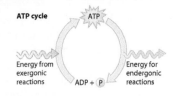

How Enzymes Function (5.13–5.16)

5.13 Enzymes speed up the cell's chemical reactions by lowering energy barriers. Enzymes are protein catalysts that decrease the activation energy (E_A) needed to begin a reaction.

5.14 A specific enzyme catalyzes each cellular reaction. An enzyme's substrate binds specifically to its active site.

5.15 Enzyme inhibitors can regulate enzyme activity in a cell. A competitive inhibitor competes with the substrate for the active site. A noncompetitive inhibitor alters an enzyme's function by changing its shape. Feedback inhibition helps regulate metabolism.

5.16 Many drugs, pesticides, and poisons are enzyme inhibitors.

Connecting the Concepts

1. Fill in the following concept map to review the processes by which molecules move across membranes.

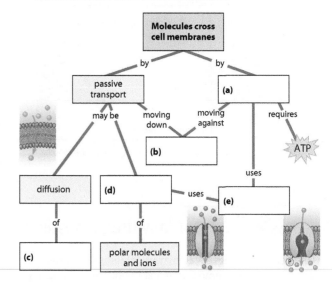

2. Label the parts of the following diagram illustrating the catalytic cycle of an enzyme.

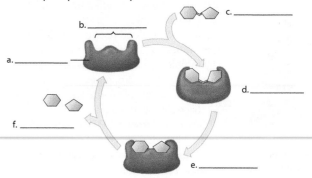

Testing Your Knowledge

Multiple Choice

3. Which best describes the structure of a cell membrane?
   a. proteins between two bilayers of phospholipids
   b. proteins embedded in a bilayer of phospholipids
   c. a bilayer of protein coating a layer of phospholipids
   d. phospholipids between two layers of protein
   e. cholesterol embedded in a bilayer of phospholipids

4. Consider the following: chemical bonds in the gasoline in a car's gas tank and the movement of the car along the road; a biker at the top of a hill and the ride he took to get there. The first parts of these situations illustrate _____, and the second parts illustrate _____.
   a. the first law of thermodynamics ... the second law
   b. kinetic energy ... potential energy
   c. an exergonic reaction ... an endergonic reaction
   d. potential energy ... kinetic energy
   e. the second law of thermodynamics ... the first law

5. A plant cell placed in distilled water will _____; an animal cell placed in distilled water will _____.
   a. burst ... burst
   b. become flaccid ... shrivel
   c. become flaccid ... be normal in shape
   d. become turgid ... be normal in shape
   e. become turgid ... burst

6. The sodium concentration in a cell is 10 times less than the concentration in the surrounding fluid. How can the cell move sodium out of the cell? (*Explain.*)
   a. passive transport
   b. diffusion
   c. active transport
   d. osmosis
   e. any of these processes

7. The synthesis of ATP from ADP and P
   a. is an exergonic process.
   b. involves the hydrolysis of a phosphate bond.
   c. transfers a phosphate, priming a protein to do work.
   d. stores energy in a form that can drive cellular work.
   e. releases energy.

8. Facilitated diffusion across a membrane requires _____ and moves a solute _____ its concentration gradient.
   a. transport proteins ... up (against)
   b. transport proteins ... down
   c. energy ... up
   d. energy and transport proteins ... up
   e. energy and transport proteins ... down

Describing, Comparing, and Explaining

9. What are aquaporins? Where would you expect to find them?

10. How do the two laws of thermodynamics apply to living organisms?

11. What are the main types of cellular work? How does ATP provide the energy for this work?

12. Why is the barrier of the activation energy beneficial for organic molecules? Explain how enzymes lower E_A.

13. How do the components and structure of cell membranes relate to the functions of membranes?

14. Sometimes inhibitors can be harmful to a cell; often they are beneficial. Explain.

Applying the Concepts

15. Explain how each of the following food preservation methods would interfere with a microbe's enzyme activity and ability to break down food: canning (heating), freezing, pickling (soaking in acetic acid), salting.

16. A biologist performed two series of experiments on lactase, the enzyme that hydrolyzes lactose to glucose and galactose. First, she made up 10% lactose solutions containing different concentrations of enzyme and measured the rate at which galactose was produced (grams of galactose per minute). Results of these experiments are shown in Table A below. In the second series of experiments (Table B), she prepared 2% enzyme solutions containing different concentrations of lactose and again measured the rate of galactose production.

Table A: Rate and Enzyme Concentration					
Lactose concentration	10%	10%	10%	10%	10%
Enzyme concentration	0%	1%	2%	4%	8%
Reaction rate	0	25	50	100	200

Table B: Rate and Substrate Concentration					
Lactose concentration	0%	5%	10%	20%	30%
Enzyme concentration	2%	2%	2%	2%	2%
Reaction rate	0	25	50	65	65

   a. Graph and explain the relationship between the reaction rate and the enzyme concentration.

   b. Graph and explain the relationship between the reaction rate and the substrate concentration. How and why did the results of the two experiments differ?

17. The following graph shows the rate of reaction for two different enzymes: One is pepsin, a digestive enzyme found in the stomach; the other is trypsin, a digestive enzyme found in the intestine. As you may know, gastric juice in the stomach contains hydrochloric acid. Which curve belongs to which enzyme?

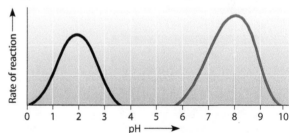

A lysosome, a digestive organelle in a cell, has an internal pH of around 4.5. Draw a curve on the graph that you would predict for a lysosomal enzyme, labeling its optimal pH.

18. Organophosphates (organic compounds containing phosphate groups) are commonly used as insecticides to improve crop yield. Organophosphates typically interfere with nerve signal transmission by inhibiting the enzymes that degrade transmitter molecules. They affect humans and other vertebrates as well as insects. Thus, the use of organophosphate pesticides poses some health risks. On the other hand, these molecules break down rapidly upon exposure to air and sunlight. As a consumer, what level of risk are you willing to accept in exchange for an abundant and affordable food supply?

Answers to all questions can be found in Appendix 4.

How Cells Harvest Chemical Energy

BIG IDEAS

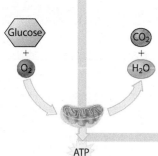

Cellular Respiration: Aerobic Harvesting of Energy
(6.1–6.5)

Cellular respiration oxidizes fuel molecules and generates ATP for cellular work.

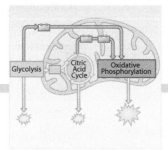

Stages of Cellular Respiration
(6.6–6.12)

The main stages of cellular respiration are glycolysis, the citric acid cycle, and oxidative phosphorylation.

Fermentation: Anaerobic Harvesting of Energy
(6.13–6.14)

Fermentation regenerates NAD⁺, allowing glycolysis and ATP production to continue without oxygen.

Connections Between Metabolic Pathways
(6.15–6.16)

The breakdown pathways of cellular respiration intersect with biosynthetic pathways.

In Chapter 5, you learned about energy transformations—how potential energy stored in the chemical bonds of fuel molecules can be converted to kinetic energy, such as the movement of a car or, as you can see here, the leaping of a lemur. Where did the lemur get the energy for this dramatic leap? The obvious answer is, of course, from its food. But the more complete answer, as you will learn in this chapter, is from the harvesting of energy from food molecules that takes place in every cell in an animal's body. In fact, this process, called cellular respiration, also occurs in the cells of plants, fungi, and protists. And a similar process takes place in most prokaryotic organisms.

Cellular respiration is the breakdown of sugars and other food molecules in the presence of oxygen to carbon dioxide and water, generating a large amount of ATP, the energy currency that "pays for" cellular work. In the muscle cells of this leaping lemur, ATP powers the contraction of its muscles. The lemur's cells also use the energy of ATP to build and maintain cell structure, transport materials across membranes, manufacture products, grow, and divide.

In this chapter, we present some basic concepts about cellular respiration and then focus on the key stages of the process: glycolysis, the citric acid cycle, and oxidative phosphorylation. We'll also consider fermentation, an extended version of glycolysis that has deep evolutionary roots. We complete the chapter with a look at how the metabolic pathways that break down organic molecules connect to those that build such molecules.

But first let's take a step back and consider the original source of the energy for most cellular work on Earth today.

Cellular Respiration: Aerobic Harvesting of Energy

6.1 Photosynthesis and cellular respiration provide energy for life

Life requires energy. In almost all ecosystems, that energy ultimately comes from the sun. Photosynthesis, the process by which the sun's energy is captured, is the topic of Chapter 7. But a brief overview here of the relationship between photosynthesis and cellular respiration will illustrate how these two processes provide energy for life (Figure 6.1). In photosynthesis, which takes place in a plant cell's chloroplast, the energy of sunlight is used to rearrange the atoms of carbon dioxide (CO_2) and water (H_2O) to produce glucose and oxygen (O_2). The lemur in Figure 6.1 obtains energy for leaping from tree to tree by eating plants. In **cellular respiration**, O_2 is consumed as glucose is broken down to CO_2 and H_2O; the cell captures the energy released in ATP. Cellular respiration takes place in the mitochondria of all eukaryotic cells.

This figure also shows that in these energy conversions, some energy is lost as heat. Life on Earth is solar powered, and energy makes a one-way trip through an ecosystem. Chemicals, however, are recycled. The CO_2 and H_2O released by cellular respiration are converted through photosynthesis to glucose and O_2, which are then used in respiration.

> **?** What is misleading about the following statement? "Plant cells perform photosynthesis, and animal cells perform cellular respiration."

their cellular work.
In fact, almost all eukaryotic cells use cellular respiration to obtain energy for
The statement implies that cellular respiration does not occur in plant cells.

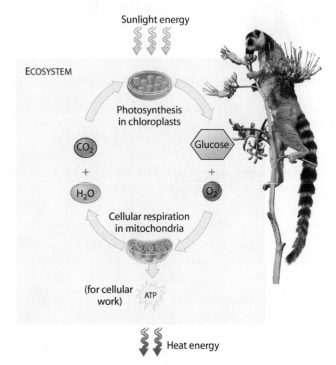

▲ **Figure 6.1** The connection between photosynthesis and cellular respiration

6.2 Breathing supplies O_2 for use in cellular respiration and removes CO_2

We often use the word *respiration* as a synonym for "breathing," the meaning of its Latin root. In that sense of the word, respiration refers to an exchange of gases: An organism obtains O_2 from its environment and releases CO_2 as a waste product. Biologists also define respiration as the aerobic (oxygen-requiring) harvesting of energy from food molecules by cells. This process is called cellular respiration to distinguish it from breathing.

Breathing and cellular respiration are closely related. As the runner in Figure 6.2 breathes in air, her lungs take up O_2 and pass it to her bloodstream. The bloodstream carries the O_2 to her muscle cells. Mitochondria in the muscle cells use the O_2 in cellular respiration to harvest energy from glucose and other organic molecules and generate ATP. Muscle cells use ATP to contract. The runner's bloodstream and lungs also perform the vital function of disposing of the CO_2 waste , which, as you can see by the equation at the bottom of the figure, is produced in cellular respiration.

> **?** How is your breathing related to your cellular respiration?

fuel, releasing CO_2 as a waste product.
cellular respiration, cells use the O_2, obtained through breathing to break down
In breathing, CO_2 and O_2 are exchanged between your lungs and the air. In

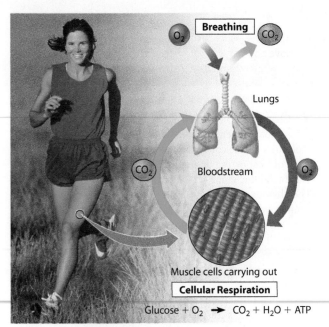

▲ **Figure 6.2** The connection between breathing and cellular respiration

6.3 Cellular respiration banks energy in ATP molecules

As the runner example in Figure 6.2 implies, oxygen usage is only a means to an end. Generating ATP for cellular work is the fundamental function of cellular respiration.

The balanced chemical equation in Figure 6.3 summarizes cellular respiration as carried out by cells that use O_2 in harvesting energy from glucose. The simple sugar glucose ($C_6H_{12}O_6$) is the fuel that cells use most often, although other organic molecules can also be "burned" in cellular respiration. The equation tells us that the atoms of the reactant molecules $C_6H_{12}O_6$ and O_2 are rearranged to form the products CO_2 and H_2O. In this exergonic process, the chemical energy of the bonds in glucose is released and stored (or "banked") in the chemical bonds of ATP (see Modules 5.10–5.12). The series of arrows in Figure 6.3 indicates that cellular respiration consists of many steps, not just a single reaction.

Cellular respiration can produce up to 32 ATP molecules for each glucose molecule, a capture of about 34% of the energy originally stored in glucose. The rest of the energy is released as heat (see Module 5.10). This may seem inefficient, but it

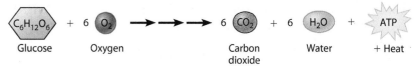

▲ **Figure 6.3** Summary equation for cellular respiration:
$C_6H_{12}O_6 + 6\ O_2 \longrightarrow 6\ CO_2 + 6\ H_2O + \text{Energy (ATP + Heat)}$

compares very well with the efficiency of most energy-conversion systems. For instance, the average automobile engine is able to convert only about 25% of the energy in gasoline to the kinetic energy of movement.

How great are the energy needs of a cell? If ATP could not be regenerated through cellular respiration, you would use up nearly your body weight in ATP each day. Let's consider the energy requirements for various human activities next.

? **Why are sweating and other body-cooling mechanisms necessary during vigorous exercise?**

● The demand for ATP is supported by an increased rate of cellular respiration, but about 66% of the energy from food produces heat instead of ATP.

CONNECTION | ## 6.4 The human body uses energy from ATP for all its activities

Your body requires a continuous supply of energy just to stay alive—to keep the heart pumping, to breathe, and to maintain body temperature. Your brain requires a huge amount of energy; its cells burn about 120 grams (g)—a quarter of a pound!—of glucose a day, accounting for about 15% of total oxygen consumption. Maintaining brain cells and other life-sustaining activities uses as much as 75% of the energy a person takes in as food during a typical day.

Above and beyond the energy you need for body maintenance, cellular respiration provides energy for voluntary activities. Figure 6.4 shows the amount of energy it takes to perform some of these activities. The energy units are **kilocalories (kcal)**, the quantity of heat required to raise the temperature of 1 kilogram (kg) of water by 1°C. (The "Calories" listed on food packages are actually kilocalories, usually signified by a capital C.) The values shown do not include the energy the body consumes for its basic life-sustaining activities. Even sleeping or lying quietly requires energy for metabolism.

The U.S. National Academy of Sciences estimates that the average adult human needs to take in food that provides about 2,200 kcal of energy per day. This includes the energy expended in both maintenance and voluntary activity. We will explore nutritional needs (and the maintenance of a healthy weight) in Chapter 21. But now we begin the study of how cells liberate the energy stored in fuel molecules to produce the ATP used to power the work of cells and thus the activities of the body.

Activity	kcal consumed per hour by a 67.5-kg (150-lb) person*
Running (8–9 mph)	979
Dancing (fast)	510
Bicycling (10 mph)	490
Swimming (2 mph)	408
Walking (4 mph)	341
Walking (3 mph)	245
Dancing (slow)	204
Driving a car	61
Sitting (writing)	28

*Not including kcal needed for body maintenance

▲ **Figure 6.4** Energy consumed by various activities

? **Walking at 3 mph, how far would you have to travel to "burn off" the equivalent of an extra slice of pizza, which has about 475 kcal? How long would that take?**

● You would have to walk about 6 miles, which would take you about 2 hours. (Now you understand why the most effective exercise for losing weight is pushing away from the table!)

6.5 Cells tap energy from electrons "falling" from organic fuels to oxygen

How do your cells extract energy from glucose? The answer involves the transfer of electrons during chemical reactions.

Redox Reactions During cellular respiration, electrons are transferred from glucose to oxygen, releasing energy. Oxygen attracts electrons very strongly, and an electron loses potential energy when it "falls" to oxygen. If you burn a cube of sugar, this electron fall happens very rapidly, releasing energy in the form of heat and light. Cellular respiration is a more controlled descent of electrons—more like stepping down an energy staircase, with energy released in small amounts that can be stored in the chemical bonds of ATP.

The movement of electrons from one molecule to another is an oxidation-reduction reaction, or **redox reaction** for short. In a redox reaction, the loss of electrons from one substance is called **oxidation**, and the addition of electrons to another substance is called **reduction**. A molecule is said to become oxidized when it loses one or more electrons and reduced when it gains one or more electrons. Because an electron transfer requires both a donor and an acceptor, oxidation and reduction always go together.

In the cellular respiration equation in **Figure 6.5A** below, you cannot see any electron transfers. What you do see are changes in the location of hydrogen atoms. These hydrogen movements represent electron transfers because each hydrogen atom consists of an electron (e^-) and a proton (hydrogen ion, or H^+). Glucose ($C_6H_{12}O_6$) loses hydrogen atoms (electrons) as it becomes oxidized to CO_2; simultaneously, O_2 gains hydrogen atoms (electrons) as it becomes reduced to H_2O. As they pass from glucose to oxygen, the electrons lose potential energy.

NADH and Electron Transport Chains An important player in the process of oxidizing glucose is a coenzyme called **NAD$^+$**, which accepts electrons and becomes reduced to NADH. NAD$^+$ (nicotinamide adenine dinucleotide) is an organic molecule that cells make from the vitamin niacin and use to shuttle electrons in redox reactions. The top equation in **Figure 6.5B** depicts the oxidation of an organic molecule. We show only its three carbons (⬤) and a few of its other atoms. An enzyme called dehydrogenase strips two hydrogen atoms from this molecule. Simultaneously, as shown in the lower equation, NAD$^+$ picks up the two electrons (⊖) and becomes reduced to NADH. One hydrogen ion (H$^+$) is released. (NADH is represented throughout this chapter as a light brown box carrying two blue electrons.)

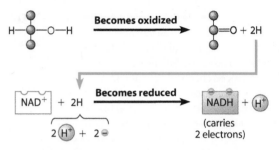

▲ **Figure 6.5B** A pair of redox reactions occuring simultaneously

Using the energy staircase analogy for electrons falling from glucose to oxygen, the transfer of electrons from an organic molecule to NAD$^+$ represents the first step. **Figure 6.5C** shows NADH delivering these electrons to the rest of the staircase— an **electron transport chain**. The steps in the chain are electron carrier molecules, shown here as purple ovals, built into the inner membrane of a mitochondrion. At the bottom of the staircase is O_2, the final electron acceptor.

The electron transport chain undergoes a series of redox reactions in which electrons pass from carrier to carrier down to oxygen. The redox steps in the staircase release energy in amounts small enough to be used by the cell to make ATP.

With an understanding of this basic mechanism of electron transfer and energy release, we can now explore cellular respiration in more detail.

❓ **What chemical characteristic of the element oxygen accounts for its function in cellular respiration?**

● Oxygen is very electronegative (see Module 2.6), making it very powerful in pulling electrons down the electron transport chain.

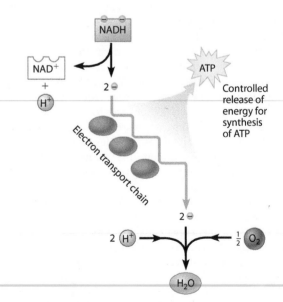

▲ **Figure 6.5C** In cellular respiration, electrons fall down an energy staircase and finally reduce O_2.

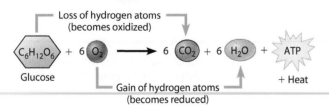

▲ **Figure 6.5A** Rearrangement of hydrogen atoms (with their electrons) in the redox reactions of cellular respiration

Stages of Cellular Respiration

6.6 Overview: Cellular respiration occurs in three main stages

Cellular respiration consists of a sequence of steps that can be divided into three main stages. Figure 6.6 gives an overview of the three stages and shows where they occur in a eukaryotic cell. (In prokaryotic cells that use aerobic respiration, these steps occur in the cytoplasm, and the electron transport chain is built into the plasma membrane.)

Stage 1: Glycolysis (shown with an aqua background throughout this chapter) occurs in the cytoplasmic fluid of the cell. Glycolysis begins cellular respiration by breaking glucose into two molecules of a three-carbon compound called pyruvate.

Stage 2: Pyruvate oxidation and the citric acid cycle (shown in a salmon color) take place within the mitochondria. Pyruvate is oxidized to a two-carbon compound. The citric acid cycle then completes the breakdown of glucose to carbon dioxide. As suggested by the smaller ATP symbols in the diagram, the cell makes a small amount of ATP during glycolysis and the citric acid cycle. The main function of these first two stages, however, is to supply the third stage of respiration with electrons (shown with gold arrows).

Stage 3: Oxidative phosphorylation (purple background) requires an electron transport chain and a process known as chemiosmosis. NADH and a related electron carrier, $FADH_2$ (flavin adenine dinucleotide), shuttle electrons to an electron transport chain embedded in the inner mitochondrion membrane. Most of the ATP produced by cellular respiration is generated by oxidative phosphorylation, which uses the energy released by the downhill fall

of electrons from NADH and $FADH_2$ to O_2 to phosphorylate ADP. (Recall from Module 5.12 that cells generate ATP by adding a phosphate group to ADP.)

What couples the electron transport chain to ATP synthesis? As the electron transport chain passes electrons down the energy staircase, it also pumps hydrogen ions (H^+) across the inner mitochondrial membrane into the narrow intermembrane space (see Figure 4.13). The result is a concentration gradient of H^+ across the membrane. In **chemiosmosis**, the potential energy of this concentration gradient is used to make ATP. The details of this process are explored in Module 6.10. In 1978, British biochemist Peter Mitchell was awarded the Nobel Prize for developing the theory of chemiosmosis.

The small amount of ATP produced in glycolysis and the citric acid cycle is made by substrate-level phosphorylation, a process we discuss in the next module. In the next several modules, we look more closely at the three stages of cellular respiration and the two mechanisms of ATP synthesis.

? **Of the three main stages of cellular respiration represented in Figure 6.6, which one uses oxygen to extract chemical energy from organic compounds?**

● Oxidative phosphorylation, using the electron transport chain, which eventually transfers electrons to oxygen

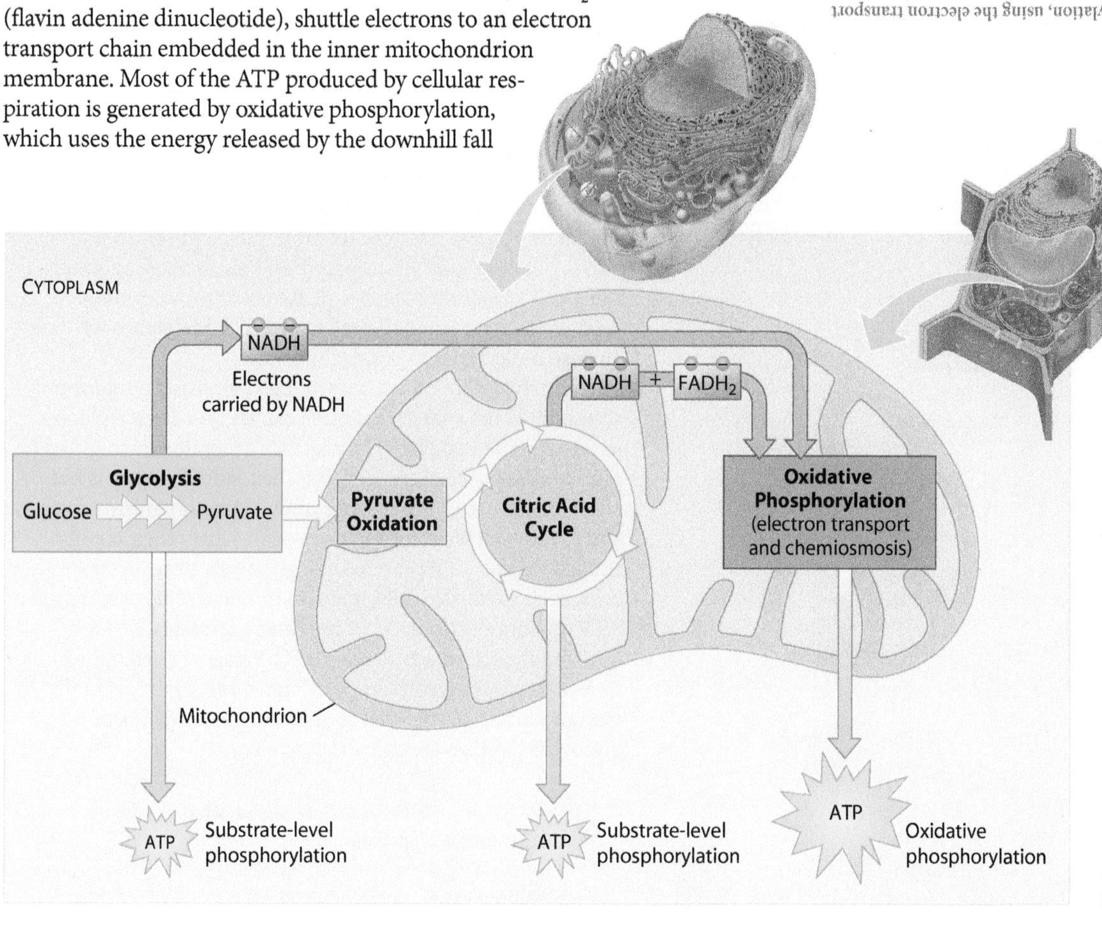

◀ **Figure 6.6** An overview of cellular respiration

6.7 Glycolysis harvests chemical energy by oxidizing glucose to pyruvate

Now that you have been introduced to the major players and processes, it's time to focus on the individual stages of cellular respiration. The term for the first stage, *glycolysis*, means "splitting of sugar" (*glyco*, sweet, and *lysis*, split), and that's exactly what happens during this phase.

Figure 6.7A below gives an overview of glycolysis in terms of input and output. Glycolysis begins with a single molecule of glucose and concludes with two molecules of pyruvate. (Pyruvate is the ionized form of pyruvic acid.) The gray balls represent the carbon atoms in each molecule; glucose has six carbons, and these same six carbons end up in the two molecules of pyruvate (three carbons in each). The straight arrow from glucose to pyruvate actually represents nine chemical steps, each catalyzed by its own enzyme. As these reactions occur, two molecules of NAD⁺ are reduced to two molecules of NADH, and a net gain of two molecules of ATP is produced.

Figure 6.7B illustrates how ATP is formed in glycolysis by the process called **substrate-level phosphorylation**. In this process, an enzyme transfers a phosphate group from a substrate molecule directly to ADP, forming ATP. You will meet substrate-level phosphorylation again in the citric acid cycle, where a small amount of ATP is generated by this process.

The energy extracted from glucose during glycolysis is banked in a combination of ATP and NADH. The cell can use the energy in ATP immediately, but for it to use the energy in NADH, electrons from NADH must pass down an electron transport chain located in the inner mitochondrial membrane. And the pyruvate molecules still hold most of the energy of glucose; these molecules will be oxidized in the citric acid cycle.

Let's take a closer look at glycolysis. **Figure 6.7C**, on the next page, shows all the organic compounds that form in the nine chemical reactions of glycolysis. Commentary on the left

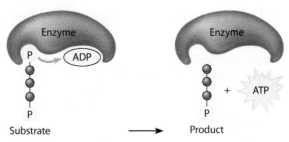

▲ **Figure 6.7B** Substrate-level phosphorylation: transfer of a phosphate group ⓟ from a substrate to ADP, producing ATP

highlights the main features of these reactions. The gray balls represent the carbon atoms in each of the compounds named on the right side of the figure.

The compounds that form between the initial reactant, glucose, and the final product, pyruvate, are known as **intermediates**. Glycolysis is an example of a *metabolic pathway*, in which each chemical step leads to the next one. For instance, the intermediate glucose 6-phosphate is the product of step 1 and the reactant for step 2. Similarly, fructose 6-phosphate is the product of step 2 and the reactant for step 3. Also essential are the specific enzymes that catalyze each chemical step; however, to help keep the figure simple, we have not included the enzymes.

As indicated in Figure 6.7C, the steps of glycolysis can be grouped into two main phases. Steps ❶–❹, the energy investment phase, actually *consume* energy. In this phase, ATP is used to energize a glucose molecule, which is then split into two small sugars that are now primed to release energy. The figure follows both of these three-carbon sugars through the second phase.

Steps ❺–❾, the energy payoff phase, *yield* energy for the cell. In this phase, two NADH molecules are produced for each initial glucose molecule, and four ATP molecules are generated. Remember that the first phase used two molecules of ATP, so the net gain to the cell is two ATP molecules for each glucose molecule that enters glycolysis.

These two ATP molecules from glycolysis account for only about 6% of the energy that a cell can harvest from a glucose molecule. The two NADH molecules generated during step 5 represent about another 16%, but their stored energy is not available for use in the absence of O_2. Some organisms—yeasts and certain bacteria, for instance—can satisfy their energy needs with the ATP produced by glycolysis alone. And some cells, such as muscle cells, may use this anaerobic production of ATP for short periods. Most cells and organisms, however, have far greater energy demands. The stages of cellular respiration that follow glycolysis release much more energy. In the next modules, we see what happens in most organisms after glycolysis oxidizes glucose to pyruvate.

? **For each glucose molecule processed, what are the net molecular products of glycolysis?**

● Two molecules of pyruvate, two molecules of ATP, and two molecules of NADH

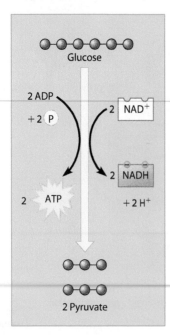

▶ **Figure 6.7A**
An overview
of glycolysis

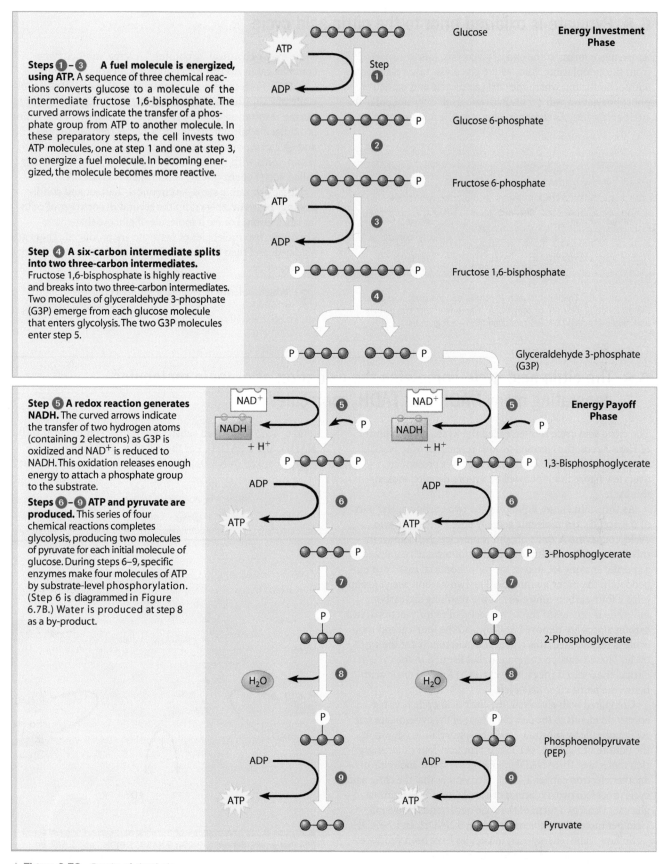

Steps ①–③ A fuel molecule is energized, using ATP. A sequence of three chemical reactions converts glucose to a molecule of the intermediate fructose 1,6-bisphosphate. The curved arrows indicate the transfer of a phosphate group from ATP to another molecule. In these preparatory steps, the cell invests two ATP molecules, one at step 1 and one at step 3, to energize a fuel molecule. In becoming energized, the molecule becomes more reactive.

Step ④ A six-carbon intermediate splits into two three-carbon intermediates. Fructose 1,6-bisphosphate is highly reactive and breaks into two three-carbon intermediates. Two molecules of glyceraldehyde 3-phosphate (G3P) emerge from each glucose molecule that enters glycolysis. The two G3P molecules enter step 5.

Step ⑤ A redox reaction generates NADH. The curved arrows indicate the transfer of two hydrogen atoms (containing 2 electrons) as G3P is oxidized and NAD^+ is reduced to NADH. This oxidation releases enough energy to attach a phosphate group to the substrate.

Steps ⑥–⑨ ATP and pyruvate are produced. This series of four chemical reactions completes glycolysis, producing two molecules of pyruvate for each initial molecule of glucose. During steps 6–9, specific enzymes make four molecules of ATP by substrate-level phosphorylation. (Step 6 is diagrammed in Figure 6.7B.) Water is produced at step 8 as a by-product.

Glucose

ATP

ADP

Step ①

Glucose 6-phosphate

②

Fructose 6-phosphate

ATP

ADP

③

Fructose 1,6-bisphosphate

④

Glyceraldehyde 3-phosphate (G3P)

Energy Investment Phase

NAD^+ ⑤ NAD^+ ⑤   **Energy Payoff Phase**

NADH   P   NADH   P

+ H^+ + H^+

1,3-Bisphosphoglycerate

ADP   ⑥   ADP   ⑥

ATP   ATP

3-Phosphoglycerate

⑦   ⑦

2-Phosphoglycerate

H_2O ⑧ H_2O ⑧

Phosphoenolpyruvate (PEP)

ADP   ⑨   ADP   ⑨

ATP   ATP

Pyruvate

▲ **Figure 6.7C** Details of glycolysis

6.8 Pyruvate is oxidized prior to the citric acid cycle

As pyruvate forms at the end of glycolysis, it is transported from the cytoplasmic fluid, where glycolysis takes place, into a mitochondrion, where the citric acid cycle and oxidative phosphorylation will occur. Pyruvate itself does not enter the citric acid cycle. As shown in **Figure 6.8**, it first undergoes

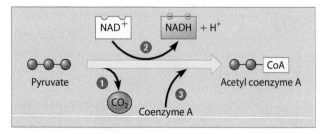

▲ **Figure 6.8** The link between glycolysis and the citric acid cycle: the oxidation of pyruvate to acetyl CoA. (Remember that two pyruvate, and thus two acetyl CoA, are produced from each glucose.)

some major chemical "grooming." A large, multienzyme complex catalyzes three reactions: ❶ A carboxyl group ($-COO^-$) is removed from pyruvate and given off as a molecule of CO_2 (this is the first step in which CO_2 is released during respiration); ❷ the two-carbon compound remaining is oxidized while a molecule of NAD^+ is reduced to NADH; and ❸ a compound called coenzyme A, derived from a B vitamin, joins with the two-carbon group to form a molecule called acetyl coenzyme A, abbreviated **acetyl CoA**.

These grooming steps—a chemical "haircut and conditioning" of pyruvate—set up the second major stage of cellular respiration. For each molecule of glucose that enters glycolysis, two molecules of pyruvate are produced. These are oxidized, and then two molecules of acetyl CoA enter the citric acid cycle.

? Which molecule in Figure 6.8 has been reduced?

● NAD^+ has been reduced to NADH.

6.9 The citric acid cycle completes the oxidation of organic molecules, generating many NADH and FADH$_2$ molecules

The citric acid cycle is often called the Krebs cycle in honor of Hans Krebs, the German-British researcher who worked out much of this pathway in the 1930s. We present an overview figure first, followed by a more detailed look at this cycle.

As shown in **Figure 6.9A**, only the two-carbon acetyl part of the acetyl CoA molecule actually enters the citric acid cycle; coenzyme A splits off and is recycled. Not shown in this figure are the multiple steps that follow, each catalyzed by a specific enzyme located in the mitochondrial matrix or embedded in the inner membrane. The two-carbon acetyl group joins a four-carbon molecule. As the resulting six-carbon molecule is processed through a series of redox reactions, two carbon atoms are removed as CO_2, and the four-carbon molecule is regenerated; this regeneration accounts for the word cycle. The six-carbon compound first formed in the cycle is citrate, the ionized (negatively charged) form of citric acid; hence the name *citric acid cycle*.

Compared with glycolysis, the citric acid cycle pays big energy dividends to the cell. Each turn of the cycle makes one ATP molecule by substrate-level phosphorylation (shown at the bottom of Figure 6.9A). It also produces four other energy-rich molecules: three NADH molecules and one molecule of another electron carrier, $FADH_2$. Remember that the citric acid cycle processes two molecules of acetyl CoA for each initial glucose. Thus, two turns of the cycle occur, and the overall yield per molecule of glucose is 2 ATP, 6 NADH, and 2 $FADH_2$.

So how many energy-rich molecules have been produced by processing one molecule of glucose through glycolysis and the citric acid cycle? Up to this point, the cell has gained a

total of 4 ATP (all from substrate-level phosphorylation), 10 NADH, and 2 $FADH_2$. For the cell to be able to harvest the energy banked in NADH and $FADH_2$, these molecules must

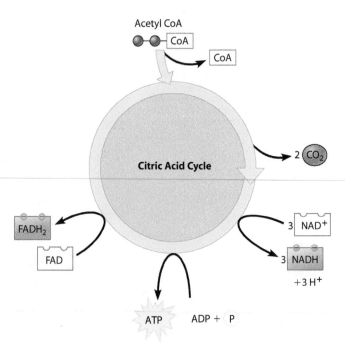

▲ **Figure 6.9A** An overview of the citric acid cycle: For each acetyl CoA that enters the cycle, 2 CO_2, 3 NADH, 1 $FADH_2$, and 1 ATP are produced. (Remember that 2 acetyl CoA are produced from glucose, so multiply by 2 to calculate a per-glucose return.)

shuttle their high-energy electrons to an electron transport chain. There the energy from the *oxidation* of organic molecules is used to *phosphorylate* ADP to ATP—hence the name *oxidative phosphorylation*. Before we look at how oxidative phosphorylation works, you may want to examine the inner workings of the citric acid cycle in **Figure 6.9B**, below.

? **What is the total number of NADH molecules generated during the complete breakdown of one glucose molecule to six molecules of CO_2?** (*Hint*: Combine the outputs of Modules 6.7–6.9.)

● 10 NADH: 2 from glycolysis; 2 from the oxidation of pyruvate; 6 from the citric acid cycle. (Did you remember to double the output due to the sugar-splitting step of glycolysis?)

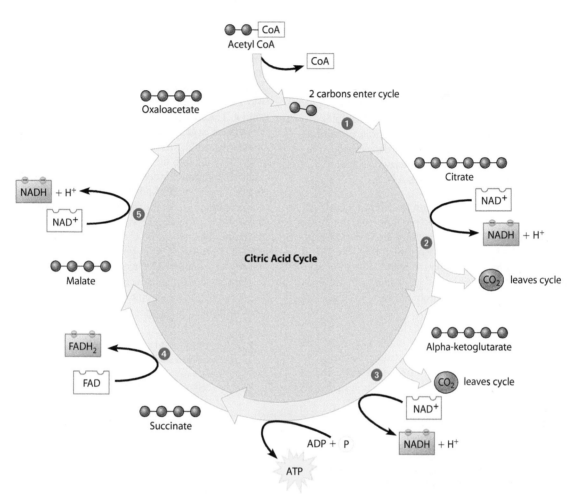

Step ❶
Acetyl CoA stokes the furnace.

A turn of the citric acid cycle begins (top center) as enzymes strip the CoA portion from acetyl CoA and combine the remaining two-carbon acetyl group with the four-carbon molecule oxaloacetate (top left) already present in the mitochondrion. The product of this reaction is the six-carbon molecule citrate. Citrate is the ionized form of citric acid. All the acid compounds in this cycle exist in the cell in their ionized form, hence the suffix *-ate*.

Steps ❷–❸
NADH, ATP, and CO_2 are generated during redox reactions.

Successive redox reactions harvest some of the energy of the acetyl group by stripping hydrogen atoms from organic acid intermediates (such as alpha-ketoglutarate) and producing energy-laden NADH molecules. In two places, an intermediate compound loses a CO_2 molecule. Energy is harvested by substrate-level phosphorylation of ADP to produce ATP. A four-carbon compound called succinate emerges at the end of step 3.

Steps ❹–❺
Further redox reactions generate $FADH_2$ and more NADH.

Enzymes rearrange chemical bonds, eventually completing the citric acid cycle by regenerating oxaloacetate. Redox reactions reduce the electron carriers FAD and NAD^+ to $FADH_2$ and NADH, respectively. One turn of the citric acid cycle is completed with the conversion of a molecule of malate to oxaloacetate. This compound is then ready to start the next turn of the cycle by accepting another acetyl group from acetyl CoA.

▲ **Figure 6.9B** A closer look at the citric acid cycle. (Each glucose molecule yields two molecules of acetyl CoA, so the cycle runs two times for each glucose molecule oxidized.)

6.10 Most ATP production occurs by oxidative phosphorylation

Your main objective in this chapter is to learn how cells harvest the energy of glucose to make ATP. But so far, you've seen the production of only 4 ATP per glucose molecule. Now it's time for the big energy payoff. The final stage of cellular respiration is oxidative phosphorylation, which uses the electron transport chain and chemiosmosis—a process introduced in Module 6.6. Oxidative phosphorylation clearly illustrates the concept of structure fitting function: The arrangement of electron carriers built into a membrane makes it possible to create an H⁺ concentration gradient across the membrane and then use the energy of that gradient to drive ATP synthesis.

Figure 6.10 shows how an electron transport chain is built into the inner membrane of the mitochondrion. The folds (cristae) of this membrane enlarge its surface area, providing space for thousands of copies of the chain. Also embedded in the membrane are multiple copies of an enzyme complex called **ATP synthase**, which synthesizes ATP.

Electron Transport Chain   Starting on the left in Figure 6.10, the gold arrow traces the path of electron flow from the shuttle molecules NADH and $FADH_2$ through the electron transport chain to oxygen, the final electron acceptor. It is in this end stage of cellular respiration that oxygen finally steps in to play its critical role. Each oxygen atom $\left(\frac{1}{2}O_2\right)$ accepts 2 electrons from the chain and picks up 2 H⁺ from the surrounding solution, forming H_2O.

Most of the carrier molecules of the chain reside in four main protein complexes (labeled I to IV in the diagram), while two mobile carriers transport electrons between the complexes. All of the carriers bind and release electrons in redox reactions, passing electrons down the "energy staircase." Three of the

protein complexes use the energy released from these electron transfers to actively transport H⁺ across the membrane, from where H⁺ is less concentrated to where it is more concentrated. The green vertical arrows show H⁺ being transported from the matrix of the mitochondrion (its innermost compartment) into the narrow intermembrane space.

Chemiosmosis   Recall that chemiosmosis is a process that uses the energy stored in a hydrogen ion gradient across a membrane to drive ATP synthesis. How does that work? The H⁺ concentration gradient stores potential energy, much the way a dam stores energy by holding back the elevated water behind it. The energy stored by a dam can be harnessed to do work (such as generating electricity) when the water is allowed to rush downhill, turning giant wheels called turbines. The ATP synthases built into the inner mitochondrial membrane act like miniature turbines. Indeed, ATP synthase is considered the smallest rotary motor known. The energy of the concentration gradient of H⁺ across the membrane drives hydrogen ions through a channel in ATP synthase, as shown on the far right of the figure. The rush of H⁺ through the channel spins a component of the complex, activating catalytic sites that attach phosphate groups to ADP to generate ATP.

We will account for how much ATP is made by oxidative phosphorylation in Module 6.12. But first, let's see what happens if something disrupts these processes.

> ❓ **What effect would an absence of oxygen (O_2) have on the process illustrated in Figure 6.10?**
>
> ● Without oxygen to "pull" electrons down the electron transport chain, the energy stored in NADH could not be harnessed for ATP synthesis.

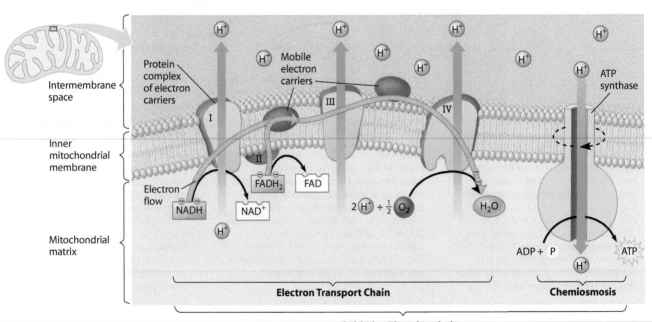

▲ **Figure 6.10** Oxidative phosphorylation: electron transport and chemiosmosis in a mitochondrion

6.11 Interrupting cellular respiration can have both harmful and beneficial effects

A number of poisons produce their deadly effects by interfering with some of the events of cellular respiration that we have just discussed. Figure 6.11 shows the places where three different categories of poisons obstruct the process of oxidative phosphorylation.

Poisons in one category block the electron transport chain. A substance called rotenone, for instance, binds tightly with one of the electron carrier molecules in the first protein complex, preventing electrons from passing to the next carrier molecule. By blocking the electron transport chain near its start and thus preventing ATP synthesis, rotenone literally starves an organism's cells of energy. Rotenone is often used to kill pest insects and fish.

Two other poisons in this category, cyanide and carbon monoxide, bind to an electron carrier in the fourth protein complex, where they block the passage of electrons to oxygen. This blockage is like turning off a faucet; electrons can no longer flow through the "pipe." The result is the same as with rotenone: No H$^+$ gradient is generated, and no ATP can be made. Cyanide was the lethal agent in an infamous case of product tampering: the Tylenol murders of 1982. Seven people in the Chicago area died after ingesting Tylenol capsules that had been laced with cyanide.

A second category of respiratory poison inhibits ATP synthase. An example of this type of poison is the antibiotic oligomycin, a compound used on the skin to combat fungal infections there. The right side of the figure shows that oligomycin blocks the passage of H$^+$ through the channel in ATP synthase, preventing fungal cells from making ATP and thereby killing them. The drug does not harm human cells because it cannot get through our outer layer of dead skin cells.

Poisons in a third category, called uncouplers, make the membrane of the mitochondrion leaky to hydrogen ions. Electron transport continues normally, but ATP cannot be made because leakage of H$^+$ through the membrane destroys the H$^+$ gradient. Cells continue to burn fuel and consume oxygen, often at a higher than normal rate, but to no avail, for they cannot make any ATP through chemiosmosis because no H$^+$ gradient exists.

A highly toxic uncoupler called dinitrophenol (DNP) is shown in the figure. When DNP is present, all steps of cellular respiration except chemiosmosis continue to run, even though almost all the energy is lost as heat. DNP poisoning produces an enormous increase in metabolic rate, profuse sweating as the body attempts to dissipate excess heat, and finally death.

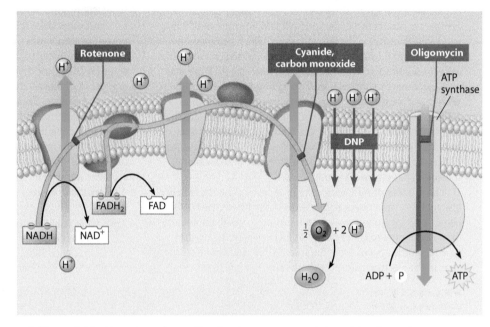

▲ **Figure 6.11** How some poisons affect the electron transport chain and chemiosmosis

For a short time in the 1930s, some physicians prescribed DNP in low doses as weight loss pills, but fatalities soon made it clear that there were far safer ways to lose weight.

Under certain conditions, however, an uncoupler that generates heat by abolishing the H$^+$ gradient in a mitochondrion may be beneficial. A remarkable adaptation is found in hibernating mammals and newborn infants in a tissue called brown fat. The cells of brown fat are packed full of mitochondria. The inner mitochondrial membrane contains an uncoupling protein, which allows H$^+$ to flow back down its concentration gradient without generating ATP. Activation of these uncouplers results in ongoing oxidation of stored fuel stores (fats) and the generation of heat, which protects hibernating mammals and newborns from dangerous drops in body temperature. In 2009, scientists discovered that adults retain deposits of brown fat. These tissues were found to be more active in colder weather, not surprisingly, and also in individuals who were thinner. This second finding suggests that brown fat may cause lean individuals to burn calories faster than other people do, and prompted some researchers to propose that these tissues could be a target for obesity-fighting drugs.

In the next module, we take a final look at the stages of cellular respiration and calculate the total amount of ATP harvested as a cell oxidizes glucose in the presence of oxygen to carbon dioxide and water.

? Looking at Figure 6.11, explain where uncoupling proteins would be found in the mitochondria of brown fat cells.

● They would span the inner mitochondrial membrane, providing a channel through which H$^+$ would diffuse down its concentration gradient back into the matrix.

6.12 Review: Each molecule of glucose yields many molecules of ATP

Let's review what the cell accomplishes by oxidizing a molecule of glucose. Figure 6.12 shows where each stage of cellular respiration occurs in a eukaryotic cell and how much ATP it produces. Starting on the left, glycolysis, which occurs in the cytoplasmic fluid, and the citric acid cycle, which occurs in the mitochondrial matrix, contribute a net total of 4 ATP per glucose molecule by substrate-level phosphorylation. The cell harvests much more energy than this via the carrier molecules NADH and $FADH_2$, which are produced in glycolysis and the citric acid cycle. The energy of the electrons they carry is used to make (according to current estimates) about 28 molecules of ATP by oxidative phosphorylation. Thus, the total yield of ATP molecules per glucose is about 32.

The number of ATP molecules produced cannot be stated exactly for several reasons. As shown in the figure, the NADH produced in glycolysis passes its electrons across the mitochondrial membrane to either NAD^+ or FAD, depending on the type of shuttle system used. Because $FADH_2$ adds its electrons later in the electron transport chain (see Figure 6.10), it

contributes less to the H^+ gradient and thus generates less ATP. In addition, some of the energy of the H^+ gradient may be used for work other than ATP production, such as the active transport of pyruvate into the mitochondrion.

More important than the actual number of ATP molecules is the point that a cell can harvest a great deal of energy from glucose—up to about 34% of the molecule's potential energy. Because most of the ATP generated by cellular respiration results from oxidative phosphorylation, the ATP yield depends on an adequate supply of oxygen to the cell. Without oxygen to function as the final electron acceptor, electron transport and ATP production stop. But as we see next, some cells can oxidize organic fuel and generate ATP *without* oxygen.

> **?** What would a cell's net ATP yield per glucose be in the presence of the poison DNP? (See Module 6.11.)

4 ATP, all from substrate-level phosphorylation. The uncoupler would destroy the H^+ concentration gradient necessary for chemiosmosis.

▶ **Figure 6.12** An estimated tally of the ATP produced by substrate-level and oxidative phosphorylation in cellular respiration

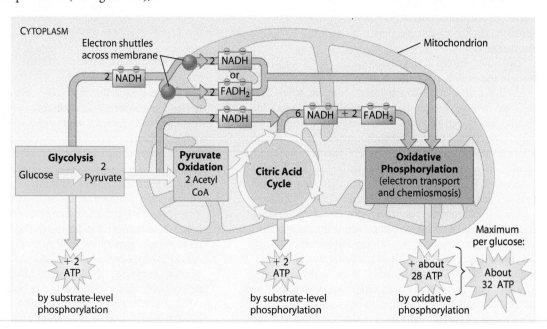

Fermentation: Anaerobic Harvesting of Energy

6.13 Fermentation enables cells to produce ATP without oxygen

Fermentation is a way of harvesting chemical energy that does not require oxygen. The metabolic pathway that generates ATP during fermentation is glycolysis, the same pathway that functions in the first stage of cellular respiration. Remember that glycolysis uses no oxygen; it simply generates a net gain of 2 ATP while oxidizing glucose to two molecules of pyruvate and reducing NAD^+ to NADH. The yield of 2 ATP is certainly a lot less than the possible

32 ATP per glucose generated during aerobic respiration, but it is enough to keep your muscles contracting for a short period of time when oxygen is scarce. And many microorganisms supply all their energy needs with the 2 ATP per glucose yield of glycolysis.

There is more to fermentation, however, than just glycolysis. To oxidize glucose in glycolysis, NAD^+ must be present as an electron acceptor. This is no problem under aerobic conditions, because the cell regenerates its pool of NAD+ when NADH passes its electrons into the mitochondrion, to be transported to the electron transport chain. Fermentation provides an anaerobic path for recycling NADH back to NAD+.

Lactic Acid Fermentation   One common type of fermentation is called **lactic acid fermentation**. Your muscle cells and certain bacteria can regenerate NAD+ by this process, as illustrated in Figure 6.13A. You can see that NADH is oxidized to NAD+ as pyruvate is reduced to lactate (the ionized form of lactic acid). Muscle cells can switch to lactic acid fermentation when the need for ATP outpaces the delivery of O_2 via the bloodstream. The lactate that builds up in muscle cells during strenuous exercise was previously thought to cause muscle fatigue and pain, but research now indicates that other factors are to blame. In any case, the lactate is carried in the blood to the liver, where it is converted back to pyruvate and oxidized in the mitochondria of liver cells.

The dairy industry uses lactic acid fermentation by bacteria to make cheese and yogurt. Other types of microbial fermentation turn soybeans into soy sauce and cabbage into sauerkraut.

Alcohol Fermentation   For thousands of years, people have used **alcohol fermentation** in brewing, winemaking, and baking. Yeasts are single-celled fungi that normally use aerobic respiration to process their food. But they are also able to survive in anaerobic environments. Yeasts and certain bacteria recycle their NADH back to NAD+ while converting pyruvate to CO_2 and ethanol (Figure 6.13B). The CO_2 provides the bubbles in beer and champagne. Bubbles of CO_2 generated by baker's yeast cause bread dough to rise. Ethanol (ethyl alcohol), the two-carbon end product, is toxic to the organisms that produce it. Yeasts release their alcohol wastes to their surroundings, where it usually diffuses away. When yeasts are confined in a wine vat, they die when the alcohol concentration reaches 14%.

Types of Anaerobes   Unlike muscle cells and yeasts, many prokaryotes that live in stagnant ponds and deep in the soil are *obligate anaerobes*, meaning they require anaerobic conditions and are poisoned by oxygen. Yeasts and many other bacteria are facultative anaerobes. A *facultative anaerobe* can make ATP either by fermentation or by oxidative phosphorylation, depending on whether O_2 is available. On the cellular level, our muscle cells behave as facultative anaerobes.

For a facultative anaerobe, pyruvate is a fork in the metabolic road. If oxygen is available, the organism will always use the more productive aerobic respiration. Thus, to make wine and beer, yeasts must be grown anaerobically so that they will ferment sugars and produce ethanol. For this reason, the wine barrels and beer fermentation vats in Figure 6.13C are designed to keep air out.

?   A glucose-fed yeast cell is moved from an aerobic environment to an anaerobic one. For the cell to continue generating ATP at the same rate, how would its rate of glucose consumption need to change?

The cell would have to consume glucose at a rate about 16 times the consumption rate in the aerobic environment (2 ATP per glucose molecule is made by fermentation versus 32 ATP by cellular respiration).

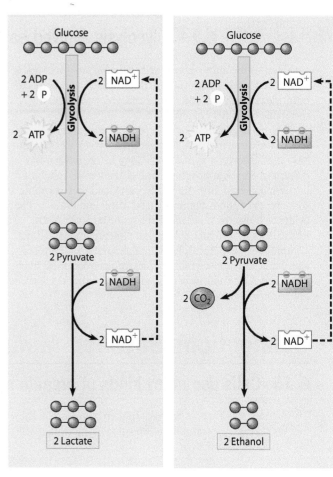

▲ **Figure 6.13A**   Lactic acid fermentation: NAD+ is regenerated as pyruvate is reduced to lactate.

▲ **Figure 6.13B**   Alcohol fermentation: NAD+ is regenerated as pyruvate is broken down to CO_2 and ethanol.

▲ **Figure 6.13C**
Wine barrels and beer fermentation vats

6.14 Glycolysis evolved early in the history of life on Earth

Glycolysis is the universal energy-harvesting process of life. If you looked inside a bacterial cell, inside one of your body cells, or inside virtually any other living cell, you would find the metabolic machinery of glycolysis.

The role of glycolysis in both fermentation and respiration has an evolutionary basis. Ancient prokaryotes are thought to have used glycolysis to make ATP long before oxygen was present in Earth's atmosphere. The oldest known fossils of bacteria date back over 3.5 billion years, and they resemble some types of photosynthetic bacteria still found today. The evidence indicates, however, that significant levels of O_2, formed as a by-product of bacterial photosynthesis, did not accumulate in the atmosphere until about 2.7 billion years ago. Thus, for almost a billion years, prokaryotes most likely generated ATP exclusively from glycolysis, a process that does not require oxygen.

The fact that glycolysis is the most widespread metabolic pathway found in Earth's organisms today suggests that it evolved very early in the history of life. The location of glycolysis within the cell also implies great antiquity; the pathway does not require any of the membrane-bounded organelles of the eukaryotic cell, which evolved more than a billion years after the prokaryotic cell. Glycolysis is a metabolic heirloom from early cells that continues to function in fermentation and as the first stage in the breakdown of organic molecules by cellular respiration.

? List some of the characteristics of glycolysis that indicate that it is an ancient metabolic pathway.

● Glycolysis occurs universally (functioning in both fermentation and respiration), does not require oxygen, and does not occur in a membrane-bounded organelle.

Connections Between Metabolic Pathways

6.15 Cells use many kinds of organic molecules as fuel for cellular respiration

Throughout this chapter, we have spoken of glucose as the fuel for cellular respiration. But free glucose molecules are not common in your diet. You obtain most of your calories as carbohydrates (such as sucrose and other disaccharide sugars and starch, a polysaccharide), fats, and proteins. You consume all three of these classes of organic molecules when you eat a handful of peanuts, for instance.

Figure 6.15 illustrates how a cell can use these three types of molecules to make ATP. A wide range of carbohydrates can be funneled into glycolysis, as indicated by the arrows on the far left of the diagram. For example, enzymes in your digestive tract hydrolyze starch to glucose, which is then broken down by glycolysis and the citric acid cycle. Similarly, glycogen, the polysaccharide stored in your liver and muscle cells, can be hydrolyzed to glucose to serve as fuel between meals.

Fats make excellent cellular fuel because they contain many hydrogen atoms and thus many energy-rich electrons. As the diagram shows (tan arrows), a cell first hydrolyzes fats to glycerol and fatty acids. It then converts the glycerol to glyceraldehyde 3-phosphate (G3P), one of the intermediates in glycolysis. The fatty acids are broken into two-carbon fragments that enter the citric acid cycle as acetyl CoA. A gram of fat yields more than twice as much ATP as a gram of carbohydrate. Because so many calories are stockpiled in each gram of fat, you must expend a large amount of energy to burn fat stored in your body. This helps explain why it is so difficult for a dieter to lose excess fat.

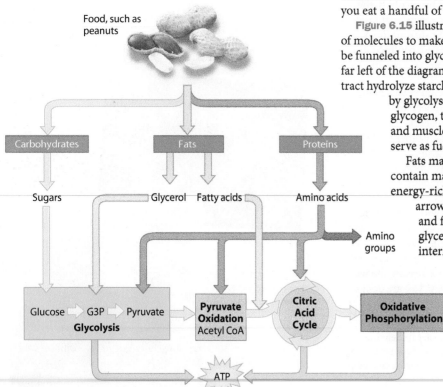

▲ Figure 6.15 Pathways that break down various food molecules

Proteins (purple arrows in Figure 6.15) can also be used for fuel, although your body preferentially burns sugars and fats first. To be oxidized as fuel, proteins must first be digested to their constituent amino acids. Typically, a cell will use most of these amino acids to make its own proteins. Enzymes can convert excess amino acids to intermediates of glycolysis or the citric acid cycle, and their energy is then harvested by cellular respiration. During the conversion, the amino groups are stripped off and later disposed of in urine.

> **?** Animals store most of their energy reserves as fats, not as polysaccharides. What is the advantage of this mode of storage for an animal?
>
> ● Most animals are mobile and benefit from a compact and concentrated form of energy storage. Also, because fats are hydrophobic, they can be stored without extra water associated with them (see Module 3.8).

6.16 Food molecules provide raw materials for biosynthesis

Not all food molecules are destined to be oxidized as fuel for making ATP. Food also provides the raw materials your cells use for biosynthesis—the production of organic molecules using energy-requiring metabolic pathways. A cell must be able to make its own molecules to build its structures and perform its functions. Some raw materials, such as amino acids, can be incorporated directly into your macromolecules. However, your cells also need to make molecules that are not present in your food. Indeed, glycolysis and the citric acid cycle function as metabolic interchanges that enable your cells to convert some kinds of molecules to others as you need them.

Figure 6.16 outlines the pathways by which your cells can make three classes of organic molecules using some of the intermediate molecules of glycolysis and the citric acid cycle. By comparing Figures 6.15 and 6.16, you can see clear connections between the energy-harvesting processes of cellular respiration and the biosynthetic pathways used to construct the organic molecules of the cell.

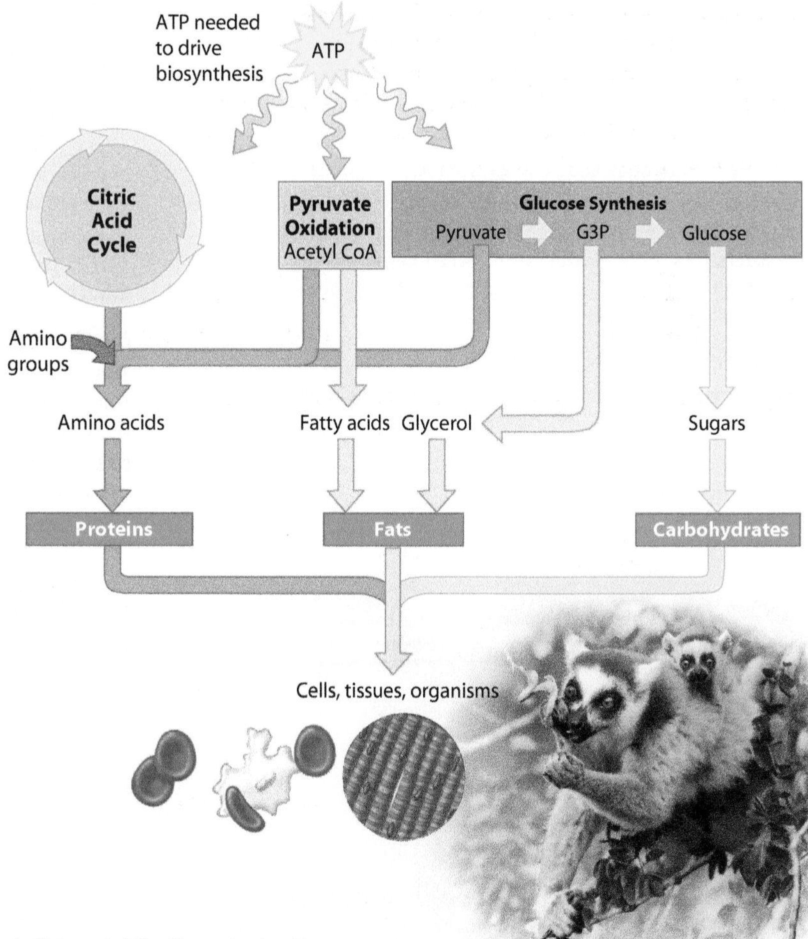

Basic principles of supply and demand regulate these pathways. If there is an excess of a certain amino acid, for example, the pathway that synthesizes it is switched off. The most common mechanism for this control is feedback inhibition: The end product inhibits an enzyme that catalyzes an early step in the pathway (see Module 5.16). Feedback inhibition also controls cellular respiration. If ATP accumulates in a cell, it inhibits an early enzyme in glycolysis, slowing down respiration and conserving resources. On the other hand, the same enzyme is activated by a buildup of ADP in the cell, signaling the need for more energy.

The cells of all living organisms—including those of the lemurs shown in Figure 6.16 and the plants they eat—have the ability to harvest energy from the breakdown of organic molecules. When the process is cellular respiration, the atoms of the starting materials end up in carbon dioxide and water. In contrast, the ability to make organic molecules from carbon

▲ **Figure 6.16** Biosynthesis of large organic molecules from intermediates of cellular respiration

dioxide and water is not universal. Animal cells lack this ability, but plant cells can actually produce organic molecules from inorganic ones using the energy of sunlight. This process, photosynthesis, is the subject of Chapter 7.

> **?** Explain how someone can gain weight and store fat even when on a low-fat diet. (*Hint:* Look for G3P and acetyl CoA in Figures 6.15 and 6.16.)
>
> ● If caloric intake is excessive, body cells use metabolic pathways to convert the excess to fat. The glycerol and fatty acids of fats are made from G3P and acetyl CoA, respectively, both produced from the oxidation of carbohydrates.

For Practice Quizzes, BioFlix, MP3 Tutors, and Activities, go to www.masteringbiology.com.

Reviewing the Concepts

Cellular Respiration: Aerobic Harvesting of Energy (6.1–6.5)

6.1 Photosynthesis and cellular respiration provide energy for life. Photosynthesis uses solar energy to produce glucose and O_2 from CO_2 and H_2O. In cellular respiration, O_2 is consumed during the breakdown of glucose to CO_2 and H_2O, and energy is released.

6.2 Breathing supplies O_2 for use in cellular respiration and removes CO_2.

6.3 Cellular respiration banks energy in ATP molecules. The summary equation for cellular respiration is $C_6H_{12}O_6 + 6\ O_2 \longrightarrow 6\ CO_2 + 6\ H_2O + Energy$ (ATP + Heat).

6.4 The human body uses energy from ATP for all its activities.

6.5 Cells tap energy from electrons "falling" from organic fuels to oxygen. Electrons removed from fuel molecules (oxidation) are transferred to NAD^+ (reduction). NADH passes electrons to an electron transport chain. As electrons "fall" from carrier to carrier and finally to O_2, energy is released.

Stages of Cellular Respiration (6.6–6.12)

6.6 Overview: Cellular respiration occurs in three main stages.

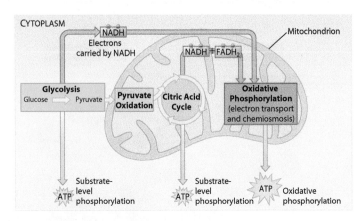

6.7 Glycolysis harvests chemical energy by oxidizing glucose to pyruvate. ATP is used to prime a glucose molecule, which is split in two. These three-carbon intermediates are oxidized to two molecules of pyruvate, yielding a net of 2 ATP and 2 NADH. ATP is formed by substrate-level phosphorylation, in which a phosphate group is transferred from an organic molecule to ADP.

6.8 Pyruvate is oxidized prior to the citric acid cycle. In the oxidation of pyruvate to acetyl CoA, CO_2 and NADH are produced.

6.9 The citric acid cycle completes the oxidation of organic molecules, generating many NADH and $FADH_2$ molecules. For each turn of the cycle, two carbons from acetyl CoA are added and 2 CO_2 are released; the energy yield is 1 ATP, 3 NADH, and 1 $FADH_2$.

6.10 Most ATP production occurs by oxidative phosphorylation. In mitochondria, electrons from NADH and $FADH_2$ travel down the electron transport chain to O_2, which picks up H^+ to form

water. Energy released by these redox reactions is used to pump H^+ from the mitochondrial matrix into the intermembrane space. In chemiosmosis, the H^+ diffuses back across the inner membrane through ATP synthase complexes, driving the synthesis of ATP.

6.11 Interrupting cellular respiration can have both harmful and beneficial effects. Poisons can block electron flow, block the movement of H^+ through ATP synthase, or allow H^+ to leak through the membrane. Uncouplers in brown fat produce body heat.

6.12 Review: Each molecule of glucose yields many molecules of ATP. Substrate-level phosphorylation and oxidative phosphorylation produce up to 32 ATP molecules for every glucose molecule oxidized in cellular respiration.

Fermentation: Anaerobic Harvesting of Energy (6.13–6.14)

6.13 Fermentation enables cells to produce ATP without oxygen. Under anaerobic conditions, muscle cells, yeasts, and certain bacteria produce ATP by glycolysis. NAD^+ is recycled from NADH as pyruvate is reduced to lactate (lactic acid fermentation) or, in microbes, alcohol and CO_2 (alcohol fermentation).

6.14 Glycolysis evolved early in the history of life on Earth. Glycolysis occurs in the cytoplasm of nearly all organisms and is thought to have evolved in ancient prokaryotes.

Connections Between Metabolic Pathways (6.15–6.16)

6.15 Cells use many kinds of organic molecules as fuel for cellular respiration. Carbohydrates, fats, and proteins can all fuel cellular respiration.

6.16 Food molecules provide raw materials for biosynthesis. Cells use intermediates from cellular respiration and ATP for biosynthesis of other organic molecules. Metabolic pathways are often regulated by feedback inhibition.

Connecting the Concepts

1. Fill in the blanks in this summary map to help you review the key concepts of cellular respiration.

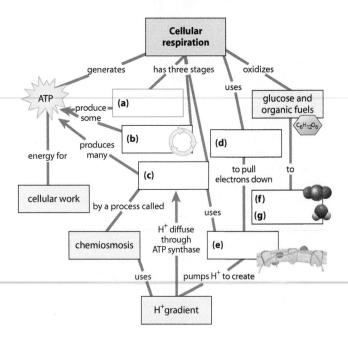

Testing Your Knowledge

Multiple Choice

2. What is the role of oxygen in cellular respiration?
   a. It is reduced in glycolysis as glucose is oxidized.
   b. It provides electrons to the electron transport chain.
   c. It combines with the carbon removed during the citric acid cycle to form CO_2.
   d. It is required for the production of heat and light.
   e. It accepts electrons from the electron transport chain.

3. When the poison cyanide blocks the electron transport chain, glycolysis and the citric acid cycle soon grind to a halt as well. Why do you think they stop?
   a. They both run out of ATP.
   b. Unused O_2 interferes with cellular respiration.
   c. They run out of NAD^+ and FAD.
   d. Electrons are no longer available.
   e. They run out of ADP.

4. A biochemist wanted to study how various substances were used in cellular respiration. In one experiment, he allowed a mouse to breathe air containing O_2 "labeled" by a particular isotope. In the mouse, the labeled oxygen first showed up in
   a. ATP.
   b. glucose ($C_6H_{12}O_6$).
   c. NADH.
   d. CO_2.
   e. H_2O.

5. In glycolysis, _____ is oxidized and _____ is reduced.
   a. NAD^+ . . . glucose
   b. glucose . . . oxygen
   c. ATP . . . ADP
   d. glucose . . . NAD^+
   e. ADP . . . ATP

6. Which of the following is the most immediate source of energy for making most of the ATP in your cells?
   a. the reduction of oxygen
   b. the transfer of Ⓟ from intermediate substrates to ADP
   c. the movement of H^+ across a membrane down its concentration gradient
   d. the splitting of glucose into two molecules of pyruvate
   e. electrons moving through the electron transport chain

7. In which of the following is the first molecule becoming reduced to the second molecule?
   a. pyruvate $\longrightarrow$ acetyl CoA
   b. pyruvate $\longrightarrow$ lactate
   c. glucose $\longrightarrow$ pyruvate
   d. $NADH + H^+ \longrightarrow NAD^+ + 2\ H$
   e. $C_6H_{12}O_6 \longrightarrow 6\ CO_2$

8. Which of the following is a true distinction between cellular respiration and fermentation?
   a. NADH is oxidized by the electron transport chain in respiration only.
   b. Only respiration oxidizes glucose.
   c. Fermentation is an example of an endergonic reaction; cellular respiration is an exergonic reaction.
   d. Substrate-level phosphorylation is unique to fermentation; cellular respiration uses oxidative phosphorylation.
   e. Fermentation is the metabolic pathway found in prokaryotes; cellular respiration is unique to eukaryotes.

Describing, Comparing, and Explaining

9. Which of the three stages of cellular respiration is considered the most ancient? Explain your answer.

10. Explain in terms of cellular respiration why you need oxygen and why you exhale carbon dioxide.

11. Compare and contrast fermentation as it occurs in your muscle cells and as it occurs in yeast cells.

12. Explain how your body can convert excess carbohydrates in the diet to fats. Can excess carbohydrates be converted to protein? What else must be supplied?

Applying the Concepts

13. An average adult human requires 2,200 kcal of energy per day. Suppose your diet provides an average of 2,300 kcal per day. How many hours per week would you have to walk to burn off the extra calories? Swim? Run? (See Figure 6.4.)

14. Your body makes NAD^+ and FAD from two B vitamins, niacin and riboflavin. The Recommended Dietary Allowance for niacin is 20 mg and for riboflavin, 1.7 mg. These amounts are thousands of times less than the amount of glucose your body needs each day to fuel its energy needs. Why is the daily requirement for these vitamins so small?

15. In a detail of the citric acid cycle not shown in Figure 6.9B, an enzyme converts succinate to a compound called fumarate, with the release of H^+. You are studying this reaction using a suspension of bean cell mitochondria and a blue dye that loses its color as it takes up H^+. You know that the higher the concentration of succinate, the more rapid the decolorization of the dye. You set up reaction mixtures with mitochondria, dye, and three different concentrations of succinate (0.1 mg/L, 0.2 mg/L, and 0.3 mg/L). Which of the following graphs represents the results you would expect, and why?

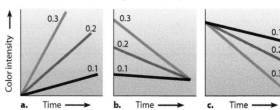

16. ATP synthase enzymes are found in the prokaryotic plasma membrane and in the inner membrane of a mitochondrion. What does this suggest about the evolutionary relationship of this eukaryotic organelle to prokaryotes?

17. Excess consumption of alcohol by a pregnant woman can cause a complex of birth defects called fetal alcohol syndrome (FAS). Symptoms of FAS include head and facial irregularities, heart defects, mental retardation, and behavioral problems. The U.S. Surgeon General's Office recommends that pregnant women abstain from drinking alcohol, and the government has mandated a warning label on liquor bottles: "Women should not drink alcoholic beverages during pregnancy because of the risk of birth defects." Imagine you are a server in a restaurant. An obviously pregnant woman orders several alcoholic drinks. How would you respond? Is it the woman's right to make those decisions about her unborn child's health? Do you bear any responsibility in the matter? Is a restaurant responsible for monitoring the health habits of its customers?

Answers to all questions can be found in Appendix 4.

CHAPTER 7

Photosynthesis: *Using Light to Make Food*

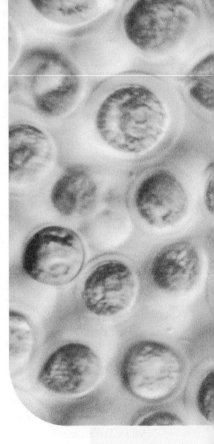

BIG IDEAS

An Overview of Photosynthesis
(7.1–7.5)

Plants and other photoautotrophs use the energy of sunlight to convert CO_2 and H_2O to sugar and O_2.

The Light Reactions: Converting Solar Energy to Chemical Energy
(7.6–7.9)

In the thylakoids of a chloroplast, the light reactions generate ATP and NADPH.

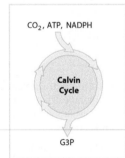

CO$_2$, ATP, NADPH

Calvin Cycle

G3P

The Calvin Cycle: Reducing CO_2 to Sugar
(7.10–7.11)

The Calvin cycle, which takes place in the stroma of the chloroplast, uses ATP and NADPH to reduce CO_2 to sugar.

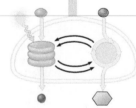

Photosynthesis Reviewed and Extended
(7.12–7.14)

Photosynthesis provides the energy and building material for ecosystems. It also affects global climate and the ozone layer.

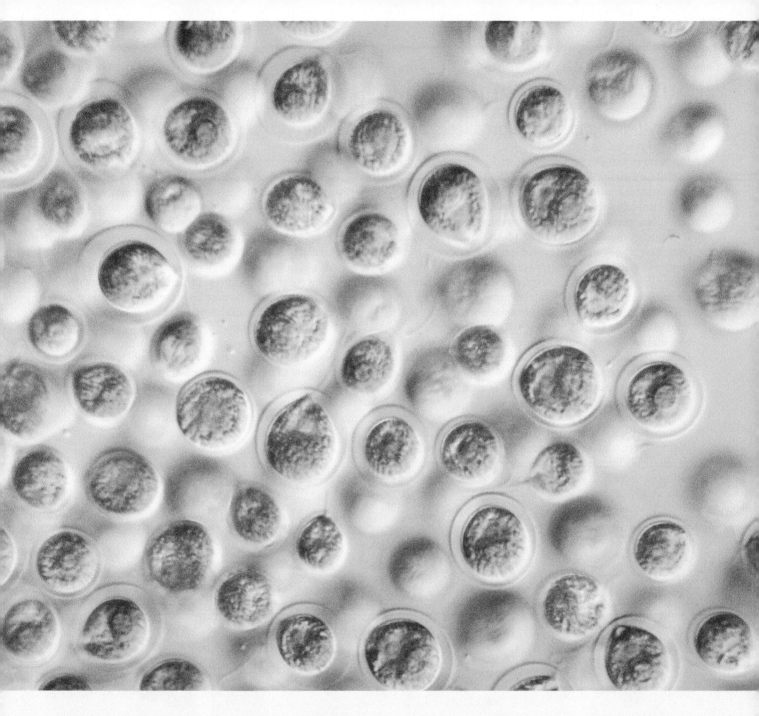

What do you think of when you see brilliant green cells like these? You might think about photosynthesis (especially if you are studying for a biology test). Others might simply admire nature's palette. But a new group of entrepreneurs has a different kind of green in mind—money.

The cells of plants, algae, and certain prokaryotes produce energy by the process of photosynthesis, which converts light energy to chemical energy, and then stores the chemical energy in sugar made from carbon dioxide and water. This stored energy is a valuable commodity. You purchase it—in the form of fruits and vegetables—to supply your body with energy. But now, enterprises ranging from small start-ups to giant oil companies are researching methods of harnessing photosynthesis for other energy needs, using single-celled algae as their "factories." For example, some algal species produce lipids that could be extracted and converted to biodiesel—green oil. Alternatively, carbohydrates produced by algae could be used to make ethanol. Unlike biofuel crops such as corn or oil palms, algae don't require large areas of fertile soil, and they grow very fast. Some designs even include using the CO_2 emissions from coal-fired power plants—a major contributor to climate change—as the carbon source for their photosynthesis.

In this chapter, you will learn how photosynthesis works. Because photosynthesis is a complex process, we begin with some basic concepts. Then we look more closely at the two stages of photosynthesis: the light reactions, in which solar energy is transformed into chemical energy, and the Calvin cycle, in which that chemical energy is used to make organic molecules. Finally, we explore ways in which photosynthesis affects our global environment.

An Overview of Photosynthesis

7.1 Autotrophs are the producers of the biosphere

Plants are **autotrophs** (meaning "self-feeders" in Greek) in that they make their own food and thus sustain themselves without consuming organic molecules derived from any other organisms. Plant cells capture light energy that has traveled 150 million kilometers from the sun and convert it to chemical energy. Because they use the energy of light, plants are specifically called *photoautotrophs*. Through the process of **photosynthesis**, plants convert CO_2 and H_2O to their own organic molecules and release O_2 as a by-product. Photoautotrophs are the ultimate source of organic molecules for almost all other organisms. They are often referred to as the producers of the biosphere because they produce its food supply. (In Chapter 16, you will learn about chemoautotrophs—prokaryotes that use inorganic chemicals as their energy source and are the producers in deep-sea vent communities.) Producers feed the consumers of the biosphere—the **heterotrophs** that consume other plants or animals or decompose organic material (*hetero* means "other").

The photographs on this page illustrate some of the diversity among photoautotrophs. On land, plants, such as those in the forest scene in **Figure 7.1A**, are the predominant producers. In aquatic environments, there are several types of photoautotrophs. **Figure 7.1B** is a micrograph of unicellular photosynthetic protists. **Figure 7.1C** shows kelp, a large alga that forms extensive underwater "forests" off the coast of California. **Figure 7.1D** is a micrograph of cyanobacteria, abundant and important producers in freshwater and marine ecosystems.

In this chapter, we focus on photosynthesis in plants, which takes place in chloroplasts. The remarkable ability to harness light energy and use it to drive the synthesis of organic compounds emerges from the structural organization of these organelles: Photosynthetic pigments, enzymes, and other molecules are grouped together in membranes, allowing the sequences of reactions to be carried out efficiently. The process of photosynthesis most likely originated in a group of bacteria that had infolded regions of the plasma membrane containing such clusters of enzymes and other molecules. In fact, according to the widely accepted theory of endosymbiosis, chloroplasts originated from a photosynthetic prokaryote that took up residence inside a eukaryotic cell (see Module 4.15).

Let's begin our study of photosynthesis with an overview of the location and structure of plant chloroplasts.

? What do "self-feeding" photoautotrophs require from the environment in order to make their own food?

● Light, carbon dioxide, and water. (Minerals are also required; you'll learn about the needs of plants in Chapter 32.)

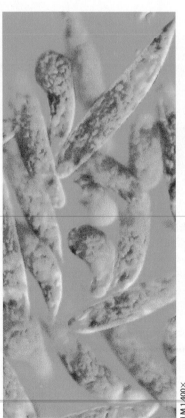

LM 1,400×

LM 460×

▲ **Figure 7.1A** Forest plants   ▲ **Figure 7.1B** Photosynthetic protists   ▲ **Figure 7.1C** Kelp, a multicellular alga   ▲ **Figure 7.1D** Cyanobacteria (photosynthetic prokaryotes)

7.2 Photosynthesis occurs in chloroplasts in plant cells

All green parts of a plant have chloroplasts in their cells and can carry out photosynthesis. In most plants, however, the leaves have the most chloroplasts (about half a million in a square millimeter surface area of a leaf) and are the major sites of photosynthesis. Their green color comes from **chlorophyll**, a light-absorbing pigment in the chloroplasts that plays a central role in converting solar energy to chemical energy.

Figure 7.2 zooms in on a leaf to show the actual sites of photosynthesis. The leaf cross section shows a slice through a leaf. Chloroplasts are concentrated in the cells of the **mesophyll**, the green tissue in the interior of the leaf. Carbon dioxide enters the leaf, and oxygen exits, by way of tiny pores called **stomata** (singular, *stoma*, meaning "mouth"). Water absorbed by the roots is delivered to the leaves in veins. Leaves also use veins to export sugar to roots and other parts of the plant.

As you can see in the light micrograph of a single mesophyll cell, each cell has numerous chloroplasts. A typical mesophyll cell has about 30 to 40 chloroplasts. The bottom drawing and electron micrograph show the structures in a single chloroplast. Membranes in the chloroplast form the framework where many of the reactions of photosynthesis occur, just as mitochondrial membranes are the site for much of the energy-harvesting machinery we discussed in Chapter 6. In the chloroplast, an envelope of two membranes encloses an inner compartment, which is filled with a thick fluid called **stroma**. Suspended in the stroma is a system of interconnected membranous sacs, called **thylakoids**, which enclose another internal compartment, called the thylakoid space. (As you will see later, this thylakoid space plays a role analogous to the intermembrane space of a mitochondrion in the generation of ATP.) In many places, thylakoids are concentrated in stacks called **grana** (singular, *granum*). Built into the thylakoid membranes are the chlorophyll molecules that capture light energy. The thylakoid membranes also house much of the machinery that converts light energy to chemical energy, which is used in the stroma to make sugar.

Later in the chapter, we examine the function of these structures in more detail. But first, let's look more closely at the general process of photosynthesis.

? How do the reactant molecules of photosynthesis reach the chloroplasts in leaves?

● CO₂ enters leaves through stomata, and H₂O enters the roots and is carried to leaves through veins.

Leaf Cross Section

Mesophyll

Leaf

Vein

CO₂   O₂

Stoma

Mesophyll Cell

LM 2,600×

Chloroplast

Inner and outer membranes

Granum

Thylakoid

Thylakoid space

Stroma

Colorized TEM 1,000×

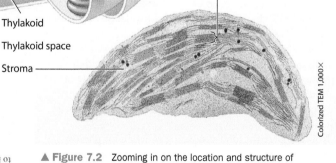

▲ **Figure 7.2** Zooming in on the location and structure of chloroplasts

7.3 Scientists traced the process of photosynthesis using isotopes

The leaves of plants that live in lakes and ponds are often covered with bubbles like the ones shown in Figure 7.3A. The bubbles are oxygen gas (O_2) produced during photosynthesis. But where does this O_2 come from?

The overall process of photosynthesis has been known since the 1800s: In the presence of light, green plants produce sugar and oxygen from carbon dioxide and water. Consider the basic equation for photosynthesis:

$$6 CO_2 + 6 H_2O \longrightarrow C_6H_{12}O_6 + 6 O_2$$

Looking at this equation, you can understand why scientists hypothesized that photosynthesis first splits carbon dioxide ($CO_2 \longrightarrow C + O_2$), releasing oxygen gas, and then adds water (H_2O) to the carbon to produce sugar. In the 1930s, this idea was challenged by C. B. van Niel, who was working with photosynthesizing bacteria that produce sugar from CO_2 but do not release O_2. He hypothesized that in plants, H_2O is split, with the hydrogen becoming incorporated into sugar and the O_2 released as gas.

▲ **Figure 7.3A** Oxygen bubbles on the leaves of an aquatic plant

In the 1950s, scientists confirmed van Niel's hypothesis by using a heavy isotope of oxygen, ^{18}O, to follow the fate of oxygen atoms during photosynthesis. (This was one of the first uses of isotopes as tracers in biological research. Remember from Module 2.3 that isotopes are atoms with differing numbers of neutrons.) The photosynthesis equation you will see in the description of these experiments is slightly more detailed than the summary equation written above. It shows that water is actually both a reactant and a product in the reaction. (As is often done, glucose is shown as a product, although the direct product of photosynthesis is a three-carbon sugar that can be used to make glucose.) In these equations, the red type denotes the labeled oxygen—^{18}O.

Experiment 1: $6 CO_2 + 12 H_2O \longrightarrow C_6H_{12}O_6 + 6 H_2O + 6 O_2$

Experiment 2: $6 CO_2 + 12 H_2O \longrightarrow C_6H_{12}O_6 + 6 H_2O + 6 O_2$

In experiment 1, a plant given CO_2 containing ^{18}O gave off no labeled (^{18}O-containing) oxygen gas. But in experiment 2, a plant given H_2O containing ^{18}O did produce labeled O_2. These experiments show that the O_2 produced during photosynthesis comes from water and not from CO_2.

Additional experiments have revealed that the oxygen atoms in CO_2 and the hydrogen atoms in the reactant H_2O molecules end up in the sugar molecule and in water that is formed as a product. Figure 7.3B summarizes the fates of all the atoms that start out in the reactant molecules of photosynthesis.

The synthesis of sugar in photosynthesis involves numerous chemical reactions. Working out the details of these reactions also involved the use of isotopes, in this case, radioactive isotopes. In the mid-1940s, American biochemist Melvin Calvin and his colleagues began using radioactive ^{14}C to trace the sequence of intermediates formed in the cyclic pathway that produces sugar from CO_2. They worked for 10 years to elucidate this cycle, which is now called the Calvin cycle. Calvin received the Nobel Prize in 1961 for this work.

? **Photosynthesis produces billions of tons of carbohydrate a year. Where does most of the mass of this huge amount of organic matter come from?**

● Mostly from CO_2 in the air, which provides both the carbon and oxygen in carbohydrate. Water supplies only the hydrogen.

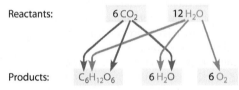

Reactants: 6 CO_2 12 H_2O

Products: $C_6H_{12}O_6$ 6 H_2O 6 O_2

▲ **Figure 7.3B** Fates of all the atoms in photosynthesis

7.4 Photosynthesis is a redox process, as is cellular respiration

What actually happens when CO_2 and water are converted to sugar and O_2? Photosynthesis is a redox (oxidation-reduction) process, just as cellular respiration is (see Module 6.5). As indicated in the summary equation for photosynthesis (Figure 7.4A), CO_2 becomes reduced to sugar as electrons, along with hydrogen ions (H^+) from water, are added to it. Meanwhile, water molecules are oxidized; that is, they lose electrons, along with hydrogen ions. Recall that oxidation and reduction always go hand in hand.

Now compare the food-producing equation for photosynthesis with the energy-releasing equation for cellular respiration that you learned about in Chapter 6 (Figure 7.4B). Overall,

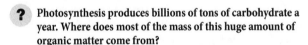

Becomes reduced

$$6 CO_2 + 6 H_2O \longrightarrow C_6H_{12}O_6 + 6 O_2$$

Becomes oxidized

▲ **Figure 7.4A** Photosynthesis (uses light energy)

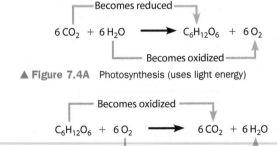

Becomes oxidized

$$C_6H_{12}O_6 + 6 O_2 \longrightarrow 6 CO_2 + 6 H_2O$$

Becomes reduced

▲ **Figure 7.4B** Cellular respiration (releases chemical energy) cellular respiration harvests energy stored in a glucose molecule by oxidizing the sugar and reducing O_2 to H_2O. This process involves a number of energy-releasing redox reactions, with electrons losing potential energy as they "fall" down an electron transport chain to O_2. Along the way, the mitochondrion uses some of the energy to synthesize ATP.

In contrast, the food-producing redox reactions of photosynthesis require energy. The potential energy of electrons increases as they move from H_2O to CO_2 during photosynthesis. The light energy captured by chlorophyll molecules in the chloroplast provides this energy boost. Photosynthesis converts light energy to chemical energy and stores it in the chemical bonds of sugar molecules, which can provide energy for later use or raw materials for biosynthesis.

> ❓ **Which redox process, photosynthesis or cellular respiration, is endergonic?** (*Hint*: See Module 5.12.)
>
> ● Photosynthesis

7.5 Overview: The two stages of photosynthesis are linked by ATP and NADPH

The equation for photosynthesis is a simple summary of a very complex process. Actually, photosynthesis occurs in two stages, each with multiple steps. **Figure 7.5** shows the inputs and outputs of the two stages and how the stages are related.

The **light reactions** include the steps that convert light energy to chemical energy and release O_2. As shown in the figure, the light reactions occur in the thylakoid membranes. Water is split, providing a source of electrons and giving off O_2 as a by-product. Light energy absorbed by chlorophyll molecules built into the membranes is used to drive the transfer of electrons and H^+ from water to the electron acceptor **NADP$^+$**, reducing it to NADPH. This electron carrier is first cousin to NADH, which transports electrons in cellular respiration; the two differ only in the extra phosphate group in NADPH. NADPH temporarily stores electrons and hydrogen ions and provides "reducing power" to the Calvin cycle. The light reactions also generate ATP from ADP and a phosphate group.

In summary, the light reactions absorb solar energy and convert it to chemical energy stored in both ATP and NADPH. Notice that these reactions produce no sugar; sugar is not made until the Calvin cycle, which is the second stage of photosynthesis.

The **Calvin cycle** occurs in the stroma of the chloroplast (see Figure 7.5). It is a cyclic series of reactions that assembles sugar molecules using CO_2 and the energy-rich products of the light reactions. The incorporation of carbon from CO_2 into organic compounds, shown in the figure as CO_2 entering the Calvin cycle, is called **carbon fixation**. After carbon fixation, enzymes of the cycle make sugars by further reducing the carbon compounds.

As the figure suggests, it is NADPH produced by the light reactions that provides the electrons for reducing carbon in the Calvin cycle. And ATP from the light reactions provides chemical energy that powers several of the steps of the Calvin

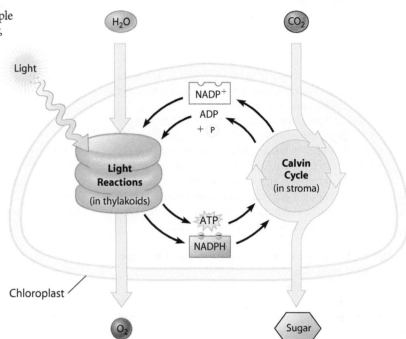

▲ **Figure 7.5** An overview of the two stages of photosynthesis in a chloroplast

cycle. The Calvin cycle is sometimes referred to as the dark reactions, or light-independent reactions, because none of the steps requires light directly. However, in most plants, the Calvin cycle occurs during daylight, when the light reactions power the cycle's sugar assembly line by supplying it with NADPH and ATP.

The word *photosynthesis* encapsulates the two stages. *Photo*, from the Greek word for "light," refers to the light reactions; *synthesis*, meaning "putting together," refers to sugar construction by the Calvin cycle. In the next several modules, we look at these two stages in more detail. But first, let's consider some of the properties of light, the energy source that powers photosynthesis.

> ❓ **For chloroplasts to produce sugar from carbon dioxide in the dark, they would need to be supplied with _____ and _____.**
>
> ● ATP . . . NADPH

The Light Reactions: Converting Solar Energy to Chemical Energy

7.6 Visible radiation absorbed by pigments drives the light reactions

What do we mean when we say that photosynthesis is powered by light energy from the sun? Sunlight is a type of energy called electromagnetic energy or electromagnetic radiation.

The Nature of Sunlight   Electromagnetic energy travels in space as rhythmic waves analogous to those made by a pebble dropped in a puddle of water. **Figure 7.6A** shows the **electromagnetic spectrum**, the full range of electromagnetic wavelengths from the very short gamma rays to the very long-wavelength radio waves. As you can see in the center of the figure, visible light—the radiation your eyes see as different colors—is only a small fraction of the spectrum. It consists of wavelengths from about 380 nm to about 750 nm. The distance between the crests of two adjacent waves is called a **wavelength** (illustrated at the bottom right of the figure).

The model of light as waves explains many of light's properties. However, light also behaves as discrete packets of energy called photons. A **photon** has a fixed quantity of energy, and the shorter the wavelength of light, the greater the energy of its photons. In fact, the photons of wavelengths that are shorter than those of visible light have enough energy to damage molecules such as proteins and nucleic acids. This is why ultraviolet (UV) radiation can cause sunburns and skin cancer.

Photosynthetic Pigments   **Figure 7.6B** shows what happens to visible light in the chloroplast. Light-absorbing molecules called *pigments*, built into the thylakoid membranes, absorb some wavelengths of light and reflect or transmit other wavelengths. We do not see the absorbed wavelengths; their energy has been absorbed by pigment molecules. What we see when we look at a leaf are the green wavelengths that the pigments transmit and reflect.

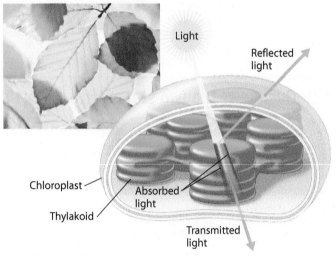

▲ **Figure 7.6B**   The interaction of light with a chloroplast

Different pigments absorb light of different wavelengths, and chloroplasts contain more than one type of pigment. **Chlorophyll *a***, which participates directly in the light reactions, absorbs mainly blue-violet and red light. It looks blue-green because it reflects mainly green light. A very similar molecule, chlorophyll *b*, absorbs mainly blue and orange light and reflects (appears) yellow-green. Chlorophyll *b* broadens the range of light that a plant can use by conveying absorbed energy to chlorophyll *a*, which then puts the energy to work in the light reactions.

Chloroplasts also contain pigments called carotenoids, which are various shades of yellow and orange. The spectacular colors of fall foliage in certain parts of the world are due partly to the yellow-orange hues of longer-lasting carotenoids that show through once the green chlorophyll breaks down. Carotenoids may broaden the spectrum of colors that can drive photosynthesis. However, a more important function seems to be *photoprotection*: Some carotenoids absorb and dissipate excessive light energy that would otherwise damage chlorophyll or interact with oxygen to form reactive oxidative molecules that can damage cell molecules. Similar carotenoids, which we obtain from carrots and some other plants, have a photoprotective role in our eyes.

Each type of pigment absorbs certain wavelengths of light because it is able to absorb the specific amounts of energy in those photons. Next we see what happens when a pigment molecule such as chlorophyll absorbs a photon of light.

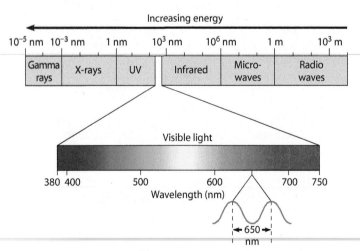

▲ **Figure 7.6A**   The electromagnetic spectrum and the wavelengths of visible light. (A wavelength of 650 nm is illustrated.)

? You may hear about the proposed health benefits of "phytochemicals" found in deep orange or red fruits and vegetables. How might such chemicals benefit a cell?

As antioxidants that protect from reactive forms of oxidative molecules ●

7.7 Photosystems capture solar energy

Energy cannot be destroyed, but it can be transformed. Let's see how light energy can be transformed to other types of energy. When a pigment molecule absorbs a photon of light, one of the pigment's electrons jumps to an energy level farther from the nucleus. In this location, the electron has more potential energy, and we say that the electron has been raised from a ground state to an excited state. The excited state, like all high-energy states, is unstable. Generally, when isolated pigment molecules absorb light, their excited electrons drop back down to the ground state in a billionth of a second, releasing their excess energy as heat. This conversion of light energy to heat is what makes a black car so hot on a sunny day (black pigments absorb all wavelengths of light).

Some isolated pigments, including chlorophyll, emit light as well as heat after absorbing photons. We can demonstrate this phenomenon in the laboratory with a chlorophyll solution, as shown on the left in **Figure 7.7A**. When illuminated, the chlorophyll emits photons of light that produce a reddish afterglow called fluorescence. The right side of Figure 7.7A illustrates what happens in fluorescence: An absorbed photon boosts an electron of chlorophyll to an excited state, from which it falls back to the ground state, emitting its energy as heat and light.

But chlorophyll behaves very differently in isolation than it does in an intact chloroplast. In their native habitat of the thylakoid membrane, chlorophyll and other pigment molecules that absorb photons transfer the energy to other pigment molecules and eventually to a special pair of chlorophyll molecules. This pair passes off an excited electron to a neighboring molecule before it has a chance to drop back to the ground state.

In the thylakoid membrane, chlorophyll molecules are organized along with other pigments and proteins into clusters called photosystems **(Figure 7.7B)**. A **photosystem** consists of a number of light-harvesting complexes surrounding a reaction-center complex. A *light-harvesting complex* contains various

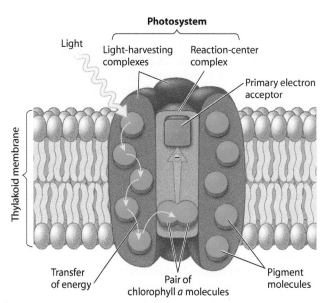

▲ **Figure 7.7B** A light-excited pair of chlorophyll molecules in the reaction center of a photosystem passing an excited electron to a primary electron acceptor

pigment molecules bound to proteins. Collectively, the light-harvesting complexes function as a light-gathering antenna. The pigments absorb photons and pass the energy from molecule to molecule (thin yellow arrows) until it reaches the reaction center. The *reaction-center complex* contains the pair of special chlorophyll *a* molecules and a molecule called the *primary electron acceptor*, which is capable of accepting electrons and becoming reduced. The solar-powered transfer of an electron from the reaction-center chlorophyll *a* to the primary electron acceptor is the first step in the transformation of light energy to chemical energy in the light reactions.

Two types of photosystems have been identified, and they cooperate in the light reactions. They are referred to as photosystem I and photosystem II, in order of their discovery, although photosystem II actually functions first in the sequence of steps that make up the light reactions. Each photosystem has a characteristic reaction-center complex. In photosystem II, the chlorophyll *a* of the reaction-center complex is called P680 because the light it absorbs best is red light with a wavelength of 680 nm. The reaction-center chlorophyll of photosystem I is called P700 because the wavelength of light it absorbs best is 700 nm (in the far-red part of the spectrum). Now let's see how the two photosystems work together in the light reactions to generate ATP and NADPH.

? Compared with a solution of isolated chlorophyll, why do intact chloroplasts release less heat and fluorescence when illuminated?

● In the chloroplasts, energy is passed from pigment molecule to pigment molecule, and eventually the light-excited electrons of reaction-center chlorophyll molecules are trapped by a primary electron acceptor rather than giving up their energy as heat and light.

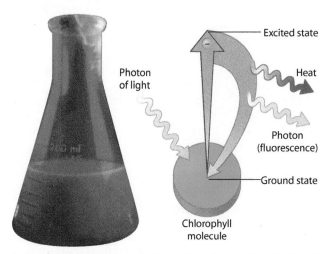

▲ **Figure 7.7A** A solution of chlorophyll glowing red when illuminated (left); a diagram of an isolated, light-excited chlorophyll molecule that releases a photon of red light (right)

7.8 Two photosystems connected by an electron transport chain generate ATP and NADPH

In the light reactions, light energy is transformed into the chemical energy of ATP and NADPH. In this process, electrons removed from H_2O pass from photosystem II to photosystem I to $NADP^+$. Between the two photosystems, the electrons move down an electron transport chain (similar to the one in cellular respiration) and provide energy for the synthesis of ATP.

Let's follow the flow of electrons (represented by gold arrows) in **Figure 7.8A**, which shows the two photosystems embedded in a thylakoid membrane. **①** A pigment molecule in a light-harvesting complex absorbs a photon of light. The energy is passed to other pigment molecules and finally to the reaction center of photosystem II, where it excites an electron of chlorophyll P680 to a higher energy state. **②** This electron is captured by the primary electron acceptor. **③** Water is split, and its electrons are supplied one by one to P680, each replacing an electron lost to the primary electron acceptor. The oxygen atom combines with a second oxygen from another split water molecule, forming O_2.

④ Each photoexcited electron passes from photosystem II to photosystem I via an electron transport chain. The exergonic "fall" of electrons provides energy for the synthesis of ATP by pumping H^+ across the membrane (not shown here). **⑤** Meanwhile, light energy excites an electron of chlorophyll P700 in the reaction center of photosystem I. An adjacent primary electron acceptor captures the electron, and an electron that reaches the bottom of the electron transport chain from photosystem II replaces the lost electron in P700. **⑥** Photoexcited electrons of photosystem I are passed through a short electron transport chain to $NADP^+$, reducing it to NADPH.

Admittedly, the scheme shown in Figure 7.8A is complicated. **Figure 7.8B** provides a mechanical analogy to help you focus on the key point: how the two photosystems cooperate in generating

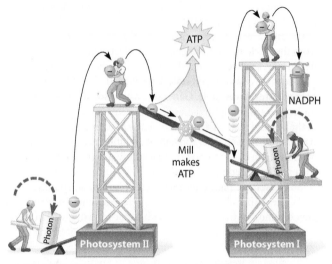

▲ **Figure 7.8B** A mechanical analogy of the light reactions

ATP and NADPH. The input of light energy, represented by the large yellow mallets, boosts electrons in the reaction-center complexes of both photosystems up to the excited state. The electrons are caught by the primary electron acceptor on top of the platform in each photosystem. Photosystem II passes the electrons through an ATP mill. Photosystem I hands its electrons off to reduce $NADP^+$ to NADPH.

NADPH, ATP, and O_2 are the products of the light reactions. Next we look in more detail at how ATP is formed.

? Tracing the light reactions in Figure 7.8A, there is a flow of electrons from _____ to _____, which is reduced to _____, the source of electrons for sugar synthesis in the _____ cycle.

● water . . . NADP⁺ . . . NADPH . . . Calvin

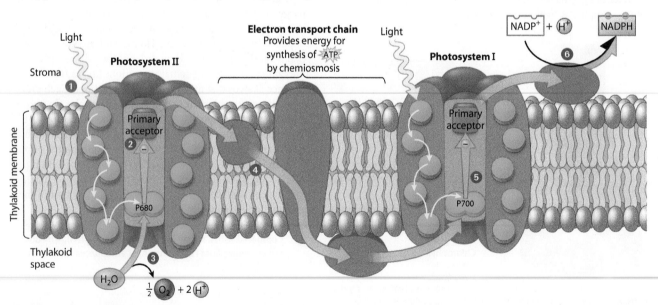

▲ **Figure 7.8A** Electron flow in the light reactions: light energy driving electrons from water to NADPH

7.9 Chemiosmosis powers ATP synthesis in the light reactions

You first encountered chemiosmosis in Modules 6.6 and 6.10 as the mechanism of oxidative phosphorylation (ATP formation) in cellular respiration in a mitochondrion. Chemiosmosis is also the mechanism that generates ATP in a chloroplast. Recall that in chemiosmosis, the potential energy of a concentration gradient of hydrogen ions (H^+) across a membrane powers ATP synthesis. This gradient is created when an electron transport chain uses the energy released as it passes electrons down the chain to pump H^+ across a membrane.

Figure 7.9 illustrates the relationship between chloroplast structure and function in the light reactions. As in Figure 7.8A, we show the two photosystems and electron transport chains, all located within the thylakoid membrane of a chloroplast. Here you can see that as photoexcited electrons are passed down the electron transport chain connecting the two photosystems, hydrogen ions are pumped across the membrane from the stroma into the thylakoid space (inside the thylakoid sacs). This generates a concentration gradient across the membrane.

The flask-shaped structure in the figure represents an ATP synthase complex, which is very similar to the ones found in a mitochondrion. The energy of the concentration gradient drives H^+ back across the membrane through ATP synthase, which couples the flow of H^+

to the phosphorylation of ADP. Because the initial energy input is light, this chemiosmotic production of ATP in photosynthesis is called **photophosphorylation**.

How does photophosphorylation compare with oxidative phosphorylation? In cellular respiration, the high-energy electrons passed down the electron transport chain come from the oxidation of organic molecules. In photosynthesis, light energy is used to drive electrons that originally came from water to the top of the transport chain. Mitochondria transfer chemical energy from food to ATP; chloroplasts transform light energy into the chemical energy of ATP.

Notice that in the light-driven flow of electrons through the two photosystems, the final electron acceptor is $NADP^+$, not O_2 as in cellular respiration. Electrons do not end up at a low energy level in H_2O, as they do in respiration. Instead, they are stored at a high state of potential energy in NADPH.

In summary, the light reactions provide the chemical energy (ATP) and reducing power (NADPH) for the next stage of photosynthesis, the Calvin cycle. In the next module we see how that cycle makes sugar.

? **What is the advantage of the light reactions producing NADPH and ATP on the stroma side of the thylakoid membrane?**

● The Calvin cycle, which uses the NADPH and ATP, occurs in the stroma.

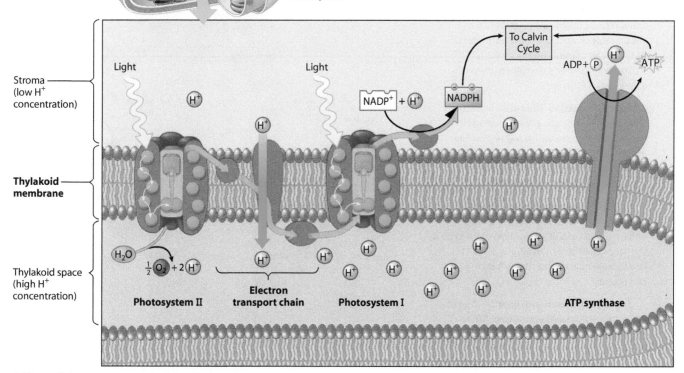

▲ **Figure 7.9** The production of ATP by chemiosmosis (numerous copies of these components present in each thylakoid)

The Calvin Cycle: Reducing CO_2 to Sugar

7.10 ATP and NADPH power sugar synthesis in the Calvin cycle

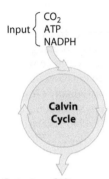

Input: CO_2, ATP, NADPH

Calvin Cycle

Output: G3P

▲ **Figure 7.10A** An overview of the Calvin cycle

The Calvin cycle functions like a sugar factory within a chloroplast. As Figure 7.10A shows, inputs to this all-important food-making process are CO_2 (from the air) and ATP and NADPH (both generated by the light reactions). Using CO_2, energy from ATP, and high-energy electrons from NADPH, the Calvin cycle constructs an energy-rich, three-carbon sugar, glyceraldehyde 3-phosphate (G3P). A plant cell can use G3P to make glucose and other organic molecules as needed. (You already met G3P in glycolysis: It is the three-carbon sugar formed by the splitting of glucose.)

Figure 7.10B presents the details of the Calvin cycle. It is called a cycle because, like the citric acid cycle in cellular respiration, the starting material is regenerated with each turn of the cycle. In this case, the starting material is a five-carbon sugar named ribulose bisphosphate (RuBP). ❶ In the carbon fixation step, the enzyme rubisco attaches CO_2 to RuBP. (Rubisco is thought to be the most abundant protein on Earth.) ❷ In the next step, a reduction reaction, NADPH reduces the organic acid 3-PGA to G3P using the energy of ATP. To make a molecule of G3P, the cycle must incorporate the carbon atoms from three molecules of CO_2. The cycle actually incorporates one carbon at a time, but we show it starting with three CO_2 molecules so that we end up with a complete G3P molecule.

For this to be a cycle, RuBP must be regenerated. ❸ For every three CO_2 molecules fixed, one G3P molecule leaves the cycle as product, and the remaining five G3P molecules are rearranged, ❹ using energy from ATP to regenerate three molecules of RuBP.

Note that for the net synthesis of one G3P molecule, the Calvin cycle consumes nine ATP and six NADPH molecules, which were provided by the light reactions.

> **?** To synthesize one glucose molecule, the Calvin cycle uses _____ CO_2, _____ ATP, and _____ NADPH. Explain why this high number of ATP and NADPH molecules is consistent with the value of glucose as an energy source.

● 6 . . . 18 . . . 12. Glucose is a valuable energy source because it is highly reduced, storing lots of potential energy in its electrons. The more energy a molecule stores, the more energy and reducing power required to produce that molecule.

Step ❶ Carbon fixation. An enzyme called rubisco combines CO_2 with a five-carbon sugar called ribulose bisphosphate (abbreviated RuBP). The unstable product splits into two molecules of the three-carbon organic acid, 3-phosphoglyceric acid (3-PGA). For three CO_2 entering, six 3-PGA result.

Step ❷ Reduction. Two chemical reactions (indicated by the two blue arrows) consume energy from six molecules of ATP and oxidize six molecules of NADPH. Six molecules of 3-PGA are reduced, producing six molecules of the energy-rich three-carbon sugar, G3P.

Step ❸ Release of one molecule of G3P. Five of the G3Ps from step 2 remain in the cycle. The single molecule of G3P you see leaving the cycle is the net product of photosynthesis. A plant cell uses G3P to make glucose and other organic compounds.

Step ❹ Regeneration of RuBP. A series of chemical reactions uses energy from ATP to rearrange the atoms in the five G3P molecules (15 carbons total), forming three RuBP molecules (15 carbons). These can start another turn of the cycle.

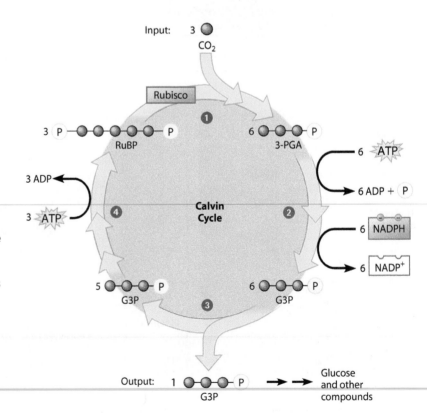

▲ **Figure 7.10B** Details of the Calvin cycle, which takes place in the stroma of a chloroplast

7.11 Other methods of carbon fixation have evolved in hot, dry climates

As you just learned in the previous module, the first step of the Calvin cycle is carbon fixation. Most plants use CO_2 directly from the air, and carbon fixation occurs when the enzyme rubisco adds CO_2 to RuBP (see step 1 of Figure 7.10B). Such plants are called **C_3 plants** because the first product of carbon fixation is the three-carbon compound 3-PGA. C_3 plants are widely distributed; they include such important agricultural crops as soybeans, oats, wheat, and rice. One problem that farmers face in growing C_3 plants is that hot, dry weather can decrease crop yield. In response to such conditions, plants close their stomata, the pores in their leaves. This adaptation reduces water loss and helps prevent dehydration, but it also prevents CO_2 from entering the leaf and O_2 from leaving. As a result, CO_2 levels get very low in the leaf and photosynthesis slows. And the O_2 released from the light reactions begins to accumulate, creating another problem.

As O_2 builds up in a leaf, rubisco adds O_2 instead of CO_2 to RuBP. A two-carbon product of this reaction is then broken down in the cell. This process is called **photorespiration** because it occurs in the light and, like respiration, it consumes O_2 and releases CO_2. But unlike cellular respiration, it uses ATP instead of producing it; and unlike photosynthesis, it yields no sugar. Photorespiration can, however, drain away as much as 50% of the carbon fixed by the Calvin cycle.

According to one hypothesis, photorespiration is an evolutionary relic from when the atmosphere had less O_2 than it does today. In the ancient atmosphere that prevailed when rubisco first evolved, the inability of the enzyme's active site to exclude O_2 would have made little difference. It is only after O_2 became so concentrated in the atmosphere that the "sloppiness" of rubisco presented a problem. New evidence also indicates that photorespiration may play a protective role when the products of the light reactions build up in a cell (as occurs when the Calvin cycle slows due to a lack of CO_2).

C_4 Plants   In some plant species found in hot, dry climates, alternate modes of carbon fixation have evolved that minimize photorespiration and optimize the Calvin cycle. **C_4 plants** are so named because they first fix CO_2 into a four-carbon compound. When the weather is hot and dry, a C_4 plant keeps its stomata mostly closed, thus conserving water. It continues making sugars by photosynthesis using the pathway and the two types of cells shown on the left side of **Figure 7.11**. An enzyme in the mesophyll cells has a high affinity for CO_2 and can fix carbon even when the CO_2 concentration in the leaf is low. The resulting four-carbon compound then acts as a carbon shuttle; it moves into bundle-sheath cells, which are packed around the veins of the leaf, and releases CO_2. Thus, the CO_2 concentration in these cells remains high enough for the Calvin cycle to make sugars and avoid photorespiration. Corn and sugarcane are examples of agriculturally important C_4 plants.

CAM Plants   A second photosynthetic adaptation has evolved in pineapples, many cacti, and other succulent (water-storing)

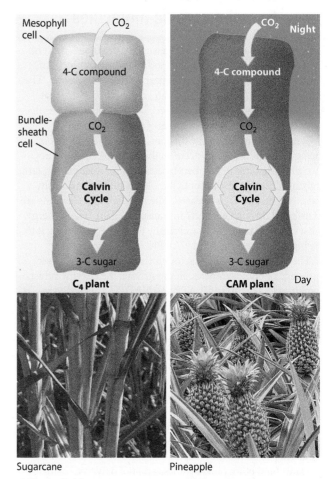

Sugarcane   Pineapple

▲ **Figure 7.11**   Comparison of C_4 and CAM photosynthesis: The fixing of CO_2 into a four-carbon compound and the Calvin cycle occur in different cells in C_4 plants and at different times of day in CAM plants.

plants, such as aloe and jade plants. Called **CAM plants**, these species are adapted to very dry climates. A CAM plant (right side of Figure 7.11) conserves water by opening its stomata and admitting CO_2 only at night. CO_2 is fixed into a four-carbon compound, which banks CO_2 at night and releases it during the day. Thus, the Calvin cycle can operate, even with the leaf's stomata closed during the day.

In C_4 plants, carbon fixation and the Calvin cycle occur in different types of cells. In CAM plants, these processes occur in the same cells, but at different times of the day. Keep in mind that CAM, C_4, and C_3 plants all eventually use the Calvin cycle to make sugar from CO_2. The C_4 and CAM pathways are two evolutionary adaptations that minimize photorespiration and maximize photosynthesis in hot, dry climates.

?   Why would you expect photorespiration on a hot, dry day to occur less in C_4 and CAM plants than in C_3 plants?

● Because of their initial fixing of carbon, both C_4 and CAM plants can supply rubisco with CO_2. When a C_3 plant closes its stomata, CO_2 levels drop and O_2 rises, making it more likely that rubisco will add O_2 to RuBP.

7.12 Review: Photosynthesis uses light energy, carbon dioxide, and water to make organic molecules

Life on Earth is solar powered. As we have discussed, most of the living world depends on the food-making machinery of photosynthesis. **Figure 7.12** summarizes this vital process. The production of sugar from CO_2 is an emergent property that arises from the structure of a chloroplast—a structural arrangement that integrates the two stages of photosynthesis.

Starting on the left in the diagram, you see a summary of the light reactions, which occur in the thylakoid membranes. Two photosystems in the membranes capture solar energy, energizing electrons in chlorophyll molecules. Simultaneously, water is split, and O_2 is released. The photoexcited electrons are transferred through an electron transport chain, where energy is harvested to make ATP, and finally to $NADP^+$, reducing it to the high-energy compound NADPH.

The chloroplast's sugar factory is the Calvin cycle, the second stage of photosynthesis. In the stroma, the enzyme rubisco combines CO_2 with RuBP. ATP and NADPH are used to reduce 3-PGA to G3P. Sugar molecules made from G3P serve as a plant's own food supply.

About 50% of the carbohydrate made by photosynthesis is consumed as fuel for cellular respiration in the mitochondria of plant cells. Sugars also serve as starting material for making other organic molecules, such as a plant's proteins and lipids. Many glucose molecules are linked together to make cellulose, the main component of cell walls. Cellulose is the most abundant organic molecule in a plant—and probably on the surface of the planet. Most plants make much more food each day than they need. They store the excess in roots, tubers, seeds, and fruits.

Plants (and other photosynthesizers) not only feed themselves but also are the ultimate source of food for virtually all other organisms. Humans and other animals make none of their own food and are totally dependent on the organic matter made by photosynthesizers. Even the energy we acquire when we eat meat was originally captured by photosynthesis. The energy in a hamburger, for instance, came from sunlight that was originally converted to a chemical form in the grasses eaten by cattle.

The collective productivity of the tiny chloroplasts is truly amazing: Photosynthesis makes an estimated 160 billion metric tons of carbohydrate per year (about 176 billion tons). That's equivalent in mass to a stack of about 100 trillion copies of this textbook. No other chemical process on Earth can match the output of photosynthesis.

This review of photosynthesis is an appropriate place to reflect on the metabolic ground we have covered in this chapter and the previous one. In Chapter 6, we saw that virtually all organisms, plants included, use cellular respiration to obtain the energy they need from fuel molecules such as glucose. We followed the chemical pathways of glycolysis and the citric acid cycle, which oxidize glucose and release energy from it. We have now come full circle, seeing how plants trap sunlight energy and use it to reduce carbon dioxide to make glucose.

In tracing glucose synthesis and its breakdown, we have also seen that cells use several of the same mechanisms—electron transport, redox reactions, and chemiosmosis—in energy storage (photosynthesis) and energy harvest (cellular respiration).

? **Explain this statement: No process is more important than photosynthesis to the welfare of life on Earth.**

● Photosynthesis is the ultimate source of the food for almost all organisms and the oxygen they need for cellular respiration.

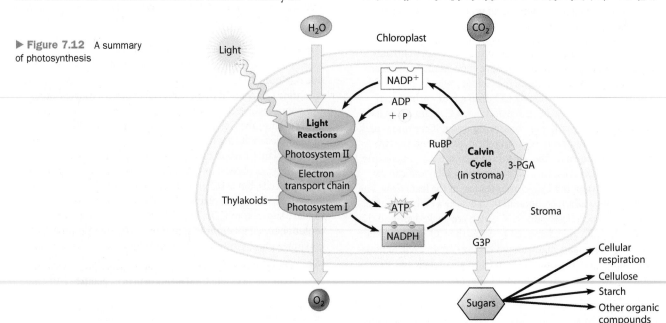

▶ **Figure 7.12** A summary of photosynthesis

7.13 Photosynthesis may moderate global climate change

The greenhouse in Figure 7.13A is used to grow plants when the weather outside is too cold. The glass or plastic walls of a greenhouse allow solar radiation to pass through. The sunlight heats the soil, which in turn warms the air. The walls trap the warm air, raising the temperature inside.

An analogous process, called the **greenhouse effect**, operates on a global scale (Figure 7.13B). Solar radiation reaching Earth's atmosphere includes ultraviolet radiation and visible light. As we discuss in the next module, the ozone layer filters out most of the damaging UV radiation. Visible light passes through and is absorbed by the planet's surface, warming it. Heat radiating from the warmed planet is absorbed by gases in the atmosphere, which then reflect some of the heat back to Earth. This natural heating effect is highly beneficial. Without it, Earth would be much colder, and most life as we know it could not exist.

The gases in the atmosphere that absorb heat radiation are called greenhouse gases. Some occur naturally, such as water vapor, carbon dioxide, and methane, while others are synthetic, such as the chlorofluorocarbons we discuss in the next module. Human activities add to the levels of these greenhouse gases.

Carbon dioxide is one of the most important greenhouse gases. You have just learned that CO_2 is a raw material for photosynthesis and a waste product of cellular respiration. These two processes, taking place in microscopic chloroplasts and mitochondria, keep carbon cycling between CO_2 and more complex organic compounds on a global scale. Photosynthetic organisms absorb billions of tons of CO_2 each year. Most of that fixed carbon returns to the atmosphere via cellular respiration, the action of decomposers, and fires. But much of it remains locked in large tracts of forests and undecomposed organisms. And large amounts of carbon are in long-term storage in fossil fuels buried deep under Earth's surface.

Since 1850, the start of the Industrial Revolution, the atmospheric concentration of CO_2 has increased about 40%, mostly due to the combustion of fossil fuels, such as coal, oil, and gasoline. Increasing concentrations of greenhouse gases have been linked to **global climate change**, of which the major aspect is *global warming*. The predicted consequences of this slow but steady increase in average global temperature include melting of polar ice, rising sea levels, extreme weather patterns, droughts, increased extinction rates, and the spread of tropical diseases. Indeed, many of these effects are already being documented.

Unfortunately, the rise in atmospheric CO_2 levels during the last century coincided with widespread deforestation, which aggravated the global warming problem by reducing an effective CO_2 sink. As forests are cleared for lumber or agriculture, and as population growth increases the demand for fossil fuels, CO_2 levels will continue to rise. We discuss global climate change in more detail in Chapter 38.

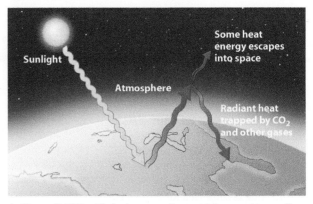

▲ Figure 7.13B CO_2 in the atmosphere and the greenhouse effect

Can photosynthesis offset this increase in atmospheric CO_2? Certainly, slowing the destruction of our forests will sustain their photosynthetic and carbon-storing contributions. Taking a lesson from plants, we can explore technologies that utilize solar energy for some of our energy needs. And as you read in the chapter introduction, biofuels hold out the promise of a renewable fuel source. As the plants or algae used for biofuels grow, their photosynthesis removes CO_2 from the atmosphere. The burning of these fuels releases CO_2 to the atmosphere, just as fossils fuels do. A key difference, however, is that fossil fuels come from the remains of ancient organisms, and their burning releases CO_2 that had been removed from the atmosphere by photosynthesis over the course of hundreds of millions of years. Growing and using alternative fuels could keep the cycle of CO_2 removal in photosynthesis balanced with CO_2 release in fuel burning.

? **Explain the greenhouse effect.**

Sunlight warms Earth's surface, which radiates heat to the atmosphere. CO_2 and other greenhouse gases absorb and radiate some heat back to Earth.

▲ Figure 7.13A Plants growing in a greenhouse

7.14 Scientific study of Earth's ozone layer has global significance

The process and importance of scientific discovery are illustrated by the story of how synthetic chemicals were destroying Earth's protective ozone layer and how the work of many scientists led to changes in worldwide environmental policies. As you now know, photosynthesis produces the O_2 on which almost all organisms depend for cellular respiration. This O_2 has another benefit: High in the atmosphere, high-energy solar radiation converts it to ozone (O_3). Acting as sunscreen for the planet, the ozone layer shields Earth from ultraviolet radiation. The balance between ozone formation and its natural destruction in the atmosphere, however, has been upset by human actions.

Chlorofluorocarbons (CFCs) are chemicals developed in the 1930s that became widely used in aerosol sprays, refrigerators, and Styrofoam production. In 1970, a scientist wondered whether CFCs were accumulating in the environment and sent a homemade detector on a boat trip to Antarctica. He found CFCs in the air all along the journey. When he reported his findings at a scientific meeting in 1972, two chemists, Sherwood Rowland and Mario Molina, wondered what happened to CFCs once they entered the atmosphere. A search of the literature found that these chemicals were not broken down in the lower atmosphere.

But the intense solar radiation in the upper atmosphere could break down CFCs, releasing chlorine atoms. Molina learned that chlorine reacts with ozone, reducing it to O_2. Other reactions liberate the chlorine, allowing it to destroy more ozone. In 1974, Molina and Rowland published their work predicting that the release of CFCs would damage the ozone layer.

As other researchers tested the CFC-ozone depletion hypothesis, the evidence accumulated, and more people became concerned about ozone depletion. Others worried about the economic impact of banning CFCs, and CFC manufacturers mounted a campaign to cast doubt on the Molina-Rowland hypothesis in any way they could. A timetable for phasing out CFCs in aerosols was announced by the U.S. government in 1977, but worldwide production continued to increase.

Then, in 1982, a researcher noted a dramatic dip in the ozone layer over Antarctica. At first he suspected an instrument malfunction. After recording this decline for two more years, he published his observations. A reanalysis of data collected by NASA (National Aeronautics and Space Administration) over that period confirmed a gigantic hole in the ozone layer. This hole has appeared every spring over Antarctica since the late 1970s and continues today. **Figure 7.14A** shows an image produced from atmospheric data from 2006. Blue and purple colors show where there is the least ozone. The ozone depletion was much greater than had been predicted by Molina and Rowland. How could it be explained?

Susan Solomon (**Figure 7.14B**), with the National Oceanic and Atmospheric Administration (NOAA), developed a hypothesis that the unusual ice clouds that appear during early

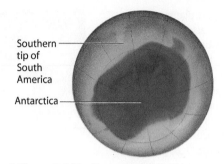

Southern tip of South America

Antarctica

▲ **Figure 7.14A** The ozone hole in the Southern Hemisphere, spring 2006

spring in Antarctica could speed up the reactions that destroy ozone. The then 30-year-old scientist led two research expeditions to the Antarctic. The data that she and her team collected indicated that chemical reactions occurring on the icy particles made CFCs hundreds of times more damaging than they normally are.

Further laboratory tests and field measurements taken from the ground, balloons, and airplanes supported Solomon's hypothesis. In response to these scientific findings, the first treaty to address Earth's environment was signed in 1987. In the Montreal Protocol, many nations agreed to phase out CFCs. As research continued to establish the extent and danger of ozone depletion, these agreements were strengthened in 1990. In 1995, Molina and Rowland shared a Nobel Prize for their work on how CFCs were damaging the atmosphere.

Global emissions of CFCs are near zero now, but because these compounds are so stable, recovery of the ozone layer is not expected until around 2060. Meanwhile, unblocked UV radiation is predicted to increase skin cancer and cataracts, as well as damage crops and phytoplankton in the oceans.

In addition to being ozone destroyers, CFCs are also potent greenhouse gases. The phaseout of CFCs has avoided what would have been the equivalent of adding 10 gigatons of CO_2 to the atmosphere. (For comparison, the Kyoto Protocol of 1997 set a 2012 target of a reduction of 2 gigatons of CO_2 emissions.)

Whether an environmental problem involves CFCs or CO_2, the scientific research is often complicated and the solutions complex. The connections between science, technology, and society, so clearly exemplified by the work of the scientists studying the ozone layer, are a major theme of this book.

? **Where does the ozone layer come from, and why is it so important to life on Earth?**

● High in the atmosphere, radiation from the sun converts O_2 to ozone. The ozone layer absorbs potentially damaging UV radiation.

▲ Figure 7.14B Susan Solomon with a globe showing Antarctica

For Practice Quizzes, BioFlix, MP3 Tutors, and Activities, go to www.masteringbiology.com.

Reviewing the Concepts

An Overview of Photosynthesis (7.1–7.5)

7.1 Autotrophs are the producers of the biosphere. Plants, algae, and some protists and bacteria are photoautotrophs, the producers of food consumed by virtually all heterotrophic organisms.

7.2 Photosynthesis occurs in chloroplasts in plant cells. Chloroplasts are surrounded by a double membrane and contain stacks of thylakoids and a thick fluid called stroma.

7.3 Scientists traced the process of photosynthesis using isotopes. Experiments using both heavy and radioactive isotopes helped determine the details of the process of photosynthesis.

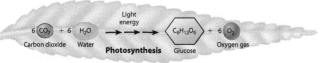

7.4 Photosynthesis is a redox process, as is cellular respiration. In photosynthesis, H_2O is oxidized and CO_2 is reduced.

7.5 Overview: The two stages of photosynthesis are linked by ATP and NADPH. The light reactions occur in the thylakoids, producing ATP and NADPH for the Calvin cycle, which takes place in the stroma.

The Light Reactions: Converting Solar Energy to Chemical Energy (7.6–7.9)

7.6 Visible radiation absorbed by pigments drives the light reactions. Certain wavelengths of visible light are absorbed by chlorophyll and other pigments. Carotenoids also function in photoprotection from excessive light.

7.7 Photosystems capture solar energy. Thylakoid membranes contain photosystems, each consisting of light-harvesting complexes and a reaction-center complex. A primary electron acceptor receives photoexcited electrons from chlorophyll.

7.8 Two photosystems connected by an electron transport chain generate ATP and NADPH. Electrons shuttle from photosystem II to photosystem I, providing energy to make ATP, and then reduce $NADP^+$ to NADPH. Photosystem II regains electrons as water is split and O_2 released.

7.9 Chemiosmosis powers ATP synthesis in the light reactions. In photophosphorylation, the electron transport chain pumps H^+ into the thylakoid space. The concentration gradient drives H^+ back through ATP synthase, driving the synthesis of ATP.

The Calvin Cycle: Reducing CO_2 to Sugar (7.10–7.11)

7.10 ATP and NADPH power sugar synthesis in the Calvin cycle. The steps of the Calvin cycle include carbon fixation, reduction, release of G3P, and regeneration of RuBP. Using carbon from CO_2, electrons from NADPH, and energy from ATP, the cycle constructs G3P, which is used to build glucose and other organic molecules.

7.11 Other methods of carbon fixation have evolved in hot, dry climates. In C_3 plants, a drop in CO_2 and rise in O_2 when stomata close divert the Calvin cycle to photorespiration. C_4 plants and CAM plants first fix CO_2 into a four-carbon compound that provides CO_2 to the Calvin cycle even when stomata close on hot, dry days.

Photosynthesis Reviewed and Extended (7.12–7.14)

7.12 Review: Photosynthesis uses light energy, carbon dioxide, and water to make organic molecules.

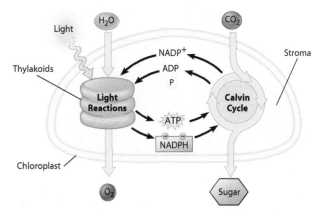

7.13 Photosynthesis may moderate global climate change. Reducing deforestation and fossil fuel use and growing biofuel crops, which remove CO_2 from the atmosphere, may help moderate the global warming caused by increasing CO_2 levels.

7.14 Scientific study of Earth's ozone layer has global significance. Solar radiation converts O_2 high in the atmosphere to ozone (O_3), which shields organisms from damaging UV radiation. Industrial chemicals called CFCs have caused dangerous thinning of the ozone layer, but international restrictions on CFC use are allowing a slow recovery.

Connecting the Concepts

1. The following diagram compares the chemiosmotic synthesis of ATP in mitochondria and chloroplasts. Fill in the blanks, which label the molecules shared by both processes and the regions in the chloroplast. Then, for both organelles, indicate which side of the membrane has the higher H^+ concentration.

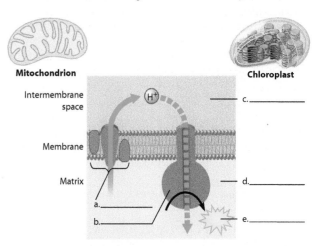

2. Continue your comparison of chemiosmosis and electron transport in mitochondria and chloroplasts. In each case,
   a. where do the electrons come from?
   b. how do the electrons get their high potential energy?
   c. what picks up the electrons at the end of the chain?
   d. how is the energy given up by the electrons used?

3. Complete this summary map of photosynthesis.

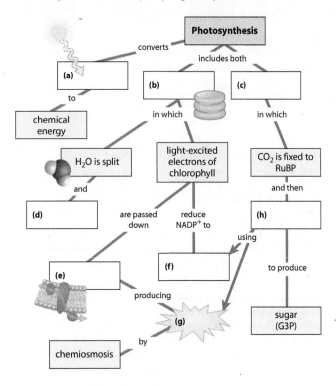

Testing Your Knowledge

Multiple Choice

4. In photosynthesis, _____ is oxidized and _____ is reduced.
   a. glucose . . . oxygen
   b. carbon dioxide . . . water
   c. water . . . carbon dioxide
   d. glucose . . . carbon dioxide
   e. water . . . oxygen

5. Which of the following are produced by reactions that take place in the thylakoids and consumed by reactions in the stroma?
   a. CO_2 and H_2O
   b. $NADP^+$ and ADP
   c. ATP and NADPH
   d. ATP, NADPH, and CO_2
   e. O_2 and ATP

6. When light strikes chlorophyll molecules in the reaction-center complex, they lose electrons, which are ultimately replaced by
   a. splitting water.
   b. breaking down ATP.
   c. oxidizing NADPH.
   d. fixing carbon.
   e. oxidizing glucose.

7. The reactions of the Calvin cycle are not directly dependent on light, but they usually do not occur at night. Why? (*Explain.*)
   a. It is often too cold at night for these reactions to take place.
   b. Carbon dioxide concentrations decrease at night.
   c. The Calvin cycle depends on products of the light reactions.
   d. Plants usually close their stomata at night.
   e. Most plants do not make four-carbon compounds, which they would need for the Calvin cycle at night.

8. How many "turns" of the Calvin cycle are required to produce one molecule of glucose? (Assume one CO_2 is fixed in each turn of the cycle.)
   a. 1
   b. 2
   c. 3
   d. 6
   e. 12

9. Which of the following does *not* occur during the Calvin cycle?
   a. carbon fixation
   b. oxidation of NADPH
   c. consumption of ATP
   d. regeneration of RuBP, the CO_2 acceptor
   e. release of oxygen

10. Why is it difficult for most plants to carry out photosynthesis in very hot, dry environments such as deserts?
    a. The light is too intense and destroys the pigment molecules.
    b. The closing of stomata keeps CO_2 from entering and O_2 from leaving the plant.
    c. They must rely on photorespiration to make ATP.
    d. Global warming is intensified in a desert environment.
    e. CO_2 builds up in the leaves, blocking carbon fixation.

11. How is photosynthesis similar in C_4 plants and CAM plants?
    a. In both cases, the light reactions and the Calvin cycle are separated in both time and location.
    b. Both types of plants make sugar without the Calvin cycle.
    c. In both cases, rubisco is not used to fix carbon initially.
    d. Both types of plants make most of their sugar in the dark.
    e. In both cases, thylakoids are not involved in photosynthesis.

Describing, Comparing, and Explaining

12. What are the major inputs and outputs of the two stages of photosynthesis?

13. Explain why a poison that inhibits an enzyme of the Calvin cycle will also inhibit the light reactions.

14. What do plants do with the sugar they produce in photosynthesis?

Applying the Concepts

15. Most experts agree that global warming is already occurring and will increase rapidly in this century. Many countries have made a commitment to reduce CO_2 emissions. Recent international negotiations, however, including a 2009 meeting in Copenhagen, Denmark, have yet to reach a consensus on a global strategy to reduce greenhouse gas emissions. Some countries have resisted taking action because a few scientists and policymakers think that the warming trend may be just a random fluctuation in temperature and/or not related to human activities or that cutting CO_2 emissions would sacrifice economic growth. Do you think we need more evidence before taking action? Or is it better to act now to reduce CO_2 emissions? What are the possible costs and benefits of each of these two strategies?

16. The use of biofuels (see chapter introduction) avoids many of the problems associated with gathering, refining, transporting, and burning fossil fuels. Yet biofuels are not without their own set of problems. What challenges do you think would arise from a large-scale conversion to biofuels? How do these challenges compare with those encountered with fossil fuels? Do you think any other types of energy sources have more benefits and fewer costs than the others? Which ones, and why?

Answers to all questions can be found in Appendix 4.

Cellular Reproduction and Genetics

The Cellular Basis of Reproduction and Inheritance

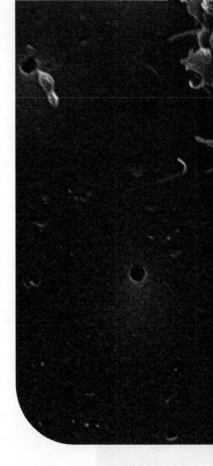

Cell Division and Reproduction
(8.1–8.2)

Cell division underlies many of life's important processes.

The Eukaryotic Cell Cycle and Mitosis
(8.3–8.10)

Cells produce genetic duplicates through an ordered, tightly controlled series of steps.

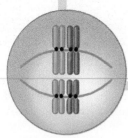

Meiosis and Crossing Over
(8.11–8.17)

The process of meiosis produces genetically varied haploid gametes from diploid cells.

Alterations of Chromosome Number and Structure
(8.18–8.23)

Errors in cell division can produce organisms with abnormal numbers of chromosomes.

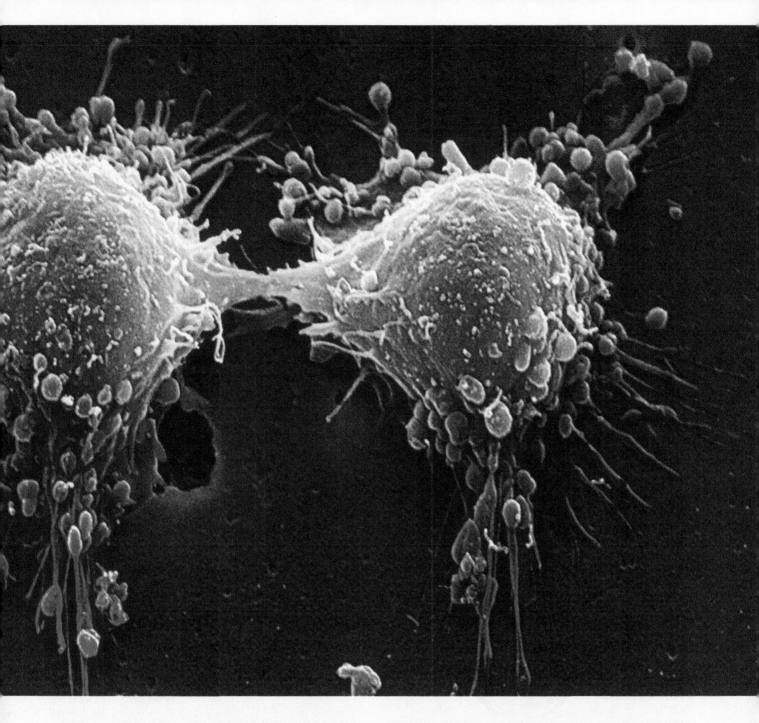

The photo above shows a cancer cell undergoing cell division, the creation of two cells from one. Cancer cells start as normal body cells that, because of genetic mutations, lose the ability to control the tempo of their own division. The result is rapid cell division that is no longer under the control of the host body—cell growth run amok! If left untreated, cancer cells may continue to divide and spread, invading other tissues and eventually killing the host. Most cancer treatments seek to prevent this outcome by disrupting one or more steps in cell division. Some anticancer drugs target dividing DNA; others disrupt cellular structures that assist in cell division. The goal of cancer treatment is to slow the spread of cancerous cells to the point that the body's immune system can overtake the growth, destroying the abnormal cells and restoring proper control of cell division.

Although cell division is harmful when it happens in a cancer cell, it is a necessary process for all forms of life. Why must cells divide? Some organisms, such as single-celled prokaryotes, reproduce themselves by splitting a single parent cell via cell division, creating two genetically identical offspring. In your body and the bodies of all other multicellular organisms, cell division allows for growth, replacement of damaged cells, and development of an embryo into an adult. Furthermore, in sexually reproducing organisms, eggs and sperm result from a particular type of cell division.

These examples illustrate the main point of this chapter: The perpetuation of life, including all aspects of reproduction and inheritance, is based on the reproduction of cells, or cell division. In this chapter, we discuss the two main types of cell division—mitosis and meiosis—and how they function within organisms.

Cell Division and Reproduction

8.1 Cell division plays many important roles in the lives of organisms

The ability of organisms to reproduce their own kind is the one characteristic that best distinguishes living things from nonliving matter (see Module 1.1 to review the characteristics of life). Only amoebas produce more amoebas, only people make more people, and only maple trees produce more maple trees. These simple facts of life have been recognized for thousands of years and are summarized by the age-old saying, "Like begets like."

However, the biological concept of reproduction includes more than just the birth of new organisms: Reproduction actually occurs much more often at the cellular level. When a cell undergoes reproduction, or **cell division**, the two "daughter" cells that result are genetically identical to each other and to the original "parent" cell. (Biologists traditionally use the word *daughter* in this context; it does not imply gender.) Before the parent cell splits into two, it duplicates its **chromosomes**, the structures that contain most of the cell's DNA. Then, during the division process, one set of chromosomes is distributed to each daughter cell. As a rule, the daughter cells receive identical sets of chromosomes from the lone, original parent cell. Each offspring cell will thus be genetically identical to the other and to the original parent cell.

Sometimes, cell division results in the reproduction of a whole organism. Many single-celled organisms, such as prokaryotes or the eukaryotic yeast cell in **Figure 8.1A**, reproduce by dividing in half, and the offspring are genetic replicas. This is an example of **asexual reproduction**, the creation of genetically identical offspring by a single parent, without the participation of sperm and egg. Many multicellular organisms can

Colorized TEM 5,000×

▲ **Figure 8.1A**
A yeast cell producing a genetically identical daughter cell by asexual reproduction

reproduce asexually as well. For example, some sea star species have the ability to grow new individuals from fragmented pieces (**Figure 8.1B**). And if you've ever grown a house-plant from a clipping, you've observed asexual reproduction in plants (**Figure 8.1C**). In asexual reproduction, there is one simple principle of inheritance: The lone parent and each of its offspring have identical genes.

▲ **Figure 8.1B** A sea star reproducing asexually

Sexual reproduction is different; it requires fertilization of an egg by a sperm. The production of gametes—egg and sperm—involves a special type of cell division that occurs only in reproductive organs (such as testes and ovaries in humans). As you'll learn later in the chapter, a gamete has only half as many chromosomes as the parent cell that gave rise to it, and these chromosomes contain unique combinations of genes. Therefore, in sexually reproducing species, like does not precisely beget like (**Figure 8.1D**). Offspring produced by sexual reproduction generally resemble their parents more closely than they resemble unrelated individuals of the same species, but they are not identical to their parents or to each other. Each offspring inherits a unique combination of genes from its two

▲ **Figure 8.1C** An African violet reproducing asexually from a cutting (the large leaf on the left)

▼ **Figure 8.1D** Sexual reproduction produces offspring with unique combinations of genes

▲ **Figure 8.1E** Dividing cells in an early human embryo

parents, and this one-and-only set of genes programs a unique combination of traits. As a result, sexual reproduction can produce great variation among offspring.

In multicellular organisms, cell division plays other important roles, in addition to the production of gametes. Cell division enables sexually reproducing organisms to develop from a single cell—the fertilized egg, or zygote—into an adult organism (Figure 8.1E). All of the trillions of cells in your body arose via repeated cell divisions that began in your mother's body with a single fertilized egg cell. After an organism is fully grown, cell division continues to function in renewal and repair, replacing cells that die from normal wear and tear or accidents. Within your body, millions of cells must divide every second to replace damaged or lost cells (Figure 8.1F).

The type of cell division responsible for asexual reproduction and for the growth and maintenance of multicellular organisms involves a process called called mitosis. The production of egg and sperm cells involves a special type of cell division called meiosis. In the remainder of this chapter, you will learn the details of both types of cell division. To start, we'll look briefly at prokaryotic cell division in the next module.

▲ **Figure 8.1F** A human kidney cell dividing

? What function does cell division play in an amoeba? What functions does it play in your body?

● Reproduction, development, growth, and repair

8.2 Prokaryotes reproduce by binary fission

Prokaryotes (bacteria and archaea) reproduce by a type of cell division called **binary fission** ("dividing in half"). In typical prokaryotes, the majority of genes are carried on a single circular DNA molecule that, with associated proteins, constitutes

the organism's chromosome. Although prokaryotic chromosomes are much smaller than those of eukaryotes, duplicating them in an orderly fashion and distributing the copies equally to two daughter bacteria is still a formidable task. Consider, for example, that when stretched out, the chromosome of the bacterium *Escherichia coli* (*E. coli*) is about 500 times longer than the cell itself. Accurately replicating this molecule when it is coiled and packed inside the cell is no small achievement.

Figure 8.2A illustrates binary fission in a prokaryote. ❶ As the chromosome is duplicating, the copies move toward the opposite ends of the cell. ❷ Meanwhile, the cell elongates. ❸ When chromosome duplication is complete and the cell has reached about twice its initial size, the plasma membrane grows inward and more cell wall is made, dividing the parent cell into two daughter cells. Figure 8.2B is an electron micrograph of a dividing bacterium (this cell is at a stage similar to the third illustration in Figure 8.2A).

? Why is binary fission classified as asexual reproduction?

● Because the genetically identical offspring inherit their DNA from a single parent.

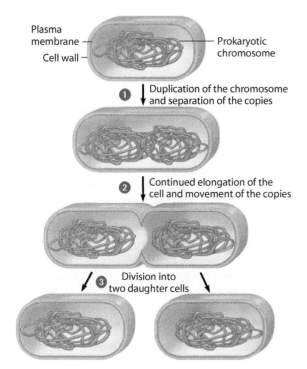

Plasma membrane
Cell wall
Prokaryotic chromosome

❶ Duplication of the chromosome and separation of the copies

❷ Continued elongation of the cell and movement of the copies

❸ Division into two daughter cells

▲ **Figure 8.2A** Binary fission of a prokaryotic cell

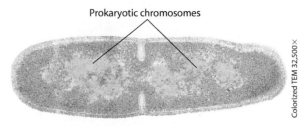

Prokaryotic chromosomes

▲ **Figure 8.2B** An electron micrograph of a dividing bacterium

The Eukaryotic Cell Cycle and Mitosis

8.3 The large, complex chromosomes of eukaryotes duplicate with each cell division

Eukaryotic cells, in general, are more complex and much larger than prokaryotic cells, and they have many more genes. Human cells, for example, carry around 21,000 genes, versus about 3,000 for a typical bacterium. Almost all the genes in the cells of humans, and in all other eukaryotes, are found in the cell nucleus, grouped into multiple chromosomes. (The exceptions include genes on the small DNA molecules of mitochondria and, in plants, chloroplasts.)

Most of the time, chromosomes exist as a diffuse mass of long, thin fibers that are far too long to fit in a cell's nucleus. In fact, if stretched out, the DNA in just one of your cells would be taller than you! DNA in this loose state is called **chromatin**, fibers composed of roughly equal amounts of DNA and protein molecules. Chromatin is too thin to be seen using a light microscope.

As a cell prepares to divide, its chromatin coils up, forming tight, distinct chromosomes that are visible under a light microscope. Why is it necessary for a cell's chromosomes to be compacted in this way? Imagine a situation from your own life: Your belongings are spread out over a considerable area of your home, but as you prepare to move to a new home, you need to gather them all up and pack them into small containers. Similarly, before a cell can undergo division, it must compact all its DNA into manageable packages. **Figure 8.3A** is a micrograph of a plant cell that is about to divide; each thick purple thread is a tightly packed individual chromosome.

Like a prokaryotic chromosome, each eukaryotic chromosome contains one long DNA molecule bearing hundreds or thousands of genes and, attached to the DNA, a number of protein molecules. However, the eukaryotic chromosome has a much more complex structure than the prokaryotic chromosome. The eukaryotic chromosome includes many more protein molecules, which help maintain the chromosome's structure and control the activity of its genes. The number of

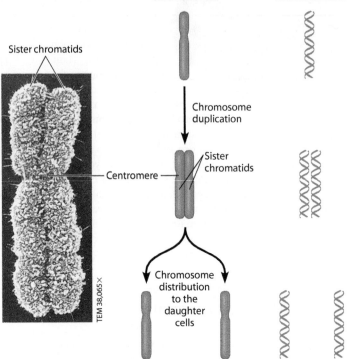

▲ **Figure 8.3B** Chromosome duplication and distribution

chromosomes in a eukaryotic cell depends on the species. For example, human body cells generally have 46 chromosomes, while the body cells of a dog have 78.

The chromosomes of a eukaryotic cell are duplicated before they condense and the cell divides. The DNA molecule of each chromosome is replicated (as you'll learn in Chapter 10), and new protein molecules attach as needed. Each chromosome now consists of two copies called **sister chromatids**, which contain identical copies of the DNA molecule (**Figure 8.3B**). The two sister chromatids are joined together especially tightly at a narrow "waist" called the **centromere** (visible near the center of each chromosome shown in the figure).

When the cell divides, the sister chromatids of a duplicated chromosome separate from each other. Once separated from its sister, each chromatid is called a chromosome, and it is identical to the chromosome the cell started with. One of the new chromosomes goes to one daughter cell, and the other goes to the other daughter cell. In this way, each daughter cell receives a complete and identical set of chromosomes. In humans, for example, a typical dividing cell has 46 duplicated chromosomes (or 92 chromatids), and each of the two daughter cells that results from it has 46 single chromosomes.

▶ **Figure 8.3A**
A plant cell (from an African blood lily) just before cell division

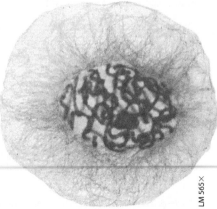

? When does a chromosome consist of two identical chromatids?

● When the cell is preparing to divide and has duplicated its chromosomes, but before the duplicates actually separate

8.4 The cell cycle multiplies cells

How do chromosome duplication and cell division fit into the life of a cell—and the life of an organism? As discussed in Module 8.1, cell division is essential to all life. Cell division is the basis of reproduction for every organism. It enables a multicellular organism to grow to adult size. It also replaces worn-out or damaged cells, keeping the total cell number in a mature individual relatively constant. In your own body, for example, millions of cells must divide every second to maintain the total number of about 10 trillion cells. Some cells divide once a day, others less often, and highly specialized cells, such as our mature muscle cells, not at all. The fact that some mature cells never divide explains why some kinds of damage—such as the death of cardiac muscle cells during a heart attack or the death of brain cells during a stroke—can never be reversed.

The process of cell division is a key component of the **cell cycle**, an ordered sequence of events that extends from the time a cell is first formed from a dividing parent cell until its own division into two cells. The cell cycle consists of two main stages: a growing stage (called interphase), during which the cell roughly doubles everything in its cytoplasm and precisely replicates its chromosomal DNA, and the actual cell division (called the mitotic phase).

As **Figure 8.4** indicates, most of the cell cycle is spent in **interphase**. This is a time when a cell's metabolic activity is very high and the cell performs its various functions within the organism. For example, a cell in your intestine might release digestive enzymes and absorb nutrients, while a white blood cell might circulate in your bloodstream, interacting with invading microbes. During interphase, a cell makes more cytoplasm. It increases its supply of proteins, creates more cytoplasmic organelles (such as mitochondria and ribosomes), and grows in size. Additionally, the chromosomes duplicate during this period. Typically, interphase lasts for at least 90% of the total time required for the cell cycle.

Interphase can be divided into three subphases: the G_1 phase ("first gap"), the S phase, and the G_2 phase ("second gap"). During all three subphases, the cell grows. However, chromosomes are duplicated only during the S phase. S stands for *synthesis* of DNA—also known as DNA replication. At the beginning of the S phase, each chromosome is single. At the end of this phase, after DNA replication, the chromosomes are double, each consisting of two sister chromatids. To summarize interphase: A cell grows (G_1), continues to grow as it copies its chromosomes (S), and then grows more as it completes preparations for cell division (G_2).

The **mitotic phase (M phase;** the blue area of the figure), the part of the cell cycle when the cell actually divides, accounts for only about 10% of the total time required for the cell cycle. The mitotic phase is itself divided into two overlapping stages, called mitosis and cytokinesis. In **mitosis**, the nucleus and its contents—most importantly the duplicated chromosomes—divide and are evenly distributed, forming two daughter nuclei. During **cytokinesis**, which usually begins before mitosis ends, the cytoplasm is divided in two. The combination of mitosis and cytokinesis produces two genetically identical

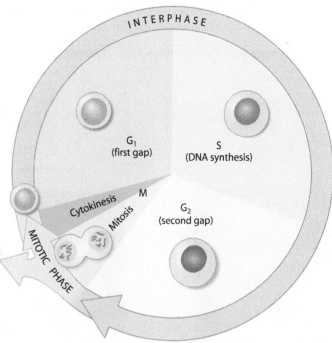

▲ **Figure 8.4** The eukaryotic cell cycle

daughter cells, each with a single nucleus, surrounding cytoplasm stocked with organelles, and a plasma membrane. Each newly produced daughter cell may then proceed through G_1 and repeat the cycle.

Mitosis is unique to eukaryotes and is the evolutionary solution to the problem of allocating identical copies of all the separate chromosomes to two daughter cells. Mitosis is a remarkably accurate mechanism. Experiments with yeast, for example, indicate that an error in chromosome distribution occurs only once in about 100,000 cell divisions.

The extreme accuracy of mitosis is essential to the development of your own body. All of us began as a single cell. Mitotic cell division ensures that all your body cells receive copies of the 46 chromosomes that were found in this original cell. Thus, every one of the trillions of cells in your body today can trace its ancestry back through mitotic divisions to that first cell produced when your father's sperm and mother's egg fused about nine months before your birth.

During the mitotic phase, a living cell viewed through a light microscope undergoes dramatic changes in the appearance of the chromosomes and other structures. In the next module, we'll use these visible changes as a guide to the stages of mitosis.

? A researcher treats cells with a chemical that prevents DNA synthesis from starting. This treatment would trap the cells in which part of the cell cycle?

G_1 ●

8.5 Cell division is a continuum of dynamic changes

Figure 8.5 illustrates the cell cycle for an animal cell using micrographs, drawings (simplified to include just four chromosomes), and text. The micrographs show cells from a newt, with chromosomes in blue and the mitotic spindle in green. Interphase is included, but the emphasis is on the dramatic changes that occur during cell division, the mitotic phase. Mitosis is a continuum, but biologists distinguish five main stages: **prophase**, **prometaphase**, **metaphase**, **anaphase**, and **telophase**.

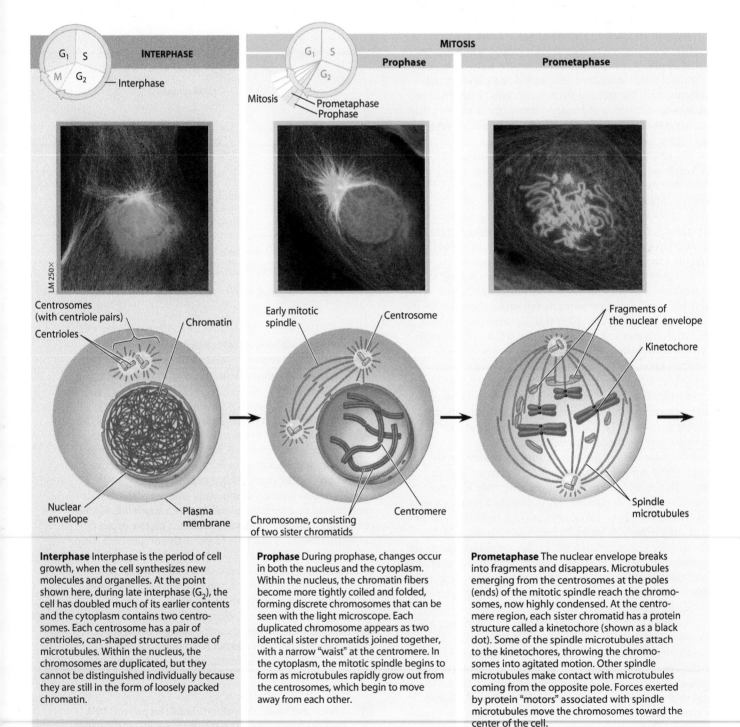

Interphase Interphase is the period of cell growth, when the cell synthesizes new molecules and organelles. At the point shown here, during late interphase (G_2), the cell has doubled much of its earlier contents and the cytoplasm contains two centrosomes. Each centrosome has a pair of centrioles, can-shaped structures made of microtubules. Within the nucleus, the chromosomes are duplicated, but they cannot be distinguished individually because they are still in the form of loosely packed chromatin.

Prophase During prophase, changes occur in both the nucleus and the cytoplasm. Within the nucleus, the chromatin fibers become more tightly coiled and folded, forming discrete chromosomes that can be seen with the light microscope. Each duplicated chromosome appears as two identical sister chromatids joined together, with a narrow "waist" at the centromere. In the cytoplasm, the mitotic spindle begins to form as microtubules rapidly grow out from the centrosomes, which begin to move away from each other.

Prometaphase The nuclear envelope breaks into fragments and disappears. Microtubules emerging from the centrosomes at the poles (ends) of the mitotic spindle reach the chromosomes, now highly condensed. At the centromere region, each sister chromatid has a protein structure called a kinetochore (shown as a black dot). Some of the spindle microtubules attach to the kinetochores, throwing the chromosomes into agitated motion. Other spindle microtubules make contact with microtubules coming from the opposite pole. Forces exerted by protein "motors" associated with spindle microtubules move the chromosomes toward the center of the cell.

▲ **Figure 8.5** The stages of cell division by mitosis

The chromosomes are the stars of the mitotic drama. Their movements depend on the **mitotic spindle**, a football-shaped structure of microtubules that guides the separation of the two sets of daughter chromosomes. The spindle microtubules emerge from two **centrosomes**, clouds of cytoplasmic material that in animal cells contain pairs of centrioles (see Module 4.16 for more information on centrioles). Centrosomes are also known as *microtubule-organizing centers*, a term describing their function.

? You view an animal cell through a microscope and observe dense, duplicated chromosomes scattered throughout the cell. Which state of mitosis are you looking at?

Prophase (since the chromosomes are condensed but not yet aligned)

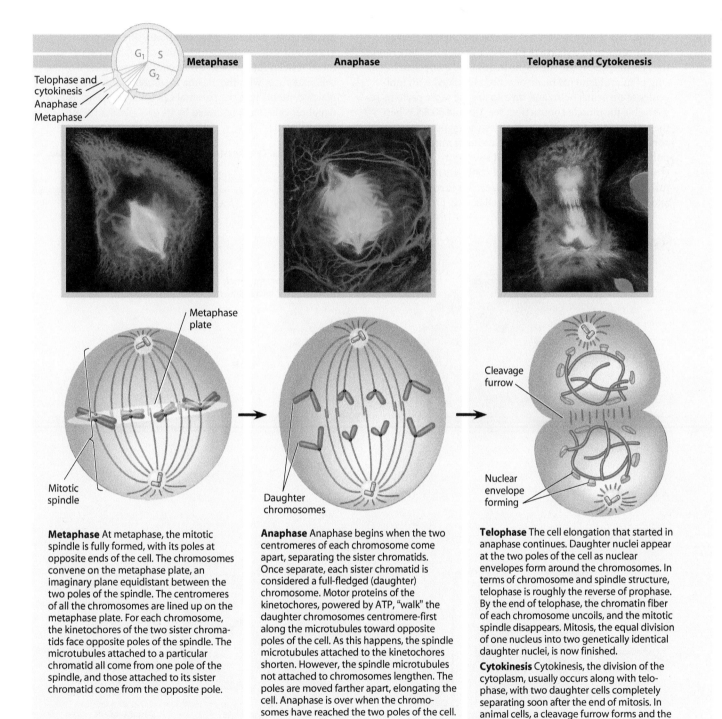

Metaphase At metaphase, the mitotic spindle is fully formed, with its poles at opposite ends of the cell. The chromosomes convene on the metaphase plate, an imaginary plane equidistant between the two poles of the spindle. The centromeres of all the chromosomes are lined up on the metaphase plate. For each chromosome, the kinetochores of the two sister chromatids face opposite poles of the spindle. The microtubules attached to a particular chromatid all come from one pole of the spindle, and those attached to its sister chromatid come from the opposite pole.

Anaphase Anaphase begins when the two centromeres of each chromosome come apart, separating the sister chromatids. Once separate, each sister chromatid is considered a full-fledged (daughter) chromosome. Motor proteins of the kinetochores, powered by ATP, "walk" the daughter chromosomes centromere-first along the microtubules toward opposite poles of the cell. As this happens, the spindle microtubules attached to the kinetochores shorten. However, the spindle microtubules not attached to chromosomes lengthen. The poles are moved farther apart, elongating the cell. Anaphase is over when the chromosomes have reached the two poles of the cell.

Telophase The cell elongation that started in anaphase continues. Daughter nuclei appear at the two poles of the cell as nuclear envelopes form around the chromosomes. In terms of chromosome and spindle structure, telophase is roughly the reverse of prophase. By the end of telophase, the chromatin fiber of each chromosome uncoils, and the mitotic spindle disappears. Mitosis, the equal division of one nucleus into two genetically identical daughter nuclei, is now finished.

Cytokinesis Cytokinesis, the division of the cytoplasm, usually occurs along with telophase, with two daughter cells completely separating soon after the end of mitosis. In animal cells, a cleavage furrow forms and the cell pinches into two.

8.6 Cytokinesis differs for plant and animal cells

Cytokinesis, the division of the cytoplasm into two cells, typically begins during telophase. Given the differences between animal and plant cells (particularly the presence of a stiff cell wall in plant cells), it isn't surprising that cytokinesis proceeds differently for these two types of eukaryotic cells.

In animal cells, cytokinesis occurs by a process known as cleavage. As shown in **Figure 8.6A**, the first sign of cleavage is the appearance of a **cleavage furrow**, a shallow indentation in the cell surface. At the site of the furrow, the cytoplasm has a ring of microfilaments made of actin, associated with molecules of myosin. (Actin and myosin are the same proteins responsible for muscle contraction; see Module 30.8.) When the actin microfilaments interact with the myosin, the ring contracts. Contraction of the myosin ring is much like the pulling of a drawstring on a hooded sweatshirt: As the drawstring is pulled, the ring of the hood contracts inward, eventually pinching shut. Similarly, the cleavage furrow deepens and eventually pinches the parent cell in two, producing two completely separate daughter cells, each with its own nucleus and share of cytoplasm.

Cytokinesis is markedly different in plant cells, which possess cell walls **(Figure 8.6B)**. During telophase, membranous vesicles containing cell wall material collect at the middle of the parent cell. The vesicles fuse, forming a membranous disk called the **cell plate**. The cell plate grows outward, accumulating more cell wall materials as more vesicles fuse with it. Eventually, the membrane of the cell plate fuses with the plasma membrane, and the cell plate's contents join the parental cell wall. The result is two daughter cells, each bounded by its own plasma membrane and cell wall.

? **Contrast cytokinesis in animals with cytokinesis in plants.**

In animals, cytokinesis involves a cleavage furrow in which contracting microfilaments pinch the cell in two. In plants, it involves formation of a cell plate, a fusion of vesicles that forms new plasma membranes and new cell walls between the cells.

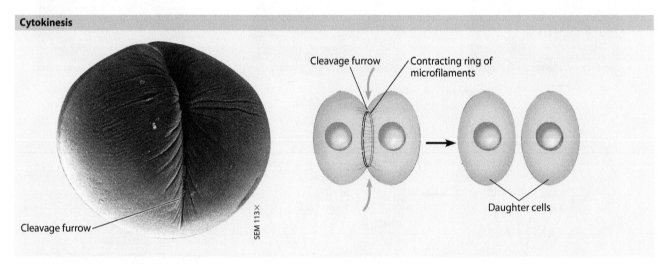

Cytokinesis

Cleavage furrow

Contracting ring of microfilaments

Daughter cells

Cleavage furrow

SEM 113×

▲ **Figure 8.6A** Cleavage of an animal cell

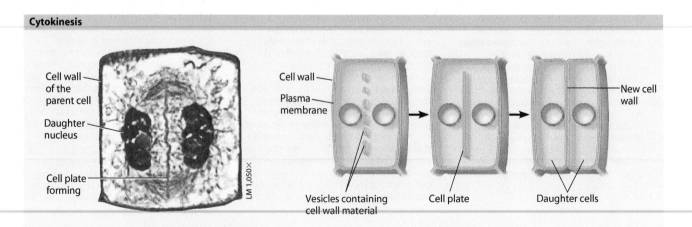

Cytokinesis

Cell wall of the parent cell

Daughter nucleus

Cell plate forming

LM 1,050×

Cell wall

Plasma membrane

New cell wall

Vesicles containing cell wall material

Cell plate

Daughter cells

▲ **Figure 8.6B** Cell plate formation in a plant cell

8.7 Anchorage, cell density, and chemical growth factors affect cell division

For a plant or an animal to grow and develop normally and maintain its tissues once fully grown, it must be able to control the timing of cell division in different parts of its body. For example, in the adult human, skin cells and the cells lining the digestive tract divide frequently throughout life, replacing cells that are constantly being abraded and sloughed off. In contrast, cells in the human liver usually do not divide unless the liver is damaged.

By growing animal cells in culture, researchers have been able to identify many factors, both physical and chemical, that can influence cell division. For example, cells fail to divide if an essential nutrient is left out of the culture medium. And most types of mammalian cells divide in culture only if certain specific growth factors are included. A **growth factor** is a protein secreted by certain body cells that stimulates other cells to divide (Figure 8.7A). Researchers have discovered at least 50 different growth factors that can trigger cell division. Different cell types respond specifically to certain growth factors or a combination of growth factors. For example, injury to the skin causes blood platelets to release a protein called platelet-derived growth factor. This protein promotes the rapid growth of connective tissue cells that help seal the wound. Another well-studied example is a protein called vascular endothelial growth factor (VEGF), which stimulates the growth of new blood vessels during fetal development and after injury. Interestingly, VEGF overproduction is a hallmark of many dangerous cancers; several anticancer drug therapies work by inhibiting the action of VEGF.

The effect of a physical factor on cell division is clearly seen in **density-dependent inhibition**, a phenomenon in

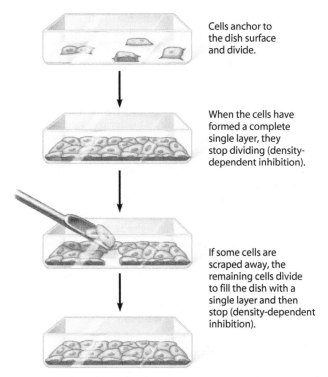

Cells anchor to the dish surface and divide.

When the cells have formed a complete single layer, they stop dividing (density-dependent inhibition).

If some cells are scraped away, the remaining cells divide to fill the dish with a single layer and then stop (density-dependent inhibition).

▲ Figure 8.7B   An experiment demonstrating density-dependent inhibition, using animal cells grown in culture

which crowded cells stop dividing. For example, animal cells growing on the surface of a dish multiply to form a single layer and usually stop dividing when they fill the space and touch one another (Figure 8.7B). If some cells are removed, those bordering the open space begin dividing again and continue until the vacancy is filled. What actually causes the cessation of growth? Studies of cultured cells suggest that physical contact of cell-surface proteins between adjacent cells is responsible for inhibiting cell division. One of the characteristics that distinguishes cancerous cells from normal body cells is their failure to exhibit density-dependent inhibition; cancer cells continue to divide even at high densities, piling up on one another.

Most animal cells also exhibit **anchorage dependence**; they must be in contact with a solid surface—such as the inside of a culture dish or the extracellular matrix of a tissue—to divide. Anchorage dependence, density-dependent inhibition, and the availability of growth factors are all important regulatory mechanisms controlling the division of the body's cells. How exactly do growth factors work? We pursue answers to this question in the next module.

? Compared to a control culture, the cells in an experimental culture are fewer but much larger in size when they cover the dish surface and stop growing. What is a reasonable hypothesis for this difference?

● The experimental culture is deficient in one or more growth factors.

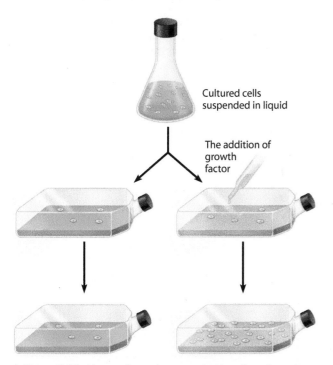

Cultured cells suspended in liquid

The addition of growth factor

▲ Figure 8.7A   An experiment demonstrating the effect of growth factors on the division of cultured animal cells

8.8 Growth factors signal the cell cycle control system

In a living animal, most cells are anchored in a fixed position and bathed in a solution of nutrients supplied by the blood, yet they usually do not divide unless they are signaled by other cells to do so. Growth factors are the main signals, and their role in promoting cell division leads us back to our earlier discussion of the cell cycle.

The sequential events of the cell cycle, represented by the circle of flat blocks in Figure 8.8A, are directed by a distinct cell cycle control system, represented by the knob in the center. The gray bar extending from the center represents the current position in the cell cycle. The **cell cycle control system** is a cyclically operating set of molecules in the cell that both triggers and coordinates key events in the cell cycle. The cell cycle is *not* like a row of falling dominoes, with each event causing the next one in line. Within the M phase, for example, metaphase does not automatically lead to anaphase. Instead, proteins of the cell cycle control system must trigger the separation of sister chromatids that marks the start of anaphase.

A checkpoint in the cell cycle is a critical control point where stop and go-ahead signals (represented by stop/go lights in the figure) can regulate the cycle. The default state in most animal cells is to halt the cell cycle at these checkpoints unless overridden by specific go-ahead signals.

The red and white gates in Figure 8.8A represent three major checkpoints in the cell cycle: during the G_1 and G_2 subphases of interphase and in the M phase. Intracellular signals detected by the control system tell it whether key cellular processes up to each point have been completed and thus whether or not the cell cycle should proceed past that point. The control system also receives messages from outside the cell, indicating both general environmental conditions and the presence of specific signal molecules from other cells. For many cells, the G_1 checkpoint seems to be the most important. If a cell receives a go-ahead signal—for example, from a growth factor—at the G_1 checkpoint, it will usually enter the S phase, eventually going on to complete its cycle and divide. If such a signal never arrives, the cell will switch to a permanently nondividing state called the G_0 phase. Many cells in the human body, such as mature nerve cells and muscle cells, are in the G_0 phase.

Figure 8.8B shows a simplified model for how a growth factor might affect the cell cycle control system at the G_1 checkpoint. A cell that responds to a growth factor (▽) has molecules of a specific receptor protein in its plasma membrane. Binding of the growth factor to the receptor triggers a signal transduction pathway in the cell. A signal transduction pathway is a series of protein molecules that conveys a message (see Modules 5.1 and 11.10). In this case, that message leads to cell division. The "signals" are changes that each protein molecule induces in the next molecule in the pathway. Via a series of relay proteins, a signal finally reaches the cell cycle control system and overrides the brakes that otherwise prevent progress of the cell cycle. In Figure 8.8B, the cell cycle is set off from the cell in a separate diagram because

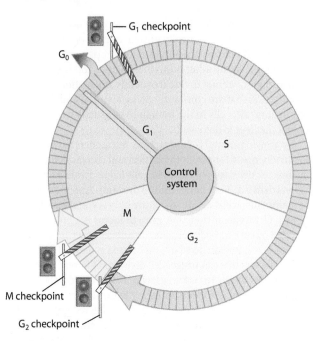

▲ Figure 8.8A   A schematic model for the cell cycle control system

the proteins making up the control system in the cell are not actually located together in one place.

Research on the control of the cell cycle is one of the hottest areas in biology today. This research is leading to a better understanding of cancer, which we discuss next.

? At which of the three checkpoints described in this module do the chromosomes exist as duplicated sister chromatids?

G_2 and the first half of M

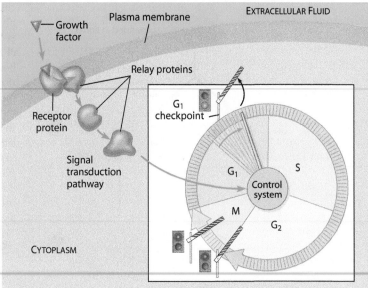

▲ Figure 8.8B   How a growth factor signals the cell cycle control system

| ## 8.9 Growing out of control, cancer cells produce malignant tumors

Cancer, which currently claims the lives of one out of every five people in the United States and other industrialized nations, is a disease of the cell cycle. Cancer cells do not heed the normal signals that regulate the cell cycle; they divide excessively and may invade other tissues of the body. If unchecked, cancer cells may continue to grow until they kill the organism.

The abnormal behavior of cancer cells begins when a single cell undergoes transformation, a process that converts a normal cell to a cancer cell. Transformation occurs following a mutation in one or more genes that encode for proteins in the cell cycle control system. Because a transformed cell grows abnormally, the immune system usually recognizes it and destroys it. However, if the cell evades destruction, it may proliferate to form a **tumor**, an abnormally growing mass of body cells. If the abnormal cells remain at the original site, the lump is called a **benign tumor**. Benign tumors can cause problems if they grow in and disrupt certain organs, such as the brain, but often they can be completely removed by surgery.

In contrast, a **malignant tumor** can spread into neighboring tissues and other parts of the body, displacing normal tissue and interrupting organ function as it goes (Figure 8.9). An individual with a malignant tumor is said to have **cancer**. Cancer cells may separate from the original tumor or secrete signal molecules that cause blood vessels to grow toward the tumor. A few tumor cells may then enter the blood and lymph vessels and move to other parts of the body, where they may proliferate and form new tumors. The spread of cancer cells beyond their original site is called **metastasis**.

Cancers are named according to the organ or tissue in which they originate. Liver cancer, for example, starts in liver tissue and may or may not spread from there. Based on their site of origin, cancers are grouped into four categories. **Carcinomas** are cancers that originate in the external or internal coverings of the body, such as the skin or the lining of the intestine. **Sarcomas** arise in tissues that support the body, such as bone and muscle. Cancers of blood-forming tissues, such as bone marrow, spleen, and lymph nodes, are called **leukemias** and **lymphomas**.

From studying cancer cells in culture, researchers have learned that these cells do not heed the normal signals that regulate the cell cycle. For example, many cancer cells have defective cell cycle control systems that proceed past checkpoints even in the absence of growth factors. Other cancer cells synthesize growth factors themselves, making them divide continuously. If cancer cells do stop dividing, they seem to do so at random points in the cell cycle, rather than at the

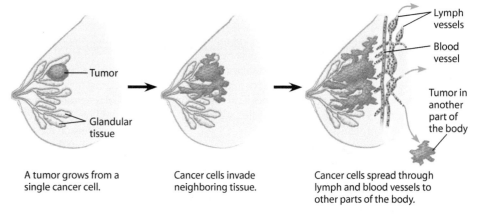

A tumor grows from a single cancer cell.

Cancer cells invade neighboring tissue.

Cancer cells spread through lymph and blood vessels to other parts of the body.

▲ **Figure 8.9** Growth and metastasis of a malignant (cancerous) tumor of the breast

normal cell cycle checkpoints. Moreover, in culture, cancer cells are "immortal"; they can go on dividing indefinitely, as long as they have a supply of nutrients (whereas normal mammalian cells divide only about 20 to 50 times before they stop).

Luckily, many tumors can be successfully treated. A tumor that appears to be localized may be removed surgically. Alternatively, it can be treated with concentrated beams of high-energy radiation, which usually damages DNA in cancer cells more than it does in normal cells, perhaps because cancer cells have lost the ability to repair such damage. However, there is sometimes enough damage to normal body cells to produce harmful side effects. For example, radiation damage to cells of the ovaries or testes can lead to sterility.

To treat widespread or metastatic tumors, chemotherapy is used. During periodic chemotherapy treatments, drugs are administered that disrupt specific steps in the cell cycle. For instance, the drug paclitaxel (trade name Taxol) freezes the mitotic spindle after it forms, which stops actively dividing cells from proceeding past metaphase. (Interestingly, Taxol was originally discovered in the bark of the Pacific yew tree, found mainly in the northwestern United States.) Vinblastin, a chemotherapeutic drug first obtained from the periwinkle plant (found in the rain forests of Madagascar), prevents the mitotic spindle from forming.

The side effects of chemotherapy are due to the drugs' effects on normal cells that rapidly divide. Nausea results from chemotherapy's effects on intestinal cells, hair loss from effects on hair follicle cells, and susceptibility to infection from effects on immune cell production.

We will return to the topic of cancer in Chapter 11, after studying the structure and function of genes. You will see that cancer results from changes in genes that code for proteins that control cell division.

 What is metastasis?

Metastasis is the spread of cancer cells from their original site of formation to other sites in the body.

8.10 Review: Mitosis provides for growth, cell replacement, and asexual reproduction

The three micrographs in Figures 8.10A–8.10C summarize the roles that mitotic cell division plays in the lives of multicellular organisms. **Figure 8.10A** shows some of the cells from the tip of a rapidly growing onion plant root. Notice the two cells in the middle row, whose nuclei are in the process of mitosis, as evidenced by the visibly compact chromosomes. Cell division in the root tip produces new cells, which elongate and bring about growth of the root.

Figure 8.10B shows a dividing bone marrow cell. Mitotic cell division within the red marrow of your body's bones—particularly within your ribs, vertebrae, breastbone, and hip—continuously creates new blood cells that replace older ones. Similar processes replace cells throughout your body. For example, dividing cells within your epidermis continuously replace dead cells that slough off the surface of your skin.

Figure 8.10C is a micrograph of a hydra, a cnidarian (relative of a sea jelly) that is a common inhabitant of freshwater lakes. A hydra is a tiny multicellular animal that reproduces by either sexual or asexual means. This individual is reproducing asexually by budding. A bud starts out as a mass of mitotically dividing cells growing on the side of the parent. Eventually, the offspring detaches from the parent and takes up life on its own. The offspring is literally a "chip off the old block," being genetically identical to (a clone of) its parent.

In all of the examples described here, the new cells have exactly the same number and types of chromosomes as the parent cells because of the way duplicated chromosomes divide during mitosis. Mitosis makes it possible for organisms to grow, regenerate and repair tissues, and reproduce asexually by producing cells that carry the same genes as the parent cells.

If we examine the cells of any individual organism or those from individuals of any one species, we see that almost all of them contain the same number and types of chromosomes. In the next module, we take a look at how genetic material is organized in chromosomes.

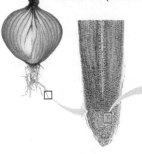

▶ **Figure 8.10A**
Growth (in an onion root)

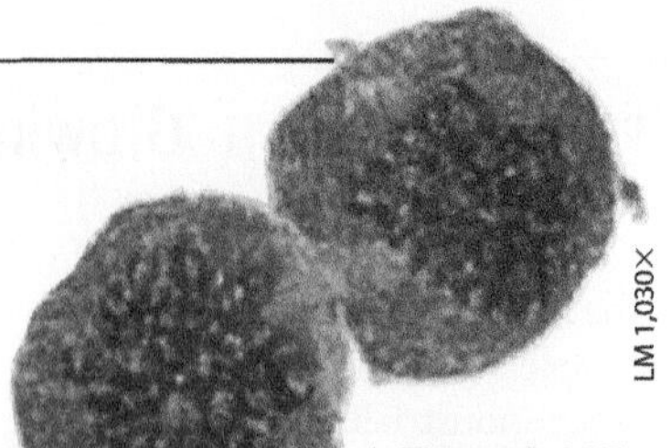

LM 700×

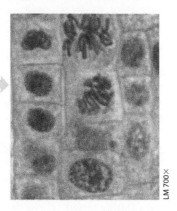

LM 1,030×

▲ **Figure 8.10B**
Cell replacement
(in bone marrow)

LM 22×

▲ **Figure 8.10C**
Asexual reproduction
(of a hydra)

? The body cells of elephants have 56 chromosomes. If an elephant skin cell with 56 chromosomes divides by mitosis, each daughter cell will have _____ chromosomes.

95

Meiosis and Crossing Over

8.11 Chromosomes are matched in homologous pairs

In humans, a typical body cell, called a **somatic cell**, has 46 chromosomes. If we use a microscope to examine human chromosomes in metaphase of mitosis, we see that the chromosomes, each consisting of two sister chromatids, can be arranged into matching pairs; **Figure 8.11** illustrates one pair of metaphase chromosomes. A human cell at metaphase contains 23 sets of duplicated chromosomes. Other species have different numbers of chromosomes, but these, too, usually occur in matched pairs. Moreover, when treated with special dyes, the chromosomes of a pair display matching staining patterns (represented by colored stripes in Figure 8.11).

Notice that each chromosome is duplicated, consisting of two sister chromatids joined at the centromere. Every (or almost every) chromosome has a twin that resembles it in length and centromere position. The two chromosomes of such a matching pair are called **homologous chromosomes** (or homologs) because they both carry genes controlling the same inherited characteristics. For example, if a gene that determines whether a person has freckles is located at a particular place, or **locus** (plural, *loci*), on one chromosome—within the narrow orange band in our drawing, for instance—then the homologous chromosome has that same gene at that same locus. However, the two chromosomes of a homologous pair may have different versions of the same gene.

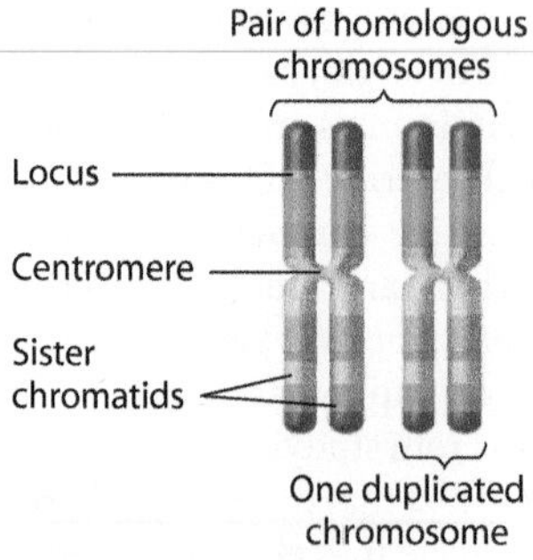

Pair of homologous chromosomes

Locus
Centromere
Sister chromatids

One duplicated chromosome

▲ **Figure 8.11** A pair of homologous chromosomes

In human females, the 46 chromosomes fall neatly into 23 homologous pairs. For a male, however, the chromosomes in one pair do not look alike. The nonidentical pair, only partly homologous, is the male's sex chromosomes. These **sex chromosomes** determine an individual's sex (male versus female), although these chromosomes carry genes that perform other functions as well. In mammals, males have one X chromosome and one Y chromosome. Females have two X chromosomes. The 22 remaining pairs of chromosomes, found in both males and females, are called **autosomes**. In the next module, we discuss how chromosomes are inherited.

? **Are all of *your* chromosomes fully homologous?**

● If you are female, then yes. If you are male, then no (your X and Y are only partly homologous).

8.12 Gametes have a single set of chromosomes

The development of a fertilized egg into a new adult organism is one phase of a multicellular organism's **life cycle**, the sequence of stages leading from the adults of one generation to the adults of the next (Figure 8.12A). Having two sets of chromosomes, one inherited from each parent, is a key factor in the life cycle of humans and all other species that reproduce sexually.

Humans, as well as most other animals and many plants, are said to be **diploid** organisms because all body cells contain pairs of homologous chromosomes. The total number of chromosomes is called the diploid number (abbreviated $2n$). For humans, the diploid number is 46; that is, $2n = 46$. The exceptions are the egg and sperm cells, collectively known as **gametes**. Each gamete has a single set of chromosomes: 22 autosomes plus a sex chromosome, either X or Y. A cell with a single chromosome set is called a **haploid** cell; it has only one member of each homologous pair. For humans, the haploid number (abbreviated n) is 23; that is, $n = 23$.

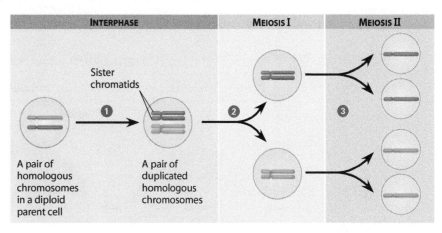

▲ **Figure 8.12B** How meiosis halves chromosome number

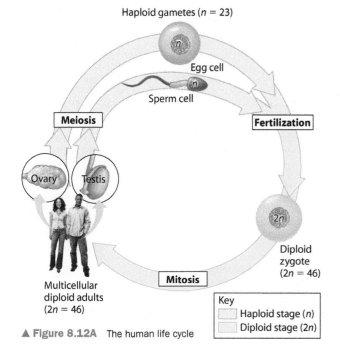

▲ **Figure 8.12A** The human life cycle

In the human life cycle, a haploid sperm cell from the father fuses with a haploid egg cell from the mother in the process of **fertilization**. The resulting fertilized egg, called a **zygote**, has two sets of homologous chromosomes and so is diploid. One set of homologous chromosomes comes from each parent. The life cycle is completed as a sexually mature adult develops from the zygote.

All sexual life cycles, including our own, involve an alternation of diploid and haploid stages. Producing haploid gametes prevents the chromosome number from doubling in every generation. Gametes are made by a special sort of cell division called meiosis, which occurs only in reproductive organs (ovaries and testes in animals). Whereas mitosis produces daughter cells with the same number of chromosomes as the parent cell, meiosis reduces the chromosome number by half. Figure 8.12B tracks one pair of homologous chromosomes. ❶ Each of the chromosomes is duplicated during interphase (before meiosis). ❷ The first division, meiosis I, segregates the two chromosomes of the homologous pair, packaging them in separate (haploid) daughter cells. But each chromosome is still doubled. ❸ Meiosis II separates the sister chromatids. Each of the four daughter cells is haploid and contains only a single chromosome from the homologous pair. We turn to meiosis next.

? **Imagine you stain a human cell and view it under a microscope. You observe 23 chromosomes, including a Y chromosome. You could conclude that this must be a _____ cell taken from the organ called the _____ .**

● sperm (since it is haploid) . . . testis (since it is from a male)

8.13 Meiosis reduces the chromosome number from diploid to haploid

Meiosis is a type of cell division that produces haploid gametes in diploid organisms. Two haploid gametes may then combine via fertilization to restore the diploid state in the zygote. Were it not for meiosis, each generation would have twice as much genetic material as the generation before!

Many of the stages of meiosis closely resemble corresponding stages in mitosis. Meiosis, like mitosis, is preceded by the duplication of chromosomes. However, this single duplication is followed by two consecutive cell divisions, called meiosis I and meiosis II. Because one duplication of the

chromosomes is followed by two divisions, each of the four daughter cells resulting from meiosis has a haploid set of chromosomes—half as many chromosomes as the parent cell. The drawings in Figure 8.13 show the two meiotic divisions for an animal cell with a diploid number of 6. The members of a pair of homologous chromosomes in Figure 8.13 (and later figures) are colored red and blue to help distinguish them. (Imagine that the red chromosomes were inherited from the mother and the blue chromosomes from the father.) One of the most important events in meiosis occurs

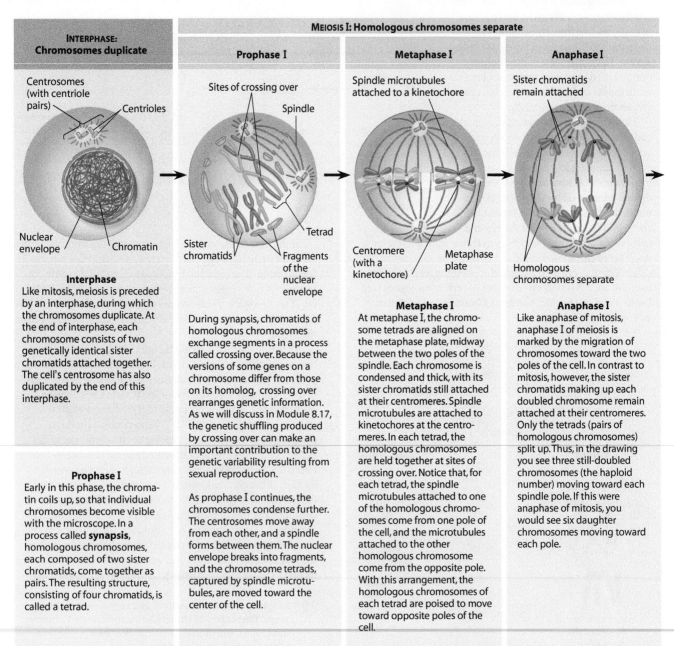

INTERPHASE: Chromosomes duplicate

Centrosomes (with centriole pairs)
Centrioles
Nuclear envelope
Chromatin

Interphase
Like mitosis, meiosis is preceded by an interphase, during which the chromosomes duplicate. At the end of interphase, each chromosome consists of two genetically identical sister chromatids attached together. The cell's centrosome has also duplicated by the end of this interphase.

Prophase I
Early in this phase, the chromatin coils up, so that individual chromosomes become visible with the microscope. In a process called **synapsis**, homologous chromosomes, each composed of two sister chromatids, come together as pairs. The resulting structure, consisting of four chromatids, is called a tetrad.

MEIOSIS I: Homologous chromosomes separate

Prophase I

Sites of crossing over
Spindle
Sister chromatids
Fragments of the nuclear envelope
Tetrad

During synapsis, chromatids of homologous chromosomes exchange segments in a process called crossing over. Because the versions of some genes on a chromosome differ from those on its homolog, crossing over rearranges genetic information. As we will discuss in Module 8.17, the genetic shuffling produced by crossing over can make an important contribution to the genetic variability resulting from sexual reproduction.

As prophase I continues, the chromosomes condense further. The centrosomes move away from each other, and a spindle forms between them. The nuclear envelope breaks into fragments, and the chromosome tetrads, captured by spindle microtubules, are moved toward the center of the cell.

Metaphase I

Spindle microtubules attached to a kinetochore
Centromere (with a kinetochore)
Metaphase plate

Metaphase I
At metaphase I, the chromosome tetrads are aligned on the metaphase plate, midway between the two poles of the spindle. Each chromosome is condensed and thick, with its sister chromatids still attached at their centromeres. Spindle microtubules are attached to kinetochores at the centromeres. In each tetrad, the homologous chromosomes are held together at sites of crossing over. Notice that, for each tetrad, the spindle microtubules attached to one of the homologous chromosomes come from one pole of the cell, and the microtubules attached to the other homologous chromosome come from the opposite pole. With this arrangement, the homologous chromosomes of each tetrad are poised to move toward opposite poles of the cell.

Anaphase I

Sister chromatids remain attached
Homologous chromosomes separate

Anaphase I
Like anaphase of mitosis, anaphase I of meiosis is marked by the migration of chromosomes toward the two poles of the cell. In contrast to mitosis, however, the sister chromatids making up each doubled chromosome remain attached at their centromeres. Only the tetrads (pairs of homologous chromosomes) split up. Thus, in the drawing you see three still-doubled chromosomes (the haploid number) moving toward each spindle pole. If this were anaphase of mitosis, you would see six daughter chromosomes moving toward each pole.

▲ Figure 8.13 The stages of meiosis

during prophase I. At this stage, four chromosomes (two sets of sister chromatids) are aligned and physically touching each other. When in this configuration, nonsister chromatids may trade segments. As you will learn in Module 8.17, this exchange of chromosome segments—called crossing over—is a key step in the generation of genetic diversity that occurs during sexual reproduction.

? **A cell has the haploid number of chromosomes, but each chromosome has two chromatids. The chromosomes are arranged singly at the center of the spindle. What is the meiotic stage?**

● Metaphase II (since the chromosomes line up two by two in metaphase I)

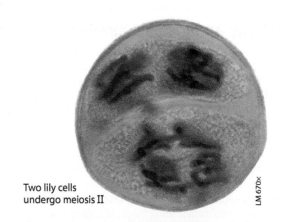

Two lily cells undergo meiosis II

LM 670×

MEIOSIS II: Sister chromatids separate

Telophase I and Cytokenesis	Prophase II	Metaphase II	Anaphase II	Telophase II and Cytokenesis

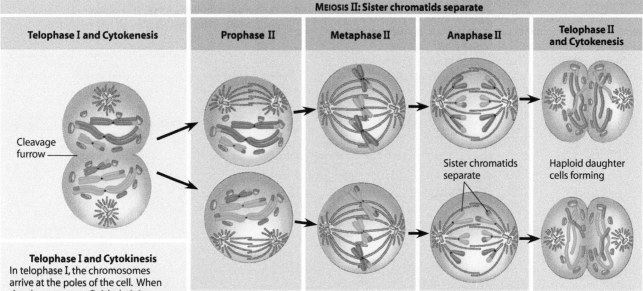

Cleavage furrow

Sister chromatids separate

Haploid daughter cells forming

Telophase I and Cytokinesis

In telophase I, the chromosomes arrive at the poles of the cell. When the chromosomes finish their journey, each pole of the cell has a haploid chromosome set, although each chromosome is still in duplicate form at this point. In other words, each chromosome still consists of two sister chromatids. Usually, cytokinesis occurs along with telophase I, and two haploid daughter cells are formed.

Following telophase I in some organisms, the chromosomes uncoil and the nuclear envelope re-forms, and there is an interphase before meiosis II begins. In other species, daughter cells produced in the first meiotic division immediately begin preparation for the second meiotic division. In either case, no chromosome duplication occurs between telophase I and the onset of meiosis II.

Meiosis II

Meiosis II is essentially the same as mitosis. The important difference is that meiosis II starts with a haploid cell.

During prophase II, a spindle forms and moves the chromosomes toward the middle of the cell. During metaphase II, the chromosomes are aligned on the metaphase plate as they are in mitosis, with the kinetochores of the sister chromatids of each chromosome pointing toward opposite poles. In anaphase II, the centromeres of sister chromatids finally separate, and the sister chromatids of each pair, now individual daughter chromosomes, move toward opposite poles of the cell. In telophase II, nuclei form at the cell poles, and cytokinesis occurs at the same time. There are now four daughter cells, each with the haploid number of (single) chromosomes.

8.14 Mitosis and meiosis have important similarities and differences

You have now learned the two ways that cells of eukaryotic organisms divide. Mitosis, which provides for growth, tissue repair, and asexual reproduction, produces daughter cells that are genetically identical to the parent cell. Meiosis, needed for sexual reproduction, yields genetically unique haploid daughter cells—cells with only one member of each homologous chromosome pair.

For both mitosis and meiosis, the chromosomes duplicate only once, during the S phase of the preceding interphase. Mitosis involves one division of the nucleus, and it is usually accompanied by cytokinesis, producing two identical diploid cells. Meiosis entails two nuclear and cytoplasmic divisions, yielding four haploid cells.

Figure 8.14 compares mitosis and meiosis, tracing these two processes for a diploid parent cell with four chromosomes. Homologous chromosomes are those matching in size.

Notice that all the events unique to meiosis occur during meiosis I. In prophase I, duplicated homologous chromosomes pair to form **tetrads**, sets of four chromatids, with each pair of sister chromatids joined at their centromeres. In metaphase I, tetrads (not individual chromosomes) are aligned at the metaphase plate. During anaphase I, pairs of homologous chromosomes separate, but the sister chromatids of each chromosome stay together. At the end of meiosis I, there are two haploid cells, but each chromosome still has two sister chromatids.

Meiosis II is virtually identical to mitosis in that it separates sister chromatids. But unlike mitosis, each daughter cell produced by meiosis II has only a *haploid* set of chromosomes.

? Explain how mitosis conserves chromosome number while meiosis reduces the number from diploid to haploid.

● In mitosis, the duplication of chromosomes is followed by one division of the cell. In meiosis, homologous chromosomes separate in the first of two cell divisions; after the second division, each new cell ends up with just a single haploid set.

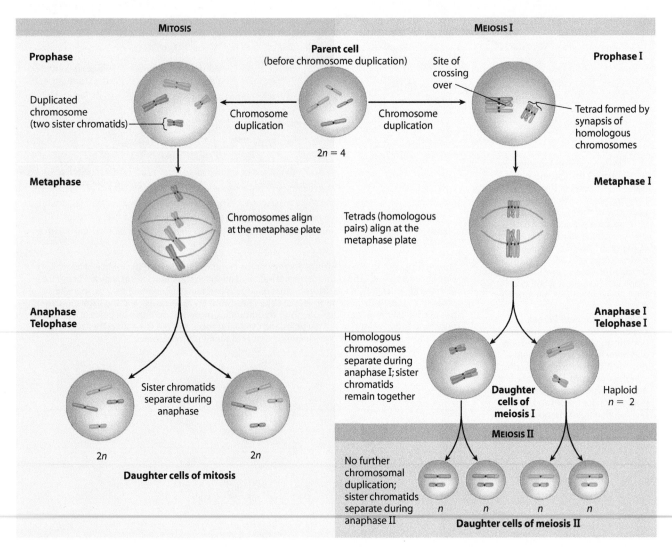

▲ Figure 8.14 Comparison of mitosis and meiosis

8.15 Independent orientation of chromosomes in meiosis and random fertilization lead to varied offspring

As we discussed in Module 8.1, offspring that result from sexual reproduction are highly varied; they are genetically different from their parents and from one another. How does this genetic variation account result from meiosis?

Figure 8.15 illustrates one way in which the process of meiosis contributes to genetic differences in gametes. The figure shows how the arrangement of homologous chromosome pairs at metaphase of meiosis I affects the resulting gametes. Once again, our example is from a diploid organism with four chromosomes (two homologous pairs), with colors used to differentiate homologous chromosomes (red for chromosomes inherited from the mother and blue for those from the father).

The orientation of the pairs of homologous chromosomes (tetrads) at metaphase I—whether the maternal (red) or paternal (blue) chromosome is closer to a given pole—is as random as the flip of a coin. Thus, there is a 50% chance that a particular daughter cell will get the maternal chromosome of a certain homologous pair and a 50% chance that it will receive the paternal chromosome. In this example, there are two possible ways that the two tetrads can align during metaphase I. In possibility A, the tetrads are oriented with both red chromosomes on the same side of the metaphase plate. Therefore, the gametes produced in possibility A can each have either two red *or* two blue chromosomes (bottom row, combinations 1 and 2).

In possibility B, the tetrads are oriented differently (blue/red and red/blue). This arrangement produces gametes that each have one red and one blue chromosome. Furthermore, half the gametes have a big blue chromosome and a small red one (combination 3), and half have a big red chromosome and a small blue one (combination 4).

So we see that for this example, four chromosome combinations are possible in the gametes, and in fact the organism will produce gametes of all four types in equal quantities. For a species with more than two pairs of chromosomes, such as humans, *all* the chromosome pairs orient independently at metaphase I. (Chromosomes X and Y behave as a homologous pair in meiosis.)

For any species, the total number of combinations of chromosomes that meiosis can package into gametes is 2^n, where n is the haploid number. For the organism in this figure, $n = 2$, so the number of chromosome combinations is 2^2, or 4. For a human ($n = 23$), there are 2^{23}, or about 8 million possible chromosome combinations! This means that each gamete you produce contains one of roughly 8 million possible combinations of chromosomes inherited from your mother and father.

How many possibilities are there when a gamete from one individual unites with a gamete from another individual in fertilization? In humans, the random fusion of a single sperm with a single ovum during fertilization will produce a zygote with any of about 64 trillion (8 million $\times$ 8 million) combinations of chromosomes! While the random nature of fertilization adds a huge amount of potential variability to the offspring of sexual reproduction, there is in fact even more variety created during meiosis, as we see in the next two modules.

? **A particular species of worm has a diploid number of 10. How many chromosomal combinations are possible for gametes formed by meiosis?**

⊙ 32; $2n = 10$, so $n = 5$ and $2^n = 32$

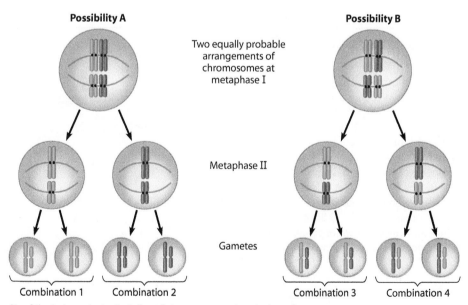

▲ Figure 8.15 Results of the independent orientation of chromosomes at metaphase I

8.16 Homologous chromosomes may carry different versions of genes

So far, we have focused on genetic variability in gametes and zygotes at the whole-chromosome level. We have yet to discuss the actual genetic information—the genes—contained in the chromosomes. The question we need to answer now is this: What is the significance of the independent orientation of metaphase chromosomes at the level of genes?

Let's take a simple example, the single tetrad in Figure 8.16. The letters on the homologous chromosomes represent genes. Recall that homologous chromosomes have genes for the same characteristic at corresponding loci. Our example involves hypothetical genes controlling the appearance of mice. C and c are different versions of a gene for one characteristic, coat color; E and e are different versions of a gene for another characteristic, eye color. (As you'll learn in later chapters, different versions of a gene contain slightly different nucleotide sequences in the chromosomal DNA.)

Let's say that C represents the gene for a brown coat and that c represents the gene for white coat. In the chromosome diagram, notice that C is at the same locus on the red homolog as c is on the blue one. Likewise, gene E (for black eyes) is at the same locus as e (pink eyes).

The fact that homologous chromosomes can bear two different kinds of genetic information for the same characteristic (for instance, coat color) is what really makes gametes—and therefore offspring—different from one another. In our example, a gamete carrying a red chromosome would have genes specifying brown coat color and black eye color, while a gamete

with the homologous blue chromosome would have genes for white coat and pink eyes. Thus, we see how a tetrad with genes shown for only two characteristics can yield two genetically different kinds of gametes. In the next module, we go a step further and see how this same tetrad can actually yield *four* different kinds of gametes.

? In the tetrad of Figure 8.16, use labels to distinguish the pair of homologous chromosomes from sister chromatids.

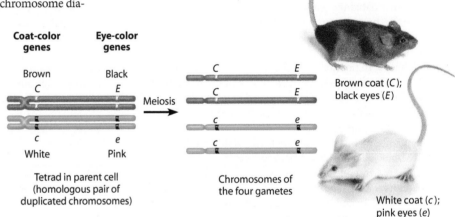

▲ **Figure 8.16** Differing genetic information (coat color and eye color) on homologous chromosomes

---

8.17 Crossing over further increases genetic variability

Crossing over is an exchange of corresponding segments between nonsister chromatids of homologous chromosomes. The micrograph and drawing in Figure 8.17A show the results of crossing over between two homologous chromosomes during prophase I of meiosis. The chromosomes are a tetrad—a set of four chromatids, with each pair of sister chromatids joined together. The sites of crossing over appear as X-shaped regions; each is called a **chiasma** (Greek for "cross"). A chiasma (plural, *chiasmata*) is a place where two homologous (nonsister) chromatids are attached to each other. Figure 8.17B illustrates how crossing over can produce new combinations of genes, using as examples the hypothetical mouse genes mentioned in the previous module.

Crossing over begins very early in prophase I of meiosis. At that time, homologous chromosomes are paired all along their

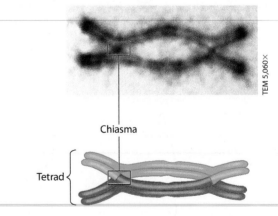

▲ **Figure 8.17A** Chiasmata, the sites of crossing over

lengths, with a precise gene-by-gene alignment. At the top of the figure is a tetrad with coat-color (*C, c*) and eye-color (*E, e*) genes labeled. ① The DNA molecules of two nonsister chromatids—one maternal (red) and one paternal (blue)—break at the same place. ② Immediately, the two broken chromatids join together in a new way (red to blue and blue to red). In effect, the two homologous segments trade places, or cross over, producing hybrid chromosomes (red/blue and blue/red) with new combinations of maternal and paternal genes. ③ When the homologous chromosomes separate in anaphase I, each contains a new segment originating from its homolog. ④ Finally, in meiosis II, the sister chromatids separate, each going to a different gamete.

In this example, if there were no crossing over, meiosis could produce only two genetic types of gametes. These would be the ones ending up with the "parental" types of chromosomes (either all blue or all red), carrying either genes *C* and *E* or genes *c* and *e*. These are the same two kinds of gametes we saw in Figure 8.16. With crossing over, two other types of gametes can result, ones that are part blue and part red. One of these carries genes *C* and *e,* and the other carries genes *c* and *E.* Chromosomes with these combinations of genes would not exist if not for crossing over. They are called "recombinant" because they result from **genetic recombination**, the production of gene combinations different from those carried by the original parental chromosomes.

In meiosis in humans, an average of one to three crossover events occur per chromosome pair. Thus, if you were to examine a chromosome from one of your gametes, you would most likely find that it is not exactly like any one of your own chromosomes. Rather, it is probably a patchwork of segments derived from a pair of homologous chromosomes, cut and pasted together to form a chromosome with a unique combination of genes.

We have now examined three sources of genetic variability in sexually reproducing organisms: independent orientation of chromosomes at metaphase I, random fertilization, and crossing over during prophase I of meiosis. When we take up molecular genetics in Chapter 10, we will see yet another source of variability: mutations, or rare changes in the DNA of genes. The different versions of genes that homologous chromosomes may have at each locus originally arise from mutations, so mutations are ultimately responsible for genetic diversity in living organisms. Once these differences arise, reshuffling of the different versions during sexual reproduction increases genetic variation. When we discuss natural selection and evolution in Unit III, we will see that this genetic variety in offspring is the raw material for natural selection.

Our discussion of meiosis to this point has focused on the process as it normally occurs. In the next, and last, major section of the chapter, we consider some of the consequences of errors in the process.

❓ **Describe how crossing over and the random alignment of homologous chromosomes on the metaphase I plate account for the genetic variation among gametes formed by meiosis.**

● Crossing over creates recombinant chromosomes having a combination of genes that were originally on different, though homologous, chromosomes. Homologous chromosome pairs are oriented randomly at metaphase of meiosis I.

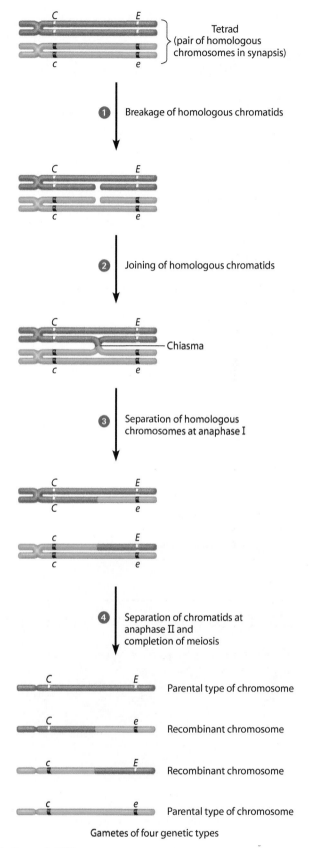

Tetrad (pair of homologous chromosomes in synapsis)

① Breakage of homologous chromatids

② Joining of homologous chromatids

Chiasma

③ Separation of homologous chromosomes at anaphase I

④ Separation of chromatids at anaphase II and completion of meiosis

Parental type of chromosome

Recombinant chromosome

Recombinant chromosome

Parental type of chromosome

Gametes of four genetic types

▲ **Figure 8.17B** How crossing over leads to genetic recombination

Alterations of Chromosome Number and Structure

8.18 A karyotype is a photographic inventory of an individual's chromosomes

Errors in meiosis can lead to gametes containing chromosomes in abnormal numbers or with major alterations in their structure. Fertilization involving such abnormal gametes results in offspring with chromosomal abnormalities. Such conditions can be readily detected in a **karyotype**, an ordered display of magnified images of an individual's chromosomes arranged in pairs. A karyotype shows the chromosomes condensed and doubled, as they appear in metaphase of mitosis.

To prepare a karyotype, medical scientists often use lymphocytes, a type of white blood cell. A blood sample is treated with a chemical that stimulates mitosis. After growing

in culture for several days, the cells are treated with another chemical to arrest mitosis at metaphase, when the chromosomes, each consisting of two joined sister chromatids, are most highly condensed. **Figure 8.18** outlines the steps in one method for the preparation of a karyotype from a blood sample.

The photograph in step 5 shows the karyotype of a normal human male. Images of the 46 chromosomes from a single diploid cell are arranged in 23 homologous pairs: autosomes numbered from 1 to 22 (starting with the largest) and one pair of sex chromosomes (X and Y in this case). The chromosomes had been stained to reveal band patterns, which are helpful in

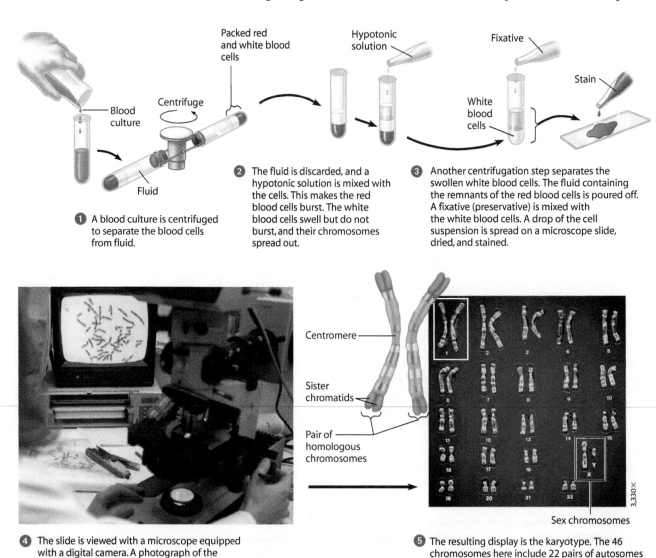

1 A blood culture is centrifuged to separate the blood cells from fluid.

2 The fluid is discarded, and a hypotonic solution is mixed with the cells. This makes the red blood cells burst. The white blood cells swell but do not burst, and their chromosomes spread out.

3 Another centrifugation step separates the swollen white blood cells. The fluid containing the remnants of the red blood cells is poured off. A fixative (preservative) is mixed with the white blood cells. A drop of the cell suspension is spread on a microscope slide, dried, and stained.

4 The slide is viewed with a microscope equipped with a digital camera. A photograph of the chromosomes is entered into a computer, which electronically arranges them by size and shape.

5 The resulting display is the karyotype. The 46 chromosomes here include 22 pairs of autosomes and two sex chromosomes, X and Y. Although difficult to discern in the karyotype, each of the chromosomes consists of two sister chromatids lying very close together (as shown in the diagram).

▲ **Figure 8.18** Preparation of a karyotype from a blood sample

differentiating the chromosomes and in detecting structural abnormalities. Among the alterations that can be detected by karyotyping is trisomy 21, the basis of Down syndrome, which we discuss next.

The karyotype in Figure 8.18 shows the normal human complement of 23 pairs of chromosomes. Compare it with **Figure 8.19A**; besides having two X chromosomes (because it's from a female), notice that there are three number 21 chromosomes, making 47 chromosomes in total. This condition is called **trisomy 21**.

In most cases, a human embryo with an abnormal number of chromosomes is spontaneously aborted (miscarried) long before birth. But some aberrations in chromosome number, including trisomy 21, appear to upset the genetic balance less drastically, and individuals carrying them can survive. These people have a characteristic set of symptoms, called a syndrome. A person with trisomy 21, for instance, has a condition called **Down syndrome**, named after John Langdon Down, who described the syndrome in 1866.

Trisomy 21 is the most common chromosome number abnormality. Affecting about one out of every 700 children born, it is also the most common serious birth defect in the United States. Chromosome 21 is one of our smallest chromosomes, but an extra copy produces a number of effects. Down syndrome includes characteristic facial features—frequently a round face, a skin fold at the inner corner of the eye, a flattened nose bridge, and small, irregular teeth—as well as short stature, heart defects, and susceptibility to respiratory infections, leukemia, and Alzheimer's disease.

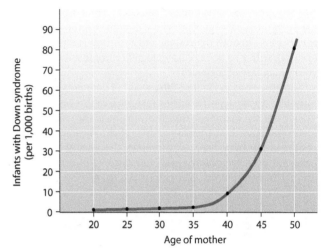

▲ Figure 8.19B   Maternal age and incidence of Down syndrome

People with Down syndrome usually have a life span shorter than normal. They also exhibit varying degrees of mental retardation. However, some individuals with the syndrome live to middle age or beyond, and many are socially adept and able to hold jobs. A few women with Down syndrome have had children, though most people with the syndrome are sexually underdeveloped and sterile. Half the eggs produced by a woman with Down syndrome will have the extra chromosome 21, so there is a 50% chance that she will transmit the syndrome to her child.

As indicated in **Figure 8.19B**, the incidence of Down syndrome in the offspring of normal parents increases markedly with the age of the mother. Down syndrome affects less than 0.05% of children (fewer than one in 2,000) born to women under age 30. The risk climbs to 1% (ten in 1,000) for mothers at age 40 and is even higher for older mothers. Because of this relatively high risk, pregnant women over 35 are candidates for fetal testing for trisomy 21 and other chromosomal abnormalities (see Module 9.10).

What causes trisomy 21? We address that question in the next module.

Trisomy 21

▲ Figure 8.19A   A karyotype showing trisomy 21, and an individual with Down syndrome

8.20 Accidents during meiosis can alter chromosome number

Within the human body, meiosis occurs repeatedly as the testes or ovaries produce gametes. Almost always, the meiotic spindle distributes chromosomes to daughter cells without error. But there is an occasional mishap in which the members of a chromosome pair fail to separate. Such an error is called a **nondisjunction**. Figures 8.20A and 8.20B illustrate two ways that a nondisjunction can occur. For simplicity, we use a hypothetical organism whose diploid chromosome number is 4. In both figures, the cell at the top is diploid ($2n = 4$), with two pairs of homologous chromosomes undergoing anaphase of meiosis I.

Sometimes, as in Figure 8.20A, a pair of homologous chromosomes do not separate during meiosis I. In this case, even though the rest of meiosis occurs normally, all the resulting gametes end up with abnormal numbers of chromosomes. Two of the gametes have three chromosomes; the other two gametes have only one chromosome each. In Figure 8.20B, meiosis I is normal, but one pair of sister chromatids fail to move apart

during meiosis II. In this case, two of the resulting gametes are abnormal; the other two gametes are normal.

If an abnormal gamete produced by nondisjunction unites with a normal gamete during fertilization, the result is a zygote with an abnormal number of chromosomes. Mitosis will then transmit the mistake to all embryonic cells. If this were a real organism and it survived, it would have an abnormal karyotype and probably a syndrome of disorders caused by the abnormal number of genes. For example, if there is nondisjunction affecting human chromosome 21, some resulting gametes will carry an extra chromosome 21. If one of these gametes unites with a normal gamete, trisomy 21 (Down syndrome) will result. Nondisjunction can also affect chromosomes other than 21, as we see next.

? **Explain how nondisjunction could result in a diploid gamete.**

● A diploid gamete would result if the nondisjunction affected all the chromosomes during one of the meiotic divisions.

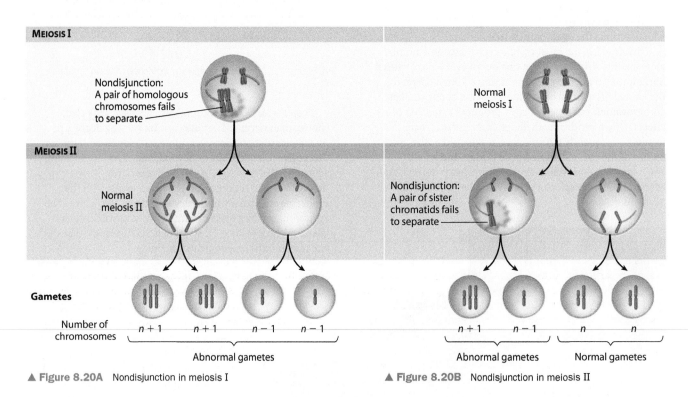

▲ Figure 8.20A   Nondisjunction in meiosis I

▲ Figure 8.20B   Nondisjunction in meiosis II

CONNECTION | ## 8.21 Abnormal numbers of sex chromosomes do not usually affect survival

Nondisjunction can result in abnormal numbers of sex chromosomes, X and Y. Unusual numbers of sex chromosomes seem to upset the genetic balance less than unusual numbers of autosomes. This may be because the Y chromosome is very

small and carries relatively few genes. Furthermore, mammalian cells usually operate with only one functioning X chromosome because other copies of the chromosome become inactivated in each cell (as you'll learn in Module 11.2).

TABLE 8.21 | ABNORMALITIES OF SEX CHROMOSOME NUMBER IN HUMANS

Sex Chromosomes	Syndrome	Origin of Nondisjunction	Frequency in Population
XXY	Klinefelter syndrome (male)	Meiosis in egg or sperm formation	$\frac{1}{2,000}$
XYY	None (normal male)	Meiosis in sperm formation	$\frac{1}{2,000}$
XXX	None (normal female)	Meiosis in egg or sperm formation	$\frac{1}{1,000}$
XO	Turner syndrome (female)	Meiosis in egg or sperm formation	$\frac{1}{5,000}$

Table 8.21 lists the most common human sex chromosome abnormalities. An extra X chromosome in a male, making him XXY, occurs approximately once in every 2,000 live births (once in every 1,000 male births). Men with this disorder, called Klinefelter syndrome, have male sex organs and normal intelligence, but the testes are abnormally small, the individual is sterile, and he often has breast enlargement and other female body characteristics. Klinefelter syndrome is also found in individuals with more than three sex chromosomes, such as XXYY, XXXY, or XXXXY. These abnormal numbers of sex chromosomes result from multiple nondisjunctions; such men are more likely to have developmental disabilities than XY or XXY individuals.

Human males with an extra Y chromosome (XYY) do not have any well-defined syndrome, although they tend to be taller than average. Females with an extra X chromosome (XXX) cannot be distinguished from XX females except by karyotype.

Females who lack an X chromosome are designated XO; the O indicates the absence of a second sex chromosome. These women have Turner syndrome. They have a characteristic appearance, including short stature and often a web of skin extending between the neck and the shoulders. Women with Turner syndrome are sterile because their sex organs do not fully mature at adolescence. If left untreated, girls with Turner syndrome have poor development of breasts and other secondary sexual characteristics. Artificial administration of estrogen can alleviate these symptoms. Women with Turner syndrome have normal intelligence. The XO condition is the sole known case where having only 45 chromosomes is not fatal in humans.

The sex chromosome abnormalities described here illustrate the crucial role of the Y chromosome in determining sex. In general, a single Y chromosome is enough to produce "maleness," even in combination with several X chromosomes. The absence of a Y chromosome yields "femaleness."

? What is the total number of autosomes you would expect to find in the karyotype of a female with Turner syndrome?

● 44 (plus one sex chromosome)

8.22 New species can arise from errors in cell division

Errors in meiosis or mitosis do not always lead to problems. In fact, biologists hypothesize that such errors have been instrumental in the evolution of many species. Numerous plant species, in particular, seem to have originated from accidents during cell division that resulted in extra sets of chromosomes. The new species is polyploid, meaning that it has more than two sets of homologous chromosomes in each somatic cell. At least half of all species of flowering plants are polyploid, including such useful ones as wheat, potatoes, apples, and cotton.

Let's consider one scenario by which a diploid (2n) plant species might generate a tetraploid (4n) plant. Imagine that, like many plants, our diploid plant produces both sperm and egg cells and can self-fertilize. If meiosis fails to occur in the plant's reproductive organs and gametes are instead produced by mitosis, the gametes will be diploid. The union of a diploid (2n) sperm with a diploid (2n) egg during self-fertilization will produce a tetraploid (4n) zygote, which may develop into a mature tetraploid plant that can itself reproduce by self-fertilization. The tetraploid plants will constitute a new species, one that has evolved in just one generation.

Although polyploid animal species are less common than polyploid plants, they are known to occur among the fishes and amphibians (Figure 8.22). Moreover, researchers in Chile have identified the first candidate for polyploidy among the mammals—a rat whose cells seem to be tetraploid. Tetraploid organisms are sometimes strikingly different from their recent diploid ancestors; they may be larger, for example. Scientists don't yet understand exactly how polyploidy brings about such differences.

? What is a polyploid organism?

● One with more than two sets of homologous chromosomes in its body cells.

▶ Figure 8.22 The gray tree frog (*Hyla versicolor*), a tetraploid organism

8.23 Alterations of chromosome structure can cause birth defects and cancer

Even if all chromosomes are present in normal numbers, abnormalities in chromosome structure may cause disorders. Breakage of a chromosome can lead to a variety of rearrangements affecting the genes of that chromosome (**Figure 8.23A**). If a fragment of a chromosome is lost, the remaining chromosome will then have a **deletion**. If a fragment from one chromosome joins to a sister chromatid or homologous chromosome, it will produce a **duplication**. If a fragment reattaches to the original chromosome but in the reverse orientation, an **inversion** results.

Inversions are less likely than deletions or duplications to produce harmful effects, because in inversions all genes are still present in their normal number. Many deletions in human chromosomes, however, cause serious physical and mental problems. One example is a specific deletion in chromosome 5 that causes *cri du chat* ("cry of the cat") syndrome. A child born with this syndrome is mentally retarded, has a small head with unusual facial features, and has a cry that sounds like the mewing of a distressed cat. Such individuals usually die in infancy or early childhood.

Another type of chromosomal change is chromosomal **translocation**, the attachment of a chromosomal fragment to a nonhomologous chromosome. As shown in the figure, a translocation may be reciprocal; that is, two nonhomologous chromosomes may exchange segments. Like inversions, translocations may or may not be harmful. Some people with Down syndrome have only part of a third chromosome 21; as the result of a translocation, this partial chromosome is attached to another (nonhomologous) chromosome.

Whereas chromosomal changes present in sperm or egg can cause congenital disorders, such changes in a somatic cell may contribute to the development of cancer. For example, a chromosomal translocation in somatic cells in the bone marrow is associated with chronic myelogenous leukemia (CML). CML is one of the most common types of leukemia.

(Leukemias are cancers affecting cells that give rise to white blood cells, or leukocytes.) In the cancerous cells of most CML patients, a part of chromosome 22 has switched places with a small fragment from a tip of chromosome 9 (**Figure 8.23B**). This reciprocal translocation creates a hybrid gene that codes for an abnormal protein. This protein stimulates cell division, leading to leukemia. The chromosome ending up with the activated cancer-causing gene is called the "Philadelphia chromosome," after the city where it was discovered.

Because the chromosomal changes in cancer are usually confined to somatic cells, cancer is not usually inherited. We'll return to cancer in Chapter 11. In Chapter 9, we continue our study of genetic principles, looking first at the historical development of the science of genetics and then at the rules governing the way traits are passed from parents to offspring.

? **How is reciprocal translocation different from normal crossing over?**

● Reciprocal translocation swaps chromosome segments between nonhomologous chromosomes. Crossing over normally exchanges corresponding segments between homologous chromosomes.

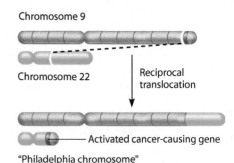

▲ **Figure 8.23B** The translocation associated with chronic myelogenous leukemia

Deletion	Inversion
A segment of a chromosome is removed	A segment of a chromosome is removed and then reinserted "backward" to its original orientation
Duplication	**Reciprocal translocation**
A segment of a chromosome is copied and inserted into the homologous chromosome	Segments of two nonhomologous chromosomes swap locations with each other

Homologous chromosomes

Nonhomologous chromosomes

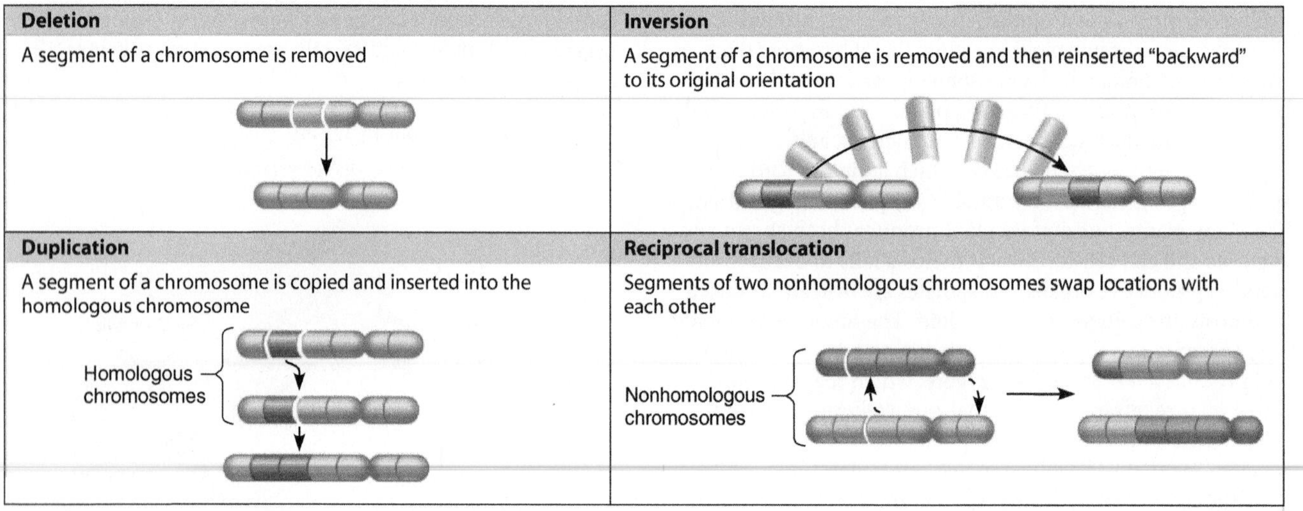

▲ **Figure 8.23A** Alterations of chromosome structure

For Practice Quizzes, BioFlix, MP3 Tutors, and Activities, go to www.masteringbiology.com.

Reviewing the Concepts

Cell Division and Reproduction (8.1–8.2)

8.1 Cell division plays many important roles in the lives of organisms. Cell division is at the heart of the reproduction of cells and organisms because cells come only from preexisting cells. Some organisms reproduce through asexual reproduction, and their offspring are all genetic copies of the parent and of each other. Others reproduce through sexual reproduction, creating a variety of offspring, each with a unique combination of traits.

8.2 Prokaryotes reproduce by binary fission. Prokaryotic cells reproduce asexually by cell division. As the cell replicates its single chromosome, the copies move apart; the growing membrane then divides the cell.

The Eukaryotic Cell Cycle and Mitosis (8.3–8.10)

8.3 The large, complex chromosomes of eukaryotes duplicate with each cell division. A eukaryotic cell has many more genes than a prokaryotic cell, and they are grouped into multiple chromosomes in the nucleus. Each chromosome contains one very long DNA molecule associated with proteins. Individual chromosomes are visible only when the cell is in the process of dividing; otherwise, they are in the form of thin, loosely packed chromatin fibers. Before a cell starts dividing, the chromosomes duplicate, producing sister chromatids (containing identical DNA) that are joined together. Cell division involves the separation of sister chromatids and results in two daughter cells, each containing a complete and identical set of chromosomes.

8.4 The cell cycle multiplies cells.

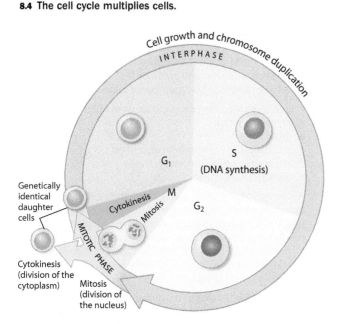

8.5 Cell division is a continuum of dynamic changes. Mitosis distributes duplicated chromosomes into two daughter nuclei. After the chromosomes are coiled up, a mitotic spindle made of microtubules moves them to the middle of the cell. The sister

chromatids then separate and move to opposite poles of the cell, where two new nuclei form. Cytokinesis, in which the cell divides in two, overlaps the end of mitosis.

8.6 Cytokinesis differs for plant and animal cells. In animals, cytokinesis occurs by a constriction of the cell (cleavage). In plants, a membranous cell plate splits the cell in two.

8.7 Anchorage, cell density, and chemical growth factors affect cell division. Most animal cells divide only when stimulated by growth factors, and some not at all. Growth factors are proteins secreted by cells that stimulate other cells to divide. In laboratory cultures, most normal cells divide only when attached to a surface. They continue dividing until they touch one another.

8.8 Growth factors signal the cell cycle control system. A set of proteins within the cell controls the cell cycle. Signals affecting critical checkpoints in the cell cycle determine whether a cell will go through the complete cycle and divide. The binding of growth factors to specific receptors on the plasma membrane is usually necessary for cell division.

8.9 Growing out of control, cancer cells produce malignant tumors. Cancer cells divide excessively to form masses called tumors. Malignant tumors can invade other tissues. Radiation and chemotherapy are effective as cancer treatments because they interfere with cell division.

8.10 Review: Mitosis provides for growth, cell replacement, and asexual reproduction. When the cell cycle operates normally, mitotic cell division functions in growth, replacement of damaged and lost cells, and asexual reproduction.

Meiosis and Crossing Over (8.11–8.17)

8.11 Chromosomes are matched in homologous pairs. The somatic (body) cells of each species contain a specific number of chromosomes; for example, human cells have 46, consisting of 23 pairs (two sets) of homologous chromosomes. The chromosomes of a homologous pair of autosomes carry genes for the same characteristics at the same place, or locus. X and Y chromosomes are only partly homologous.

8.12 Gametes have a single set of chromosomes. Cells with two sets of homologous chromosomes are diploid. Gametes—eggs and sperm—are haploid cells with a single set of chromosomes. Sexual life cycles involve the alternation of haploid and diploid stages.

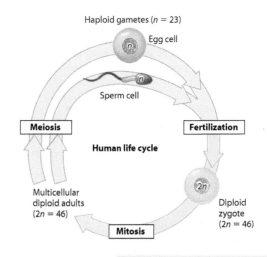

8.13 Meiosis reduces the chromosome number from diploid to haploid. Meiosis, like mitosis, is preceded by chromosome duplication, but in meiosis, the cell divides twice to form four daughter cells. The first division, meiosis I, starts with synapsis, the pairing of homologous chromosomes. In crossing over, homologous chromosomes exchange corresponding segments. Meiosis I separates the members of each homologous pair and produces two daughter cells, each with one set of chromosomes. Meiosis II is essentially the same as mitosis: In each of the cells, the sister chromatids of each chromosome separate. The result is a total of four haploid cells.

8.14 Mitosis and meiosis have important similarities and differences. Both mitosis and meiosis begin with diploid parent cells that have chromosomes duplicated during the previous interphase. But mitosis produces two genetically identical diploid somatic daughter cells, while meiosis produces four genetically unique haploid gametes.

8.15 Independent orientation of chromosomes in meiosis and random fertilization lead to varied offspring. Each chromosome of a homologous pair differs at many points from the other member of the pair. Random arrangements of chromosome pairs at metaphase I of meiosis leads to many different combinations of chromosomes in eggs and sperm. Random fertilization of eggs by sperm greatly increases this variation.

8.16 Homologous chromosomes may carry different versions of genes. The differences between homologous chromosomes are based on the fact that they can bear different versions of genes at corresponding loci.

8.17 Crossing over further increases genetic variability. Genetic recombination, which results from crossing over during prophase I of meiosis, increases variation still further.

Alterations of Chromosome Number and Structure (8.18–8.23)

8.18 A karyotype is a photographic inventory of an individual's chromosomes. To prepare a karyotype, white blood cells are isolated, stimulated to grow, arrested at metaphase, and photographed under a microscope. The chromosomes are arranged into ordered pairs so that any chromosomal abnormalities can be detected.

8.19 An extra copy of chromosome 21 causes Down syndrome. Trisomy 21, the most common chromosome number abnormality in the United States, results in a condition called Down syndrome.

8.20 Accidents during meiosis can alter chromosome number. An abnormal chromosome count is the result of nondisjunction, which can result from the failure of a pair of homologous chromosomes to separate during meiosis I or from the failure of sister chromatids to separate during meiosis II.

8.21 Abnormal numbers of sex chromosomes do not usually affect survival. Nondisjunction of the sex chromosomes during meiosis can result in individuals with a missing or extra X or Y chromosome. In some cases (such as XXY), this leads to syndromes; in other cases (such as XXX), the body is normal.

8.22 New species can arise from errors in cell division. Nondisjunction can produce polyploid organisms, ones with extra sets of chromosomes. Such errors in mitosis can be important in the evolution of new species.

8.23 Alterations of chromosome structure can cause birth defects and cancer. Chromosome breakage can lead to rearrangements—deletions, duplications, inversions, and translocations—that can produce genetic disorders or, if the changes occur in somatic cells, cancer.

Connecting the Concepts

1. Complete the following table to compare mitosis and meiosis.

	Mitosis	Meiosis
Number of chromosomal duplications		
Number of cell divisions		
Number of daughter cells produced		
Number of chromosomes in the daughter cells		
How the chromosomes line up during metaphase		
Genetic relationship of the daughter cells to the parent cell		
Functions performed in the human body		

Testing Your Knowledge

Multiple Choice

2. If an intestinal cell in a grasshopper contains 24 chromosomes, then a grasshopper sperm cell contains _____ chromosomes.
   a. 3   d. 24
   b. 6   e. 48
   c. 12

3. Which of the following phases of mitosis is essentially the opposite of prophase in terms of nuclear changes?
   a. telophase   d. interphase
   b. metaphase   e. anaphase
   c. S phase

4. A biochemist measured the amount of DNA in cells growing in the laboratory and found that the quantity of DNA in a cell doubled
   a. between prophase and anaphase of mitosis.
   b. between the G_1 and G_2 phases of the cell cycle.
   c. during the M phase of the cell cycle.
   d. between prophase I and prophase II of meiosis.
   e. between anaphase and telophase of mitosis.

5. Which of the following is *not* a function of mitosis in humans?
   a. repair of wounds
   b. growth
   c. production of gametes from diploid cells
   d. replacement of lost or damaged cells
   e. multiplication of somatic cells

6. A micrograph of a dividing cell from a mouse showed 19 chromosomes, each consisting of two sister chromatids. During which of the following stages of cell division could such a picture have been taken? (*Explain your answer.*)
   a. prophase of mitosis   d. anaphase of mitosis
   b. telophase II of meiosis   e. prophase II of meiosis
   c. prophase I of meiosis

7. Cytochalasin B is a chemical that disrupts microfilament formation. This chemical would interfere with
   a. DNA replication.
   b. formation of the mitotic spindle.
   c. cleavage.
   d. formation of the cell plate.
   e. crossing over.

8. It is difficult to observe individual chromosomes during interphase because
   a. the DNA has not been replicated yet.
   b. they are in the form of long, thin strands.
   c. they leave the nucleus and are dispersed to other parts of the cell.
   d. homologous chromosomes do not pair up until division starts.
   e. the spindle must move them to the metaphase plate before they become visible.

9. A fruit fly somatic cell contains 8 chromosomes. This means that _____ different combinations of chromosomes are possible in its gametes.
   a. 4   d. 32
   b. 8   e. 64
   c. 16

10. If a fragment of a chromosome breaks off and then reattaches to the original chromosome but in the reverse direction, the resulting chromosomal abnormality is called
    a. a deletion.   d. a nondisjunction.
    b. an inversion.   e. a reciprocal translocation.
    c. a translocation.

11. Why are individuals with an extra chromosome 21, which causes Down syndrome, more numerous than individuals with an extra chromosome 3 or chromosome 16?
    a. There are probably more genes on chromosome 21 than on the others.
    b. Chromosome 21 is a sex chromosome and chromosomes 3 and 16 are not.
    c. Down syndrome is not more common, just more serious.
    d. Extra copies of the other chromosomes are probably fatal.
    e. Chromosome 21 is more likely to produce a nondisjunction error than other chromosomes.

Describing, Comparing, and Explaining

12. An organism called a plasmodial slime mold is one large cytoplasmic mass with many nuclei. Explain how such a "megacell" could form.

13. Briefly describe how three different processes that occur during a sexual life cycle increase the genetic diversity of offspring.

14. Discuss the factors that control the division of eukaryotic cells grown in the laboratory. Cancer cells are easier to grow in the lab than other cells. Why do you suppose this is?

15. In the light micrograph below of dividing cells near the tip of an onion root, identify a cell in interphase, prophase, metaphase, anaphase, and telophase. Describe the major events occurring at each stage.

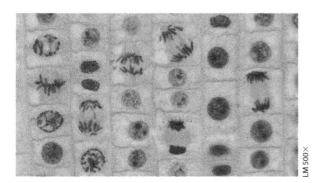

LM 500×

16. Compare cytokinesis in plant and animal cells. In what ways are the two processes similar? In what ways are they different?

17. Sketch a cell with three pairs of chromosomes undergoing meiosis, and show how nondisjunction can result in the production of gametes with extra or missing chromosomes.

Applying the Concepts

18. Suppose you read in the newspaper that a genetic engineering laboratory has developed a procedure for fusing two gametes from the same person (two eggs or two sperm) to form a zygote. The article mentions that an early step in the procedure prevents crossing over from occurring during the formation of the gametes in the donor's body. The researchers are in the process of determining the genetic makeup of one of their new zygotes. Which of the following predictions do you think they would make? Justify your choice, and explain why you rejected each of the other choices.
    a. The zygote would have 46 chromosomes, all of which came from the gamete donor (its one parent), so the zygote would be genetically identical to the gamete donor.
    b. The zygote *could* be genetically identical to the gamete donor, but it is much more likely that it would have an unpredictable mixture of chromosomes from the gamete donor's parents.
    c. The zygote would not be genetically identical to the gamete donor, but it would be genetically identical to one of the donor's parents.
    d. The zygote would not be genetically identical to the gamete donor, but it would be genetically identical to one of the donor's grandparents.

19. Bacteria are able to divide on a much faster schedule than eukaryotic cells. Some bacteria can divide every 20 minutes, while the minimum time required by eukaryotic cells in a rapidly developing embryo is about once per hour, and most cells divide much less often than that. State several testable hypotheses explaining why bacteria can divide at a faster rate than eukaryotic cells.

20. Red blood cells, which carry oxygen to body tissues, live for only about 120 days. Replacement cells are produced by cell division in bone marrow. How many cell divisions must occur each second in your bone marrow just to replace red blood cells? Here is some information to use in calculating your answer: There are about 5 million red blood cells per cubic millimeter (mm^3) of blood. An average adult has about 5 L (5,000 cm^3) of blood. (*Hint*: What is the total number of red blood cells in the body? What fraction of them must be replaced each day if all are replaced in 120 days?)

21. A mule is the offspring of a horse and a donkey. A donkey sperm contains 31 chromosomes and a horse egg cell 32 chromosomes, so the zygote contains a total of 63 chromosomes. The zygote develops normally. The combined set of chromosomes is not a problem in mitosis, and the mule combines some of the best characteristics of horses and donkeys. However, a mule is sterile; meiosis cannot occur normally in its testes (or ovaries). Explain why mitosis is normal in cells containing both horse and donkey chromosomes but the mixed set of chromosomes interferes with meiosis.

Patterns of Inheritance

Mendel's Laws
(9.1–9.10)

A few simple and long-established rules explain many aspects of heredity.

Variations on
Mendel's Laws
(9.11–9.15)

Some inheritance patterns are more complex than the ones described by Mendel.

The Chromosomal Basis
of Inheritance
(9.16–9.19)

Hereditary rules can be understood by following the behavior of chromosomes.

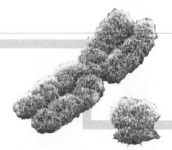

Sex Chromosomes and
Sex-Linked Genes
(9.20–9.23)

Genes found on sex chromosomes display unique patterns of inheritance.

The cute canine shown above is a purebred Labrador retriever. Displaying the traits that distinguish this breed—such as a narrow muzzle and gentle eyes—this dog, when bred to other Labradors, is expected to produce puppies that look very similar. This is a reasonable expectation because a purebred dog has a well-documented pedigree that includes several generations of ancestors with similar genetic makeup and appearance. But similarities among purebred Labs extend beyond mere appearance; Labradors are generally kind, outgoing, intelligent, and docile. Such behavioral similarities suggests that breeders can select for temperament as well as physical traits.

Purebred pooches are living proof that dogs are more than man's best friend—they are also one of our longest-running genetic experiments. For thousands of years, different groups of people have chosen and mated dogs with specific traits.

Continued over millennia, the result of such genetic tinkering is an incredibly diverse array of dog body types and behaviors.

Although humans have been applying genetics for thousands of years—by breeding food crops as well as domesticated animals—the biological basis of selective breeding has only recently been understood. In this chapter, we examine the rules that govern how inherited traits are passed from parents to offspring. We look at several kinds of inheritance patterns and how they allow us to predict the ratios of offspring with particular traits. Most importantly, we uncover a basic biological concept: how the behavior of chromosomes during gamete formation and fertilization (discussed in Chapter 8) accounts for the patterns of inheritance we observe. Along the way, we'll return several times to the Labrador retriever as an example of how basic genetic principles can help us understand the world around us.

Mendel's Laws

9.1 The science of genetics has ancient roots

Attempts to explain inheritance date back at least to ancient Greece. The physician Hippocrates (approximately 460–370 BCE) suggested an explanation called pangenesis. According to this idea, particles called pangenes travel from each part of an organism's body to the eggs or sperm and then are passed to the next generation; moreover, changes that occur in the body during an organism's life are passed on in this way. The Greek philosopher Aristotle (384–322 BCE; Figure 9.1) rejected this idea as simplistic, saying that what is inherited is the potential to produce body features rather than particles of the features themselves.

Actually, pangenesis proves incorrect in several respects. The reproductive cells are not composed of particles from somatic (body) cells, and changes in somatic cells do not influence eggs and sperm. For instance, no matter how much you enlarge your biceps by lifting weights, muscle cells in your arms do not transmit genetic information to your gametes, and your offspring will not be changed by your weight-lifting efforts. This may seem like common sense today, but the pangenesis hypothesis and the idea that traits acquired during an individual's lifetime are passed on to offspring prevailed well into the 19th century.

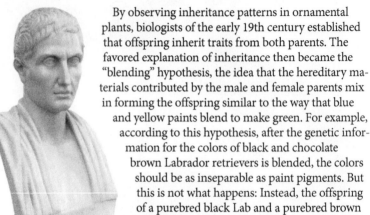

▲ Figure 9.1 Aristotle

By observing inheritance patterns in ornamental plants, biologists of the early 19th century established that offspring inherit traits from both parents. The favored explanation of inheritance then became the "blending" hypothesis, the idea that the hereditary materials contributed by the male and female parents mix in forming the offspring similar to the way that blue and yellow paints blend to make green. For example, according to this hypothesis, after the genetic information for the colors of black and chocolate brown Labrador retrievers is blended, the colors should be as inseparable as paint pigments. But this is not what happens: Instead, the offspring of a purebred black Lab and a purebred brown Lab will all be black, but some of the dogs in the next generation will be brown (you'll learn why in Module 9.6). The blending hypothesis was finally rejected because it does not explain how traits that disappear in one generation can reappear in later ones.

? Horse breeders sometimes speak of "mixing the bloodlines" of two pedigrees. In what way is this phrase inaccurate?

● It implies the blending hypothesis—that offspring are a blend of two parents, as in a liquid mixture.

9.2 Experimental genetics began in an abbey garden

Heredity is the transmission of traits from one generation to the next. The field of **genetics**, the scientific study of heredity, began in the 1860s, when an Augustinian monk named Gregor Mendel (Figure 9.2A) deduced the fundamental principles of genetics by breeding garden peas. Mendel lived and worked in an abbey in Brunn, Austria (now Brno, in the Czech Republic). Strongly influenced by his study of physics, mathematics, and chemistry at the University of Vienna, his research was both experimentally and mathematically rigorous, and these qualities were largely responsible for his success.

In a paper published in 1866, Mendel correctly argued that parents pass on to their offspring discrete "heritable factors." (It is interesting to note that Mendel's landmark publication came just seven years after Darwin's 1859 publication of *The Origin of Species*, making the 1860s a banner decade in the development of modern biology.)

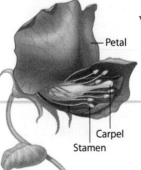

▲ Figure 9.2A
Gregor Mendel

In his paper, Mendel stressed that the heritable factors, today called genes, retain their individuality generation after generation. That is, genes are like playing cards; a deck may be shuffled, but the cards always retain their original identities, and no card is ever blended with another. Similarly, genes may be rearranged but each gene permanently retains its identity.

Mendel probably chose to study garden peas because they had short generation times, produced large numbers of offspring from each mating, and came in many readily distinguishable varieties. For example, one variety has purple flowers, and another variety has white flowers. A heritable feature that varies among individuals, such as flower color, is called a **character**. Each variant for a character, such as purple or white flowers, is called a **trait**.

Perhaps the most important advantage of pea plants as an experimental model was that Mendel could strictly control matings. As Figure 9.2B shows, the petals

— Petal

◀ Figure 9.2B The anatomy of a garden pea flower (with one petal removed to improve visibility)

Carpel
Stamen

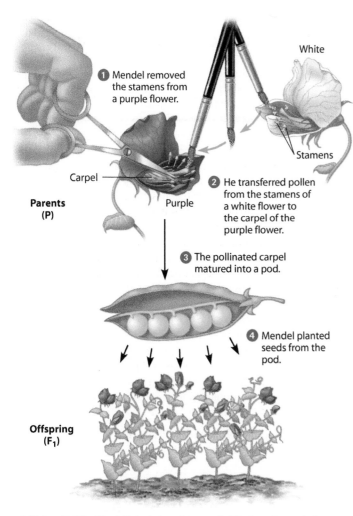

① Mendel removed the stamens from a purple flower.

White

Stamens

② He transferred pollen from the stamens of a white flower to the carpel of the purple flower.

Carpel

Parents (P)

Purple

③ The pollinated carpel matured into a pod.

④ Mendel planted seeds from the pod.

Offspring (F₁)

▲ Figure 9.2C Mendel's technique for cross-fertilization of pea plants

of the pea flower almost completely enclose the reproductive organs: the stamens and carpel. Consequently, pea plants usually are able to **self-fertilize** in nature. That is, sperm-carrying pollen grains released from the stamens land on the egg-containing carpel of the same flower. Mendel could ensure self-fertilization by covering a flower with a small bag so that no pollen from another plant could reach the carpel. When he wanted **cross-fertilization** (fertilization of one plant by pollen from a different plant), he used the method shown in **Figure 9.2C**. ① He prevented self-fertilization by cutting off the immature stamens of a plant before they produced pollen. ② To cross-fertilize the stameneless flower, he dusted its carpel with pollen from another plant. After pollination, ③ the carpel developed into a pod, containing seeds (peas) that ④ he planted. The seeds grew into offspring plants. Through these methods, Mendel could always be sure of the parentage of new plants.

Mendel's success was due not only to his experimental approach and choice of organism but also to his selection of characteristics to study. He chose to observe seven characters, each of which occurred as two distinct traits (**Figure 9.2D**). Mendel worked with his plants until he was sure he had **true-breeding** varieties—that is, varieties for which self-fertilization produced offspring all identical to the parent. For instance, he identified

a purple-flowered variety that, when self-fertilized, produced offspring plants that all had purple flowers.

Now Mendel was ready to ask what would happen when he crossed his different true-breeding varieties with each other. For example, what offspring would result if plants with purple flowers and plants with white flowers were cross-fertilized? The offspring of two different varieties are called **hybrids**, and the cross-fertilization itself is referred to as a hybridization, or simply a genetic **cross**. The true-breeding parental plants are called the **P generation** (P for parental), and their hybrid offspring are called the **F₁ generation** (F for filial, from the Latin word for "son"). When F₁ plants self-fertilize or fertilize each other, their offspring are the **F₂ generation**. We turn to Mendel's results next.

? Why was the development of true-breeding varieties critical to the success of Mendel's experiments?

● True-breeding varieties allowed Mendel to predict the outcome of specific crosses and thus to run controlled experiments.

Character	Traits	
	Dominant	**Recessive**
Flower color	Purple	White
Flower position	Axial	Terminal
Seed color	Yellow	Green
Seed shape	Round	Wrinkled
Pod shape	Inflated	Constricted
Pod color	Green	Yellow
Stem length	Tall	Dwarf

▲ Figure 9.2D The seven pea characters studied by Mendel

9.3 Mendel's law of segregation describes the inheritance of a single character

Mendel performed many experiments in which he tracked the inheritance of characters that occur in two forms, such as flower color. The results led him to formulate several hypotheses about inheritance. Let's look at some of his experiments and follow the reasoning that led to his hypotheses.

Figure 9.3A starts with a cross between a true-breeding pea plant with purple flowers and a true-breeding pea plant with white flowers. This is called a **monohybrid cross** because the parent plants differ in only one character—flower color. Mendel observed that F_1 plants all had purple flowers; they were not light purple, as predicted by the blending hypothesis. Was the white-flowered plant's genetic contribution to the hybrids lost? By mating the F_1 plants with each other, Mendel found the answer to be no. Out of 929 F_2 plants, 705 (about $\frac{3}{4}$) had purple flowers and 224 (about $\frac{1}{4}$) had white flowers, a ratio of about three plants with purple flowers to every one with white flowers (abbreviated as 3:1). Mendel reasoned that the heritable factor for white flowers did not disappear in the F_1 plants, but was masked when the purple-flower factor was present. He also deduced that the F_1 plants must have carried two factors for the flower-color character, one for purple and one for white.

Mendel observed these same patterns of inheritance for six other pea plant characters (see Figure 9.2D). From his results, he developed four hypotheses, described here using modern terminology, such as "gene" instead of "heritable factor."

1. *There are alternative versions of genes that account for variations in inherited characters.* For example, the gene for flower color in pea plants exists in two versions: one for purple and the other for white. The alternative versions of a gene are called **alleles**.

2. *For each character, an organism inherits two alleles, one from each parent.* These alleles may be the same or different. An organism that has two identical alleles for a gene is said to be **homozygous** for that gene (and is a "homozygote" for that trait). An organism that has two different alleles for a gene is said to be **heterozygous** for that gene (and is a "heterozygote").

3. *If the two alleles of an inherited pair differ, then one determines the organism's appearance and is called the* **dominant** *allele; the other has no noticeable effect on the organism's appearance and is called the* **recessive** *allele.* We use uppercase letters to represent dominant alleles and lowercase letters to represent recessive alleles.

4. *A sperm or egg carries only one allele for each inherited character because allele pairs separate (segregate) from each other during the production of gametes.* This statement is called the **law of segregation**. When sperm and egg unite at fertilization, each contributes its allele, restoring the paired condition in the offspring.

Figure 9.3B explains the results in Figure 9.3A. In this example, the letter P represents the dominant allele (for purple

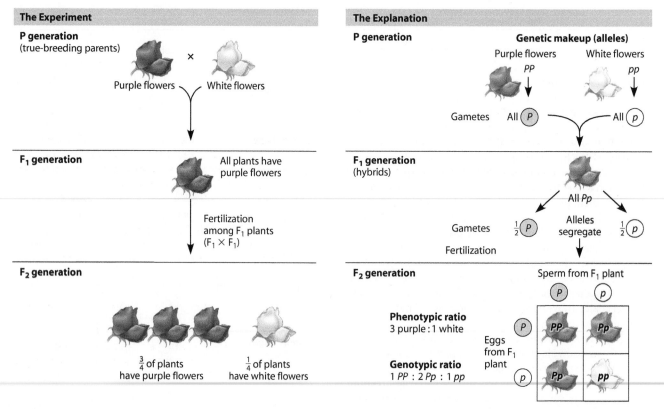

▲ Figure 9.3A   Crosses tracking one character (flower color)

▲ Figure 9.3B   An explanation of the crosses in Figure 9.3A flowers), and *p* stands for the recessive allele (for white flowers). Both parental plants (at the top of the figure) were true-breeding, and Mendel's first two hypotheses propose that one parental variety had two alleles for purple flowers (*PP*) and the other had two alleles for white flowers (*pp*).

Consistent with hypothesis 4, the gametes of Mendel's parental plants each carried one allele; thus, the parental gametes in Figure 9.3B are either *P* or *p*. As a result of fertilization, the F$_1$ hybrids each inherited one allele for purple flowers and one for white. Hypothesis 3 explains why all of the F$_1$ hybrids (*Pp*) had purple flowers: The dominant *P* allele has its full effect in the heterozygote, while the recessive *p* allele has no effect.

Mendel's hypotheses also explain the 3:1 ratio in the F$_2$ generation. Because the F$_1$ hybrids are *Pp*, they make gametes *P* and *p* in equal numbers. The bottom diagram in Figure 9.3B, called a **Punnett square**, shows the four possible combinations of alleles that could occur when these gametes combine.

The Punnett square shows the proportions of F$_2$ plants predicted by Mendel's hypotheses. If a sperm carrying allele *P* fertilizes an egg carrying allele *P*, the offspring (*PP*) will produce purple flowers. Mendel's hypotheses predict that this combination will occur in $\frac{1}{4}$ of the offspring. As shown in the Punnett square, the hypotheses also predict that $\frac{1}{2}$ (or two of four) of the offspring will inherit one *P* allele and one *p* allele. These offspring (*Pp*) will all have purple flowers because *P* is dominant. The remaining $\frac{1}{4}$ of F$_2$ plants will inherit two *p* alleles and will have white flowers.

Because an organism's appearance does not always reveal its genetic composition, geneticists distinguish between an organism's physical traits, called its **phenotype** (such as purple or white flowers), and its genetic makeup, its **genotype** (in this example, *PP*, *Pp*, or *pp*). So now we see that Figure 9.3A shows just phenotypes while Figure 9.3B shows both phenotypes and genotypes in our sample crosses. For the F$_2$ plants, the ratio of plants with purple flowers to those with white flowers (3:1) is called the phenotypic ratio. The genotypic ratio, as shown by the Punnett square, is 1 *PP*:2 *Pp*:1 *pp*.

Mendel found that each of the seven characteristics he studied exhibited the same inheritance pattern: One parental trait disappeared in the F$_1$ generation, only to reappear in $\frac{1}{4}$ of the F$_2$ offspring. The mechanism underlying this inheritance pattern is stated by Mendel's law of segregation: Pairs of alleles segregate (separate) during gamete formation. The fusion of gametes at fertilization creates allele pairs once again. Research since Mendel's time has established that due to the separation of homologous chromosomes during meiosis II (see Modules 8.12–14), the law of segregation applies to all sexually reproducing organisms, including humans. We'll return to Mendel and his experiments with pea plants in Module 9.5, but first let's see how some of the concepts we discussed in Chapter 8 fit with what we have said about genetics so far.

? **How can two plants with different genotypes for a particular inherited character be identical in phenotype?**

One could be homozygous for the dominant allele and the other heterozygous.

9.4 Homologous chromosomes bear the alleles for each character

Figure 9.4 shows the locations of three genes on a pair of homologous chromosomes (homologs)—chromosomes that carry alleles of the same gene. Recall from Module 8.11 that every diploid cell, whether from pea plant or human, has chromosomes in homologous pairs. One member of each pair comes from the organism's female parent, while the other member of the pair comes from the male parent.

Each labeled band on the chromosomes in the figure represents a gene **locus** (plural, *loci*), a specific location of a gene along the chromosome. The matching colors of the three corresponding loci on the two homologs highlight the fact that homologous chromosomes have genes for the same characters located at the same positions along their lengths. However, as the uppercase and lowercase letters next to the loci indicate, two homologous chromosomes may bear either the same alleles or different ones. This is the connection between Mendel's laws and homologous chromosomes: Alleles (alternative versions) of a gene reside at the same locus on homologous chromosomes.

The diagram here also serves as a review of some of the genetic terms we have encountered to this point. We will return to the chromosomal basis of inheritance in more detail beginning with Module 9.16.

? **An individual is heterozygous, *Bb*, for a gene. According to the law of segregation, each gamete formed by this individual will have *either* the *B* allele *or* the *b* allele. Recalling what you learned about meiosis in Chapter 8, explain the physical basis for this segregation of alleles.**

The *B* and *b* alleles are located at the same gene locus on homologous chromosomes, which separate during meiosis I and are packaged in separate gametes.

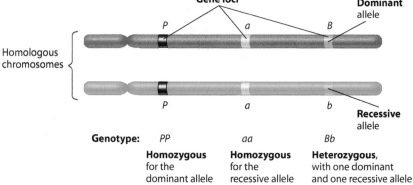

▲ **Figure 9.4** Three gene loci on homologous chromosomes

9.5 The law of independent assortment is revealed by tracking two characters at once

Recall from Module 9.3 that Mendel established his law of segregation by following one character from the P generation through the F₁ and F₂ generations. From such monohybrid crosses, Mendel knew that the allele for round seed shape (designated *R*) was dominant to the allele for wrinkled seed shape (*r*) and that the allele for yellow seed color (*Y*) was dominant to the allele for green seed color (*y*). Mendel wondered: What would happen if he crossed plants that differ in both seed shape and seed color?

To find out, Mendel set up a **dihybrid cross**, a mating of parental varieties differing in two characters. Mendel crossed homozygous plants having round yellow seeds (genotype *RRYY*) with plants having wrinkled green seeds (*rryy*). Mendel knew that an *RRYY* plant would produce only gametes with *RY* alleles; an *rryy* plant would produce only gametes with *ry* alleles. Therefore, Mendel knew there was only one possible outcome for the F₁ generation: the union of *RY* and *ry* gametes would yield hybrids heterozygous for both characters (*RrYy*)— that is, dihybrids. All of these *RrYy* offspring would have round yellow seeds, the double dominant phenotype.

The F₂ generation is a bit trickier. Would the genes for seed color and seed shape be transmitted from parent to offspring as a package, or would they be inherited separately? To find out, Mendel crossed the *RrYy* F₁ plants with each other. He hypothesized two possible outcomes from this experiment: Either the dihybrid cross would exhibit *dependent* assortment, with the genes for seed color and seed shape inherited together as a set, or it would exhibit *independent* assortment, with the genes inherited independently from each other.

As shown on the left side of **Figure 9.5A**, the hypothesis of dependent assortment leads to the prediction that each F₂ plant would inherit one of two possible sperm (*RY* or *ry*) and one of

two possible eggs (*RY* or *ry*), for a total of four combinations. The Punnett square shows that there could be only two F₂ phenotypes—round yellow or wrinkled green—in a 3:1 ratio. However, when Mendel actually performed this cross, he did not obtain these results, thus refuting the hypothesis of dependent assortment.

The alternative hypothesis—that the genes would exhibit independent assortment—is shown on the right side of Figure 9.5A. This leads to the prediction that the F₁ plants would produce four different gametes: *RY*, *Ry*, *rY*, and *ry*. Each F₂ plant would inherit one of four possible sperm and one of four possible eggs, for a total of 16 possible combinations. The Punnett square shows that fertilization among these gametes would lead to four different seed phenotypes—round yellow, round green, wrinkled yellow, or wrinkled green—in a 9:3:3:1 ratio. In fact, Mendel observed such a ratio in the F₂ plants, indicating that each pair of alleles segregates independently of the other.

The Punnett square on the right-hand side of Figure 9.5A also reveals that a dihybrid cross is equivalent to two monohybrid crosses—one for seed color and one for seed shape—occurring simultaneously. From the 9:3:3:1 ratio, we can see that there are 12 plants with round seeds to 4 with wrinkled seeds and 12 yellow-seeded plants to 4 green-seeded ones. These 12:4 ratios each reduce to 3:1, which is the F₂ ratio for a monohybrid cross; a monohybrid cross is occurring for each of the two traits. Mendel tried his seven pea characters in various dihybrid combinations and always obtained data close to the predicted 9:3:3:1 ratio. These results supported the hypothesis that each pair of alleles segregates (assorts) independently of other pairs of alleles during gamete formation. In other words, the inheritance of one character has no effect on the inheritance of another. This is called Mendel's **law of independent assortment**.

Figure 9.5B shows how this law applies to the inheritance of two characters in Labrador retrievers: black versus chocolate coat color and normal vision versus progressive retinal atrophy (PRA), an eye disorder that leads to blindness. As you would expect, these characters are controlled by separate genes. Black Labs have at

▶ **Figure 9.5A**
Two hypotheses for segregation in a dihybrid cross

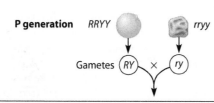

P generation   *RRYY*   ⊗   *rryy*

Gametes (*RY*) ✕ (*ry*)

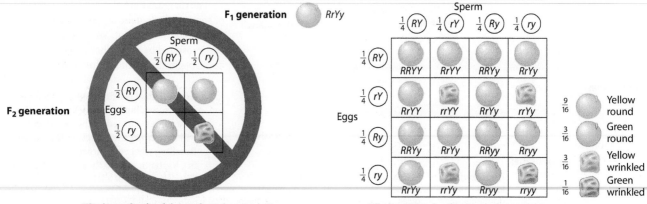

F₁ generation   *RrYy*

F₂ generation

The hypothesis of dependent assortment
Data did not support; hypothesis refuted

Sperm
½ (*RY*)   ½ (*ry*)

Eggs
½ (*RY*)
½ (*ry*)

The hypothesis of independent assortment
Actual results; hypothesis supported

Sperm
¼ (*RY*)   ¼ (*rY*)   ¼ (*Ry*)   ¼ (*ry*)

Eggs
¼ (*RY*)   *RRYY* *RrYY* *RRYy* *RrYy*
¼ (*rY*)   *RrYY* *rrYY* *RrYy* *rrYy*
¼ (*Ry*)   *RRYy* *RrYy* *RRyy* *Rryy*
¼ (*ry*)   *RrYy* *rrYy* *Rryy* *rryy*

9/16   Yellow round
3/16   Green round
3/16   Yellow wrinkled
1/16   Green wrinkled

least one copy of an allele called *B*, which gives their hairs densely packed granules of a dark pigment. The *B* allele is dominant to *b*, which leads to a less tightly packed distribution of pigment granules. As a result, the coats of dogs with genotype *bb* are chocolate in color. (If you're wondering about yellow Labs, their color is controlled by a different gene altogether.) The allele that causes PRA, called *n*, is recessive to allele *N*, which is necessary for normal vision. Thus, only dogs of genotype *nn* become blind from PRA. (In the figure, blanks in the genotypes are used where a particular phenotype may result from multiple genotypes. For example, a black Lab may have either genotype *BB* or *Bb*, which we abbreviate as *B_.*)

The lower part of Figure 9.5B shows what happens when we mate two heterozygous Labs, both of genotype *BbNn*. The F₂ phenotypic ratio will be nine black dogs with normal eyes to three black with PRA to three chocolate with normal eyes to one chocolate with PRA. These results are analogous to the results in Figure 9.5A and demonstrate that the *B* and *N* genes are inherited independently.

? **Predict the phenotypes of offspring obtained by mating a black Lab homozygous for both coat color and normal eyes with a chocolate Lab that is blind from PRA.**

● All offspring would be black with normal eyes (BBNN × bbnn → BbNn).

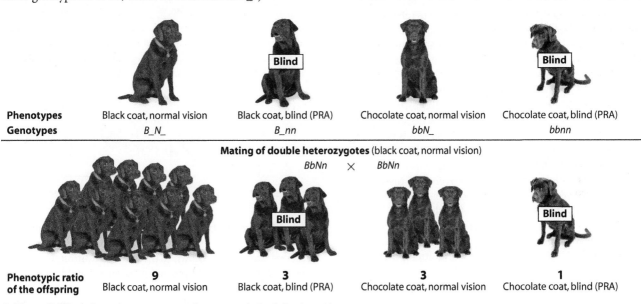

Phenotypes	Black coat, normal vision	Black coat, blind (PRA)	Chocolate coat, normal vision	Chocolate coat, blind (PRA)
Genotypes	B_N_	B_nn	bbN_	bbnn

Mating of double heterozygotes (black coat, normal vision)
BbNn × *BbNn*

Phenotypic ratio of the offspring	**9** Black coat, normal vision	**3** Black coat, blind (PRA)	**3** Chocolate coat, normal vision	**1** Chocolate coat, blind (PRA)

▲ **Figure 9.5B** Independent assortment of two genes in the Labrador retriever

9.6 Geneticists can use the testcross to determine unknown genotypes

Suppose you have a Labrador retriever with a chocolate coat. Referring to Figure 9.5B, you can tell that its genotype must be *bb*, the only combination of alleles that produces the chocolate-coat phenotype. But what if you had a black Lab? It could have one of two possible genotypes—*BB* or *Bb*—and there is no way to tell which is correct simply by looking at the dog. To determine your dog's genotype, you could perform a **testcross**, a mating between an individual of unknown genotype (your black Lab) and a homozygous recessive (*bb*) individual—in this case, a chocolate Lab.

Figure 9.6 shows the offspring that could result from such a mating. If, as shown on the bottom left, the black parent's genotype is *BB*, we would expect all the offspring to be black because a cross between genotypes *BB* and *bb* can produce only *Bb* offspring. On the other hand, if the black parent is *Bb*, as shown on the bottom right, we would expect both black (*Bb*) and chocolate (*bb*) offspring. Thus, the appearance of the offspring reveals the original black dog's genotype.

Mendel used testcrosses to verify that he had true-breeding varieties of plants. The testcross continues to be an important tool of geneticists for determining genotypes.

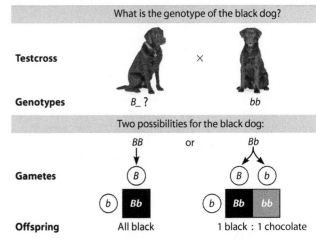

	What is the genotype of the black dog?	
Testcross		×
Genotypes	B_?	bb

Two possibilities for the black dog:

	BB	or	*Bb*
Gametes	B		B b
Offspring	All black		1 black : 1 chocolate

▲ **Figure 9.6** Using a testcross to determine genotype

? **You use a testcross to determine the genotype of a Lab with normal eyes. Half of the offspring of the testcross are normal and half develop PRA. What is the genotype of the normal parent?**

● Heterozygous (Nn)

9.7 Mendel's laws reflect the rules of probability

Mendel's strong background in mathematics served him well in his studies of inheritance. He understood, for instance, that the segregation of allele pairs during gamete formation and the re-forming of pairs at fertilization obey the rules of probability—the same rules that apply to the tossing of coins, the rolling of dice, and the drawing of cards. Mendel also appreciated the statistical nature of inheritance. He knew that he needed to obtain large samples—to count many offspring from his crosses—before he could begin to interpret inheritance patterns.

Let's see how the rules of probability apply to inheritance. The probability scale ranges from 0 to 1. An event that is certain to occur has a probability of 1, whereas an event that is certain *not* to occur has a probability of 0. For example, a tossed coin has a $\frac{1}{2}$ chance of landing heads and a $\frac{1}{2}$ chance of landing tails. These two possibilities add up to 1; the probabilities of all possible outcomes for an event to occur must always add up to 1. In another example, in a standard deck of 52 playing cards, the chance of drawing a jack of diamonds is $\frac{1}{52}$ and the chance of drawing any card other than the jack of diamonds is $\frac{51}{52}$, which together add up to 1.

An important lesson we can learn from coin tossing is that for each and every toss of the coin, the probability of heads is $\frac{1}{2}$. Even if heads has landed five times in a row, the probability of the next toss coming up heads is still $\frac{1}{2}$. In other words, the outcome of any particular toss is unaffected by what has happened on previous attempts. Each toss is an independent event.

If two coins are tossed simultaneously, the outcome for each coin is an independent event, unaffected by the other coin. What is the chance that both coins will land heads up? The probability of such a compound event is the product of the probabilities of each independent event; for the two tosses of coins, $\frac{1}{2} \times \frac{1}{2} = \frac{1}{4}$. This statistical principle is called the **rule of multiplication**, and it holds true for genetics as well as coin tosses.

Figure 9.7 represents a cross between F_1 Labrador retrievers that have the *Bb* genotype for coat color. The genetic cross is portrayed by the tossing of two coins that stand in for the two gametes (a dime for the egg and a penny for the sperm); the heads side of each coin stands for the dominant *B* allele and the tails side of each coin the recessive *b* allele. What is the probability that a particular F_2 dog will have the *bb* genotype? To produce a *bb* offspring, both egg and sperm must carry the *b* allele. The probability that an egg will have the *b* allele is $\frac{1}{2}$, and the probability that a sperm will have the *b* allele is also $\frac{1}{2}$. By the rule of multiplication, the probability that the two *b* alleles will come together at fertilization is $\frac{1}{2} \times \frac{1}{2} = \frac{1}{4}$. This is exactly the answer given by the Punnett square in Figure 9.7. If we know the genotypes of the parents, we can predict the probability for any genotype among the offspring.

Now consider the probability that an F_2 Lab will be heterozygous for the coat-color gene. As Figure 9.7 shows, there are two ways in which F_1 gametes can combine to produce a heterozygous offspring. The dominant (*B*) allele can come from the egg and the recessive (*b*) allele from the sperm, or vice

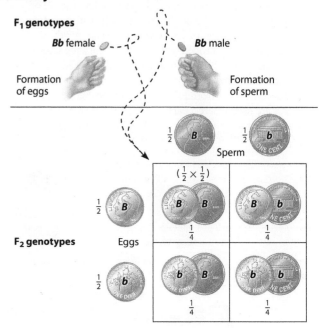

▲ **Figure 9.7** Segregation and fertilization as chance events

versa. The probability that an event can occur in two or more alternative ways is the sum of the separate probabilities of the different ways; this is known as the **rule of addition**. Using this rule, we can calculate the probability of an F_2 heterozygote as $\frac{1}{4} + \frac{1}{4} = \frac{1}{2}$.

By applying the rules of probability to segregation and independent assortment, we can solve some rather complex genetics problems. For instance, we can predict the results of trihybrid crosses, in which three different characters are involved. Consider a cross between two organisms that both have the genotype *AaBbCc*. What is the probability that an offspring from this cross will be a recessive homozygote for all three genes (*aabbcc*)? Since each allele pair assorts independently, we can treat this trihybrid cross as three separate monohybrid crosses:

Aa × *Aa*: Probability of *aa* offspring = $\frac{1}{4}$

Bb × *Bb*: Probability of *bb* offspring = $\frac{1}{4}$

Cc × *Cc*: Probability of *cc* offspring = $\frac{1}{4}$

Because the segregation of each allele pair is an independent event, we use the rule of multiplication to calculate the probability that the offspring will be *aabbcc*:

$\frac{1}{4} aa \times \frac{1}{4} bb \times \frac{1}{4} cc = \frac{1}{64}$.

We could reach the same conclusion by constructing a 64-section Punnett square, but that would take a lot of space!

? **A plant of genotype *AABbCC* is crossed with an *AaBbCc* plant. What is the probability of an offspring having the genotype *AABBCC*?**

● $\frac{1}{16}$ (that is, $\frac{1}{2} \times \frac{1}{4} \times \frac{1}{2}$)

9.8 Genetic traits in humans can be tracked through family pedigrees

While much of the classic work that led to our understanding of genetics was performed on model organisms (such as peas and fruit flies), Mendel's laws apply to the inheritance of many human traits as well. Figure 9.8A illustrates alternative forms of three human characters that are each thought to be determined by simple dominant-recessive inheritance at one gene locus. (The genetic basis of many other human characters, such as eye and hair color, involves several genes and is not well understood.)

If we call the dominant allele of a gene under consideration *A*, the dominant phenotype results from either the homozygous genotype *AA* or the heterozygous genotype *Aa*. Recessive phenotypes always result from the homozygous genotype *aa*.

In genetics, the word *dominant* does not imply that a phenotype is either normal or more common than a recessive phenotype; **wild-type traits**—those prevailing in nature—are not necessarily specified by dominant alleles. Rather, dominance means that a heterozygote (*Aa*), carrying only a single copy of a dominant allele, displays the dominant phenotype. By contrast, the phenotype of the corresponding recessive allele is seen only in a homozygote (*aa*). Recessive traits may in fact be more common in the population than dominant ones. For example, the absence of freckles is more common than their presence.

How can we determine the inheritance pattern of a particular human trait? Since we obviously cannot control human matings and run a testcross, geneticists must analyze the results of matings that have already occurred. First, a geneticist collects as much information as possible about a family's history for the trait of interest. The next step is to assemble this information into a family tree—the family **pedigree**. (You may associate pedigrees with purebred animals—such as racehorses or championship dogs—but they can represent human matings just as well.) To analyze the pedigree, the geneticist applies logic and Mendel's laws.

Let's apply this approach to the example in Figure 9.8B, a pedigree that traces the incidence of free versus attached earlobes in a hypothetical family. The letter *F* stands for the allele for free earlobes, and *f* symbolizes the allele for attached earlobes. In the pedigree, □ represents a male, ○ represents a female, and colored symbols (■ and ●) indicate that the person is affected by the trait under investigation (in this case, attached earlobes). The earliest generation studied is at the top of the pedigree, and the most recent generation is at the bottom.

Even if we didn't already know that *f* was recessive to *F*, we could apply Mendel's laws to deduce it from the pedigree. That is

Dominant Traits	Recessive Traits

Freckles / No freckles

Widow's peak / Straight hairline

Free earlobe / Attached earlobe

▲ **Figure 9.8A** Examples of single-gene inherited traits in humans

the only way that one of the third-generation sisters (at the bottom left) could have attached earlobes when both her parents did not; in the pedigree, this is represented by an affected individual (●) with two parents who are unaffected (□ and ○). We can therefore label all the individuals with attached earlobes in the pedigree—that is, all those with colored circles or squares—as homozygous recessive (*ff*).

Mendel's laws enable us to deduce the genotypes for most of the people in the pedigree. For example, both of the second-generation parents must have carried the *f* allele (which they passed on to the affected daughter) along with the *F* allele that gave them free earlobes. The same must be true of the first set of grandparents (the top left couple in the pedigree) because they both had free earlobes but their two sons had attached earlobes.

Notice that we cannot deduce the genotype of every member of the pedigree. For example, the sister with free earlobes in the bottom right of the pedigree must have at least one *F* allele, but she could be either *FF* or *Ff*. We cannot distinguish between these two possibilities using the available data.

❓ **Look at Figure 9.8B and imagine that the sister with attached earlobes married a man with free earlobes and they had a daughter. What phenotype of this daughter would allow us to deduce all three genotypes in that family?**

● If the daughter had free earlobes, then she and her father must be *ff* and her mother must be *Ff*.

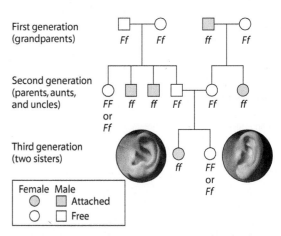

First generation (grandparents) — *Ff* *Ff* *ff* *Ff*

Second generation (parents, aunts, and uncles) — *FF or Ff* *ff* *ff* *Ff* *Ff* *ff*

Third generation (two sisters) — *ff* *FF or Ff*

Female	Male	
○	■	Attached
○	□	Free

▲ **Figure 9.8B** A pedigree showing the inheritance of attached versus free earlobes in a hypothetical family

| **9.9 Many inherited disorders in humans are controlled by a single gene**

The genetic disorders listed in Table 9.9 are known to be inherited as dominant or recessive traits controlled by a single gene locus. These human disorders therefore show simple inheritance patterns like the traits Mendel studied in pea plants. The genes discussed in this module are all located on autosomes, chromosomes other than the sex chromosomes X and Y (see Module 8.11).

Recessive Disorders   Most human genetic disorders are recessive. They range in severity from relatively mild, such as albinism (lack of pigmentation), to invariably fatal, such as Tay-Sachs disease. Most people who have recessive disorders are born to normal parents who are both heterozygotes—that is, who are **carriers** of the recessive allele for the disorder but are phenotypically normal.

Using Mendel's laws, we can predict the fraction of affected offspring likely to result from a mating between two carriers. Consider a form of inherited deafness caused by a recessive allele (Figure 9.9A). Suppose two heterozygous carriers (Dd) had a child. What is the probability that this child would be deaf? As the Punnett square in Figure 9.9A shows, each child of two carriers has a $\frac{1}{4}$ chance of inheriting two recessive alleles. To put it another way, we can say that about one-fourth of the children from such a mating are

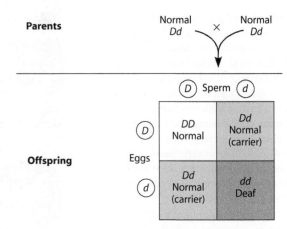

▲ Figure 9.9A   Offspring produced by parents who are both carriers for a recessive disorder, a type of deafness

likely to be deaf. We can also say that a hearing ("normal") child from such a marriage has a $\frac{2}{3}$ chance of being a Dd carrier; that is, two out of three of the offspring with the hearing phenotype will be carriers. We can apply this same

TABLE 9.9 | SOME AUTOSOMAL DISORDERS IN HUMANS

Disorder	Major Symptoms	Incidence		Comments
Recessive disorders				
Albinism	Lack of pigment in the skin, hair, and eyes	$\frac{1}{22,000}$		Prone to skin cancer
Cystic fibrosis	Excess mucus in the lungs, digestive tract, liver; increased susceptibility to infections; death in early childhood unless treated	$\frac{1}{2,500}$	Caucasians	See Module 9.9
Galactosemia	Accumulation of galactose in tissues; mental retardation; eye and liver damage	$\frac{1}{100,000}$		Treated by eliminating galactose from diet
Phenylketonuria (PKU)	Accumulation of phenylalanine in blood; lack of normal skin pigment; mental retardation	$\frac{1}{10,000}$	in U.S. and Europe	See Module 9.10
Sickle-cell disease	Sickled red blood cells; damage to many tissues	$\frac{1}{400}$	African-Americans	See Module 9.13
Tay-Sachs disease	Lipid accumulation in brain cells; mental deficiency; blindness; death in childhood	$\frac{1}{3,500}$	Jews from central Europe	See Module 4.10
Dominant disorders				
Achondroplasia	Dwarfism	$\frac{1}{25,000}$		See Module 9.9
Alzheimer's disease (one type)	Mental deterioration; usually strikes late in life	Not known		Familial (inherited) Alzheimer's is a rare form of the disease
Huntington's disease	Mental deterioration and uncontrollable movements; strikes in middle age	$\frac{1}{25,000}$		See Module 9.9
Hypercholesterolemia	Excess cholesterol in the blood; heart disease	$\frac{1}{500}$	are heterozygous	See Module 9.11

method of pedigree analysis and prediction to any genetic trait controlled by a single gene locus.

The most common life-threatening genetic disease in the United States is **cystic fibrosis (CF)**. Affecting about 30,000 Americans and 70,000 people worldwide, the recessive CF allele is carried by about one in 31 Americans. A person with two copies of this allele has cystic fibrosis, which is characterized by an excessive secretion of very thick mucus from the lungs, pancreas, and other organs. This mucus can interfere with breathing, digestion, and liver function and makes the person vulnerable to recurrent bacterial infections. Although there is no cure for this disease, strict adherence to a daily health regimen—including gentle pounding on the chest and back to clear the airway, inhaled antibiotics, and a special diet—can have a profound impact on the health of the affected person. CF was once invariably fatal in childhood, but tremendous advances in treatment have raised the median survival age of Americans with CF to 37.

Most genetic disorders are not evenly distributed across all ethnic groups. CF, for example, is most common in Caucasians. Such uneven distribution is the result of prolonged geographic isolation of certain populations. For example, the isolated lives of the early inhabitants of Martha's Vineyard (an island off the coast of Massachusetts) led to frequent **inbreeding**, matings between close blood relatives. This caused the frequency of an allele that causes deafness to be high within the community, which led to a high incidence of deafness. Because the community was geographically isolated, the deafness allele was rarely transmitted to the public beyond Martha's Vineyard.

With the increased mobility in most societies today, it is relatively unlikely that two carriers of a rare, harmful allele will meet and mate. However, the probability increases greatly if close blood relatives have children. People with recent common ancestors are more likely to carry the same recessive alleles than are unrelated people. Inbreeding is therefore likely to produce offspring homozygous for recessive traits. Geneticists have observed increased incidence of harmful recessive traits among many types of inbred animals. For example, purebred Labrador retrievers are known to have high incidences of certain genetic defects, such as weak hip, knee, and elbow joints, in addition to eye problems. The detrimental effects of inbreeding are also seen in some endangered species (see Module 13.11).

Dominant Disorders Although many harmful alleles are recessive, a number of human disorders are caused by dominant alleles. Some are harmless conditions, such as extra fingers and toes (called polydactyly) or webbed fingers and toes.

A more serious dominant disorder is **achondroplasia**, a form of dwarfism in which the head and torso of the body

▲ **Figure 9.9B** Dr. Michael C. Ain, a specialist in the repair of bone defects caused by achondroplasia and related disorders

develop normally, but the arms and legs are short **(Figure 9.9B)**. About one out of every 25,000 people have achondroplasia. The homozygous dominant genotype (*AA*) causes death of the embryo, and therefore only heterozygotes (*Aa*), individuals with a single copy of the defective allele, have this disorder. (This also means that a person with achondroplasia has a 50% chance of passing the condition on to any children.) Therefore, all those who do not have achondroplasia, more than 99.99% of the population, are homozygous for the recessive allele (*aa*). This example makes it clear that a dominant allele is not necessarily more common in a population than a corresponding recessive allele.

Dominant alleles that cause lethal diseases are much less common than lethal recessives. One reason for this difference is that the dominant lethal allele cannot be carried by heterozygotes without affecting them. Many lethal dominant alleles result from mutations in a sperm or egg that subsequently kill the embryo. And if the afflicted individual is born but does not survive long enough to reproduce, he or she will not pass on the lethal allele to future generations. This is in contrast to lethal recessive mutations, which are perpetuated from generation to generation by healthy heterozygous carriers.

A lethal dominant allele can escape elimination, however, if it does not cause death until a relatively advanced age. One such example is the allele that causes **Huntington's disease**, a degenerative disorder of the nervous system that usually does not appear until middle age. Once the deterioration of the nervous system begins, it is irreversible and inevitably fatal. Because the allele for Huntington's disease is dominant, any child born to a parent with the allele has a 50% chance of inheriting the allele and the disorder. This example makes it clear that a dominant allele is not necessarily "better" than a corresponding recessive allele.

Until relatively recently, the onset of symptoms was the only way to know if a person had inherited the Huntington's allele. This is no longer the case. By analyzing DNA samples from a large family with a high incidence of the disorder, geneticists tracked the Huntington's allele to a locus near the tip of chromosome 4, and the gene has been sequenced. This information led to development of a test that can detect the presence of the Huntington's allele in an individual's genome. This is one of several genetic tests currently available. We'll explore the topic of personal genetic screening in the next module.

? Peter is a 30-year-old man whose father died of Huntington's disease. Neither Peter's mother nor a much older sister show any signs of Huntington's. What is the probability that Peter has inherited Huntington's disease?

● Since his father had the disease, there is a $\frac{1}{2}$ chance that Peter received the gene. (The genotype of his sister is irrelevant.)

| # 9.10 New technologies can provide insight into one's genetic legacy

Some prospective parents are aware that they have an increased risk of having a baby with a genetic disease. For example, many pregnant women over age 35 know that they have a heightened risk of bearing children with Down syndrome (see Module 8.19), and some couples are aware that certain genetic diseases run in their families. These potential parents may want to learn more about their own and their baby's genetic makeup. Modern technologies offer ways to obtain such information before conception, during pregnancy, and after birth.

Genetic Testing   Because most children with recessive disorders are born to healthy parents, the genetic risk for many diseases is determined by whether the prospective parents are carriers of the recessive allele. For an increasing number of genetic disorders, including Tay-Sachs disease, sickle-cell disease, and one form of cystic fibrosis, tests are available that can distinguish between individuals who have no disease-causing alleles and those who are heterozygous carriers. Other parents may know that a dominant but late-appearing disease, such as

Huntington's disease, runs in their family. Such people may benefit from genetic tests for dominant alleles. Information from genetic testing (also called genetic screening) can inform decisions about whether to have a child.

Fetal Testing   Several technologies are available for detecting genetic conditions in a fetus. Genetic testing before birth requires the collection of fetal cells. In **amniocentesis**, performed between weeks 14 and 20 of pregnancy, a physician carefully inserts a needle through the abdomen and into the mother's uterus while watching an ultrasound imager to help avoid the fetus (**Figure 9.10A**, left). The physician extracts about 10 milliliters (2 teaspoonsful) of the amniotic fluid that bathes the developing fetus. Tests for genetic disorders can be performed on fetal cells (mostly from shed skin) that have been isolated from the fluid. Before testing, these cells are usually cultured in the laboratory for several weeks. By then, enough dividing cells can be harvested to allow karyotyping (see Module 8.18) and the detection of chromosomal abnormalities such as Down

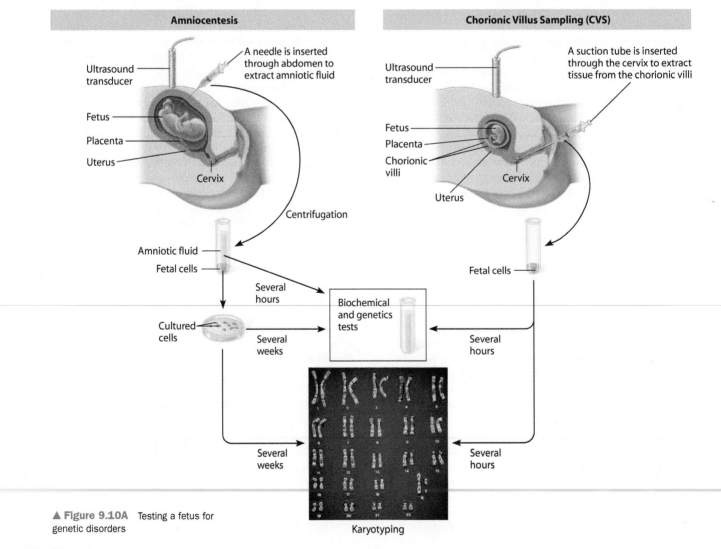

▲ **Figure 9.10A**   Testing a fetus for genetic disorders

syndrome. Biochemical tests can also be performed on the cultured cells, revealing conditions such as Tay-Sachs disease.

In another procedure, **chorionic villus sampling (CVS)**, a physician extracts a tiny sample of chorionic villus tissue from the placenta, the organ that carries nourishment and wastes between the fetus and the mother. The tissue can be obtained using a narrow, flexible tube inserted through the mother's vagina and cervix into the uterus (Figure 9.10A, right). Results of karyotyping and some biochemical tests can be available within 24 hours. The speed of CVS is an advantage over amniocentesis. Another advantage is that CVS can be performed as early as the 8th week of pregnancy.

Unfortunately, both amniocentesis and CVS pose some risk of complications, such as maternal bleeding, miscarriage, or premature birth. Complication rates for amniocentesis and CVS are about 1% and 2%, respectively. Because of the risks, these procedures are usually reserved for situations in which the possibility of a genetic disease is significantly higher than average. Newer genetic screening procedures involve isolating tiny amounts of fetal cells or DNA released into the mother's bloodstream. Although few reliable tests are yet available using this method, this promising and complication-free technology may soon replace more invasive procedures.

Blood tests on the mother at 15 to 20 weeks of pregnancy can help identify fetuses at risk for certain birth defects—and thus candidates for further testing that may require more invasive procedures (such as amniocentesis). The most widely used blood test measures the mother's blood level of alphafetoprotein (AFP), a protein produced by the fetus. High levels of AFP may indicate a neural tube defect in the fetus. (The neural tube is an embryonic structure that develops into the brain and spinal cord.) Low levels of AFP may indicate Down syndrome. For a more complete risk profile, a woman's doctor may order a "triple screen test," which measures AFP as well as two other hormones produced by the placenta. Abnormal levels of these substances in the maternal blood may also point to a risk of Down syndrome.

Fetal Imaging   Other techniques enable a physician to examine a fetus directly for anatomical deformities. The most common procedure is **ultrasound imaging**, which uses sound waves to produce a picture of the fetus. Figure 9.10B shows an ultrasound scanner, which emits high-frequency sounds, beyond the range of hearing. When the sound waves bounce off the fetus, the echoes produce an image on the monitor. The inset image in Figure 9.10B shows a fetus at about 20 weeks. Ultrasound imaging is noninvasive—no foreign objects are inserted into the mother's body—and has no known risk. In another imaging method, fetoscopy, a needle-thin tube containing a fiber optic viewing scope is inserted into the uterus. Fetoscopy can provide highly detailed images of the fetus but, unlike ultrasound, carries risk of complications.

Newborn Screening   Some genetic disorders can be detected at birth by simple tests that are now routinely performed in most hospitals in the United States. One common screening program is for phenylketonuria (PKU), a recessively inherited disorder that occurs in about one out of every 10,000 births in the United

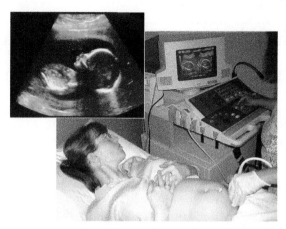

▲ Figure 9.10B   Ultrasound scanning of a fetus

States. Children with this disease cannot properly break down the naturally occurring amino acid phenylalanine; and an accumulation of phenylalanine may lead to mental retardation. However, if the deficiency is detected in the newborn, a special diet low in phenylalanine can usually prevent retardation. Unfortunately, few other genetic disorders are currently treatable.

Ethical Considerations   As new technologies such as fetal imaging and testing become more widespread, geneticists are working to make sure that they do not cause more problems than they solve. Consider the tests for identifying carriers of recessive diseases. Such information may enable people with family histories of genetic disorders to make informed decisions about having children. But these new methods for genetic screening pose problems, too. If confidentiality is breached, will carriers be stigmatized? For example, will they be denied health or life insurance, even though they themselves are healthy? Will misinformed employers equate "carrier" with disease? Geneticists stress that patients seeking genetic testing should receive counseling both before and after to clarify their family history, to explain the test, and to help them cope with the results. But with a wealth of genetic information becoming available, a full discussion of the meaning of the results might be time-consuming and costly, raising the question of who should pay for it.

Couples at risk for conceiving children with genetic disorders may now learn a great deal about their unborn children. In particular, CVS gives parents a chance to become informed very early in pregnancy. What is to be done with such information? If fetal tests reveal a serious disorder, the parents must choose between terminating the pregnancy and preparing themselves for a baby with severe problems. Identifying a genetic disease early can give families time to prepare—emotionally, medically, and financially.

Advances in biotechnology offer possibilities for reducing human suffering, but not before key ethical issues are resolved. The dilemmas posed by human genetics reinforce one of this book's central themes: the immense social implications of biology.

?   **What is the primary benefit of genetic screening by CVS? What is the primary risk?**

● CVS allows genetic screening to be performed very early in pregnancy and provides quick results, but it carries a risk of miscarriage.

Variations on Mendel's Laws

9.11 Incomplete dominance results in intermediate phenotypes

Mendel's laws explain inheritance in terms of discrete factors—genes—that are passed along from generation to generation according to simple rules of probability. Mendel's laws are valid for all sexually reproducing organisms, including garden peas, Labradors, and human beings. But just as the basic rules of musical harmony cannot account for all the rich sounds of a symphony, Mendel's laws stop short of explaining some patterns of genetic inheritance. In fact, for most sexually reproducing organisms, cases where Mendel's laws can strictly account for the patterns of inheritance are relatively rare. More often, the inheritance patterns are more complex, as we will see in this and the next four modules.

The F_1 offspring of Mendel's pea crosses always looked like one of the two parental varieties. In this situation—called **complete dominance**—the dominant allele has the same phenotypic effect whether present in one or two copies. But for some characters, the appearance of F_1 hybrids falls between the phenotypes of the two parental varieties, an effect called **incomplete dominance**. For instance, as **Figure 9.11A** illustrates, when red snapdragons are crossed with white snapdragons, all the F_1 hybrids have pink flowers. This third phenotype results from flowers of the heterozygote having less red pigment than the red homozygotes.

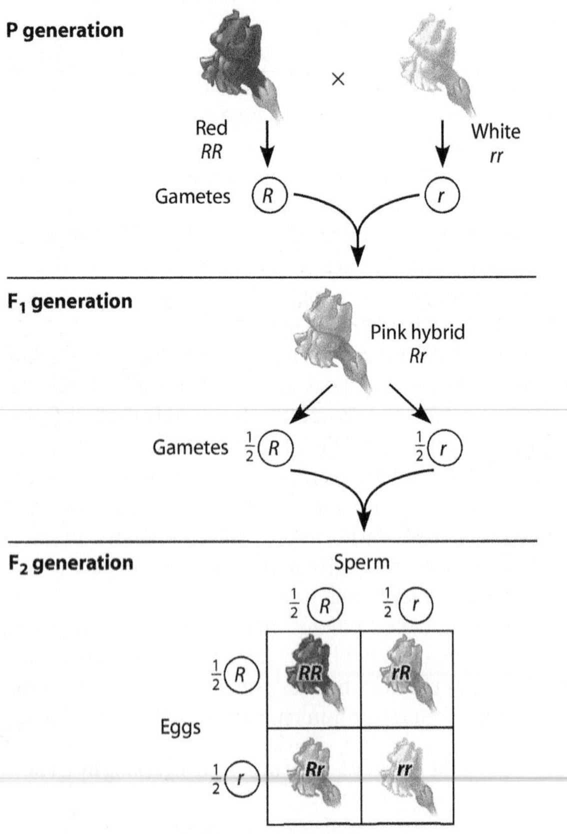

Incomplete dominance does *not* support the blending hypothesis described in Module 9.1, which would predict that the red and white traits could never be retrieved from the pink hybrids. As the Punnett square at the bottom of Figure 9.11A shows, the F_2 offspring appear in a phenotypic ratio of one red to two pink to one white, because the red and white alleles segregate during gamete formation in the pink F_1 hybrids. In incomplete dominance, the phenotypes of heterozygotes differ from the two homozygous varieties, and the genotypic ratio and the phenotypic ratio are both 1:2:1 in the F_2 generation.

We also see examples of incomplete dominance in humans. One case involves a recessive allele (h) that can cause hypercholesterolemia, dangerously high levels of cholesterol in the blood. Normal individuals are HH. Heterozygotes (Hh; about one in 500 people) have blood cholesterol levels about twice normal. They are unusually prone to atherosclerosis, the blockage of arteries by cholesterol buildup in artery walls, and they may have heart attacks from blocked heart arteries by their mid-30s. This form of the disease can often be controlled through changes in diet and by taking statins, a class of medications that can significantly lower blood cholesterol. Hypercholesterolemia is even more serious in homozygous individuals (hh; about one in a million people). Homozygotes have about five times the normal amount of blood cholesterol and may have heart attacks as early as age 2. Homozygous hypercholesterolemia is harder to treat; options include high doses of statin drugs, organ surgeries or transplants, or physically filtering lipids from the blood.

Figure 9.11B illustrates the molecular basis for hypercholesterolemia. The dominant allele (H), which normal individuals carry in duplicate (HH), specifies a cell-surface receptor protein called an LDL receptor. Low-density lipoprotein (LDL, sometimes called "bad cholesterol") is transported in the blood. In certain cells, the LDL receptors mop up excess LDL particles from the blood and promote their breakdown. This process helps prevent the accumulation of cholesterol in

P generation

Red
RR

×

White
rr

Gametes (R)   (r)

F₁ generation

Pink hybrid
Rr

Gametes ½(R)   ½(r)

F₂ generation

Sperm

½(R)   ½(r)

½(R)   *RR*   *rR*

Eggs

½(r)   *Rr*   *rr*

▲ Figure 9.11A   Incomplete dominance in snapdragon flower color

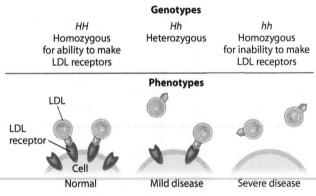

Genotypes		
HH	*Hh*	*hh*
Homozygous for ability to make LDL receptors	Heterozygous	Homozygous for inability to make LDL receptors

Phenotypes

LDL

LDL receptor

Cell

Normal   Mild disease   Severe disease

▲ Figure 9.11B   Incomplete dominance in human hypercholesterolemia

arteries. Without the receptors, lethal levels of LDL build up in the blood. Heterozygotes (*Hh*) have only half the normal number of LDL receptors, and homozygous recessives (*hh*) have none.

? Why is a testcross unnecessary to determine whether a snap-dragon with red flowers is homozygous or heterozygous?

Because the homozygotes and heterozygotes differ in phenotype: red flowers for the dominant homozygote and pink flowers for the heterozygote.

9.12 Many genes have more than two alleles in the population

So far, we have discussed inheritance patterns involving only two alleles per gene (*H* versus *h*, for example). But most genes can be found in populations in more than two versions, known as multiple alleles. Although any particular individual carries, at most, two different alleles for a particular gene, in cases of multiple alleles, more than two possible alleles exist in the population.

For instance, the **ABO blood group** phenotype in humans involves three alleles of a single gene. Various combinations of three alleles for the ABO blood type produce four phenotypes: A person's blood type may be A, B, AB, or O (Figure 9.12). These letters refer to two carbohydrates, designated A and B, that may be found on the surface of red blood cells. A person's red blood cells may be coated with carbohydrate A (in which case they are said to have type A blood), carbohydrate B (type B), both carbohydrates (type AB), or neither carbohydrate (type O). (In case you are wondering, the "positive" and "negative" notations on blood types—referred to as the Rh blood group system—are due to inheritance of a separate, unrelated gene.)

Matching compatible blood types is critical for safe blood transfusions. If a donor's blood cells have a carbohydrate (A or B) that is foreign to the recipient, then the recipient's immune system produces blood proteins called antibodies (see Module 24.9) that bind specifically to the foreign carbohydrates and cause the donor blood cells to clump together, potentially killing the recipient. The clumping reaction is also the basis of a blood-typing test performed in the laboratory. In Figure 9.12, notice that AB individuals can receive blood from anyone without fear of clumping, making them "universal recipients," while donated type O blood never causes clumping, making those with type O blood "universal donors".

The four blood groups result from various combinations of the three different alleles: I^A (for an enzyme referred to as *I*, which adds carbohydrate A to red blood cells), I^B (for B), and *i* (for neither A nor B). Each person inherits one of these alleles from each parent. Because there are three alleles, there are six possible genotypes, as listed in the figure. Both the I^A and I^B alleles are dominant to the *i* allele. Thus, $I^A I^A$ and $I^A i$ people have type A blood, and $I^B I^B$ and $I^B i$ people have type B. Recessive homozygotes, *ii*, have type O blood, with neither carbohydrate. The I^A and I^B alleles are **codominant**: Both alleles are expressed in heterozygous individuals ($I^A I^B$), who have type AB blood. Note that codominance (the expression of both alleles) is different from incomplete dominance (the expression of one intermediate trait).

? Maria has type O blood, and her sister has type AB blood. The girls know that both of their maternal grandparents are type A. What are the genotypes of the girls' parents?

Their mother is $I^A i$, their father is $I^B i$.

Blood Group (Phenotype)	Genotypes	Carbohydrates Present on Red Blood Cells	Antibodies Present in Blood	Reaction When Blood from Groups Below Is Mixed with Antibodies from Groups at Left			
				O	A	B	AB
A	$I^A I^A$ or $I^A i$	Carbohydrate A	Anti-B				
B	$I^B I^B$ or $I^B i$	Carbohydrate B	Anti-A				
AB	$I^A I^B$	Carbohydrate A and Carbohydrate B	None				
O	*ii*	Neither	Anti-A Anti-B				

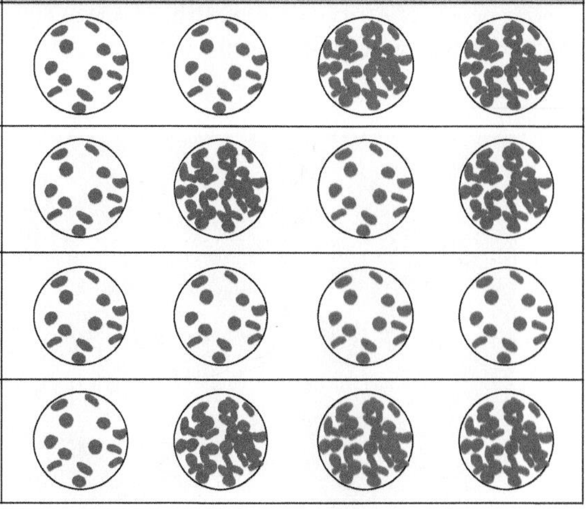

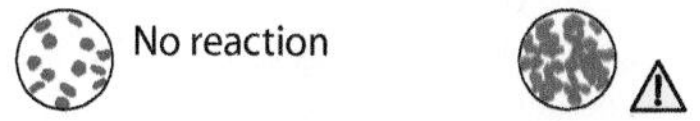

No reaction ⚠

▲ Figure 9.12 Multiple alleles for the ABO blood groups

9.13 A single gene may affect many phenotypic characters

All of our genetic examples to this point have been cases in which each gene specifies only one hereditary character. In most cases, however, one gene influences multiple characters, a property called **pleiotropy**.

An example of pleiotropy in humans is **sickle-cell disease** (sometimes called sickle-cell anemia). The direct effect of the sickle-cell allele is to make red blood cells produce abnormal hemoglobin proteins. These molecules tend to link together and crystallize, especially when the oxygen content of the blood is lower than usual because of high altitude, overexertion, or respiratory ailments. As the hemoglobin crystallizes, the normally disk-shaped red blood cells deform to a sickle shape with jagged edges (Figure 9.13A). Sickled cells are destroyed rapidly by the body, and their destruction may seriously lower the individual's red cell count, causing anemia and general weakening of the body. Also, because of their angular shape, sickled cells do not flow smoothly in the blood and tend to accumulate and clog tiny blood vessels. Blood flow to body parts is reduced, resulting in periodic fever, severe pain, and damage to various organs, including the heart, brain, and kidneys. Sickled cells also accumulate in the spleen, damaging it. The overall result is a disorder characterized by the cascade of symptoms shown in Figure 9.13B. Blood transfusions and certain drugs may relieve some of the symptoms, but there is no cure, and sickle-cell disease kills about 100,000 people in the world each year.

In most cases, only people who are homozygous for the sickle-cell allele suffer from the disease. Heterozygotes, who have one sickle-cell allele and one nonsickle allele, are usually healthy, although in rare cases they may experience some effects when oxygen in the blood is severely reduced, such as at very high altitudes. These effects may occur because the nonsickle and sickle-cell alleles are codominant at the molecular level: Both alleles are expressed in heterozygous individuals, and their red blood cells contain both normal and abnormal hemoglobin.

Sickle-cell disease is the most common inherited disorder among people of African descent, striking one in 400 African-Americans. About one in ten African-Americans is a carrier (an unaffected heterozygote). Among Americans of other ancestry, the sickle-cell allele is extremely rare.

One in ten is an unusually high frequency of carriers for an allele with such harmful effects in homozygotes. We might expect that the frequency of the sickle-cell allele in the population would be much lower because many homozygotes die before passing their genes to the next generation. The high frequency appears to be a vestige of the roots of African-Americans. Sickle-cell disease is most common in tropical Africa, where the deadly disease malaria is also prevalent. The parasite that causes malaria spends part of its life cycle inside red blood cells. When it enters those of a person with the sickle-cell allele, it triggers sickling. The body destroys most of the sickled cells, and the parasite does not grow well in those that remain. Consequently, sickle-cell carriers are resistant to malaria, and in many parts of Africa, they live longer and have more offspring than noncarriers who are exposed to malaria. In this way, malaria has kept the frequency of the sickle-cell allele relatively high in much of the African continent. To put it in evolutionary terms, as long as malaria is a danger, individuals with the sickle-cell allele have a selective advantage.

? **How does sickle-cell disease exemplify the concept of pleiotropy?**

● Homozygosity for the sickle-cell allele causes abnormal hemoglobin, and the impact of the abnormal hemoglobin on the shape of red blood cells leads to a cascade of symptoms in multiple organs of the body.

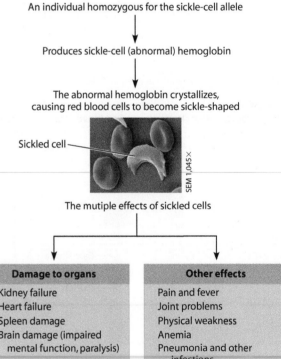

An individual homozygous for the sickle-cell allele

↓

Produces sickle-cell (abnormal) hemoglobin

↓

The abnormal hemoglobin crystallizes, causing red blood cells to become sickle-shaped

Sickled cell

SEM 1,045×

The multiple effects of sickled cells

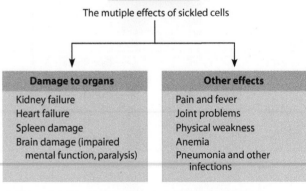

Damage to organs	Other effects
Kidney failure	Pain and fever
Heart failure	Joint problems
Spleen damage	Physical weakness
Brain damage (impaired mental function, paralysis)	Anemia
	Pneumonia and other infections

▲ Figure 9.13B Sickle-cell disease, an example of pleitropy

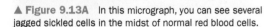

SEM 1,045×

▲ Figure 9.13A In this micrograph, you can see several jagged sickled cells in the midst of normal red blood cells.

9.14 A single character may be influenced by many genes

Mendel studied genetic characters that could be classified on an either-or basis, such as purple or white flower color. However, many characteristics, such as human skin color and height, vary in a population along a continuum. Many such features result from **polygenic inheritance**, the additive effects of two or more genes on a single phenotypic character. (This is the converse of pleiotropy, in which a single gene affects several characters.)

Let's consider a hypothetical example. Assume that the continuous variation in human skin color is controlled by three genes that are inherited separately, like Mendel's pea genes. (Actually, genetic evidence indicates that *at least* three genes control this character.) The "dark-skin" allele for each gene (*A*, *B*, or *C*) contributes one "unit" of darkness to the phenotype and is incompletely dominant to the other allele (*a*, *b*, or *c*). A person who is *AABBCC* would be very dark, whereas an *aabbcc* individual would be very light. An *AaBbCc* person (resulting, for example, from a mating between an *AABBCC* person and an *aabbcc* person) would have skin of an intermediate shade. Because the alleles have an additive effect, the genotype *AaBbCc* would produce the same skin color as any other genotype with just three dark-skin alleles, such as *AABbcc*, since both of these individuals have three "units" of darkness.

The Punnett square in **Figure 9.14** shows all possible genotypes of offspring from a mating of two triple heterozygotes, the F₁ generation here. The row of squares below the Punnett square shows the seven skin pigmentation phenotypes that would theoretically result from this mating. The seven bars in the graph at the bottom of the figure depict the relative numbers of each of the phenotypes in the F₂ generation. This hypothetical example shows how inheritance of three genes could lead to a wide variety of pigmentation phenotypes. In real human populations, skin color has even more variations than shown in the figure, in part for reasons we discuss in the next module.

Up to this point in the chapter, we have presented four types of inheritance patterns that are extensions of Mendel's laws of inheritance: incomplete dominance, codominance, pleiotropy, and polygenic inheritance. It is important to realize that these patterns are extensions of Mendel's model, rather than exceptions to it. From Mendel's garden pea experiments came data supporting a particulate theory of inheritance, with the particles (genes) being transmitted according to the same rules of chance that govern the tossing of coins. The particulate theory holds true for all inheritance patterns, even the patterns that are more complex than the ones originally considered by Mendel. In the next module, we consider another important source of deviation from Mendel's standard model: the effect of the environment.

? Based on the model for skin color in Figure 9.14, an *AaBbcc* individual would be indistinguishable in phenotype from which of the following individuals: *AAbbcc*, *aaBBcc*, *AabbCc*, *Aabbcc*, or *aaBbcc*?

● All except *AaBbcc*

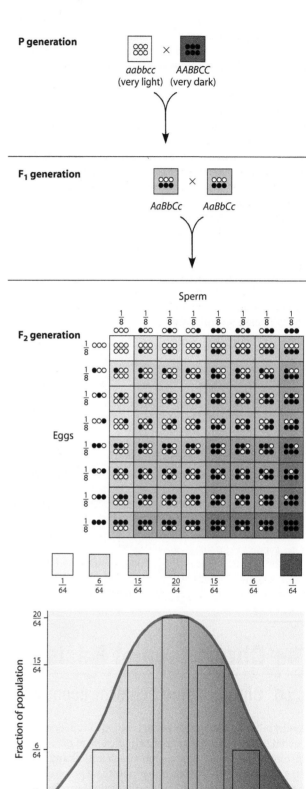

▲ **Figure 9.14** A model for polygenic inheritance of skin color

9.15 The environment affects many characters

In the previous module, we saw how a set of three hypothetical human skin-color genes could produce seven different phenotypes for skin color. If we examine a real human population for skin color, we might see more shades than just seven. The true range might be similar to the entire spectrum of color under the bell-shaped curve in Figure 9.14. In fact, no matter how carefully we characterize the genes for skin color, a purely genetic description will always be incomplete. This is because some intermediate shades of skin color result from the effects of environmental factors, such as exposure to the sun (Figure 9.15A).

Many characters result from a combination of heredity and environment. For example, the leaves of a tree all have the same genotype, but they may vary greatly in phenotype such as size, shape, and color, depending on exposure to wind and sun and the tree's nutritional state. For humans, nutrition influences height; exercise alters build; sun-tanning darkens the skin; and experience improves performance on intelligence tests. As geneticists learn more and more about our genes, it is becoming clear that many human phenotypes—such as risk of heart disease and cancer and susceptibility to alcoholism and schizophrenia—are influenced by both genes and environment.

Whether human characters are more influenced by genes or by the environment—nature or nurture—is a very old and hotly contested debate. For some characters, such as the ABO blood group, a given genotype absolutely mandates a very specific phenotype, and the environment plays no role whatsoever. In contrast, a person's counts of red and white blood cells (the numbers of blood cells per milliliter of blood) are influenced greatly by environmental factors such as the altitude, the customary level of physical activity, and the presence of infectious agents.

It is important to realize that the individual features of any organism arise from a combination of genetic and environmental factors. Simply spending time with identical twins will convince anyone that environment, and not just genes, affects a person's traits (Figure 9.15B). However, there is an important difference between these two sources of variation: Only genetic influences are inherited. Any effects of the environment are generally not passed on to the next generation.

? **If most characters result from a combination of environment and heredity, why was Mendel able to ignore environmental influences on his pea plants?**

● The characters he chose for study were all entirely genetically determined.

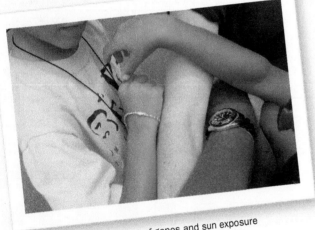

▲ **Figure 9.15A** The effect of genes and sun exposure on the skin of one of this book's authors and his family

▲ **Figure 9.15B** Varying phenotypes due to environmental factors in genetically identical twins

The Chromosomal Basis of Inheritance

9.16 Chromosome behavior accounts for Mendel's laws

Mendel published his results in 1866, but not until long after he died did biologists understand the significance of his work. Cell biologists worked out the processes of mitosis and meiosis in the late 1800s (see Chapter 8 to review these processes). Then, around 1900, researchers began to notice parallels between the behavior of chromosomes and the behavior of Mendel's heritable factors. Eventually, one of biology's most important concepts emerged. By combining these observations,

the **chromosome theory of inheritance** states that genes occupy specific loci (positions) on chromosomes, and it is the chromosomes that undergo segregation and independent assortment during meiosis. Thus, it is the behavior of chromosomes during meiosis and fertilization that accounts for inheritance patterns.

We can see the chromosomal basis of Mendel's laws by following the fates of two genes during meiosis and fertilization in pea plants. In Figure 9.16, we show the genes for seed shape (alleles *R* and *r*) and seed color (*Y* and *y*) as black bars on different chromosomes. Notice that the Punnett square is repeated from Figure 9.5A; we will now follow the chromosomes to see how they account for the results of the dihybrid cross shown in the Punnett square. We start with the F_1 generation, in which all plants have the *RrYy* genotype. To simplify the diagram, we show only two of the seven pairs of pea chromosomes and three of the stages of meiosis: metaphase I, anaphase I, and metaphase II.

To see the chromosomal basis of the law of segregation (which states that pairs of alleles separate from each other during gamete formation via meiosis; see Module 9.3), let's follow just the homologous pair of long chromosomes, the ones carrying *R* and *r*, taking either the left or the right branch from the F_1 cell. Whichever arrangement the chromosomes assume at metaphase I, the two alleles segregate as the homologous chromosomes separate in anaphase I. And at the end of meiosis II, a single long chromosome ends up in each of the gametes. Fertilization then recombines the two alleles at random, resulting in F_2 offspring that are $\frac{1}{4}$ *RR*, $\frac{1}{2}$ *Rr*, and $\frac{1}{4}$ *rr*. The ratio of round

to wrinkled phenotypes is thus 3:1 (12 round to 4 wrinkled), the ratio Mendel observed, as shown in the Punnett square in the figure.

To see the chromosomal basis of the law of independent assortment (which states that each pair of alleles sorts independently of other pairs of alleles during gamete formation; see Module 9.5), follow both the long and short (nonhomologous) chromosomes through the figure below. Two alternative, equally likely arrangements of tetrads can occur at metaphase I. The nonhomologous chromosomes (and their genes) assort independently, leading to four gamete genotypes. Random fertilization leads to the 9:3:3:1 phenotypic ratio in the F_2 generation.

? Which of Mendel's laws have their physical basis in the following phases of meiosis: (a) the orientation of homologous chromosome pairs in metaphase I; (b) the separation of homologs in anaphase I?

● (a) The law of independent assortment; (b) the law of segregation

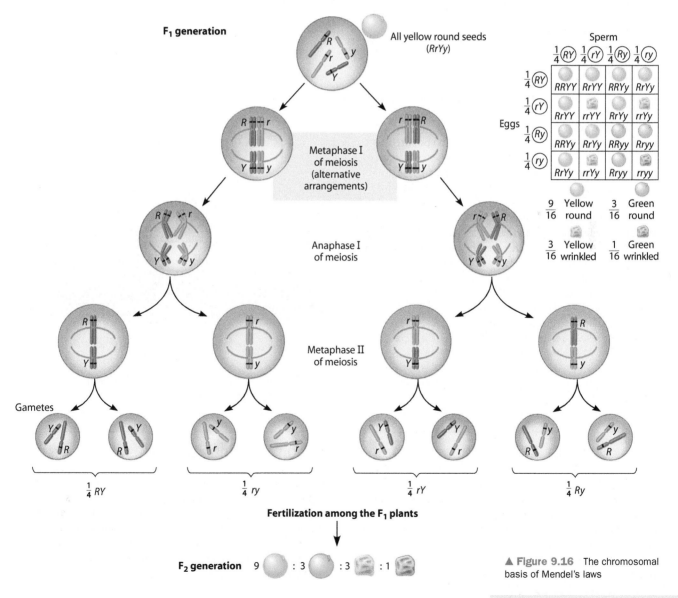

▲ Figure 9.16 The chromosomal basis of Mendel's laws

9.17 **Genes on the same chromosome tend to be inherited together**

In 1908, British biologists William Bateson and Reginald Punnett (originator of the Punnett square) observed an inheritance pattern that seemed inconsistent with Mendelian laws. Bateson and Punnett were working with two characters in sweet peas: flower color and pollen shape. They crossed doubly heterozygous plants (*PpLl*) that exhibited the dominant traits: purple flowers (expression of the *P* allele) and long pollen grains (expression of the *L* allele). The corresponding recessive traits are red flowers (in *pp* plants) and round pollen (in *ll* plants).

The top part of Figure 9.17 illustrates Bateson and Punnett's experiment. When they looked at just one of the two characters (that is, either cross *Pp* × *Pp* or cross *Ll* × *Ll*), they found that the dominant and recessive alleles segregated, producing a phenotypic ratio of approximately 3:1 for the offspring, in agreement with Mendel's law of segregation. However, when the biologists combined their data for the two characters, they did not see the predicted 9:3:3:1 ratio. Instead, as shown in the table, they found a disproportionately large number of plants with just two of the predicted phenotypes: purple long (almost 75% of the total) and red round (about 14%). The other two phenotypes (purple round and red long) were found in far fewer numbers than expected. What can account for these results?

The number of genes in a cell is far greater than the number of chromosomes; in fact, each chromosome has hundreds or thousands of genes. Genes located close together on the same chromosome tend to be inherited together and are called **linked genes**. Linked genes generally do not follow Mendel's law of independent assortment.

As shown in the explanation section of the figure, sweet-pea genes for flower color and pollen shape are located on the same chromosome. Thus, meiosis in the heterozygous (*PpLl*) sweet-pea plant yields mostly two genotypes of gametes (*PL* and *pl*) rather than equal numbers of the four types of gametes that would result if the flower-color and pollen-shape genes were not linked. The large numbers of plants with purple long and red round traits in the Bateson-Punnett experiment resulted from fertilization among the *PL* and *pl* gametes. But what about the smaller numbers of plants with purple round and red long traits? As you will see in the next module, the phenomenon of crossing over accounts for these offspring.

The Experiment

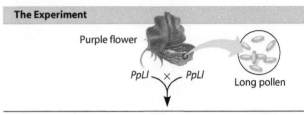

Purple flower

PpLl × *PpLl*   Long pollen

Phenotypes	Observed offspring	Prediction (9:3:3:1)
Purple long	284	215
Purple round	21	71
Red long	21	71
Red round	55	24

The Explanation: Linked Genes

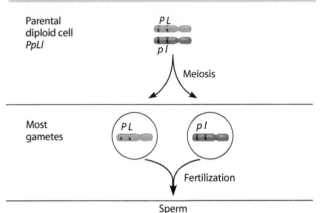

Parental diploid cell *PpLl*

P L
p l

Meiosis

Most gametes

P L   *p l*

Fertilization

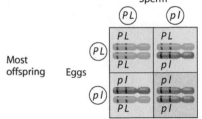

Sperm

Most offspring   Eggs

3 purple long : 1 red round
Not accounted for: purple round and red long

▲ **Figure 9.17** The experiment revealing linked genes in the sweet pea

 ? **Why do linked genes tend to be inherited together?**

Because they are located close together on the same chromosome

9.18 **Crossing over produces new combinations of alleles**

In Module 8.17, we saw that during meiosis, crossing over between homologous chromosomes produces new combinations of alleles in gametes. Using the experiment shown in Figure 9.17 as an example, Figure 9.18A reviews this process, showing that two linked genes can give rise to four different gamete genotypes. Gametes with genotypes *PL* and *pl* carry parental-type chromosomes that have not been altered by crossing over. In contrast, gametes with genotypes *Pl* and *pL* are recombinant gametes. The exchange of chromosome segments during crossing over has produced new combinations of alleles. We can now understand the results of the Bateson-Punnett experiment presented in the previous module: The small fraction of offspring with recombinant phenotypes (purple round and red long) must have resulted from fertilization involving recombinant gametes.

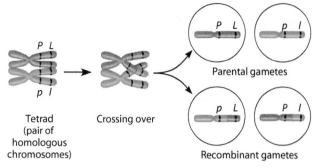

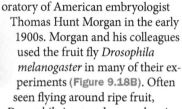

Tetrad
(pair of
homologous
chromosomes)

Crossing over

Parental gametes

Recombinant gametes

▲ **Figure 9.18A** Review: the production of recombinant gametes

The discovery of how crossing over creates gamete diversity confirmed the relationship between chromosome behavior and heredity. Some of the most important early studies of crossing over were performed in the laboratory of American embryologist Thomas Hunt Morgan in the early 1900s. Morgan and his colleagues used the fruit fly *Drosophila melanogaster* in many of their experiments (**Figure 9.18B**). Often seen flying around ripe fruit, *Drosophila* is a good research animal for genetic studies because it can be easily and inexpensively bred, producing each new generation in a couple of weeks.

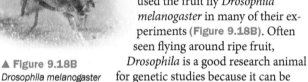

▲ **Figure 9.18B**
Drosophila melanogaster

Figure 9.18C shows one of Morgan's experiments, a cross between a wild-type fruit fly (recall from Module 9.8 that "wild-type" refers to the traits most common in nature, in this case, gray body and long wings) and a fly with a black body and undeveloped, or vestigial, wings. Morgan knew the genotypes of these flies from previous studies. Here we use the following gene symbols:

G = gray body (dominant)

g = black body (recessive)

L = long wings (dominant)

l = vestigial wings (recessive)

In mating a heterozygous gray fly with long wings (genotype *GgLl*) with a black fly with vestigial wings (genotype *ggll*), Morgan performed a testcross (see Module 9.6). If the genes were not linked, then independent assortment would produce offspring in a phenotypic ratio of 1:1:1:1 ($\frac{1}{4}$ gray body, long wings; $\frac{1}{4}$ black body, vestigial wings; $\frac{1}{4}$ gray body, vestigial wings; and $\frac{1}{4}$ black body, long wings). But because these genes are linked, Morgan obtained the results shown in the top part of Figure 9.18C: Most of the offspring had parental phenotypes, but 17% of the offspring flies were recombinants. The percentage of recombinants is called the **recombination frequency**.

When Morgan first obtained these results, he did not know about crossing over. To explain the ratio of offspring, he hypothesized that the genes were linked and that some mechanism occasionally broke the linkage. Tests of the hypothesis proved him correct, establishing that crossing over was the mechanism that "breaks linkages" between genes.

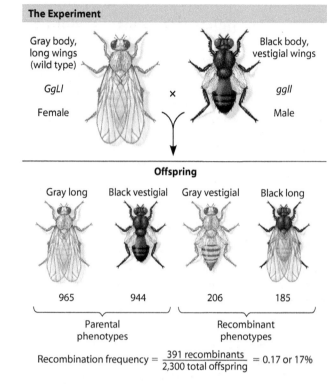

The Experiment

Gray body, long wings (wild type)

GgLl

Female

×

Black body, vestigial wings

ggll

Male

Offspring

Gray long | Black vestigial | Gray vestigial | Black long

965 | 944 | 206 | 185

Parental phenotypes | Recombinant phenotypes

Recombination frequency $= \dfrac{391 \text{ recombinants}}{2{,}300 \text{ total offspring}} = 0.17$ or 17%

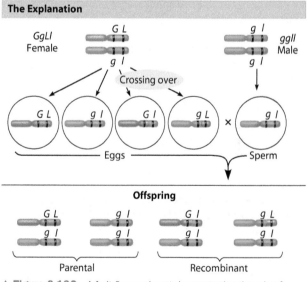

The Explanation

GgLl
Female

ggll
Male

Crossing over

Eggs

Sperm

Offspring

Parental | Recombinant

▲ **Figure 9.18C** A fruit fly experiment demonstrating the role of crossing over in inheritance

The lower part of Figure 9.18C explains Morgan's results in terms of crossing over. A crossover between chromatids of homologous chromosomes in parent *GgLl* broke linkages between the *G* and *L* alleles and between the *g* and *l* alleles, forming the recombinant chromosomes *Gl* and *gL*. Later steps in meiosis distributed the recombinant chromosomes to gametes, and random fertilization produced the four kinds of offspring Morgan observed.

? Return to the data in Figure 9.17. What is the recombination frequency between the flower-color and pollen-length genes?

11% $\left(\frac{391}{42}\right)$ ●

9.19 Geneticists use crossover data to map genes

Working with *Drosophila*, T. H. Morgan and his students—Alfred H. Sturtevant in particular—greatly advanced our understanding of genetics during the early 20th century. One of Sturtevant's major contributions to genetics was an approach for using crossover data to map gene loci. His reasoning was elegantly simple: The greater the distance between two genes, the more points there are between them where crossing over can occur. With this principle in mind, Sturtevant began using recombination data from fruit fly crosses to assign relative positions of the genes on the chromosomes—that is, to map genes.

Figure 9.19A represents a part of the chromosome that carries the linked genes for black body (*g*) and vestigial wings (*l*) that we described in Module 9.18. This same chromosome also carries a gene that has a recessive allele (we'll call it *c*) determining cinnabar eye color, a brighter red than the wild-type color. Figure 9.19A shows the actual crossover (recombination) frequencies between these alleles, taken two at a time: 17% between the *g* and *l* alleles, 9% between *g* and *c*, and 9.5% between *c* and *l*. Sturtevant reasoned that these values represent the relative distances between the genes. Because the crossover frequencies between *g* and *c* and between *l* and *c* are approximately half that between *g* and *l*, gene *c* must lie roughly midway between *g* and *l*. Thus, the sequence of these genes on one of the fruit fly chromosomes must be *g-c-l*. Such a diagram of relative gene locations is called a **linkage map**.

Sturtevant started by assuming that the chance of crossing over is approximately equal at all points along a chromosome. We now know that this assumption is only approximately true; some locations along the chromosome are more prone to crossing over than others. Still, his method of mapping genes

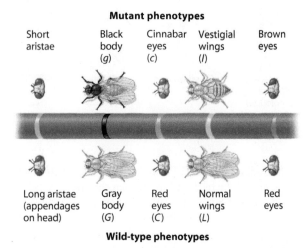

Mutant phenotypes

| Short aristae | Black body (*g*) | Cinnabar eyes (*c*) | Vestigial wings (*l*) | Brown eyes |

| Long aristae (appendages on head) | Gray body (*G*) | Red eyes (*C*) | Normal wings (*L*) | Red eyes |

Wild-type phenotypes

▲ **Figure 9.19B** A partial linkage map of a fruit fly chromosome

worked well, and it proved extremely valuable in establishing the relative positions of many other fruit fly genes. Eventually, enough data were accumulated to reveal that *Drosophila* has four groups of genes, corresponding to its four pairs of homologous chromosomes. **Figure 9.19B** is a genetic map showing just five of the gene loci on part of one chromosome: the loci labeled *g*, *c*, and *l* and two others. Notice that eye color is a character affected by more than one gene. Here we see the cinnabar-eye and brown-eye genes; still other eye-color genes are found elsewhere (see Module 9.21). For each of these genes, however, the wild-type allele specifies red eyes.

The linkage-mapping method has proved extremely valuable in establishing the relative positions of many genes in many organisms. The real beauty of the technique is that a wealth of information about genes can be learned simply by breeding and observing the organisms; no fancy equipment is required.

? You design *Drosophila* crosses to provide recombination data for a gene not included in Figure 9.19A. The gene has recombination frequencies of 3% with the vestigial-wing (*l*) locus and 7% with the cinnabar-eye (*c*) locus. Where is it located on the chromosome?

● The gene is located between the vestigial and cinnabar loci, a bit closer to the vestigial-wing locus (since it has a lower recombination frequency).

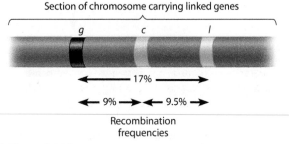

Section of chromosome carrying linked genes

g   *c*   *l*

◄——— 17% ———►

◄— 9% —►◄— 9.5% —►

Recombination frequencies

▲ **Figure 9.19A** Mapping genes from crossover data

Sex Chromosomes and Sex-Linked Genes

9.20 Chromosomes determine sex in many species

Many animals, including fruit flies and all mammals, have a pair of **sex chromosomes**, designated X and Y, that determine an individual's sex **(Figure 9.20A)**. **Figure 9.20B** reviews what you learned in Chapter 8 about sex determination in humans. Individuals with one X chromosome and one Y chromosome

▶ **Figure 9.20A** The human sex chromosomes

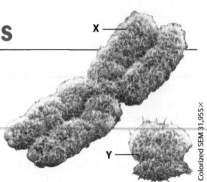

X

Y

Colorized SEM 31,955×

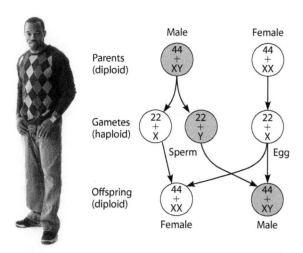

▲ **Figure 9.20B** The X-Y system

▲ **Figure 9.20D** The Z-W system

are males; XX individuals are females. Human males and females both have 44 autosomes (nonsex chromosomes). As a result of chromosome segregation during meiosis, each gamete contains one sex chromosome and a haploid set of autosomes (22 in humans). All eggs contain a single X chromosome. Of the sperm cells, half contain an X chromosome and half contain a Y chromosome. An offspring's sex depends on whether the sperm cell that fertilizes the egg bears an X chromosome or a Y chromosome. In the fruit fly's X-Y system, sex is determined by the ratio between the number of X chromosomes and the number of autosome sets, although the Y chromosome is essential for sperm formation.

The genetic basis of sex determination in humans is not yet completely understood, but one gene on the Y chromosome plays a crucial role. This gene, discovered by a British research team in 1990, is called *SRY* (for sex-determining region of Y) and triggers testis development. In the absence of *SRY*, an individual develops ovaries rather than testes. *SRY* codes for proteins that regulate other genes on the Y chromosome. These genes in turn produce proteins necessary for normal testis development.

The X-Y system is only one of several sex-determining systems. For example, grasshoppers, roaches, and some other insects have an X-O system, in which O stands for the absence of a sex chromosome (Figure 9.20C). Females have two X chromosomes (XX); males have only one sex chromosome (XO). Males produce two classes of sperm (X-bearing and lacking any sex chromosome), and sperm cells determine the sex of the offspring at fertilization.

In contrast to the X-Y and X-O systems, eggs determine sex in certain fishes, butterflies, and birds (Figure 9.20D). The sex

chromosomes in these animals are designated Z and W. Males have the genotype ZZ; females are ZW. In this system, sex is determined by whether the egg carries a Z or a W.

Some organisms lack sex chromosomes altogether. In most ants and bees, sex is determined by chromosome number rather than by sex chromosomes (Figure 9.20E). Females develop from fertilized eggs and thus are diploid. Males develop from unfertilized eggs—they are fatherless—and are haploid.

Most animals have two separate sexes; that is, individuals are either male or female. Many plant species have sperm-bearing and egg-bearing flowers borne on different individuals. Some plant species, such as date palms, have the X-Y system of sex determination; others, such as the wild strawberry, have the Z-W system. However, most plant species and some animal species have individuals that produce both sperm and eggs. In such species, all individuals have the same complement of chromosomes.

In Module 9.15, we discussed the role that environment plays in determining many characters. Among some animals, environment can even determine sex. For some species of reptiles, the temperature at which eggs are incubated during a specific period of embryonic development determines whether that embryo will develop into a male or female. For example, if green sea turtle hatchlings incubate above 30°C (86°F), nearly all the resulting turtles will be males. (Some worry that global climate change might have the unexpected consequence of affecting the makeup of turtle populations.) Such temperature-dependent sex determination is an extreme example of the environment affecting the phenotype of an individual.

? **During fertilization in humans, what determines the sex of the offspring?**

● Whether the egg is fertilized by a sperm bearing an X chromosome (producing a female offspring) or by a sperm with a Y chromosome (producing a male)

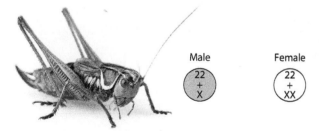

▲ **Figure 9.20C** The X-O system

▲ **Figure 9.20E** Sex determination by chromosome number

9.21 Sex-linked genes exhibit a unique pattern of inheritance

Besides bearing genes that determine sex, the sex chromosomes also contain genes for characters unrelated to femaleness or maleness. A gene located on either sex chromosome is called a **sex-linked gene**. Because the human X chromosome contains many more genes than the Y, the term has historically referred specifically to genes on the X chromosome. (Be careful not to confuse the term *sex-linked gene*, which refers to a gene on a sex chromosome, with the term *linked genes*, which refers to genes on the same chromosome that tend to be inherited together.)

The figures in this module illustrate inheritance patterns for white eye color in the fruit fly, an X-linked recessive trait. Wild-type fruit flies have red eyes; white eyes are very rare (Figure 9.21A). We use the uppercase letter R for the dominant, wild-type, red-eye allele and r for the recessive white-eye allele. Because these alleles are carried on the X chromosome, we show them as superscripts to the letter X. Thus, red-eyed male fruit flies have the genotype X^RY; white-eyed males are X^rY. The Y chromosome does not have a gene locus for eye color; therefore, the male's phenotype results entirely from his single X-linked gene. In the female, X^RX^R and X^RX^r flies have red eyes, and X^rX^r flies have white eyes.

A white-eyed male (X^rY) will transmit his X^r to all of his female offspring but to none of his male offspring. This is because his female offspring, in order to be female, must inherit his X chromosome, but his male offspring must inherit his Y chromosome.

As shown in Figure 9.21B, when the female parent is a dominant homozygote (X^RX^R) and the male parent is X^rY, all the offspring have red eyes, but the female offspring are all carriers of the allele for white eyes (X^RX^r). When those offspring are bred to each other, the classic 3:1 phenotypic ratio of red eyes to white eyes appears among the offspring (Figure 9.21C). However, there is a twist: The white-eyed trait shows up only in males. All the females have red eyes, whereas half the males have red eyes and half have white eyes. All females inherit at least one dominant allele (from their male parent); half of them are homozygous dominant, whereas the other half are heterozygous carriers, like their female parent. Among the males, half of them inherit the recessive allele their mother was carrying, producing the white-eye phenotype.

Because the white-eye allele is recessive, a female will have white eyes only if she receives that allele on both X chromosomes. For example, if a heterozygous female mates with a white-eyed male, there is a 50% chance that each offspring will have white eyes (resulting from genotype X^rX^r or X^rY), regardless of sex (Figure 9.21D). Female offspring with red eyes are heterozygotes, whereas red-eyed male offspring completely lack the recessive allele.

? A white-eyed female *Drosophila* is mated with a red-eyed (wild-type) male. What result do you predict for the numerous offspring?

All female offspring will be red-eyed but heterozygous (X^RX^r); all male offspring will be white-eyed (X^rY).

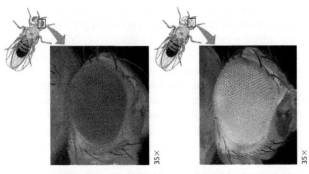

▲ **Figure 9.21A** Fruit fly eye color determined by sex-linked gene

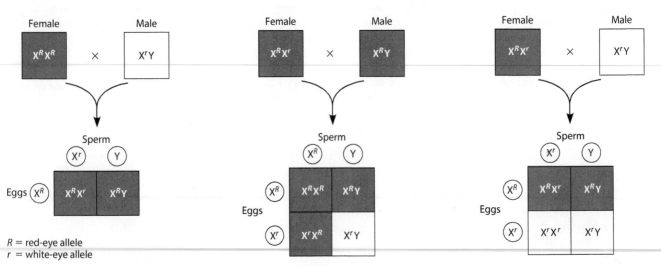

R = red-eye allele
r = white-eye allele

▲ **Figure 9.21B** A homozygous, red-eyed female crossed with a white-eyed male

▲ **Figure 9.21C** A heterozygous female crossed with a red-eyed male

▲ **Figure 9.21D** A heterozygous female crossed with a white-eyed male

9.22 Human sex-linked disorders affect mostly males

As in fruit flies, a number of human conditions result from sex-linked (X-linked) recessive alleles. Like a male fruit fly, if a man inherits only one X-linked recessive allele—from his mother—the allele will be expressed. In contrast, a woman has to inherit two such alleles—one from each parent—in order to exhibit the trait. Thus, recessive X-linked traits are expressed much more frequently in men than in women.

Hemophilia is an X-linked recessive trait with a long, well-documented history. Hemophiliacs bleed excessively when injured because they lack one or more of the proteins required for blood clotting. A high incidence of hemophilia plagued the royal families of Europe. Queen Victoria (1819–1901) of England was a carrier of the hemophilia allele. She passed it on to one of her sons and two of her daughters. Through marriage, her daughters then introduced the disease into the royal families of Prussia, Russia, and Spain. Thus, the age-old practice of strengthening international alliances by marriage effectively spread hemophilia through the royal families of several nations. The pedigree in Figure 9.22 traces the disease through one branch of the royal family. As you can see in the pedigree, Alexandra, like her mother and grandmother, was a carrier, and Alexis had the disease.

Another recessive disorder in humans that is sex-linked is **red-green colorblindness**, a malfunction of light-sensitive cells in the eyes. Colorblindness is actually a class of disorders that involves several X-linked genes. A person with normal color vision can see more than 150 colors. In contrast, someone with red-green colorblindness can see fewer than 25. Mostly males are affected, but heterozygous females have some defects.

Duchenne muscular dystrophy, a condition characterized by a progressive weakening of the muscles and loss of coordination, is another human X-linked recessive disorder. The

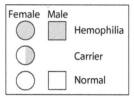
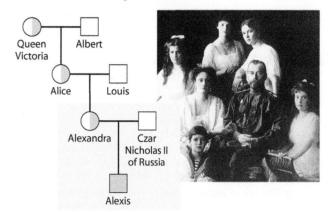

▲ Figure 9.22 Hemophilia in the royal family of Russia

first symptoms appear in early childhood, when the child begins to have difficulty standing up. He is inevitably wheelchair-bound by age 12. Eventually, muscle tissue becomes severely wasted, and normal breathing becomes difficult. Affected individuals rarely live past their early 20s.

? Neither Tom nor Sue has hemophilia, but their first son does. If the couple has a second child, what is the probability that he or she will also have the disease?

● $\frac{1}{4}$ ($\frac{1}{2}$ chance of a male child × $\frac{1}{2}$ chance that he will inherit the mutant X)

9.23 The Y chromosome provides clues about human male evolution

Barring mutations, the human Y chromosome passes essentially intact from father to son. By analyzing Y DNA, researchers can learn about the ancestry of human males.

In 2003, geneticists discovered that about 8% of males currently living in central Asia have Y chromosomes of striking genetic similarity. Further analysis traced their common genetic heritage to a single man living about 1,000 years ago. In combination with historical records, the data led to the speculation that the Mongolian ruler Genghis Kahn (Figure 9.23) may be responsible for the spread of the unusual chromosome to nearly 16 million men living today. A similar study of Irish men in 2006 suggested that nearly 10% of them were descendants of Niall of the Nine Hostages, a warlord who lived during the 5th century.

Another study of Y DNA seemed to confirm the claim by the Lemba people of southern Africa that they are descended from ancient Jews.

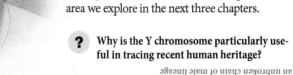

▲ Figure 9.23 Genghis Kahn

Sequences of Y DNA distinctive of the Jewish priestly caste called Cohanim (descendants of Moses' brother Aaron, according to the Bible) are found at high frequencies among the Lemba.

The discovery of the sex chromosomes and their pattern of inheritance was one of many breakthroughs in understanding how genes are passed from one generation to the next. During the first half of the 20th century, geneticists rediscovered Mendel's work, reinterpreted his laws in light of chromosomal behavior during meiosis, and firmly established the chromosome theory of inheritance. The chromosome theory set the stage for another explosion of experimental work in the second half of the 20th century. This work was in molecular genetics, an area we explore in the next three chapters.

? Why is the Y chromosome particularly useful in tracing recent human heritage?

● Because it is passed directly from father to son, forming an unbroken chain of male lineage

Reviewing the Concepts

Mendel's Laws (9.1–9.10)

9.1 The science of genetics has ancient roots.

9.2 Experimental genetics began in an abbey garden. The science of genetics began with Gregor Mendel's quantitative experiments. Mendel crossed pea plants and traced traits from generation to generation. He hypothesized that there are alternative versions of genes (alleles), the units that determine heritable traits.

9.3 Mendel's law of segregation describes the inheritance of a single character. Mendel's law of segregation predicts that each set of alleles will separate as gametes are formed:

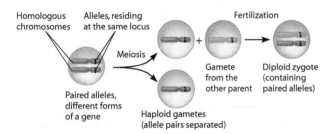

9.4 Homologous chromosomes bear the alleles for each character. When the two alleles of a gene in a diploid individual are different, the dominant allele determines the inherited trait, whereas the recessive allele has no effect.

9.5 The law of independent assortment is revealed by tracking two characters at once. Mendel's law of independent assortment states that the alleles of a pair segregate independently of other allele pairs during gamete formation.

9.6 Geneticists can use the testcross to determine unknown genotypes. The offspring of a testcross, a mating between an individual of unknown genotype and a homozygous recessive individual, can reveal the unknown's genotype.

9.7 Mendel's laws reflect the rules of probability. The rule of multiplication calculates the probability of two independent events both occurring. The rule of addition calculates the probability of an event that can occur in alternative ways.

9.8 Genetic traits in humans can be tracked through family pedigrees. The inheritance of many human traits follows Mendel's laws. Family pedigrees can help determine individual genotypes.

9.9 Many inherited disorders in humans are controlled by a single gene.

9.10 New technologies can provide insight into one's genetic legacy. Carrier screening, fetal testing, fetal imaging, and newborn screening can provide information for reproductive decisions but may create ethical dilemmas.

Variations on Mendel's Laws (9.11–9.15)

9.11 Incomplete dominance results in intermediate phenotypes. Mendel's laws are valid for all sexually reproducing species, but genotype often does not dictate phenotype in the simple way his laws describe, as shown in the figure at the top of the next column.

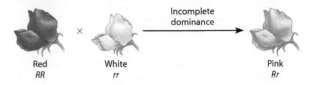

Incomplete dominance

Red RR × White rr → Pink Rr

9.12 Many genes have more than two alleles in the population. For example, the ABO blood group phenotype in humans is controlled by three alleles that produce a total of four phenotypes.

9.13 A single gene may affect many phenotypic characters:

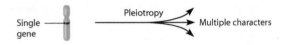

Single gene → Pleiotropy → Multiple characters

9.14 A single character may be influenced by many genes:

Multiple genes → Polygenic inheritance → Single characters (such as skin color)

9.15 The environment affects many characters. Many traits are affected, in varying degrees, by both genetic and environmental factors.

The Chromosomal Basis of Inheritance (9.16–9.19)

9.16 Chromosome behavior accounts for Mendel's laws. Genes are located on chromosomes, whose behavior during meiosis and fertilization accounts for inheritance patterns.

9.17 Genes on the same chromosome tend to be inherited together. Such genes are said to be linked; they display non-Mendelian inheritance patterns.

9.18 Crossing over produces new combinations of alleles. Crossing over can separate linked alleles, producing gametes with recombinant chromosomes.

9.19 Geneticists use crossover data to map genes. Recombination frequencies can be used to map the relative positions of genes on chromosomes.

Sex Chromosomes and Sex-Linked Genes (9.20–9.23)

9.20 Chromosomes determine sex in many species. In mammals, a male has XY sex chromosomes, and a female has XX. The Y chromosome has genes for the development of testes, whereas an absence of the Y allows ovaries to develop. Other systems of sex determination exist in other animals and plants.

9.21 Sex-linked genes exhibit a unique pattern of inheritance. All genes on the sex chromosomes are said to be sex-linked. However, the X chromosome carries many genes unrelated to sex.

9.22 Human sex-linked disorders affect mostly males. Most sex-linked (X-linked) human disorders are due to recessive alleles and are seen mostly in males. A male receiving a single X-linked recessive allele from his mother will have the disorder; a female must receive the allele from both parents to be affected.

9.23 The Y chromosome provides clues about human male evolution. Because they are passed on intact from father to son, Y chromosomes can provide data about recent human evolutionary history.

Connecting the Concepts

1. Complete this concept map to help you review some key concepts of genetics.

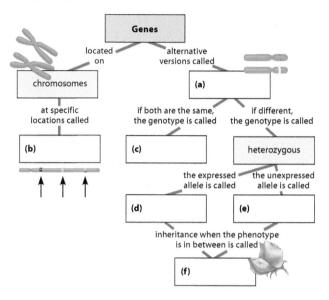

Testing Your Knowledge

Multiple Choice

2. Edward was found to be heterozygous (*Ss*) for sickle-cell trait. The alleles represented by the letters *S* and *s* are
   a. on the X and Y chromosomes.
   b. linked.
   c. on homologous chromosomes.
   d. both present in each of Edward's sperm cells.
   e. on the same chromosome but far apart.

3. Whether an allele is dominant or recessive depends on
   a. how common the allele is, relative to other alleles.
   b. whether it is inherited from the mother or the father.
   c. which chromosome it is on.
   d. whether it or another allele determines the phenotype when both are present.
   e. whether or not it is linked to other genes.

4. Two fruit flies with eyes of the usual red color are crossed, and their offspring are as follows: 77 red-eyed males, 71 ruby-eyed males, 152 red-eyed females. The allele for ruby eyes is
   a. autosomal (carried on an autosome) and dominant.
   b. autosomal and recessive.
   c. sex-linked and dominant.
   d. sex-linked and recessive.
   e. impossible to determine without more information.

5. A man who has type B blood and a woman who has type A blood could have children of which of the following phenotypes?
   a. A or B only
   b. AB only
   c. AB or O
   d. A, B, or O
   e. A, B, AB, or O

Additional Genetics Problems

6. Why do more men than women have colorblindness?

7. In fruit flies, the genes for wing shape and body stripes are linked. In a fly whose genotype is *WwSs*, *W* is linked to *S*, and *w* is linked to *s*. Show how this fly can produce gametes containing four different combinations of alleles. Which are parental-type gametes? Which are recombinant gametes? How are the recombinants produced?

8. Adult height in humans is at least partially hereditary; tall parents tend to have tall children. But humans come in a range of sizes, not just tall and short. Which extension of Mendel's model accounts for the hereditary variation in human height?

9. Tim and Jan both have freckles (see Module 9.8), but their son Mike does not. Show with a Punnett square how this is possible. If Tim and Jan have two more children, what is the probability that both will have freckles?

10. Both Tim and Jan (problem 9) have a widow's peak (see Module 9.8), but Mike has a straight hairline. What are their genotypes? What is the probability that Tim and Jan's next child will have freckles and a straight hairline?

11. In rabbits, black hair depends on a dominant allele, *B*, and brown hair on a recessive allele, *b*. Short hair is due to a dominant allele, *S*, and long hair to a recessive allele, *s*. If a true-breeding black, short-haired male is mated with a brown, long-haired female, describe their offspring. What will be the genotypes of the offspring? If two of these F₁ rabbits are mated, what phenotypes would you expect among their offspring? In what proportions?

12. A fruit fly with a gray body and red eyes (genotype *BbPp*) is mated with a fly having a black body and purple eyes (genotype *bbpp*). What ratio of offspring would you expect if the body-color and eye-color genes are on different chromosomes (unlinked)? When this mating is actually carried out, most of the offspring look like the parents, but 3% have a gray body and purple eyes, and 3% have a black body and red eyes. Are these genes linked or unlinked? What is the recombination frequency?

13. A series of matings shows that the recombination frequency between the black-body gene (problem 12) and the gene for dumpy (shortened) wings is 36%. The recombination frequency between purple eyes and dumpy wings is 41%. What is the sequence of these three genes on the chromosome?

14. A couple are both phenotypically normal, but their son suffers from hemophilia, a sex-linked recessive disorder. What fraction of their children are likely to suffer from hemophilia? What fraction are likely to be carriers?

15. Heather was surprised to discover she suffered from red-green colorblindness. She told her biology professor, who said, "Your father is colorblind too, right?" How did her professor know this? Why did her professor not say the same thing to the colorblind males in the class?

Applying the Concepts

16. In 1981, a stray black cat with unusual rounded, curled-back ears was adopted by a family in Lakewood, California. Hundreds of descendants of this cat have since been born, and cat fanciers hope to develop the "curl" cat into a show breed. The curl allele is apparently dominant and autosomal (carried on an autosome). Suppose you owned the first curl cat and wanted to breed it to develop a true-breeding variety. Describe tests that would determine whether the curl gene is dominant or recessive and whether it is autosomal or sex-linked. Explain why you think your tests would be conclusive. Describe a test to determine that a cat is true-breeding.

CHAPTER
10

Molecular Biology of the Gene

BIG IDEAS

The Structure of the Genetic Material
(10.1–10.3)

A series of experiments established DNA as the molecule of heredity.

DNA Replication
(10.4–10.5)

Each DNA strand can serve as a template for another.

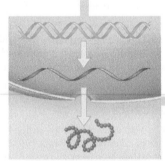

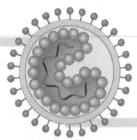

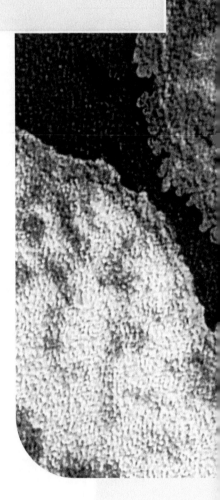

The Flow of Genetic Information from DNA to RNA to Protein
(10.6–10.16)

Genotype controls phenotype through the production of proteins.

The Genetics of Viruses and Bacteria
(10.17–10.23)

Viruses and bacteria are useful model systems for the study of molecular biology.

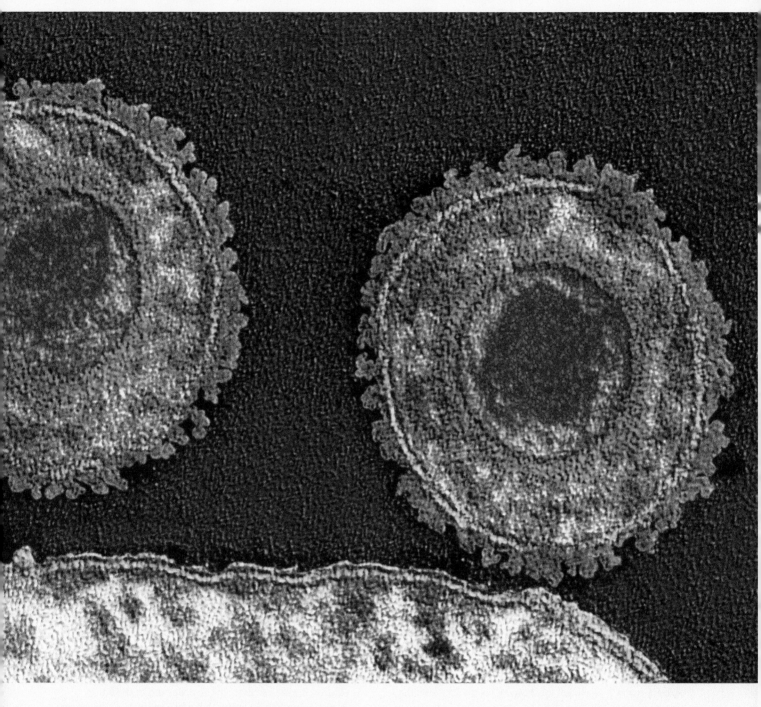

The electron micrograph above shows herpesvirus, an infectious microbe that causes cold sores, genital herpes, chicken pox, and other human diseases. In the micrograph, protein spikes protrude from the exterior of the virus, while the genetic material, colored orange, is visible inside the cell.

Once it enters the human body, a herpesvirus tumbles along until it finds a suitable target cell, recognized when the virus's spikes bind to protein receptor molecules on the cell's surface. The outer membrane of the virus then fuses with the plasma membrane of the cell, and the inner part of the virus enters the cell. The virus DNA, its genetic material, soon enters the nucleus. In the nuclei of certain nerve cells, the viral DNA can remain dormant for long periods of time. Once activated, often under conditions of physical or emotional stress, the viral DNA hijacks the cell's own molecules and organelles and uses them to produce new copies of the virus. Virus production eventually causes host cells to burst. Such destruction causes the sores that are characteristic of herpes diseases. The released viruses can then infect other cells.

Viruses share some of the characteristics of living organisms, but are generally not considered alive because they are not cellular and cannot reproduce on their own. Because viruses have much less complex structures than cells, they are relatively easy to study on the molecular level. For this reason, we owe our first glimpses of the functions of DNA, the molecule that controls hereditary traits, to the study of viruses.

This chapter is about molecular biology—the study of DNA and how it serves as the basis of heredity. We'll explore the structure of DNA, how it replicates, and how it controls the cell by directing RNA and protein synthesis. We end with an examination of the genetics of viruses and bacteria.

The Structure of the Genetic Material

10.1 Experiments showed that DNA is the genetic material

Today, even schoolchildren have heard of DNA, and scientists routinely manipulate DNA in the laboratory and use it to change the heritable characteristics of cells. Early in the 20th century, however, the precise identity of the molecular basis for inheritance was unknown. Biologists knew that genes were located on chromosomes and that the two chemical components of chromosomes were DNA and protein. Therefore, DNA and protein were the likely candidates to be the genetic material. Until the 1940s, the case for proteins seemed stronger because proteins appeared to be more structurally complex: Proteins were known to be made from 20 different amino acid building blocks, whereas DNA was known to be made from a mere four kinds of nucleotides. It seemed to make sense that the more complex molecule would serve as the hereditary material. Biologists finally established the role of DNA in heredity through experiments with bacteria and the viruses that infect them. This breakthrough ushered in the field of **molecular biology**, the study of heredity at the molecular level.

We can trace the discovery of the genetic role of DNA back to 1928. British medical officer Frederick Griffith was studying two strains (varieties) of a bacterium: a harmless strain and a pathogenic (disease-causing) strain that causes pneumonia. Griffith was surprised to find that when he killed the pathogenic bacteria and then mixed the bacterial remains with living harmless bacteria, some living bacterial cells were converted to the disease-causing form. Furthermore, all of the descendants of the transformed bacteria inherited the newly acquired ability to cause disease. Clearly, some chemical component of the dead bacteria could act as a "transforming factor" that brought about a heritable change in live bacteria.

Griffith's work set the stage for a race to discover the identity of the transforming factor. In 1952, American biologists Alfred Hershey and Martha Chase performed a very convincing set of experiments that showed DNA to be the genetic material of T2, a virus that infects the bacterium *Escherichia coli* (*E. coli*). Viruses that exclusively infect bacteria are called **bacteriophages** ("bacteria-eaters"), or **phages** for short. Figure 10.1A shows the structure of phage T2, which consists solely of DNA (blue) and protein (gold). Resembling a lunar landing craft, T2 has a DNA-containing head and a hollow tail with six jointed protein fibers extending from it. The fibers attach to the surface of a susceptible bacterium. Hershey and Chase knew that T2 could reprogram its host cell to produce new phages, but they did not know which component—DNA or protein—was responsible for this ability.

Hershey and Chase found the answer by devising an experiment to determine what kinds of molecules the phage transferred to *E. coli* during infection. Their experiment used only a few relatively simple tools: chemicals containing radioactive isotopes (see Module 2.4); a radioactivity detector; a kitchen blender; and a centrifuge, a device that spins test tubes to separate particles of different weights. (These are still basic tools of molecular biology.)

Hershey and Chase used different radioactive isotopes to label the DNA and protein in T2. First, they grew T2 with *E. coli* in a solution containing radioactive sulfur (bright yellow in Figure 10.1B). Protein contains sulfur but DNA does not, so as new phages were made, the radioactive sulfur atoms were incorporated only into the proteins of the bacteriophage. The researchers grew a separate batch of phages in a solution containing radioactive phosphorus (green). Because nearly all the phage's phosphorus is in DNA, this labeled only the phage DNA.

Armed with the two batches of labeled T2, Hershey and Chase were ready to perform the experiment outlined in Figure 10.1B. ❶ They allowed the two batches of T2 to infect separate samples of nonradioactive bacteria. ❷ Shortly after the onset of infection, they agitated the cultures in a blender to shake loose any parts of the phages that remained outside the bacterial cells. ❸ Then, they spun the mixtures in a centrifuge. The cells were deposited as a pellet at the bottom of the centrifuge tubes, but phages and parts of phages, being lighter, remained suspended in the liquid. ❹ The researchers then measured the radioactivity in the pellet and in the liquid.

Hershey and Chase found that when the bacteria had been infected with T2 phages containing labeled protein, the radioactivity ended up mainly in the liquid within the centrifuge tube, which contained phages but not bacteria. This result suggested that the phage protein did not enter the cells. But when the bacteria had been infected with phages whose DNA was tagged, then most of the radioactivity was in the pellet of bacterial cells at the bottom of the centrifuge tube. Furthermore, when these bacteria were returned to liquid growth medium, they soon lysed, or broke open, releasing new phages with radioactive phosphorus in their DNA but no radioactive sulfur in their proteins.

Figure 10.1C outlines our current understanding—as originally outlined by Hershey and Chase—of the replication cycle of phage T2. After the virus ❶ attaches to the host bacterial cell, it ❷ injects its DNA into the host. Notice that virtually all

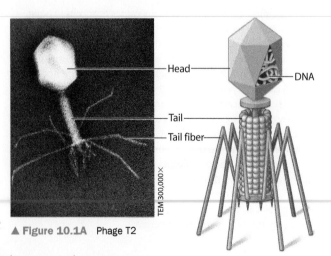

▲ Figure 10.1A Phage T2

Head
DNA
Tail
Tail fiber

TEM 300,000×

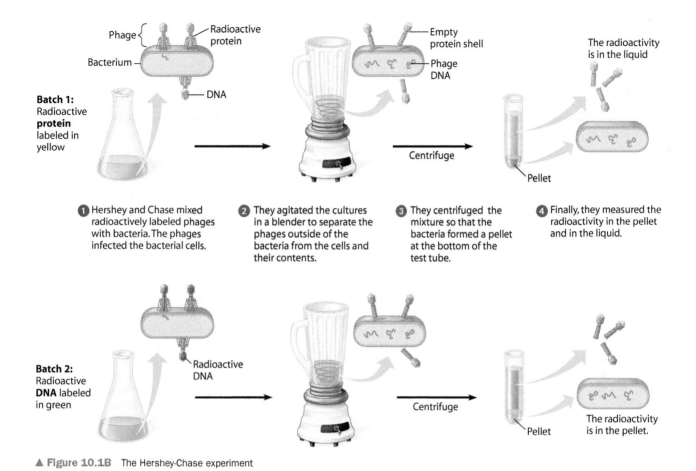

Batch 1:
Radioactive **protein** labeled in yellow

Phage
Radioactive protein
Bacterium
DNA
Empty protein shell
Phage DNA
The radioactivity is in the liquid
Pellet

Batch 2:
Radioactive **DNA** labeled in green

Radioactive DNA
Centrifuge
Pellet
The radioactivity is in the pellet.

1 Hershey and Chase mixed radioactively labeled phages with bacteria. The phages infected the bacterial cells.

2 They agitated the cultures in a blender to separate the phages outside of the bacteria from the cells and their contents.

3 They centrifuged the mixture so that the bacteria formed a pellet at the bottom of the test tube.

4 Finally, they measured the radioactivity in the pellet and in the liquid.

▲ **Figure 10.1B** The Hershey-Chase experiment

of the viral protein (yellow) is left outside (which is why the radioactive protein did not show up in the host cells during the experiment shown at the top of Figure 10.1B). Once injected, the viral DNA causes the bacterial cells to **3** produce new phage proteins and DNA molecules—indeed, complete new phages—which soon **4** cause the cell to lyse, releasing the newly produced phages. In agreement with the experimental results of Hershey and Chase, it is the viral DNA that contains the instructions for making phages.

Once DNA was shown to be the molecule of heredity, understanding its structure became the most important quest in biology. In the next two modules, we'll review the structure of DNA and discuss how it was discovered.

? **What convinced Hershey and Chase that DNA, rather than protein, is the genetic material of phage T2?**

● Radioactively labeled phage DNA, but not labeled protein, entered the host cell during infection and directed the synthesis of new viruses.

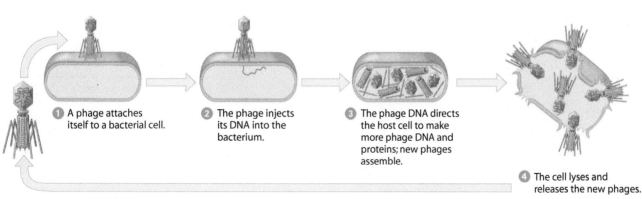

1 A phage attaches itself to a bacterial cell.

2 The phage injects its DNA into the bacterium.

3 The phage DNA directs the host cell to make more phage DNA and proteins; new phages assemble.

4 The cell lyses and releases the new phages.

▲ **Figure 10.1C** A phage replication cycle

10.2 DNA and RNA are polymers of nucleotides

By the time Hershey and Chase performed their experiments, much was already known about DNA. Scientists had identified all its atoms and knew how they were covalently bonded to one another. What was not understood was the specific arrangement of atoms that gave DNA its unique properties—the capacity to store genetic information, copy it, and pass it from generation to generation. However, only one year after Hershey and Chase published their results, scientists figured out the three-dimensional structure of DNA and the basic strategy of how it works. We will examine that momentous discovery in Module 10.3, but first, let's look at the underlying chemical structure of DNA and its chemical cousin RNA.

Recall from Module 3.15 that DNA and RNA are nucleic acids, consisting of long chains (polymers) of chemical units (monomers) called **nucleotides**. Figure 10.2A shows four representations of various parts of the same molecule. At left is a view of a DNA double helix. One of the strands is opened up (center) to show two different views of an individual DNA **polynucleotide**, a nucleotide polymer (chain). The view on the far right zooms into a single nucleotide from the chain. Each type of DNA nucleotide has a different nitrogen-containing base: adenine (A), cytosine (C), thymine (T), or guanine (G). Because

nucleotides can occur in a polynucleotide in any sequence and polynucleotides vary in length from long to very long, the number of possible polynucleotides is enormous. The chain shown in this figure has the sequence ACTGG, only one of many possible arrangements of the four types of nucleotides that make up DNA.

Looking more closely at our polynucleotide, we see in the center of Figure 10.2A that each nucleotide consists of three components: a nitrogenous base (in DNA: A, C, T, or G), a sugar (blue), and a phosphate group (yellow). The nucleotides are joined to one another by covalent bonds between the sugar of one nucleotide and the phosphate of the next. This results in a **sugar-phosphate backbone**, a repeating pattern of sugar-phosphate-sugar-phosphate. The nitrogenous bases are arranged like ribs that project from the backbone.

Examining a single nucleotide in even more detail (on the right in Figure 10.2A), you can see the chemical structure of its three components. The phosphate group has a phosphorus atom (P) at its center and is the source of the word *acid* in *nucleic acid*. The sugar has five carbon atoms, shown in red here for emphasis—four in its ring and one extending above the ring. The ring also includes an oxygen atom. The sugar is called deoxyribose because, compared with the sugar ribose, it is missing an oxygen atom. (Notice that the C atom in the lower right corner of the ring is bonded to an H atom instead of to an —OH group, as it is in ribose; see Figure 10.2C. Hence, DNA is "deoxy"—which means "without an oxygen"—compared to RNA.)

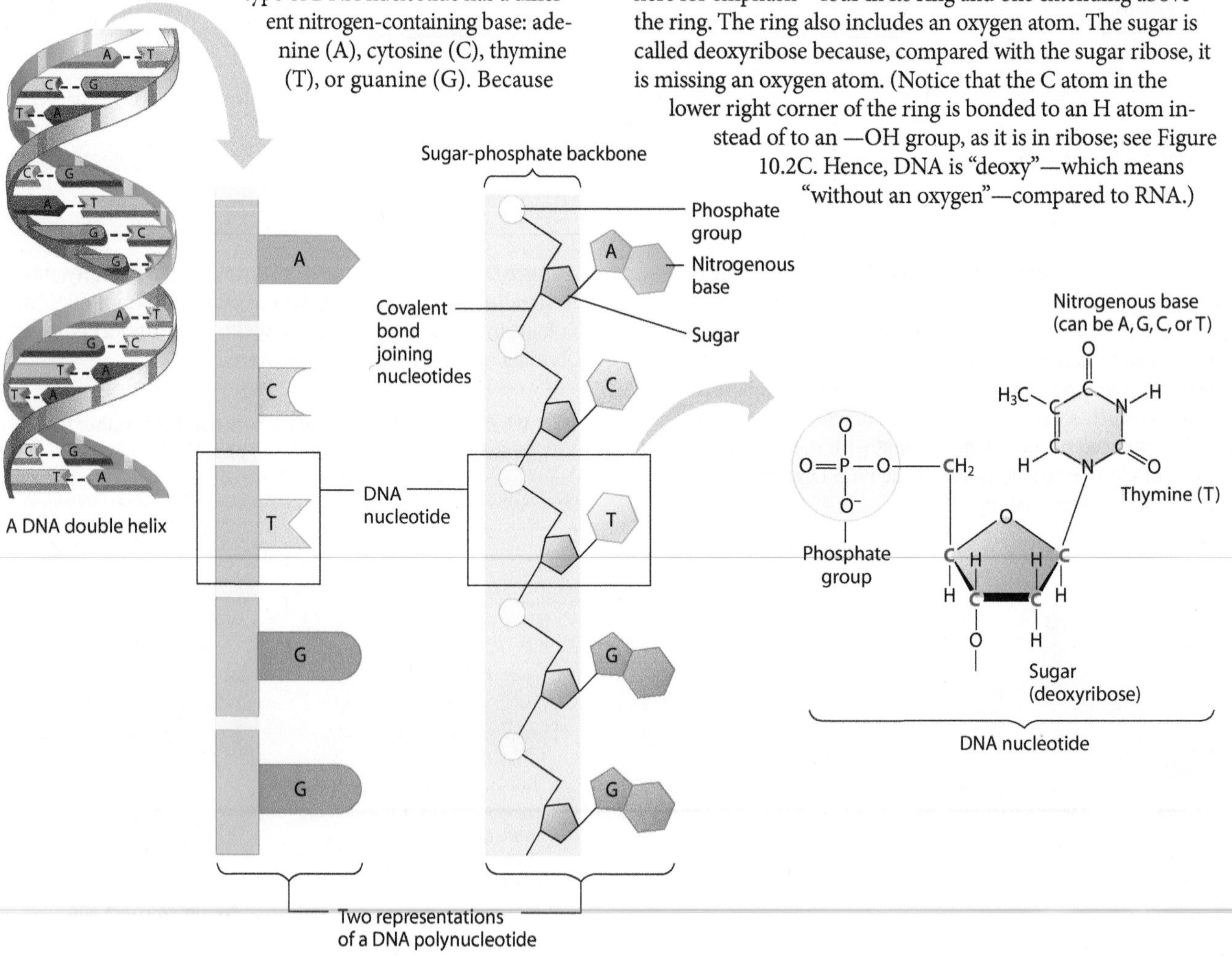

▲ Figure 10.2A The structure of a DNA polynucleotide

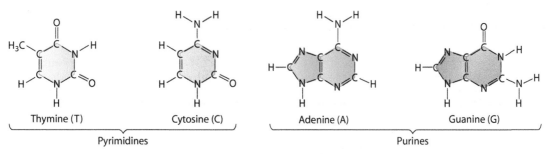

Thymine (T)   Cytosine (C)   Adenine (A)   Guanine (G)

Pyrimidines   Purines

▲ **Figure 10.2B**   The nitrogenous bases of DNA

The full name for **DNA** is **deoxyribonucleic acid**, with the *nucleic* portion of the word referring to DNA's location in the nuclei of eukaryotic cells. Each nitrogenous base (thymine, in our example at the right in Figure 10.2A) has a single or double ring consisting of nitrogen and carbon atoms with various functional groups attached. Recall from Module 3.2 that a functional group is a chemical group that affects a molecule's function by participating in specific chemical reactions. In the case of DNA, the main role of the functional groups is to determine which other kind of bases each base can hydrogen-bond with. For example, the NH_2 group hanging off cytosine is capable of forming a hydrogen bond to the C=O group hanging off guanine, but not with the NH_2 group protruding from adenine. The chemical groups of the bases are therefore responsible for DNA's most important property, which you will learn more about in the next module. In contrast to the acidic phosphate group, nitrogenous bases are basic, hence their name.

The four nucleotides found in DNA differ only in the structure of their nitrogenous bases **(Figure 10.2B)**. At this point, the structural details are not as important as the fact that the bases are of two types. **Thymine (T)** and **cytosine (C)** are single-ring structures called pyrimidines. **Adenine (A)** and **guanine (G)** are larger, double-ring structures called purines. The one-letter abbreviations can be used either for the bases alone or for the nucleotides containing them.

What about RNA **(Figure 10.2C)**? As its name—ribonucleic acid—implies, its sugar is ribose rather than deoxyribose. Notice the ribose in the RNA nucleotide in Figure 10.2C;

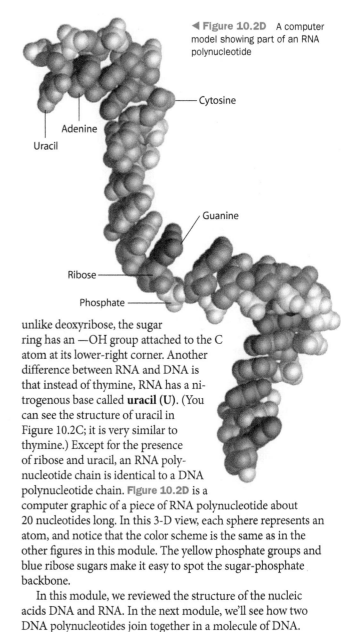

◀ **Figure 10.2D**   A computer model showing part of an RNA polynucleotide

Cytosine

Adenine

Uracil

Guanine

Ribose

Phosphate

unlike deoxyribose, the sugar ring has an —OH group attached to the C atom at its lower-right corner. Another difference between RNA and DNA is that instead of thymine, RNA has a nitrogenous base called **uracil (U)**. (You can see the structure of uracil in Figure 10.2C; it is very similar to thymine.) Except for the presence of ribose and uracil, an RNA polynucleotide chain is identical to a DNA polynucleotide chain. **Figure 10.2D** is a computer graphic of a piece of RNA polynucleotide about 20 nucleotides long. In this 3-D view, each sphere represents an atom, and notice that the color scheme is the same as in the other figures in this module. The yellow phosphate groups and blue ribose sugars make it easy to spot the sugar-phosphate backbone.

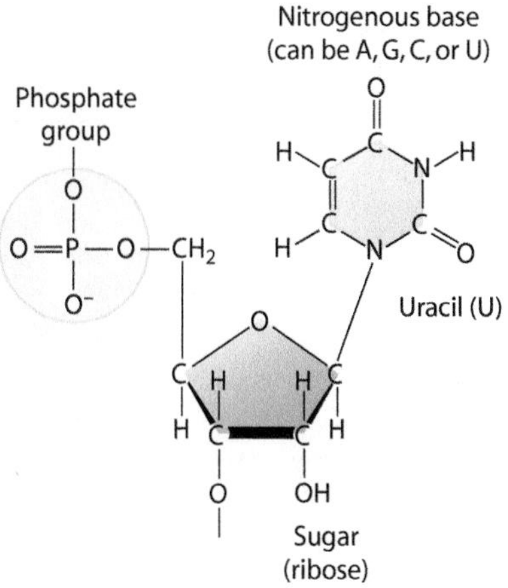

In this module, we reviewed the structure of the nucleic acids DNA and RNA. In the next module, we'll see how two DNA polynucleotides join together in a molecule of DNA.

Phosphate group

Nitrogenous base (can be A, G, C, or U)

Uracil (U)

Sugar (ribose)

▲ **Figure 10.2C**   An RNA nucleotide

? **Compare and contrast DNA and RNA polynucleotides.**

● Both are polymers of nucleotides consisting of a sugar, a nitrogenous base, and a phosphate. In RNA, the sugar is ribose; in DNA, it is deoxyribose. Both RNA and DNA have the bases A, G, and C, but DNA has a T and RNA has a U.

10.3 DNA is a double-stranded helix

After the 1952 Hershey-Chase experiment convinced most biologists that DNA was the material that stored genetic information, a race was on to determine how the structure of this molecule could account for its role in heredity. By that time, the arrangement of covalent bonds in a nucleic acid polymer was well established, and researchers focused on discovering the three-dimensional shape of DNA. First to the finish line were two scientists who were relatively unknown at the time—American James D. Watson and Englishman Francis Crick.

The brief but celebrated partnership that solved the puzzle of DNA structure began soon after Watson, a 23-year-old newly minted Ph.D., journeyed to Cambridge University in England, where the more senior Crick was studying protein structure with a technique called X-ray crystallography. While visiting the laboratory of Maurice Wilkins at King's College in London, Watson saw an X-ray crystallographic image of DNA produced by Wilkins's colleague Rosalind Franklin (Figure 10.3A). A careful study of the image enabled Watson to deduce the basic shape of DNA to be a helix with a uniform diameter of 2 nanometers (nm), with its nitrogenous bases stacked about one-third of a nanometer apart. (For comparison, the plasma membrane of a cell is about 8 nm thick.) The diameter of the helix suggested that it was made up of two polynucleotide strands, a **double helix**.

Watson and Crick began trying to construct a wire model of a double helix that would conform both to Franklin's data and to what was then known about the chemistry of DNA (Figure 10.3B). They had concluded that the sugar-phosphate backbones must be on the outside of the double helix, forcing the nitrogenous bases to swivel to the interior of the molecule. But how were the bases arranged in the interior of the double helix?

At first, Watson and Crick imagined that the bases paired like with like—for example, A with A and C with C. But that kind of pairing did not fit the X-ray data, which suggested that the DNA molecule has a uniform diameter. An A-A pair, with two double-ring bases, would be almost twice as wide as a C-C pair. It soon became apparent that a double-ringed base (purine) must always be paired with a single-ringed base (pyrimidine) on the opposite strand. Moreover, Watson and Crick realized that the individual structures of the bases dictated the pairings even more specifically. As discussed in the previous module, each base has functional groups protruding from its six-sided ring that can best form hydrogen bonds with one appropriate partner (to review the hydrogen bond, see Module 2.8).

Adenine can best form hydrogen bonds with thymine, and guanine with cytosine. In the biologist's shorthand, A pairs with T, and G pairs with C. A is also said to be "complementary" to T, and G to C.

Watson and Crick's pairing scheme not only fit what was known about the physical attributes and chemical bonding of DNA, but also explained some data obtained several years earlier by American biochemist Erwin Chargaff. Chargaff had discovered that the amount of adenine in the DNA of any one species was equal to the amount of thymine and that the amount of guanine was equal to that of cytosine. Chargaff's rules, as they are called, are explained by the fact that A on one of DNA's polynucleotide chains always pairs with T on the other polynucleotide chain, and G on one chain pairs only with C on the other chain.

You can picture the model of the DNA double helix proposed by Watson and Crick as a rope ladder with wooden rungs, with the ladder twisting into a spiral (Figure 10.3C). The side ropes are the equivalent of the sugar-phosphate backbones, and the rungs represent pairs of nitrogenous bases joined by hydrogen bonds.

Figure 10.3D shows three representations of the double helix. The shapes of the base symbols in the ribbonlike diagram on the left indicate the bases' complementarity; notice that the shape of any kind of base matches only one other kind of base. In the center of the diagram is an atomic-level version showing four base pairs, with the helix untwisted and the hydrogen bonds specified by dotted lines. Notice that a C-G base pair has functional groups that form three hydrogen bonds,

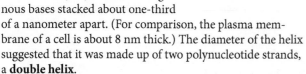

▲ Figure 10.3A
Rosalind Franklin and her X-ray image of DNA

▲ Figure 10.3B Watson and Crick in 1953 with their model of the DNA double helix

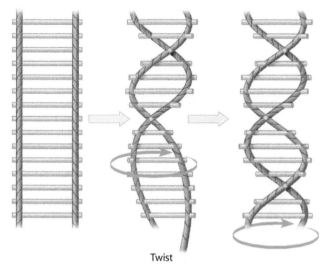

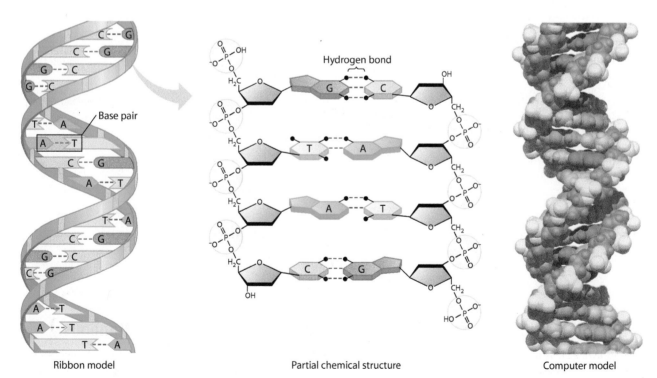

▲ Figure 10.3C A rope ladder model for the double helix

Although the Watson-Crick base-pairing rules dictate the side-by-side combinations of nitrogenous bases that form the rungs of the double helix, they place no restrictions on the sequence of nucleotides along the length of a DNA strand. In fact, the sequence of bases can vary in countless ways, and each gene has a unique order of nucleotides, or base sequence.

In April 1953, Watson and Crick rocked the scientific world with a succinct paper explaining their molecular model for DNA in the journal *Nature*. In 1962, Watson, Crick, and Wilkins received the Nobel Prize for their work. (Rosalind Franklin probably would have received the prize as well but for her death from cancer in 1958; Nobel Prizes are never awarded posthumously.) Few milestones in the history of biology have had as broad an impact as the discovery of the double helix, with its A-T and C-G base pairing.

The Watson-Crick model gave new meaning to the words *genes* and *chromosomes*—and to the chromosome theory of inheritance (see Module 9.16). With a complete picture of DNA, we can see that the genetic information in a chromosome must be encoded in the nucleotide sequence of the molecule. One powerful aspect of the Watson-Crick model is that the structure of DNA suggests a molecular explanation for genetic inheritance, as we will see in the next module.

while an A-T base pair has functional groups that form two hydrogen bonds. This difference means that C-G base pairs are somewhat stronger than A-T base pairs. You can see that the two sugar-phosphate backbones of the double helix are oriented in opposite directions. (Notice that the sugars on the two strands are upside down with respect to each other.) On the right is a computer graphic showing most of the atoms of part of a double helix. The atoms that compose the deoxyribose sugars are shown as blue, phosphate groups as yellow, and nitrogenous bases as shades of green and orange.

? Along one strand of a double helix is the nucleotide sequence GGCATAGGT. What is the complementary sequence for the other DNA strand?

● CCGTATCCA

Ribbon model

Partial chemical structure

Computer model

▲ Figure 10.3D Three representations of DNA

DNA Replication

10.4 DNA replication depends on specific base pairing

One of biology's overarching themes—the relationship between structure and function—is evident in the double helix. The idea that there is specific pairing of bases in DNA was the flash of inspiration that led Watson and Crick to the correct structure of the double helix. At the same time, they saw the functional significance of the base-pairing rules. They ended their classic 1953 paper with this statement: "It has not escaped our notice that the specific pairing we have postulated immediately suggests a possible copying mechanism for the genetic material."

The logic behind the Watson-Crick proposal for how DNA is copied—by specific pairing of complementary bases—is quite simple. You can see this by covering one of the strands in the parental DNA molecule in **Figure 10.4A**. You can determine the sequence of bases in the covered strand by applying the base-pairing rules to the unmasked strand: A pairs with T (and T with A), and G pairs with C (and C with G).

Watson and Crick predicted that a cell applies the same rules when copying its genes. As shown in Figure 10.4A, the two strands of parental DNA (blue) separate. Each then becomes a template for the assembly of a complementary strand from a supply of free nucleotides (gray) that is always available within the nucleus. The nucleotides line up one at a time along the template strand in accordance with the base-pairing rules. Enzymes link the nucleotides to form the new DNA strands. The completed new molecules, identical to the parental molecule, are known as daughter DNA (although no gender should be inferred).

Watson and Crick's model predicts that when a double helix replicates, each of the two daughter molecules will have one old strand, which was part of the parental molecule, and one newly created strand. This model for DNA replication is known as the **semiconservative model** because half of the parental molecule is maintained (conserved) in each daughter molecule. The semiconservative model of replication was confirmed by experiments performed in the 1950s.

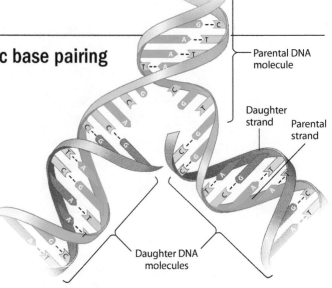

▲ Figure 10.4B   The untwisting and replication of DNA

Although the general mechanism of DNA replication is conceptually simple, the actual process is complex, requiring the coordination of more than a dozen enzymes and other proteins. Some of the complexity arises from the need for the helical DNA molecule to untwist as it replicates and for the two new strands to be made roughly simultaneously (**Figure 10.4B**). Another challenge is the speed of the process. *E. coli*, with about 4.6 million DNA base pairs, can copy its entire genome in less than an hour. Humans, with over 6 billion base pairs in 46 diploid chromosomes, require only a few hours. And yet, the process is amazingly accurate; typically, only about one DNA nucleotide per several billion is incorrectly paired. In the next module, we take a closer look at the mechanisms of DNA replication that allow it to proceed with such speed and accuracy.

? **How does complementary base pairing make possible the replication of DNA?**

● When the two strands of the double helix separate, free nucleotides can base-pair along each strand, leading to the synthesis of new complementary strands.

▶ **Figure 10.4A**
A template model for
DNA replication

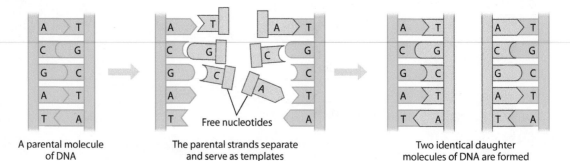

| A parental molecule of DNA | The parental strands separate and serve as templates | Two identical daughter molecules of DNA are formed |

10.5 DNA replication proceeds in two directions at many sites simultaneously

Replication of a DNA molecule begins at special sites called *origins of replication*, short stretches of DNA having a specific sequence of nucleotides where proteins attach to the DNA and separate the strands. As shown in **Figure 10.5A**, replication then proceeds in both directions, creating replication "bubbles." The parental DNA strands (blue) open up as daughter

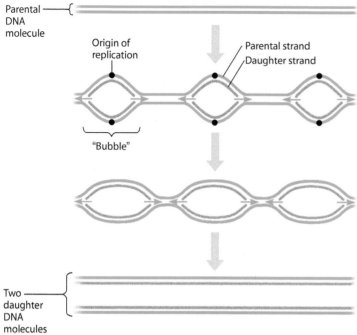

▲ **Figure 10.5A** Multiple bubbles in replicating DNA

strands (gray) elongate on both sides of each bubble. The DNA molecule of a eukaryotic chromosome has many origins where replication can start simultaneously. Thus, hundreds or thousands of bubbles can be present at once, shortening the total time needed for replication. Eventually, all the bubbles fuse, yielding two completed daughter DNA molecules (see the bottom of Figure 10.5A).

Figure 10.5B shows the molecular building blocks of a tiny segment of DNA, reminding us that the DNA's sugar-phosphate backbones run in opposite directions. Notice that each strand has a 3' ("three-prime") end and a 5' ("five-prime") end. The primed numbers refer to the carbon atoms of the nucleotide sugars. At one end of each DNA strand, the sugar's 3' carbon atom is attached to an —OH group; at the other end, the sugar's 5' carbon is attached to a phosphate group.

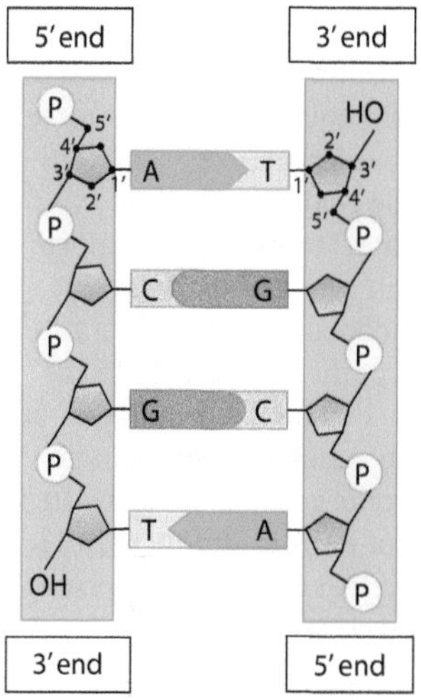

The opposite orientation of the strands is important in DNA replication. The enzymes that link DNA nucleotides to a growing daughter strand, called **DNA polymerases**, add nucleotides only to the 3' end of the strand, never to the 5' end. Thus, a daughter DNA strand can only grow in the 5' → 3' direction. You see the consequences of this enzyme specificity in Figure 10.5C, where the forked structure represents one side of a replication bubble. One

of the daughter strands (shown in gray) can be synthesized in one continuous piece by a DNA polymerase working toward the forking point of the parental DNA. However, to make the other daughter strand, polymerase molecules must work outward from the forking point. The only way this can be accomplished is if the new strand is synthesized in short pieces as the fork opens up. These pieces are called Okazaki fragments, after the Japanese husband-and-wife team of molecular biologists who discovered them. Another enzyme, called **DNA ligase**, then links, or ligates, the pieces together into a single DNA strand.

In addition to their roles in adding nucleotides to a DNA chain, DNA polymerases carry out a proofreading step that quickly removes nucleotides that have base-paired incorrectly during replication. DNA polymerases and DNA ligase are also involved in repairing DNA damaged by harmful radiation, such as ultraviolet light and X-rays, or toxic chemicals in the environment, such as those found in tobacco smoke.

DNA replication ensures that all the somatic cells in a multicellular organism carry the same genetic information. It is also the means by which genetic instructions are copied for the next generation of the organism. In the next module, we begin to pursue the connection between DNA instructions and an organism's phenotypic traits.

? **What is the function of DNA polymerase in DNA replication?**

● As free nucleotides base-pair to a parental DNA strand, the enzyme covalently bonds them to the 3' end of a growing daughter strand.

▲ **Figure 10.5B** The opposite orientations of DNA strands

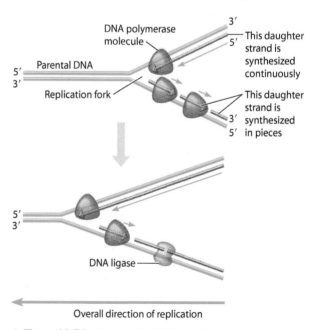

▲ **Figure 10.5C** How daughter DNA strands are synthesized

The Flow of Genetic Information from DNA to RNA to Protein

10.6 The DNA genotype is expressed as proteins, which provide the molecular basis for phenotypic traits

With our knowledge of DNA, we can now define genotype and phenotype more precisely than we did in Chapter 9. An organism's genotype, its genetic makeup, is the heritable information contained in its DNA. The phenotype is the organism's physical traits. So what is the molecular connection between genotype and phenotype?

The answer is that the DNA inherited by an organism specifies traits by dictating the synthesis of proteins. In other words, proteins are the links between the genotype and the phenotype. However, a gene does not build a protein directly. Rather, a gene dispatches instructions in the form of RNA, which in turn programs protein synthesis. This fundamental concept in biology, termed the "central dogma" by Francis Crick, is summarized in Figure 10.6A. The molecular "chain of command" is from DNA in the nucleus of the cell to RNA to protein synthesis in the cytoplasm. The two main stages are **transcription**, the synthesis of RNA under the direction of DNA, and **translation**, the synthesis of protein under the direction of RNA.

The relationship between genes and proteins was first proposed in 1909, when English physician Archibald Garrod suggested that genes dictate phenotypes through enzymes, the proteins that catalyze chemical reactions. Garrod hypothesized that an inherited disease reflects a person's inability to make a particular enzyme, and he referred to such diseases as "inborn errors of metabolism." He gave as one example the hereditary condition called alkaptonuria, in which the urine is dark because it contains a chemical called alkapton. Garrod reasoned that individuals without the disorder have an enzyme that breaks down alkapton, whereas alkaptonuric individuals cannot make the enzyme. Garrod's hypothesis was ahead of its time, but research conducted decades later proved him right. In the intervening years, biochemists accumulated evidence that cells make and break down biologically important molecules via metabolic pathways, as in the synthesis of an amino acid or the breakdown of a sugar. As we described in Unit I (see Module 5.15, for example), each step in a metabolic pathway is catalyzed by a specific enzyme. Therefore, individuals lacking one of the enzymes for a pathway are unable to complete it.

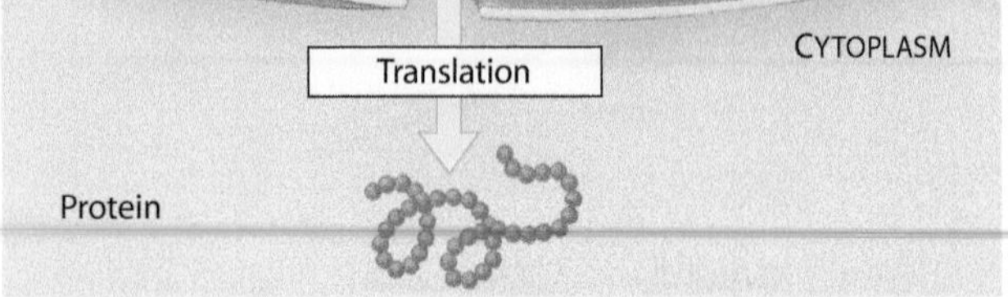

The major breakthrough in demonstrating the relationship between genes and enzymes came in the 1940s from the work of American geneticists George Beadle and Edward Tatum with the bread mold *Neurospora crassa* (Figure 10.6B). Beadle and Tatum studied strains of the mold that were unable to grow on a simple growth medium. Each of these so-called nutritional mutants turned out to lack an enzyme in a metabolic pathway that produced some molecule the mold needed, such as an amino acid. Beadle and Tatum also showed that each mutant was defective in a single gene. This result suggested the one gene–one enzyme hypothesis—the idea that the function of a gene is to dictate the production of a specific enzyme.

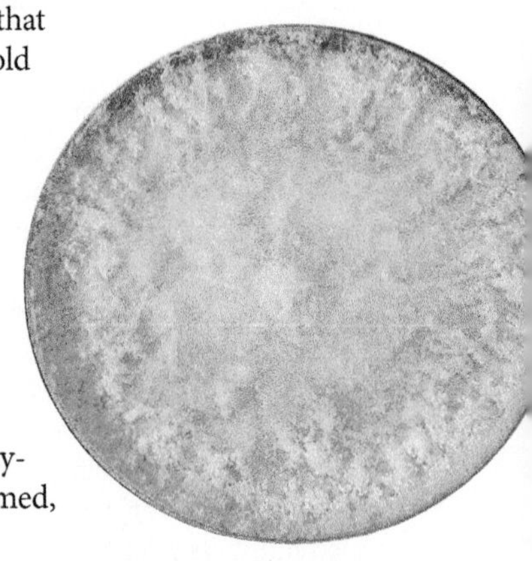

The one gene–one enzyme hypothesis has been amply confirmed, but with important modifications. First, it was extended beyond enzymes to include *all* types of proteins. For example, keratin (the structural protein of hair) and the hormone insulin are two examples of proteins that are not enzymes. So biologists began to think in terms of one gene–one protein. However, many proteins are made from two or more polypeptide chains, with each polypeptide specified by its own gene. For example, hemoglobin, the oxygen-transporting protein in your blood, is built from two kinds of polypeptides, encoded by two different genes. Thus, Beadle and Tatum's hypothesis is now stated as follows: The function of a gene is to dictate the production of a polypeptide. Even this description is not entirely accurate, in that the RNA transcribed from some genes is not translated (you'll learn about two such kinds of RNA in Modules 10.11 and 10.12). The flow of information from genotype to phenotype continues to be an active research area.

▲ **Figure 10.6B** The bread mold *Neurospora crassa* growing in a culture dish

? **What are the functions of transcription and translation?**

● Transcription is the transfer of information from DNA to RNA. Translation is the use of the information in RNA to make a polypeptide.

▲ **Figure 10.6A** The flow of genetic information in a eukaryotic cell

DNA

Transcription

RNA

NUCLEUS

CYTOPLASM

Translation

Protein

10.7 Genetic information written in codons is translated into amino acid sequences

Genes provide the instructions for making specific proteins. But a gene does not build a protein directly. As you have learned, the bridge between DNA and protein synthesis is the nucleic acid RNA: DNA is transcribed into RNA, which is then translated into protein. Put another way, information within the cell flows as DNA → RNA → protein. This is sometimes stated as: "DNA makes RNA makes protein."

Transcription and translation are linguistic terms, and it is useful to think of nucleic acids and proteins as having languages. To understand how genetic information passes from genotype to phenotype, we need to see how the chemical language of DNA is translated into the different chemical language of proteins.

What, exactly, is the language of nucleic acids? Both DNA and RNA are polymers (long chains) made of nucleotide monomers (the individual units that make up the polymer). In DNA, there are four types of nucleotides, which differ in their nitrogenous bases (A, T, C, and G). The same is true for RNA, although it has the base U instead of T.

Figure 10.7 focuses on a small region of one gene (gene 3, shown in light blue) carried by a DNA molecule. DNA's language is written as a linear sequence of nucleotide bases on a polynucleotide, a sequence such as the one you see on the enlarged DNA segment in the figure. Specific sequences of bases, each with a beginning and an end, make up the genes on a DNA strand. A typical gene consists of hundreds or thousands of nucleotides in a specific sequence.

The pink strand underneath the enlarged DNA segment represents the results of transcription: an RNA molecule. The process is called transcription because the nucleic acid language of DNA has been rewritten (transcribed) as a sequence of bases on RNA. Notice that the language is still that of nucleic acids, although the nucleotide bases on the RNA molecule are complementary to those on the DNA strand. As we will see in Module 10.9,

this is because the RNA was synthesized using the DNA as a template.

The purple chain represents the results of translation, the conversion of the nucleic acid language to the polypeptide language (recall that proteins consist of one or more polypeptides). Like nucleic acids, polypeptides are polymers, but the monomers that compose them are the 20 amino acids common to all organisms. Again, the language is written in a linear sequence, and the sequence of nucleotides of the RNA molecule dictates the sequence of amino acids of the polypeptide.

The RNA acts as a messenger carrying genetic information from DNA.

During translation, there is a change in language from the nucleotide sequence of the RNA to the amino acid sequence of the polypeptide. How is this translation achieved? Recall that there are only four different kinds of nucleotides in DNA (A, G, C, T) and RNA (A, G, C, U). In translation, these four nucleotides must somehow specify all 20 amino acids. Consider whether each single nucleotide base were to specify one amino acid. In this case, only four of the 20 amino acids could be accounted for, one for each type of base.

What if the language consisted of two-letter code words? If we read the bases of a gene two at a time—AG, for example, could specify one amino acid, whereas AT could designate a different amino acid—then only 16 arrangements would be possible (4^2), which is still not enough to specify all 20 amino acids. However, if the code word in DNA consists of a triplet, with each arrangement of three consecutive bases specifying an amino acid—AGT specifies one amino acid, for example, while AGA specifies a different one—then there can be 64 (that is, 4^3) possible code words, more than enough to specify the 20 amino acids. Indeed, there are enough triplets to allow more than one coding for each amino acid. For example, the base triplets AAT and AAC could both code for the same amino acid. Thus, triplets of bases are the smallest "words" of uniform length that can specify all the amino acids (see the brackets below the strand of RNA in Figure 10.7).

Experiments have verified that the flow of information from gene to protein is based on a **triplet code:** The genetic instructions for the amino acid sequence of a polypeptide chain are written in DNA and RNA as a series of nonoverlapping three-base "words" called **codons.** Notice in the figure that three-base codons in the DNA are transcribed into complementary three-base codons in the RNA, and then the RNA codons are translated into amino acids that form a polypeptide. We turn to the codons themselves in the next module.

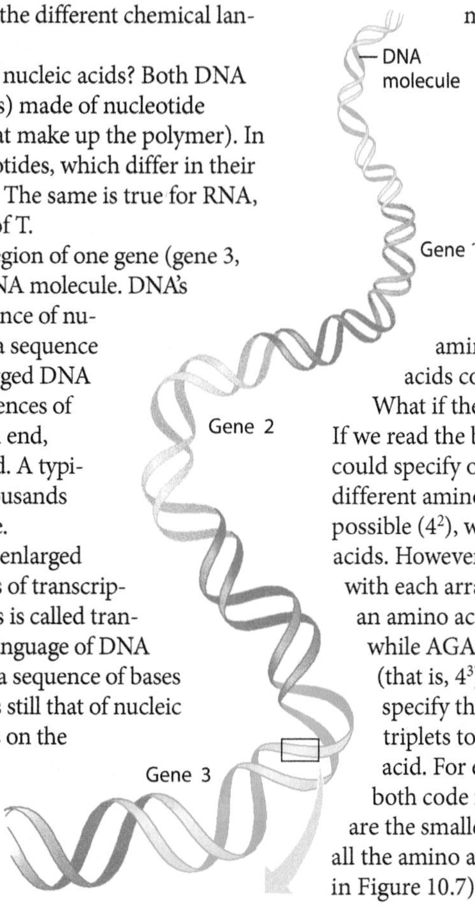

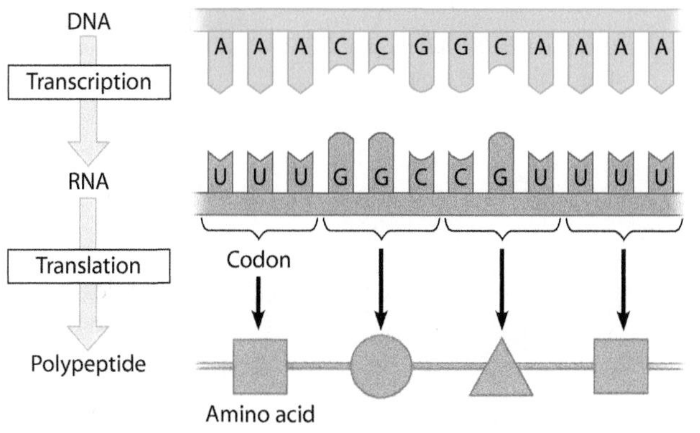

? **What is the minimum number of nucleotides necessary to code for 100 amino acids?**

▲ Figure 10.7 Transcription and translation of codons

10.8 The genetic code dictates how codons are translated into amino acids

During the 1960s, scientists cracked the **genetic code**, the set of rules that relate codons in RNA to amino acids in proteins. The rules were established by a series of elegant experiments that disclosed the amino acid translations of each of the nucleotide-triplet code words. The first codon was deciphered in 1961 by American biochemist Marshall Nirenberg. He synthesized an artificial RNA molecule by linking together identical RNA nucleotides having uracil as their only base. No matter where this message started or stopped, it could contain only one type of triplet codon: UUU. Nirenberg added this "poly-U" to a test-tube mixture containing ribosomes and the other ingredients required for polypeptide synthesis. This mixture translated the poly-U into a polypeptide containing a single kind of amino acid, phenylalanine (Phe). Thus, Nirenberg learned that the RNA codon UUU specifies the amino acid phenylalanine. By variations on this method, the amino acids specified by all the codons were soon determined.

As shown in **Figure 10.8A**, 61 of the 64 triplets code for amino acids. The triplet AUG (green box in the figure) has a dual function: It codes for the amino acid methionine (Met) and also can provide a signal for the start of a polypeptide chain. Three codons (red) do not designate amino acids. They are the stop codons that mark the end of translation.

Notice in Figure 10.8A that there is redundancy in the code but no ambiguity. For example, although codons UUU and UUC both specify phenylalanine (redundancy), neither of them ever represents any other amino acid (no ambiguity). The codons in the figure are the triplets found in RNA. They have a straightforward, complementary relationship to the

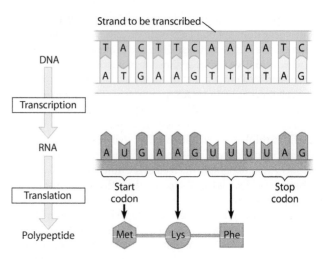

▲ **Figure 10.8B** Deciphering the genetic information in DNA

codons in DNA, with UUU in the RNA matching AAA in the DNA, for example. The nucleotides making up the codons occur in a linear order along the DNA and RNA, with no gaps or "punctuation" separating the codons.

As an exercise in translating the genetic code, consider the 12-nucleotide segment of DNA in **Figure 10.8B**. Let's read this as a series of triplets. Using the base-pairing rules (with U in RNA instead of T), we see that the RNA codon corresponding to the first transcribed DNA triplet, TAC, is AUG. As you can see in Figure 10.8A, AUG specifies, "Place Met as the first amino acid in the polypeptide." The second DNA triplet, TTC, dictates RNA codon AAG, which designates lysine (Lys) as the second amino acid. We continue until we reach a stop codon (UAG in this example).

The genetic code is nearly universal, shared by organisms from the simplest bacteria to the most complex plants and animals. As you will learn in Chapter 12, such universality is key to modern DNA technologies because it allows scientists to mix and match genes from various species (**Figure 10.8C**). A language shared by all living things must have evolved early enough in the history of life to be present in the common ancestors of all modern organisms. A shared genetic vocabulary is a reminder of the kinship that connects all life on Earth.

? Translate the RNA sequence CCAUUUACG into the corresponding amino acid sequence.

Second base

		U	C	A	G	
First base	U	UUU ⎤ Phe UUC ⎦ UUA ⎤ Leu UUG ⎦	UCU ⎤ UCC ⎥ Ser UCA ⎥ UCG ⎦	UAU ⎤ Tyr UAC ⎦ UAA Stop UAG Stop	UGU ⎤ Cys UGC ⎦ UGA Stop UGG Trp	U C A G
	C	CUU ⎤ CUC ⎥ Leu CUA ⎥ CUG ⎦	CCU ⎤ CCC ⎥ Pro CCA ⎥ CCG ⎦	CAU ⎤ His CAC ⎦ CAA ⎤ Gln CAG ⎦	CGU ⎤ CGC ⎥ Arg CGA ⎥ CGG ⎦	U C A G
	A	AUU ⎤ AUC ⎥ Ile AUA ⎦ AUG Met or start	ACU ⎤ ACC ⎥ Thr ACA ⎥ ACG ⎦	AAU ⎤ Asn AAC ⎦ AAA ⎤ Lys AAG ⎦	AGU ⎤ Ser AGC ⎦ AGA ⎤ Arg AGG ⎦	U C A G
	G	GUU ⎤ GUC ⎥ Val GUA ⎥ GUG ⎦	GCU ⎤ GCC ⎥ Ala GCA ⎥ GCG ⎦	GAU ⎤ Asp GAC ⎦ GAA ⎤ Glu GAG ⎦	GGU ⎤ GGC ⎥ Gly GGA ⎥ GGG ⎦	U C A G

Third base

▲ **Figure 10.8A** Dictionary of the genetic code (RNA codons)

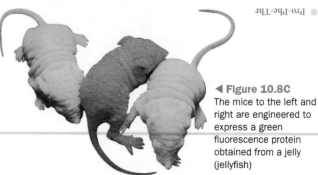

◀ **Figure 10.8C** The mice to the left and right are engineered to express a green fluorescence protein obtained from a jelly (jellyfish)

Pro-Phe-Thr

10.9 Transcription produces genetic messages in the form of RNA

In eukaryotic cells, transcription, the transfer of genetic information from DNA to RNA, occurs in the nucleus. (The nucleus, after all, contains the DNA; see Figure 10.6A for a review.) An RNA molecule is transcribed from a DNA template by a process that resembles the synthesis of a DNA strand during DNA replication (see Module 10.4).

Figure 10.9A is a close-up view of the process of transcription. As with replication, the two DNA strands must first separate at the place where the process will start. In transcription, however, only one of the DNA strands serves as a template for the newly forming RNA molecule; the other strand is unused. The nucleotides that make up the new RNA molecule take their place one at a time along the DNA template strand by forming hydrogen bonds with the nucleotide bases there. Notice that the RNA nucleotides follow the same base-pairing rules that govern DNA replication, except that U, rather than T, pairs with A. The RNA nucleotides are linked by the transcription enzyme **RNA polymerase**, symbolized in the figure by the large gray shape.

Figure 10.9B is an overview of the transcription of an entire prokaryotic gene. (We focus on prokaryotes here; eukaryotic transcription occurs via a similar but more complex process.) Specific sequences of nucleotides along the DNA mark where transcription of a gene begins and ends. The "start transcribing" signal is a nucleotide sequence called a **promoter**. A promoter is a specific binding site for RNA polymerase and determines which of the two strands of the DNA double helix is used as the template in transcription.

➊ The first phase of transcription, called initiation, is the attachment of RNA polymerase to the promoter and the start of RNA synthesis. ➋ During a second phase of transcription, elongation, the RNA grows longer. As RNA synthesis continues, the RNA strand peels away from its DNA template, allowing the two separated DNA strands to come back

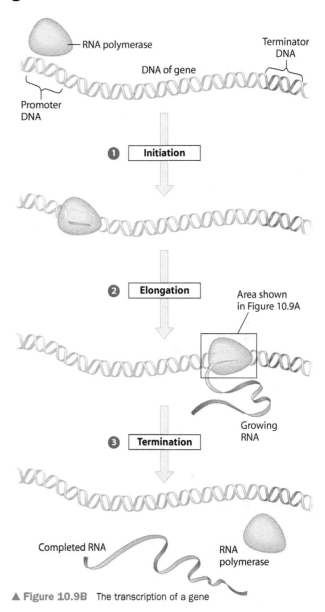

➊ **Initiation**

➋ **Elongation**

Area shown in Figure 10.9A

Growing RNA

➌ **Termination**

Completed RNA

RNA polymerase

▲ Figure 10.9B   The transcription of a gene

together in the region already transcribed. ➌ Finally, in the third phase, termination, the RNA polymerase reaches a sequence of bases in the DNA template called a **terminator**. This sequence signals the end of the gene; at that point, the polymerase molecule detaches from the RNA molecule and the gene.

In addition to producing RNA that encodes amino acid sequences, transcription makes two other kinds of RNA that are involved in building polypeptides. We discuss these three kinds of RNA—messenger RNA, transfer RNA, and ribosomal RNA—in the next three modules.

?   **What is a promoter? What molecule binds to it?**

A promoter is a specific nucleotide sequence at the start of a gene where RNA polymerase attaches and begins transcription.

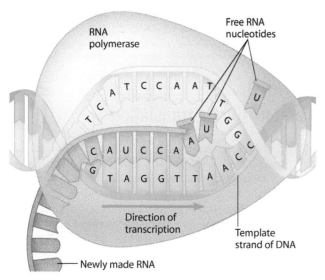

▲ Figure 10.9A   A close-up view of transcription

10.10 Eukaryotic RNA is processed before leaving the nucleus as mRNA

The kind of RNA that encodes amino acid sequences is called **messenger RNA (mRNA)** because it conveys genetic messages from DNA to the translation machinery of the cell. Messenger RNA is transcribed from DNA, and the information in the mRNA is then translated into polypeptides. In prokaryotic cells, which lack nuclei, transcription and translation occur in the same place: the cytoplasm. In eukaryotic cells, however, mRNA molecules must exit the nucleus via the nuclear pores and enter the cytoplasm, where the machinery for polypeptide synthesis is located.

Before leaving the nucleus as mRNA, eukaryotic transcripts are modified, or processed, in several ways (Figure 10.10). One kind of RNA processing is the addition of extra nucleotides to the ends of the RNA transcript. These additions include a small cap (a single G nucleotide) at one end and a long tail (a chain of 50 to 250 A nucleotides) at the other end. The cap and tail (yellow in the figure) facilitate the export of the mRNA from the nucleus, protect the mRNA from attack by cellular enzymes, and help ribosomes bind to the mRNA. The cap and tail themselves are not translated into protein.

Another type of RNA processing is made necessary in eukaryotes by noncoding stretches of nucleotides that interrupt the nucleotides that actually code for amino acids. It is as if unintelligible sequences of letters were randomly interspersed in an otherwise intelligible document. Most genes of plants and animals, it turns out, include such internal noncoding regions, which are called **introns** ("intervening sequences"). The coding regions—the parts of a gene that are expressed—are called **exons**. As Figure 10.10 shows, both exons (darker color) and introns (lighter color) are transcribed from DNA into RNA. However, before the RNA leaves the nucleus, the introns are removed, and the exons are joined to produce an mRNA molecule with a continuous coding sequence. (The short noncoding regions just inside the cap and tail are considered parts of the first and last exons.) This cutting-and-pasting process is called **RNA splicing**. In most cases, RNA splicing is catalyzed by a complex of proteins and small RNA molecules, but sometimes the RNA transcript itself catalyzes the process. In other words, RNA can sometimes act as an enzyme that removes its own introns! As we will see in the next chapter (in Module 11.4),

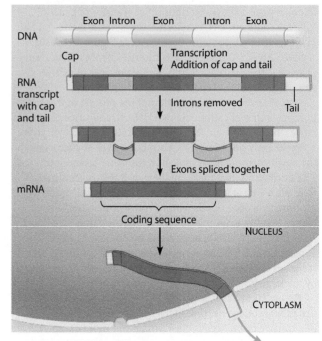

▲ **Figure 10.10** The production of eukaryotic mRNA

RNA splicing also provides a means to produce multiple polypeptides from a single gene.

As we have discussed, translation is a conversion between different languages—from the nucleic acid language to the protein language—and it involves more elaborate machinery than transcription. The first important ingredient required for translation is the processed mRNA. Once it is present, the machinery used to translate mRNA requires enzymes and sources of chemical energy, such as ATP. In addition, translation requires two heavy-duty components: ribosomes and a kind of RNA called transfer RNA, the subject of the next module.

 Explain why most eukaryotic genes are longer than the mRNA that leaves the nucleus.

● These genes have introns, noncoding sequences of nucleotides that are spliced out of the initial RNA transcript, to produce mRNA.

10.11 Transfer RNA molecules serve as interpreters during translation

Translation of any language requires an interpreter, someone or something that can recognize the words of one language and convert them to another. Translation of a genetic message carried in mRNA into the amino acid language of proteins also requires an interpreter. To convert the words of nucleic acids (codons) to the amino acid words of proteins, a cell employs a molecular interpreter, a special type of RNA called **transfer RNA (tRNA)**.

A cell that is producing proteins has in its cytoplasm a supply of amino acids, either obtained from food or made from

other chemicals. But amino acids themselves cannot recognize the codons in the mRNA. The amino acid tryptophan, for example, is no more attracted by codons for tryptophan than by any other codons. It is up to the cell's molecular interpreters, tRNA molecules, to match amino acids to the appropriate codons to form the new polypeptide. To perform this task, tRNA molecules must carry out two functions: (1) picking up the appropriate amino acids and (2) recognizing the appropriate codons in the mRNA. The unique structure of tRNA molecules enables them to perform both tasks.

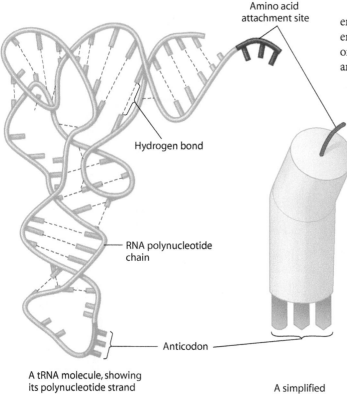

Amino acid
attachment site

Hydrogen bond

RNA polynucleotide
chain

Anticodon

A tRNA molecule, showing
its polynucleotide strand
and hydrogen bonding

A simplified
schematic of a tRNA

▲ **Figure 10.11A**   The structure of tRNA

Each amino acid is joined to the correct tRNA by a specific enzyme. There is a family of 20 versions of these enzymes, one enzyme for each amino acid. Each enzyme specifically binds one type of amino acid to all tRNA molecules that code for that amino acid, using a molecule of ATP as energy to drive the reaction. The resulting amino acid–tRNA complex can then furnish its amino acid to a growing polypeptide chain, a process that we describe in Module 10.12.

The computer graphic in **Figure 10.11B** shows a tRNA molecule (green) and an ATP molecule (purple) bound to the enzyme molecule (blue). (To help you see the two distinct molecules, the tRNA molecule is shown with a stick representation, while the enzyme is shown as space-filling spheres.) In this figure, you can see the proportional sizes of these three molecules. The amino acid that would attach to the tRNA is not shown; it would be less than half the size of the ATP.

Once an amino acid is attached to its appropriate tRNA, it can be incorporated into a growing polypeptide chain. This is accomplished within ribosomes, the cellular organelles directly responsible for the synthesis of protein. We examine ribosomes in the next module.

? **What is an anticodon, and what is its function?**

● It is the base triplet of a tRNA molecule that couples the tRNA to a complementary codon in the mRNA. This is a key step in translating mRNA to polypeptide.

Figure 10.11A shows two representations of a tRNA molecule. The structure on the left shows the backbone and bases, with hydrogen bonds between bases shown as dashed magenta lines. The structure on the right is a simplified schematic that emphasizes the most important parts of the structure. Notice from the structure on the left that a tRNA molecule is made of a single strand of RNA—one polynucleotide chain—consisting of about 80 nucleotides. By twisting and folding upon itself, tRNA forms several double-stranded regions in which short stretches of RNA base-pair with other stretches via hydrogen bonds. A single-stranded loop at one end of the folded molecule contains a special triplet of bases called an **anticodon**. The anticodon triplet is complementary to a codon triplet on mRNA. During translation, the anticodon on tRNA recognizes a particular codon on mRNA by using base-pairing rules. At the other end of the tRNA molecule is a site where one specific kind of amino acid can attach.

In the modules that follow, we represent tRNA with the simplified shape shown on the right in Figure 10.11A. This shape emphasizes the two parts of the molecule—the anticodon and the amino acid attachment site—that give tRNA its ability to match a particular nucleic acid word (a codon in mRNA) with its corresponding protein word (an amino acid). Although all tRNA molecules are similar, there is a slightly different variety of tRNA for each amino acid.

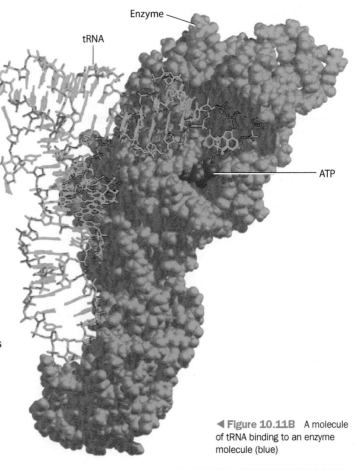

Enzyme

tRNA

ATP

◀ **Figure 10.11B**   A molecule of tRNA binding to an enzyme molecule (blue)

10.12 Ribosomes build polypeptides

We have now looked at many of the components a cell needs to carry out translation: instructions in the form of mRNA molecules, tRNA to interpret the instructions, a supply of amino acids and enzymes (for attaching amino acids to tRNA), and ATP for energy. The final components are the **ribosomes**, structures in the cytoplasm that position mRNA and tRNA close together and catalyze the synthesis of polypeptides.

A ribosome consists of two subunits, each made up of proteins and a kind of RNA called **ribosomal RNA (rRNA)**. In Figure 10.12A, you can see the actual shapes and relative sizes of the ribosomal subunits. You can also see where mRNA, tRNA, and the growing polypeptide are located during translation.

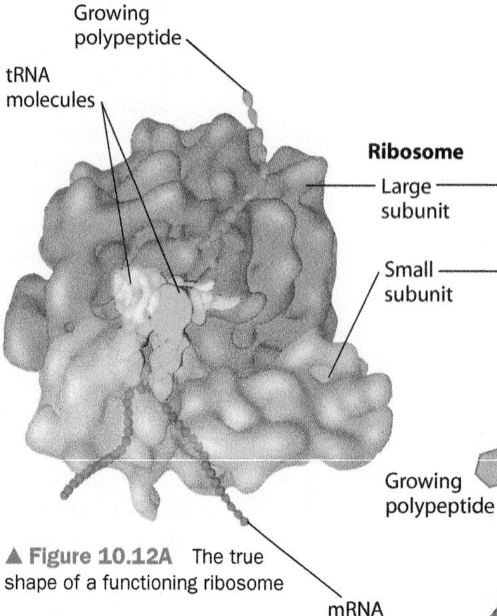

The ribosomes of prokaryotes and eukaryotes are very similar in function, but those of eukaryotes are slightly larger and different in composition. The differences are medically significant. Certain antibiotic drugs can inactivate prokaryotic ribosomes while leaving eukaryotic ribosomes unaffected. These drugs, such as tetracycline and streptomycin, are used to combat bacterial infections.

The simplified drawings in Figures 10.12B and 10.12C indicate how tRNA anticodons and mRNA codons fit together on ribosomes. As Figure 10.12B shows, each ribosome has a binding site for mRNA and the two main binding sites (P and A) for tRNA. Figure 10.12C shows tRNA molecules occupying these two sites. The subunits of the ribosome act like a vise, holding the tRNA and mRNA molecules close together, allowing the

▲ Figure 10.12A   The true shape of a functioning ribosome

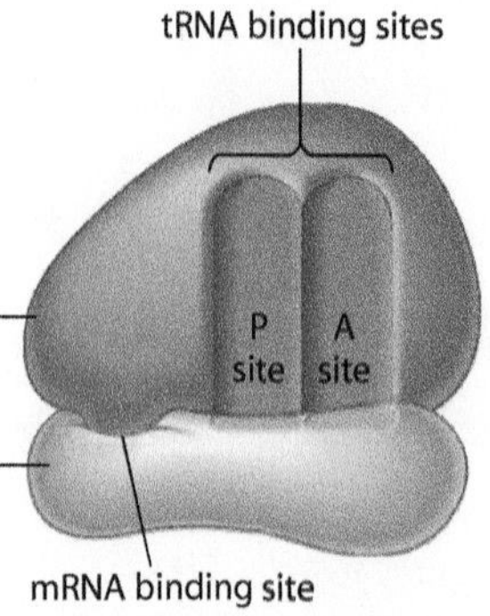

▲ Figure 10.12B   A ribosome with empty binding sites

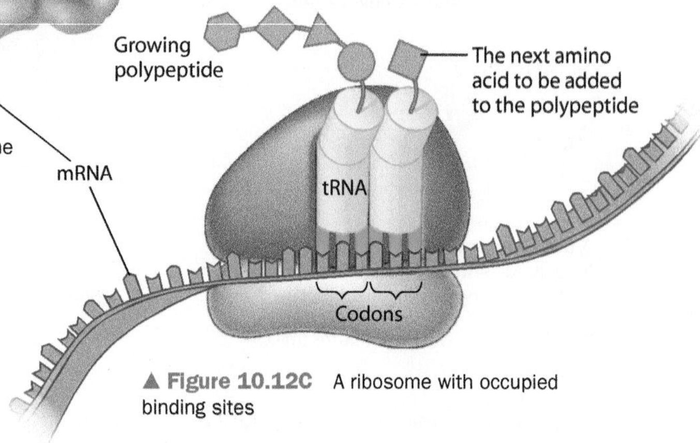

▲ Figure 10.12C   A ribosome with occupied binding sites

amino acids carried by the tRNA molecules to be connected into a polypeptide chain. In the next two modules, we examine the steps of translation in detail.

?   How does a ribosome facilitate protein synthesis?

● A ribosome holds mRNA and tRNAs together and connects amino acids from the tRNAs to the growing polypeptide chain.

10.13 An initiation codon marks the start of an mRNA message

Translation can be divided into the same three phases as transcription: initiation, elongation, and termination. The process of polypeptide initiation brings together the mRNA, a tRNA bearing the first amino acid, and the two subunits of a ribosome.

As shown in Figure 10.13A, an mRNA molecule is longer than the genetic message it carries. The light pink nucleotides at either end of the molecule are not part of the message, but help the mRNA to bind to the ribosome. The initiation process establishes

exactly where translation will begin, ensuring that the mRNA codons are translated into the correct sequence of amino acids.

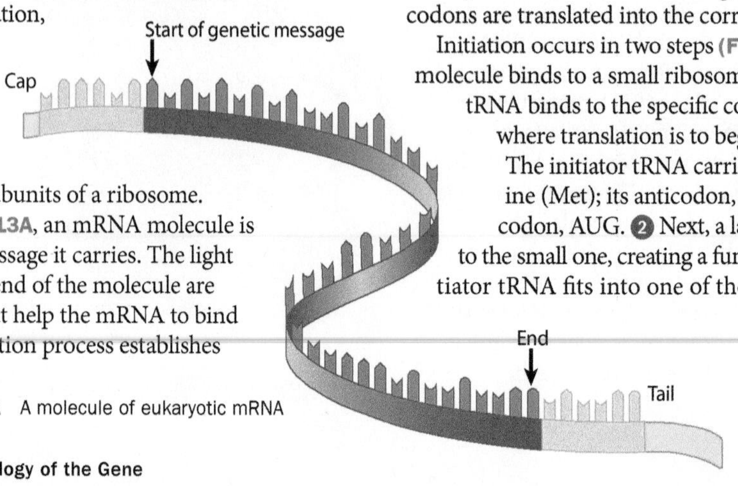

Initiation occurs in two steps (Figure 10.13B). ❶ An mRNA molecule binds to a small ribosomal subunit. A special initiator tRNA binds to the specific codon, called the **start codon**, where translation is to begin on the mRNA molecule. The initiator tRNA carries the amino acid methionine (Met); its anticodon, UAC, binds to the start codon, AUG. ❷ Next, a large ribosomal subunit binds to the small one, creating a functional ribosome. The initiator tRNA fits into one of the two tRNA binding

▶ Figure 10.13A   A molecule of eukaryotic mRNA

sites on the ribosome. This site, called the **P site**, will hold the growing polypeptide. The other tRNA binding site, called the **A site**, is vacant and ready for the next amino-acid-bearing tRNA.

? What would happen if a genetic mutation changed a start codon to some other codon?

● The messenger RNA transcribed from the mutated gene would be nonfunctional because ribosomes could not initiate translation correctly.

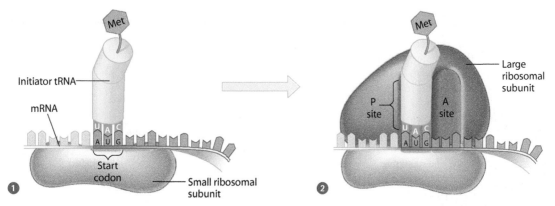

▲ Figure 10.13B The initiation of translation

10.14 Elongation adds amino acids to the polypeptide chain until a stop codon terminates translation

Once initiation is complete, amino acids are added one by one to the first amino acid. Each addition occurs in a three-step elongation process (Figure 10.14):

❶ Codon recognition. The anticodon of an incoming tRNA molecule, carrying its amino acid, pairs with the mRNA codon in the A site of the ribosome.

❷ Peptide bond formation. The polypeptide separates from the tRNA in the P site and attaches by a new peptide bond to the amino acid carried by the tRNA in the A site. The ribosome catalyzes formation of the peptide bond, adding one more amino acid to the growing polypeptide chain.

❸ Translocation. The P site tRNA now leaves the ribosome, and the ribosome translocates (moves) the remaining tRNA in the A site, with the growing polypeptide, to the P site. The codon and anticodon remain hydrogen-bonded, and the mRNA and tRNA move as a unit. This movement brings into the A site the next mRNA codon to be translated, and the process can start again with step 1.

Elongation continues until a **stop codon** reaches the ribosome's A site. Stop codons—UAA, UAG, and UGA—do not code for amino acids but instead act as signals to stop translation. This is the termination stage of translation. The completed polypeptide is freed from the last tRNA, and the ribosome splits back into its separate subunits.

? What happens as a tRNA passes through the A and P binding sites on the ribosome?

● In the A site, its amino acid receives the growing polypeptide from the tRNA that precedes it. In the P site, it gives up the polypeptide to the tRNA that follows it.

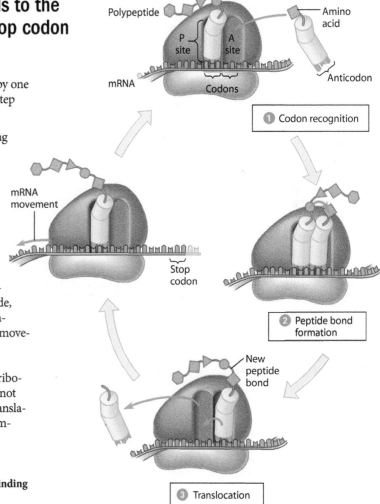

▲ Figure 10.14 Polypeptide elongation; the small green arrows indicate movement

10.15 Review: The flow of genetic information in the cell is DNA → RNA → protein

Figure 10.15 summarizes the main stages in the flow of genetic information from DNA to RNA to protein. ❶ In transcription (DNA → RNA), the mRNA is synthesized on a DNA template. In eukaryotic cells, transcription occurs in the nucleus, and the messenger RNA must travel from the nucleus to the cytoplasm. In prokaryotes, transcription occurs in the cytoplasm.

❷–❺ Translation (RNA → protein) can be divided into four steps, all of which occur in the cytoplasm in eukaryotic cells. When the polypeptide is complete at the end of step 5, the two ribosomal subunits come apart, and the tRNA and mRNA are released (not shown in this figure). Translation is rapid; a single ribosome can make an average-sized polypeptide in less than a minute. Typically, an mRNA molecule is translated simultaneously by a number of ribosomes. Once the start codon emerges from the first ribosome, a second ribosome can attach to it; thus, several ribosomes may trail along on the same mRNA molecule.

As it is made, a polypeptide coils and folds, assuming a three-dimensional shape, its tertiary structure. Several polypeptides may come together, forming a protein with quaternary structure (see Module 3.13).

What is the overall significance of transcription and translation? These are the main processes whereby genes control the structures and activities of cells—or, more broadly, the way the genotype produces the phenotype. The chain of command originates with the information in a gene, a specific linear sequence of nucleotides in DNA. The gene serves as a template, dictating transcription of a complementary sequence of nucleotides in mRNA. In turn, mRNA dictates the linear sequence in which amino acids assemble to form a specific polypeptide. Finally, the proteins that form from the polypeptides determine the appearance and the capabilities of the cell and organism.

? Which of the following molecules or structures does not participate directly in translation: ribosomes, transfer RNA, messenger RNA, DNA?

DNA

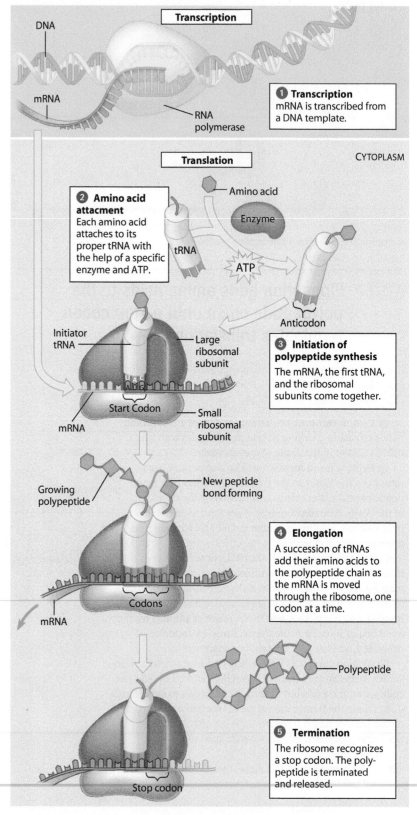

Transcription

DNA

mRNA

RNA polymerase

❶ **Transcription**
mRNA is transcribed from a DNA template.

CYTOPLASM

Translation

❷ **Amino acid attacment**
Each amino acid attaches to its proper tRNA with the help of a specific enzyme and ATP.

Amino acid

Enzyme

tRNA

ATP

Anticodon

Initiator tRNA

Large ribosomal subunit

Start Codon

mRNA

Small ribosomal subunit

❸ **Initiation of polypeptide synthesis**
The mRNA, the first tRNA, and the ribosomal subunits come together.

Growing polypeptide

New peptide bond forming

Codons

mRNA

❹ **Elongation**
A succession of tRNAs add their amino acids to the polypeptide chain as the mRNA is moved through the ribosome, one codon at a time.

Polypeptide

Stop codon

❺ **Termination**
The ribosome recognizes a stop codon. The polypeptide is terminated and released.

▲ **Figure 10.15** A summary of transcription and translation

10.16 Mutations can change the meaning of genes

Many inherited traits can be understood in molecular terms. For instance, sickle-cell disease (see Module 9.13) can be traced through a difference in a protein to one tiny change in a gene. In one of the two kinds of polypeptides in the hemoglobin protein, an individual with sickle-cell disease has a single different amino acid—valine (Val) instead of glutamate (Glu). This difference is caused by the change of a single nucleotide in the coding strand of DNA (Figure 10.16A). In the double helix, one nucleotide *pair* is changed.

Any change in the nucleotide sequence of DNA is called a **mutation**. Mutations can involve large regions of a chromosome or just a single nucleotide pair, as in sickle-cell disease. Here we consider how mutations involving only one or a few nucleotide pairs can affect gene translation.

Mutations within a gene can be divided into two general categories: nucleotide substitutions, and nucleotide insertions or deletions (Figure 10.16B). A nucleotide substitution is the replacement of one nucleotide and its base-pairing partner with another pair of nucleotides. For example, in the second row in Figure 10.16B, A replaces G in the fourth codon of the mRNA. What effect can a substitution have? Because the genetic code is redundant, some substitution mutations have no effect at all. For example, if a mutation causes an mRNA codon to change from GAA to GAG, no change in the protein product would result because GAA and GAG both code for the same amino acid (Glu; see Figure 10.8A). Such a change is called a **silent mutation**.

Other substitutions, called **missense mutations**, do change the amino acid coding. For example, if a mutation causes an mRNA codon to change from GGC to AGC, as in the second row of Figure 10.16B. The resulting protein will have a serine (Ser) instead of a glycine (Gly) at this position. Some missense mutations have little or no effect on the shape or function of the resulting protein, but others, as in the case of sickle-cell disease, prevent the protein from performing its normal function.

Occasionally, a nucleotide substitution leads to an improved protein that enhances the success of the mutant organism and its descendants. Much more often, though, mutations are harmful. Some substitutions, called **nonsense mutations**, change an amino acid codon into a stop codon. For example, if an AGA (Arg) codon is mutated to a UGA (stop) codon, the result will be a prematurely terminated protein, which probably will not function properly.

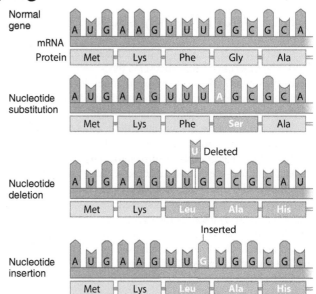

▲ Figure 10.16B Types of mutations and their effects

Mutations involving the insertion or deletion of one or more nucleotides in a gene often have disastrous effects. Because mRNA is read as a series of nucleotide triplets (codons) during translation, adding or subtracting nucleotides may alter the **reading frame** (triplet grouping) of the message. All the nucleotides that are "downstream" of the insertion or deletion will be regrouped into different codons (Figure 10.16B, bottom two rows). The result will most likely be a nonfunctional polypeptide.

The production of mutations, called **mutagenesis**, can occur in a number of ways. Spontaneous mutations are due to errors that occur during DNA replication or recombination. Other mutations are caused by physical or chemical agents, called **mutagens**. High-energy radiation, such as X-rays or ultraviolet light, is a physical mutagen. One class of chemical mutagens consists of chemicals that are similar to normal DNA bases but pair incorrectly or are otherwise disruptive when incorporated into DNA. For example, the anti-AIDS drug AZT works because its structure is similar enough to thymine that viral polymerases incorporate it into newly synthesized DNA, but different enough that the drug blocks further replication.

Although mutations are often harmful, they are also extremely useful, both in nature and in the laboratory. It is because of mutations that there is such a rich diversity of genes in the living world, a diversity that makes evolution by natural selection possible. Mutations are also essential tools for geneticists. Whether naturally occurring (as in Mendel's peas) or created in the laboratory (Morgan used X-rays to make most of his fruit fly mutants; see Module 9.18), mutations create the different alleles needed for genetic research.

? How could a single nucleotide substitution result in a shortened protein product?

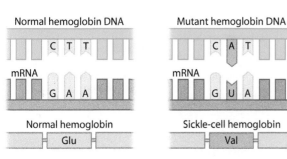

▲ Figure 10.16A The molecular basis of sickle-cell disease

● A substitution that changed an amino acid codon into a stop codon would produce a prematurely terminated polypeptide.

The Genetics of Viruses and Bacteria

10.17 Viral DNA may become part of the host chromosome

As we discussed in Module 10.1, bacteria and viruses served as models in experiments that uncovered the molecular details of heredity. Now let's take a closer look at viruses, focusing on the relationship between viral structure and the processes of nucleic acid replication, transcription, and translation.

In a sense, a **virus** is nothing more than "genes in a box": an infectious particle consisting of a bit of nucleic acid wrapped in a protein coat called a **capsid** and, in some cases, a membrane envelope. Viruses are parasites that can replicate (reproduce) only inside cells. In fact, the host cell provides most of the components necessary for replicating, transcribing, and translating the viral nucleic acid.

In Figure 10.1C, we described the replication cycle of phage T2. This sort of cycle is called a **lytic cycle** because it results in the lysis (breaking open) of the host cell and the release of the viruses that were produced within the cell. Some phages can also replicate by an alternative route called the lysogenic cycle. During a **lysogenic cycle**, viral DNA replication occurs without destroying the host cell.

In **Figure 10.17**, you see the two kinds of cycles for a phage called lambda that infects *E. coli*. Both cycles begin when the phage DNA ❶ enters the bacterium and ❷ forms a circle. The DNA then embarks on one of the two pathways. In the lytic cycle (left), ❸ lambda's DNA immediately turns the cell into a virus-producing factory, and ❹ the cell soon lyses and releases its viral products.

In the lysogenic cycle, however, ❺ viral DNA is inserted by genetic recombination into the bacterial chromosome. Once inserted, the phage DNA is referred to as a **prophage**, and most of its genes are inactive. ❻ Every time the *E. coli* cell prepares to divide, it replicates the phage DNA along with its own chromosome and passes the copies on to daughter cells. A single infected cell can thereby quickly give rise to a large population of bacterial cells that all carry prophage. The lysogenic cycle enables viruses to spread without killing the host cells on which they depend. The prophages may remain in the bacterial cells indefinitely. ❼ Occasionally, however, an environmental signal—typically, one that indicates an unfavorable turn in the environment, such as an increase in radiation, drought, or certain toxic chemicals—triggers a switchover from the lysogenic cycle to the lytic cycle. This so-called genetic switch causes the viral DNA to be excised from the bacterial chromosome, eventually leading to death of the host cell.

Sometimes, the few prophage genes active in a lysogenic bacterium can cause medical problems. For example, the bacteria that cause diphtheria, botulism, and scarlet fever would be harmless to humans if it were not for the prophage genes they carry. Certain of these genes direct the bacteria to produce the toxins responsible for making people ill. In the next module, we will explore viruses that infect animals and plants.

> **?** Describe one way a virus can perpetuate its genes without destroying its host cell. What is this type of replication cycle called?

● Some viruses can insert their DNA into a chromosome of the host cell, which replicates the viral genes when it replicates its own DNA prior to cell division. This is called the lysogenic cycle.

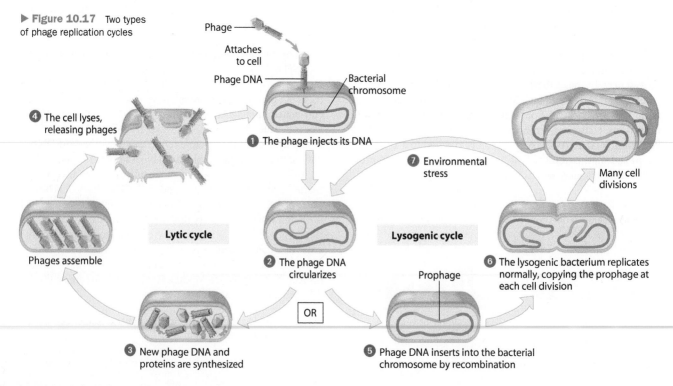

▶ **Figure 10.17** Two types of phage replication cycles

Phage
Attaches to cell
Phage DNA
Bacterial chromosome

❹ The cell lyses, releasing phages

❶ The phage injects its DNA

❼ Environmental stress

Many cell divisions

Lytic cycle

Lysogenic cycle

Phages assemble

❷ The phage DNA circularizes

Prophage

❻ The lysogenic bacterium replicates normally, copying the prophage at each cell division

OR

❸ New phage DNA and proteins are synthesized

❺ Phage DNA inserts into the bacterial chromosome by recombination

10.18 Many viruses cause disease in animals and plants

Viruses can cause disease in both animals and plants. A typical animal virus has a membranous outer envelope and projecting spikes of glycoprotein (protein molecules with attached sugars). The envelope helps the virus enter and leave the host cell. Many animal viruses have RNA rather than DNA as their genetic material. Examples of RNA viruses include those that cause the common cold, measles, mumps, polio, and AIDS. Examples of diseases caused by DNA viruses include hepatitis, chicken pox, and herpes infections.

Figure 10.18 shows the replication cycle of a typical enveloped RNA virus: the mumps virus. (Once a common childhood disease characterized by fever and painful swelling of the salivary glands, mumps has become quite rare in industrialized nations.) When the virus contacts a host cell, the glycoprotein spikes attach to receptor proteins on the cell's plasma membrane. The envelope fuses with the cell's membrane, allowing the

protein-coated RNA to ❶ enter the cytoplasm. ❷ Enzymes then remove the protein coat. ❸ An enzyme that entered the cell as part of the virus uses the virus's RNA genome as a template for making complementary strands of RNA (pink). The new strands have two functions: ❹ They serve as mRNA for the synthesis of new viral proteins, and ❺ they serve as templates for synthesizing new viral genome RNA. ❻ The new coat proteins assemble around the new viral RNA. ❼ Finally, the viruses leave the cell by cloaking themselves in the host cell's plasma membrane. Thus, the virus obtains its envelope from the host cell, leaving the cell without necessarily lysing it.

Not all animal viruses replicate in the cytoplasm. For example, herpesviruses, which you read about in the chapter introduction, are enveloped DNA viruses that replicate in the host cell's nucleus; they acquire their envelopes from the cell's nuclear membranes. While inside the nuclei of certain nerve cells, herpesvirus DNA may remain permanently dormant, without destroying these cells. From time to time, physical stress, such as a cold or sunburn, or emotional stress may stimulate the herpesvirus DNA to begin production of the virus, which then infects cells at the body's surface and brings about cold sores or genital sores.

The amount of damage a virus causes our body depends partly on how quickly our immune system responds to fight the infection and partly on the ability of the infected tissue to repair itself. We usually recover completely from colds because our respiratory tract tissue can efficiently replace damaged cells by mitosis. In contrast, the poliovirus attacks nerve cells, which are not usually replaceable. The damage to such cells, unfortunately, is permanent. In such cases, we try to prevent the disease with vaccines (see Module 24.4).

Viruses that infect plants can stunt plant growth and diminish crop yields. Most known plant viruses are RNA viruses. To infect a plant, a virus must first get past the plant's outer protective layer of cells (the epidermis). Once a virus enters a plant cell and begins replicating, it can spread throughout the entire plant through plasmodesmata, the cytoplasmic connections that penetrate the walls between adjacent plant cells (see Figure 4.21). Plant viruses may spread to other plants by insects, herbivores, humans, or farming tools. As with animal viruses, there are no cures for most viral diseases of plants. Agricultural scientists focus instead on preventing infections and on breeding resistant varieties of crop plants.

? **Explain how some viruses replicate without having DNA.**

● The genetic material of these viruses is RNA, which is replicated inside the host cell by special enzymes encoded by the virus. The viral genome (or its complement) serves as mRNA for the synthesis of viral proteins.

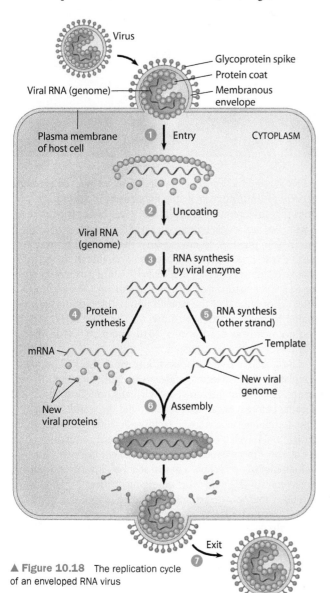

▲ Figure 10.18 The replication cycle of an enveloped RNA virus

10.19 Emerging viruses threaten human health

Viruses that appear suddenly or are new to medical scientists are called **emerging viruses**. There are many familiar examples. HIV, the AIDS virus, is a classic example: This virus appeared in New York and California in the early 1980s, seemingly out of nowhere. The deadly Ebola virus, recognized initially in 1976 in central Africa, is one of several emerging viruses that cause hemorrhagic fever, an often fatal illness characterized by fever, vomiting, massive bleeding, and circulatory system collapse. A number of other dangerous new viruses cause encephalitis, an inflammation of the brain. One example is the West Nile virus, which appeared for the first time in North America in 1999 and has since spread to all 48 contiguous U.S. states. West Nile virus is spread primarily by mosquitoes, which carry the virus in blood sucked from one victim and can transfer it to another victim. Severe acute respiratory syndrome (SARS) first appeared in China in 2002. Within eight months, about 8,000 people were infected, of whom some 10% died. Researchers quickly identified the infectious agent as a previously unknown, single-stranded RNA coronavirus, so named for its crown-like "corona" of spikes.

From where and how do such viruses burst on the human scene, giving rise to rare or previously unknown diseases? Three processes contribute to the emergence of viral diseases: mutation, contact between species, and spread from isolated populations.

The mutation of existing viruses is a major source of new viral diseases. RNA viruses tend to have unusually high rates of mutation because errors in replicating their RNA genomes are not subject to the kind of proofreading and repair mechanisms that help reduce errors in DNA replication. Some mutations enable existing viruses to evolve into new strains (genetic varieties) that can cause disease in individuals who have developed immunity to ancestral strains. That is why we need yearly flu vaccines: Mutations create new influenza virus strains to which previously vaccinated people have no immunity.

New viral diseases often arise from the spread of existing viruses from one host species to another. Scientists estimate that about three-quarters of new human diseases have originated in other animals. For example, in 1997, at least 18 people in Hong Kong were infected with a strain of flu virus called H5N1, which was previously seen only in birds. A mass culling of all of Hong Kong's 1.5 million domestic birds appeared to stop that outbreak. Beginning in 2002, however, new cases of human infection by this bird strain began to crop up around southeast Asia. As of 2009, the disease caused by this virus, now called "avian flu," has killed more than 250 people, and more than 100 million birds have either died from the disease or been killed to prevent the spread of infection.

In 2009, scientists in Mexico and then the United States became aware of a rapidly spreading new strain of flu called

Colorized TEM 8,500×

▼ Figure 10.19 People in Mexico City wearing masks in an attempt to prevent spread of the 2009 H1N1 virus (shown in the inset)

H1N1 (Figure 10.19). This particular virus evolved through genetic reshuffling of multiple flu viruses, including ones that infect humans, birds, and pigs (hence the name "swine flu," although humans cannot contract the virus directly from pigs). A vaccine against the 2009 H1N1 was rushed into production and became available in the fall of that year. Interestingly, the 2009 H1N1 flu virus is very similar to a virus that, in just 18 months during 1918 and 1919, infected one-third of the world's population, killing an estimated 50 million people worldwide. The 2009 H1N1 strain was not nearly as deadly; as of 2010, about 20,000 deaths worldwide had been reported.

The spread of a viral disease from a small, isolated human population can also lead to widespread epidemics. For instance, AIDS went unnamed and virtually unnoticed for decades before it began to spread around the world. In this case, technological and social factors—including affordable international travel, blood transfusions, sexual promiscuity, and the abuse of intravenous drugs—allowed a previously rare human disease to become a global scourge. If we ever do manage to control HIV and other emerging viruses, that success will likely follow from our understanding of molecular biology.

 Why doesn't a flu shot one year give us immunity to flu in subsequent years?

● Influenza viruses evolve rapidly by frequent mutation; thus, the strains that infect us later will most likely be different from the ones to which we've been vaccinated.

10.20 The AIDS virus makes DNA on an RNA template

The devastating disease **AIDS** (acquired immunodeficiency syndrome) is caused by **HIV** (human immunodeficiency virus), an RNA virus with some special properties. In outward appearance, HIV resembles the flu or mumps virus (**Figure 10.20A**). Its membranous envelope and glycoprotein spikes enable HIV to enter and leave a host cell much the way the mumps virus does (see Figure 10.18). Notice, however, that HIV contains two identical copies of its RNA instead of one. HIV also has a different mode of replication. HIV carries molecules of an enzyme called **reverse transcriptase**, which catalyzes reverse transcription, the synthesis of DNA on an RNA template. This unusual process, which is opposite the usual DNA → RNA flow of genetic information, characterizes **retroviruses** (retro means "backward").

Figure 10.20B illustrates what happens after HIV RNA is uncoated in the cytoplasm of a host cell. ❶ Reverse transcriptase ( ) uses the RNA as a template to make a DNA strand and then ❷ adds a second, complementary DNA strand. ❸ The resulting viral DNA enters the cell's nucleus and inserts itself into the chromosomal DNA, becoming a provirus (analogous to a prophage). The host's RNA polymerase ❹ transcribes the proviral DNA into RNA, which can then be ❺ translated by ribosomes into viral proteins. ❻ New viruses assembled from these components leave the cell and can infect other cells.

HIV infects and kills white blood cells that play important roles in the body's immune system. The loss of such cells causes the body to become susceptible to other infections that it would normally be able to fight off. Such secondary infections cause the syndrome (a collection of symptoms) that can kill an AIDS patient. We discuss AIDS in more detail when we take up the immune system in Chapter 24.

? Why is HIV classified as a retrovirus?

● It synthesizes DNA from its RNA genome. This is the reverse ("retro") of the usual DNA ⟶ RNA information flow.

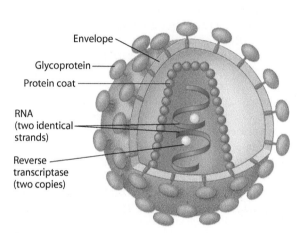

▲ **Figure 10.20A**   A model of HIV structure

Envelope
Glycoprotein
Protein coat
RNA (two identical strands)
Reverse transcriptase (two copies)

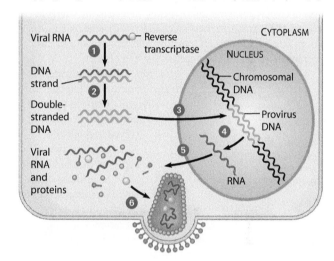

▲ **Figure 10.20B**   The behavior of HIV nucleic acid in a host cell

Viral RNA — Reverse transcriptase
CYTOPLASM
NUCLEUS
DNA strand
Chromosomal DNA
Double-stranded DNA
Provirus DNA
Viral RNA and proteins
RNA

10.21 Viroids and prions are formidable pathogens in plants and animals

Viruses may be small and simple, but they dwarf another class of pathogens: viroids. **Viroids** are small circular RNA molecules that infect plants. Unlike the nucleic acid of a virus, viroids do not encode proteins but can replicate in host plant cells, apparently using cellular enzymes. These small RNA molecules seem to cause errors in the regulatory systems that control plant growth. The typical signs of viroid diseases are abnormal development and stunted growth.

An important lesson to learn from viroids is that a single molecule can be an infectious agent. Viroids consist solely of nucleic acid, whose ability to be replicated is well known. Even more surprising are infectious proteins called **prions**, which cause a number of degenerative brain diseases in various animal species, including scrapie in sheep and goats, chronic wasting disease in deer and elk, mad cow disease (formally called bovine spongiform encephalopathy, or BSE), and Creutzfeldt-Jakob disease in humans. (The human disease is exceedingly rare, with at most a few hundred cases per year in the United States.)

A prion is thought to be a misfolded form of a protein normally present in brain cells. When the prion enters a cell containing the normal form of protein, the prion somehow converts the normal protein molecules to the misfolded prion versions. The abnormal proteins clump together, which may lead to loss of brain tissue (although *how* this occurs is the subject of much debate and ongoing research). To date, there is no cure for prion diseases, and the only hope for developing effective treatments lies in understanding and preventing the process of infection.

? What makes prions different from all other known infectious agents?

● Prions are proteins and have no nucleic acid.

10.22 Bacteria can transfer DNA in three ways

By studying viral replication, researchers also learn about the mechanisms that regulate DNA replication and gene expression in living cells. Bacteria are equally valuable as microbial models in genetics research. As prokaryotic cells, bacteria allow researchers to investigate molecular genetics in the simplest living organisms.

Most of a bacterium's DNA is found in a single chromosome, a closed loop of DNA with associated proteins. In the diagrams here, we show the chromosome much smaller than it actually is relative to the cell. A bacterial chromosome is hundreds of times longer than its cell; it fits inside the cell because it is tightly folded.

Bacterial cells reproduce by replication of the bacterial chromosome followed by binary fission (see Module 8.2). Because binary fission is an asexual process involving only a single parent, the bacteria in a colony are genetically identical to the parental cell. But this does not mean that bacteria lack ways to produce new combinations of genes. In fact, in the bacterial world, there are three mechanisms by which genes can move from one cell to another: transformation, transduction, and conjugation. Let's discuss each of these in turn.

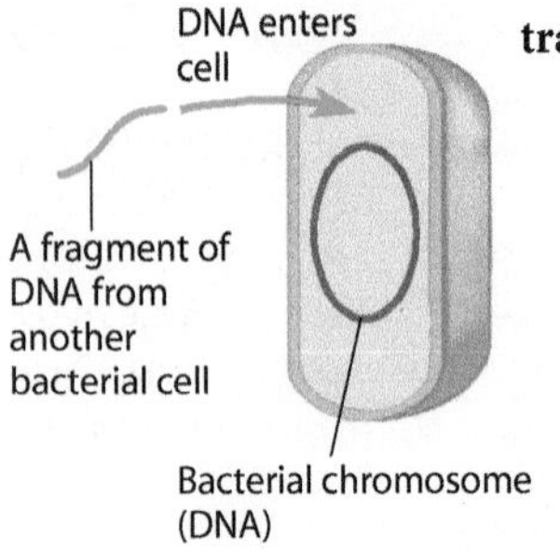

Figure 10.22A illustrates **transformation**, the uptake of foreign DNA from the surrounding environment. In Frederick Griffith's "transforming factor" experiment (see Module 10.1), a harmless strain of bacteria took up pieces of DNA left from the dead cells of a disease-causing strain. The DNA from the pathogenic bacteria carried a gene that made the cells resistant to an animal's defenses, and when the previously harmless bacteria acquired this gene, it could cause pneumonia in infected animals.

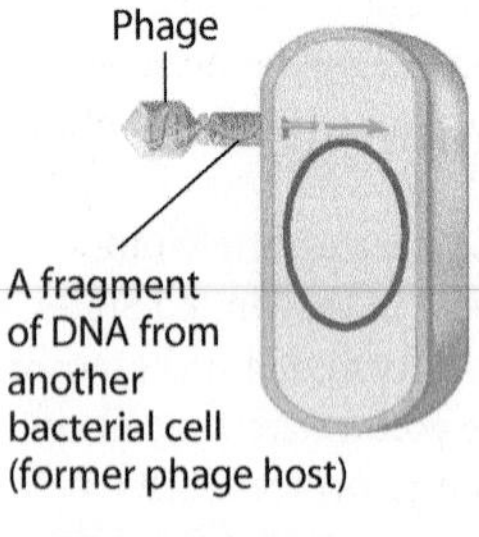

Bacteriophages, the viruses that infect bacteria, provide the second means of bringing together genes of different bacteria. The transfer of bacterial genes by a phage is called **transduction**. During a lytic infection, when new viruses are being assembled in an infected bacterial cell, a fragment of DNA belonging to the host cell may be mistakenly packaged within the phage's coat instead of the phage's DNA. When the phage infects a new bacterial cell, the DNA stowaway from the former host cell is injected into the new host (Figure 10.22B).

Figure 10.22C is an illustration of what happens at the DNA level when two bacterial cells "mate." This physical union of two bacterial cells—of the same or different species—and the DNA

transfer between them is called **conjugation**. The donor cell has hollow appendages called sex pili, one of which is attached to the recipient cell in the figure. The outside layers of the cells have fused, and a cytoplasmic bridge has formed between them. Through this mating bridge, donor cell DNA (light blue in the figure) passes to the recipient cell. The donor cell replicates its DNA as it transfers it, so the cell doesn't end up lacking any genes. The DNA replication is a special type that allows one copy to peel off and transfer into the recipient cell.

Once new DNA gets into a bacterial cell, by whatever mechanism, part of it may then integrate into the recipient's chromosome. As **Figure 10.22D** indicates, integration occurs by crossing over between the donor and recipient DNA molecules, a process similar to crossing over between eukaryotic chromosomes (see Module 8.17). Here we see that two crossovers result in a piece of the donated DNA replacing part of the recipient cell's original DNA. The leftover pieces of DNA are broken down and degraded, leaving the recipient bacterium with a recombinant chromosome.

As we'll see in the next module, the transfer of genetic material between bacteria has important medical consequences.

? The three modes of gene transfer between bacteria are _____, which is transfer via a virus; _____, which is the uptake of DNA from the surrounding environment; and _____, which is bacterial "mating."

● transduction · · · transformation · · · conjugation

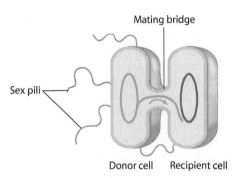

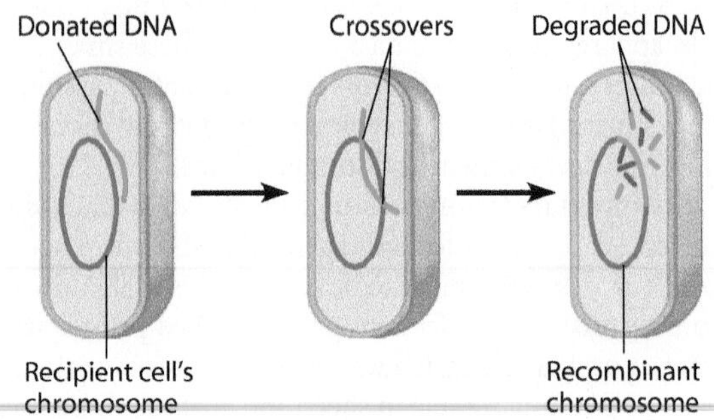

▲ Figure 10.22C   Conjugation

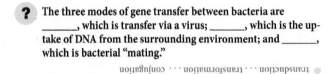

▲ **Figure 10.22D**   The integration of donated DNA into the recipient cell's chromosome

▲ **Figure 10.22A**
Transformation

▲ **Figure 10.22B**
Transduction

10.23 Bacterial plasmids can serve as carriers for gene transfer

The ability of a donor *E. coli* cell to carry out conjugation is usually due to a specific piece of DNA called the **F factor** (F for *fertility*). The F factor carries genes for making sex pili and other requirements for conjugation; it also contains an origin of replication, where DNA replication starts.

Let's see how the F factor behaves during conjugation. In Figure 10.23A, the F factor (light blue) is integrated into the donor bacterium's chromosome. When this cell conjugates with a recipient cell, the donor chromosome starts replicating at the F factor's origin of replication, indicated by the blue dot on the DNA. The growing copy of the DNA peels off the chromosome and heads into the recipient cell. Thus, part of the F factor serves as the leading end of the transferred DNA, but right behind it are genes from the donor's original chromosome. The rest of the F factor stays in the donor cell. Once inside the recipient cell, the transferred donor genes can recombine with the corresponding part of the recipient chromosome by crossing over. If crossing over occurs, the recipient cell may be genetically changed, but it usually remains a recipient because the

Plasmids

Colorized TEM 1,730×

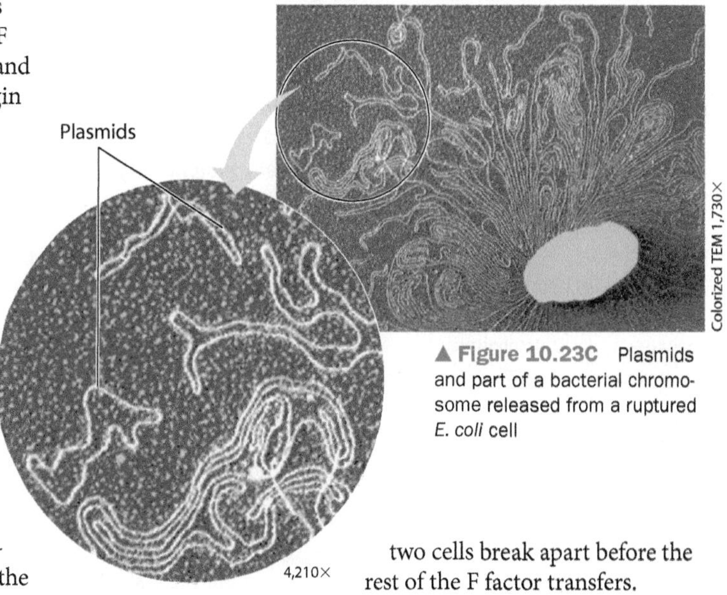

▲ **Figure 10.23C** Plasmids and part of a bacterial chromosome released from a ruptured *E. coli* cell

4,210×

two cells break apart before the rest of the F factor transfers.

Alternatively, as Figure 10.23B shows, an F factor can exist as a **plasmid**, a small, circular DNA molecule separate from the bacterial chromosome. Every plasmid has an origin of replication, required for its replication within the cell. Some plasmids, including the F factor plasmid, can bring about conjugation and move to another cell. When the donor cell in Figure 10.23B mates with a recipient cell, the F factor replicates and at the same time transfers one whole copy of itself, in linear rather than circular form, to the recipient cell. The transferred plasmid re-forms a circle in the recipient cell, and the cell becomes a donor.

E. coli and other bacteria have many different kinds of plasmids. You can see several from one cell in Figure 10.23C, along with part of the bacterial chromosome, which extends in loops from the ruptured cell. Some plasmids carry genes that can affect the survival of the cell. Plasmids of one class, called **R plasmids**, pose serious problems for human medicine. Transferable R plasmids carry genes for enzymes that destroy antibiotics such as penicillin and tetracycline. Bacteria containing R plasmids are resistant (hence the designation R) to antibiotics that would otherwise kill them. The widespread use of antibiotics in medicine and agriculture has tended to kill off bacteria that lack R plasmids, whereas those with R plasmids have multiplied. As a result, an increasing number of bacteria that cause human diseases, such as food poisoning and gonorrhea, are becoming resistant to antibiotics (see Module 13.15).

We'll return to the topic of plasmids in Chapter 12. But first, we'll continue our study of molecular genetics in Chapter 11, where we'll explore what is known about how genes themselves are controlled.

? In Chapter 12, you will learn that plasmids are useful tools for genetic engineering. Can you guess why?

● Scientists can take advantage of the ability of plasmids to carry foreign genes, to replicate, and to be inherited by progeny cells.

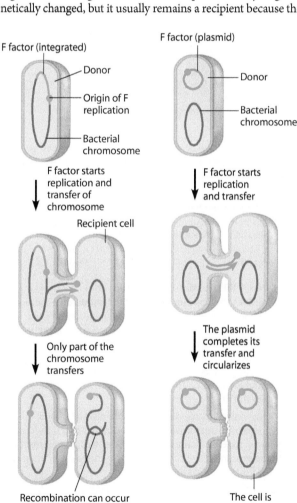

F factor (integrated)

- Donor
- Origin of F replication
- Bacterial chromosome

F factor starts replication and transfer of chromosome

Recipient cell

Only part of the chromosome transfers

Recombination can occur

▲ **Figure 10.23A** Transfer of chromosomal DNA by an integrated F factor

F factor (plasmid)

- Donor
- Bacterial chromosome

F factor starts replication and transfer

The plasmid completes its transfer and circularizes

The cell is now a donor

▲ **Figure 10.23B** Transfer of an F factor plasmid

For Practice Quizzes, BioFlix, MP3 Tutors, and Activities, go to www.masteringbiology.com.

Reviewing the Concepts

The Structure of the Genetic Material (10.1–10.3)

10.1 Experiments showed that DNA is the genetic material. One key experiment demonstrated that certain phages (bacterial viruses) reprogram host cells to produce more phages by injecting their DNA.

10.2 DNA and RNA are polymers of nucleotide.

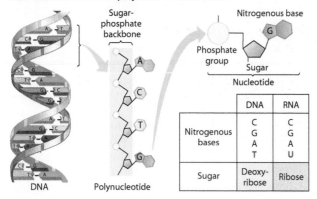

	DNA	RNA
Nitrogenous bases	C G A T	C G A U
Sugar	Deoxy-ribose	Ribose

10.3 DNA is a double-stranded helix. Watson and Crick worked out the three-dimensional structure of DNA: two polynucleotide strands wrapped around each other in a double helix. Hydrogen bonds between bases hold the strands together. Each base pairs with a complementary partner: A with T, G with C.

DNA Replication (10.4–10.5)

10.4 DNA replication depends on specific base pairing. DNA replication starts with the separation of DNA strands. Enzymes then use each strand as a template to assemble new nucleotides into a complementary strand.

10.5 DNA replication proceeds in two directions at many sites simultaneously. Using the enzyme DNA polymerase, the cell synthesizes one daughter strand as a continuous piece. The other strand is synthesized as a series of short pieces, which are then connected by the enzyme DNA ligase.

The Flow of Genetic Information from DNA to RNA to Protein (10.6–10.16)

10.6 The DNA genotype is expressed as proteins, which provide the molecular basis for phenotypic traits. The DNA of a gene—a linear sequence of many nucleotides—is transcribed into RNA, which is translated into a polypeptide.

10.7 Genetic information written in codons is translated into amino acid sequences. Codons are base triplets.

10.8 The genetic code dictates how codons are translated into amino acids. Nearly all organisms use an identical genetic code to convert the codons of a gene to the amino acid sequence of a polypeptide.

10.9 Transcription produces genetic messages in the form of RNA. In the nucleus, the DNA helix unzips, and RNA nucleotides line up and hydrogen-bond along one strand of the DNA, following the base-pairing rules.

10.10 Eukaryotic RNA is processed before leaving the nucleus as mRNA. Noncoding segments of RNA called introns are spliced out, and a cap and tail are added to the ends of the mRNA.

10.11 Transfer RNA molecules serve as interpreters during translation. Translation takes place in the cytoplasm. A ribosome attaches to the mRNA and translates its message into a specific polypeptide, aided by transfer RNAs (tRNAs). Each tRNA is a folded molecule bearing a base triplet called an anticodon on one end; a specific amino acid is added to the other end.

10.12 Ribosomes build polypeptides. Made of rRNA and proteins, ribsomes have binding sites for tRNAs and mRNA.

10.13 An initiation codon marks the start of an mRNA message.

10.14 Elongation adds amino acids to the polypeptide chain until a stop codon terminates translation. As the mRNA moves one codon at a time relative to the ribosome, a tRNA with a complementary anticodon pairs with each codon, adding its amino acid to the growing polypeptide chain.

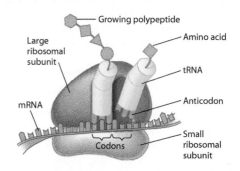

10.15 Review: The flow of genetic information in the cell is DNA → RNA → protein. The sequence of codons in DNA, via the sequence of codons in mRNA, spells out the primary structure of a polypeptide.

10.16 Mutations can change the meaning of genes. Mutations are changes in the DNA nucleotide sequence, caused by errors in DNA replication or recombination, or by mutagens. Substituting, inserting, or deleting nucleotides alters a gene, with varying effects on the organism.

The Genetics of Viruses and Bacteria (10.17–10.23)

10.17 Viral DNA may become part of the host chromosome. Viruses can be regarded as genes packaged in protein. When phage DNA enters a lytic cycle inside a bacterium, it is replicated, transcribed, and translated; the new viral DNA and protein molecules then assemble into new phages, which burst from the host cell. In the lysogenic cycle, phage DNA inserts into the host chromosome and is passed on to generations of daughter cells. Much later, it may initiate phage production.

10.18 Many viruses cause disease in animals and plants. Flu viruses and most plant viruses have RNA, rather than DNA, as their genetic material. Some animal viruses steal a bit of host cell membrane as a protective envelope. Some viruses can remain latent in the host's body for long periods.

10.19 Emerging viruses threaten human health.

10.20 The AIDS virus makes DNA on an RNA template. HIV is a retrovirus: It uses RNA as a template for making DNA, which then inserts into a host chromosome.

10.21 Viroids and prions are formidable pathogens in plants and animals. Viroids are RNA molecules that can infect plants. Prions are infectious proteins that can cause brain diseases in animals.

10.22 Bacteria can transfer DNA in three ways. Bacteria can transfer genes from cell to cell by transformation, transduction, or conjugation.

10.23 Bacterial plasmids can serve as carriers for gene transfer. Plasmids are small circular DNA molecules separate from the bacterial chromosome.

Connecting the Concepts

1. Check your understanding of the flow of genetic information through a cell by filling in the blanks.

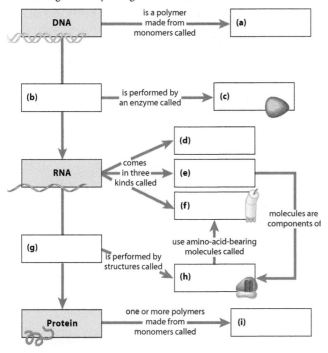

Testing Your Knowledge

Multiple Choice

2. Scientists have discovered how to put together a bacteriophage with the protein coat of phage T2 and the DNA of phage lambda. If this composite phage were allowed to infect a bacterium, the phages produced in the host cell would have _____. (*Explain your answer.*)
   a. the protein of T2 and the DNA of lambda
   b. the protein of lambda and the DNA of T2
   c. a mixture of the DNA and proteins of both phages
   d. the protein and DNA of T2
   e. the protein and DNA of lambda

3. A geneticist found that a particular mutation had no effect on the polypeptide encoded by a gene. This mutation probably involved
   a. deletion of one nucleotide.
   b. alteration of the start codon.
   c. insertion of one nucleotide.
   d. deletion of the entire gene.
   e. substitution of one nucleotide.

4. Which of the following correctly ranks the structures in order of size, from largest to smallest?
   a. gene-chromosome-nucleotide-codon
   b. chromosome-gene-codon-nucleotide
   c. nucleotide-chromosome-gene-codon
   d. chromosome-nucleotide-gene-codon
   e. gene-chromosome-codon-nucleotide

5. The nucleotide sequence of a DNA codon is GTA. A messenger RNA molecule with a complementary codon is transcribed from the DNA. In the process of protein synthesis, a transfer RNA pairs with the mRNA codon. What is the nucleotide sequence of the tRNA anticodon?
   a. CAT   d. CAU
   b. CUT   e. GT
   c. GUA

Describing, Comparing, and Explaining

6. Describe the process of DNA replication: the ingredients needed, the steps in the process, and the final product.

7. Describe the process by which the information in a eukaryotic gene is transcribed and translated into a protein. Correctly use these words in your description: tRNA, amino acid, start codon, transcription, RNA splicing, exons, introns, mRNA, gene, codon, RNA polymerase, ribosome, translation, anticodon, peptide bond, stop codon.

Applying the Concepts

8. A cell containing a single chromosome is placed in a medium containing radioactive phosphate so that any new DNA strands formed by DNA replication will be radioactive. The cell replicates its DNA and divides. Then the daughter cells (still in the radioactive medium) replicate their DNA and divide, and a total of four cells are present. Sketch the DNA molecules in all four cells, showing a normal (nonradioactive) DNA strand as a solid line and a radioactive DNA strand as a dashed line.

9. The base sequence of the gene coding for a short polypeptide is CTACGCTAGGCGATTGACT. What would be the base sequence of the mRNA transcribed from this gene? Using the genetic code in Figure 10.8A, give the amino acid sequence of the polypeptide translated from this mRNA. (*Hint:* What is the start codon?)

10. Researchers on the Human Genome Project have determined the nucleotide sequences of human genes and in many cases identified the proteins encoded by the genes. Knowledge of the nucleotide sequences of genes might be used to develop lifesaving medicines or treatments for genetic defects. In the United States, both government agencies and biotechnology companies have applied for patents on their discoveries of genes. In Britain, the courts have ruled that a naturally occurring gene cannot be patented. Do you think individuals and companies should be able to patent genes and gene products? Before answering, consider the following: What are the purposes of a patent? How might the discoverer of a gene benefit from a patent? How might the public benefit? What might be some positive and negative results of patenting genes?

Answers to all questions can be found in Appendix 4.

11

How Genes Are Controlled

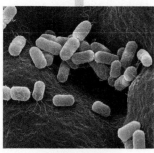

Control of Gene Expression
(11.1–11.11)

Cells can turn genes on and
off through a variety
of mechanisms.

Cloning of Plants
and Animals
(11.12–11.15)

Cloning demonstrates that many
body cells retain their full
genetic potential.

The Genetic Basis
of Cancer
(11.16–11.19)

Changes in genes that control
gene expression can lead to
out-of-control cell growth.

The smiling canine shown above is a cloned grey wolf (*Canis lupus*), born in a South Korean lab in 2007. In this context, the term *clone* refers to an individual created by asexual reproduction (that is, reproduction of a single individual that does not involve fusion of sperm and egg). First demonstrated in the 1950s with frogs, animal cloning became much more commonplace after 1997, when Scottish researchers announced the first successful cloning of a mammal: the world-famous Dolly, a sheep cloned from a mammary cell extracted from an adult ewe.

Cloning efforts to date have focused on farm animals (such as sheep), important research organisms (such as mice), and endangered species (such as wolves). Indeed, cloning may be the only way to repopulate some highly endangered species. However, conservationists argue that cloning may trivialize the tragedy of extinction and detract from efforts to preserve natural habitats. They correctly point out that cloning does not increase genetic diversity and is therefore not as beneficial to endangered species as natural reproduction.

The cloning of an animal from a single body cell demonstrates that the starting cell contained a complete genome capable of directing the production of all the cell types in an organism. The development of a multicellular organism with many different kinds of cells thus depends on the turning on and off of different genes in different cells—the control of gene expression.

Whether an organism is unicellular or multicellular, its cells may alter their patterns of gene expression in response to the organism's needs. We begin this chapter with examples of how and where this may occur. Next we look at the methods and applications of plant and animal cloning. Finally, we discuss cancer, a disease that can be caused by changes in gene expression.

Control of Gene Expression

11.1 Proteins interacting with DNA turn prokaryotic genes on or off in response to environmental changes

Picture an *Escherichia coli* (*E. coli*) bacterium living in your intestine (Figure 11.1A). Its environment changes continuously, depending on your dietary whims. For example, if you eat a sweet roll for breakfast, the bacterium will be bathed in sugars and broken-down fats. Later, if you have a salad for lunch, the *E. coli*'s environment will change drastically. How can a bacterium cope with such a constantly shifting flow of resources?

The answer is that **gene regulation**—the turning on and off of genes—can help organisms respond to environmental changes. What does it mean to turn a gene on or off? As we discussed in Chapter 10, genes determine the nucleotide sequences of specific mRNA molecules, and mRNA in turn determines the sequences of amino acids in protein molecules (DNA → RNA → protein). Thus, a gene that is turned on is being transcribed into RNA, and that message is being translated into specific protein molecules. The overall process by which genetic information flows from genes to proteins—that is, from genotype to phenotype—is called **gene expression**. The control of gene expression makes it possible for cells to produce specific kinds of proteins when and where they are needed.

It's no coincidence that we used *E. coli* as our example. Our earliest understanding of gene control came from studies of this bacterium by French biologists François Jacob and Jacques Monod. *E. coli* has a remarkable ability to change its metabolic activities in response to changes in its environment. For example, *E. coli* produces enzymes needed to metabolize a specific nutrient only when that nutrient is available. Bacterial cells that can conserve resources and energy have an advantage over cells that are unable to do so. Thus, natural selection has favored bacteria that express only the genes whose products are needed by the cell. Let's look at how the regulation of gene transcription helps *E. coli* efficiently use available resources.

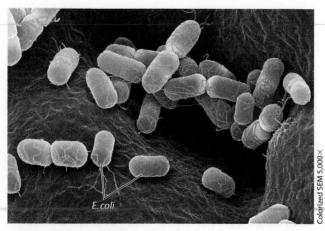

▲ **Figure 11.1A** Cells of *E. coli* bacteria

Colorized SEM 5,000×

The *lac* Operon Imagine the bacterium in your intestine soon after you drink a glass of milk. One of the main nutrients in milk is the disaccharide sugar lactose. When lactose is plentiful in the intestine, *E. coli* makes the enzymes necessary to absorb the sugar and use it as an energy source. Conversely, when lactose is not plentiful, *E. coli* does not waste its energy producing these enzymes.

Recall that enzymes are proteins; their production is an outcome of gene expression. *E. coli* can make lactose-utilization enzymes because it has genes that code for these enzymes. Figure 11.1B presents a model (first proposed in 1961 by Jacob and Monod) to explain how an *E. coli* cell can turn genes coding for lactose-utilization enzymes off or on, depending on whether lactose is available.

E. coli uses three enzymes to take up and start metabolizing lactose, and the genes coding for these three enzymes are regulated as a single unit. The DNA at the top of Figure 11.1B represents a small segment of the bacterium's chromosome. Notice that the three genes that code for the lactose-utilization enzymes (light blue) are next to each other in the DNA.

Adjacent to the group of lactose enzyme genes are two control sequences, short sections of DNA that help control the enzyme genes. One control sequence is a **promoter**, a site where the transcription enzyme, RNA polymerase, attaches and initiates transcription—in this case, transcription of all three lactose enzyme genes (as depicted in the bottom panel of Figure 11.1B). Between the promoter and the enzyme genes, a DNA control sequence called an **operator** acts as a switch. The operator determines whether RNA polymerase can attach to the promoter and start transcribing the genes.

Such a cluster of genes with related functions, along with the control sequences, is called an **operon**; with rare exceptions, operons exist only in prokaryotes. The key advantage to the grouping of related genes into operons is that a single "on-off switch" can control the whole cluster. The operon discussed here is called the *lac* operon, short for lactose operon. When an *E. coli* bacterium encounters lactose, all the enzymes needed for its metabolism are made at once because the operon's genes are all controlled by a single switch, the operator. But what determines whether the operator switch is on or off?

The top panel of Figure 11.1B shows the *lac* operon in "off" mode, its status when there is no lactose in the cell's environment. Transcription is turned off by a protein called a **repressor** ( ), a protein that functions by binding to the operator ( ) and physically blocking the attachment of RNA polymerase ( ) to the promoter ( ). On the left side of the figure, you can see where the repressor comes from. A gene called a **regulatory gene** (dark blue), located outside the operon, codes for the repressor. The regulatory gene is expressed continually, so the cell always has a small supply of repressor molecules.

Operon turned off (lactose is absent):

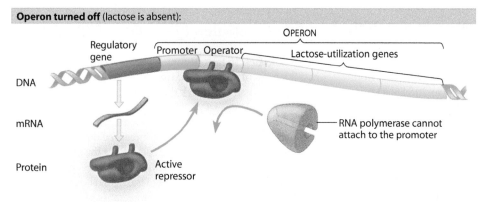

Operon turned on (lactose inactivates the repressor):

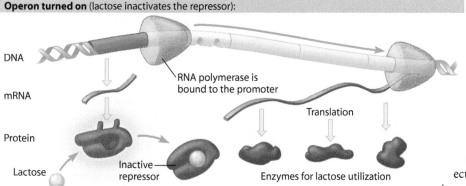

▲ **Figure 11.1B**   The *lac* operon

How can an operon be turned on if its repressor is always present? As the bottom panel of Figure 11.1B indicates, lactose ( ) interferes with the attachment of the *lac* repressor to the operator by binding to the repressor and changing its shape. With its new shape ( ), the repressor cannot bind to the operator, and the operator switch remains on. RNA polymerase can now bind to the promoter (since it is no longer being blocked) and from there transcribes the genes of the operon. The resulting mRNA carries coding sequences for all three enzymes needed for lactose metabolism. The cell can translate the message in this single mRNA into three separate polypeptides because the mRNA has multiple codons signaling the start and stop of translation.

The *lac* operon is so efficient that the addition of lactose to a bacterium's environment results in a thousandfold increase in lactose utilization enzymes in just 15 minutes. The newly produced mRNA and protein molecules will remain intact for only a short time before cellular enzymes break them down. When the synthesis of mRNA and protein stops because lactose is no longer present, the molecules quickly disappear.

Other Kinds of Operons   The *lac* operon is only one type of operon in bacteria. Other types also have a promoter, an operator, and several adjacent genes, but they differ in the way the operator switch is controlled. **Figure 11.1C** shows two types of repressor-controlled operons. The *lac* operon's repressor is active when alone and inactive when bound to lactose. A second type of operon, represented here by the *trp*

operon, is controlled by a repressor that is *inactive* alone. To be active, this type of repressor must combine with a specific small molecule. In our example, the small molecule is tryptophan (Trp), an amino acid essential for protein synthesis. *E. coli* can make tryptophan from scratch, using enzymes encoded in the *trp* operon. But it will stop making tryptophan and simply absorb it in prefabricated form from the surroundings whenever possible. When *E. coli* is swimming in tryptophan in the intestines (as occurs when you eat foods such as milk and poultry), the tryptophan binds to the repressor of the *trp* operon. This activates the *trp* repressor, enabling it to switch off the operon. Thus, this type of operon allows bacteria to stop making certain essential molecules when the molecules are already present in the environment, saving materials and energy for the cells.

Another type of operon control involves **activators**, proteins that turn operons *on* by binding to DNA. These proteins act by making it easier for RNA polymerase to bind to the promoter, rather than by blocking RNA polymerase, as repressors do. Activators help control a wide variety of operons.

Armed with a variety of operons regulated by repressors and activators, *E. coli* and other prokaryotes can thrive in frequently changing environments. Next we examine how more complex eukaryotes regulate their genes.

?   **A certain mutation in *E. coli* impairs the ability of the *lac* repressor to bind to the *lac* operator. How would this affect the cell?**

The cell would wastefully produce the enzymes for lactose metabolism continuously, even when lactose is not present.

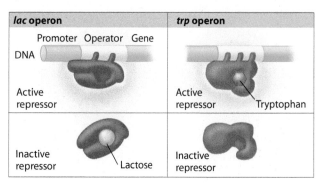

▲ **Figure 11.1C**   Two types of repressor-controlled operons

11.2 Chromosome structure and chemical modifications can affect gene expression

The cells of all organisms, whether prokaryotes or eukaryotes, must be able to turn genes on and off in response to signals from their external and internal environments. All multicellular eukaryotes also require an additional level of gene control: During the repeated cell divisions that lead from a zygote to an adult in a multicellular organism, individual cells must undergo **differentiation**—that is, they must become specialized in structure and function, with each type of cell fulfilling a distinct role. Your body, for example, contains hundreds of different types of cells. What makes a kidney cell different from, say, a bone cell?

To perform its specialized role, each cell type must maintain a specific program of gene expression in which some genes are expressed and others are not. Almost all the cells in an organism contain an identical genome, yet the subset of genes expressed in each cell type is unique, reflecting its specific function. Each adult human cell expresses only a small fraction of its total genes at any given time. And even one particular cell type can change its pattern of gene expression over time in response to developmental signals or other changes in the environment.

The differences between cell types, therefore, are due not to different genes being present, but to selective gene expression. In this module, we begin our exploration of gene regulation in eukaryotes by looking at the chromosomes, where almost all of a cell's genes are located.

DNA Packing   The DNA in just a single human chromosome would, if stretched out, average 4 cm in length, thousands of times greater than the diameter of the nucleus. All of this DNA can fit within the nucleus because of an elaborate, multilevel system of packing—coiling and folding—of the DNA in each chromosome. A crucial aspect of DNA packing is the association of the DNA with small proteins

called **histones**. In fact, histone proteins account for about half the mass of eukaryotic chromosomes. (Prokaryotes have analogous proteins, but lack the degree of DNA packing seen in eukaryotes.)

Figure 11.2A shows a model for the main levels of DNA packing. At the left, notice that the unpacked double-helical molecule of DNA has a diameter of 2 nm. At the first level of packing, histones attach to the DNA double helix. In the electron micrograph near the top left of the figure, notice how the DNA-histone complex has the appearance of beads on a string. Each "bead," called a **nucleosome**, consists of DNA wound around a protein core of eight histone molecules. Short stretches of DNA, called linkers, are the "strings" that join consecutive "beads" of nucleosomes.

At the next level of packing, the beaded string is wrapped into a tight helical fiber. This fiber coils further into a thick supercoil with a diameter of about 300 nm. Looping and folding can further compact the DNA, as you can see in the metaphase chromosome at the right of the figure. Viewed as a whole, Figure 11.2A gives a sense of how successive levels of coiling and folding enable a huge amount of DNA to fit into a cell nucleus.

DNA packing can block gene expression by preventing RNA polymerase and other transcription proteins from contacting the DNA. Cells seem to use higher levels of packing for long-term inactivation of genes. Highly compacted chromatin, which is found not only in mitotic chromosomes—such as the duplicated chromosome shown below—but also in varying regions of interphase chromosomes, is generally not expressed at all.

Chemical Modifications and Epigenetic Inheritance   In addition to being able to change their level of packing, the cells of many eukaryotic organisms have the capability to establish and maintain chemical modifications to their chromosomes in

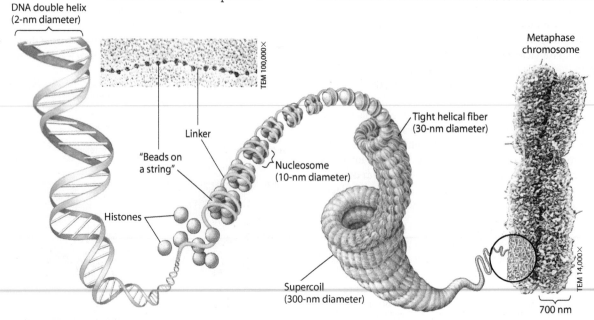

DNA double helix
(2-nm diameter)

TEM 100,000×

Linker

"Beads on a string"

Histones

Nucleosome
(10-nm diameter)

Supercoil
(300-nm diameter)

Tight helical fiber
(30-nm diameter)

Metaphase chromosome

TEM 14,000×

700 nm

▲ **Figure 11.2A**   DNA packing in a eukaryotic chromosome

ways that help regulate gene expression. For example, the addition of chemical groups to some of the amino acids in histone proteins, or their removal, can cause the proteins to bind DNA more tightly or loosely, altering the ability of transcription machinery to reach those genes.

DNA itself can also be the target of chemical modification. In one such type of modification, certain enzymes add a methyl group (CH_3) to DNA bases, usually cytosine, without changing the actual sequence of the bases. Individual genes are usually more heavily methylated in cells in which they are not expressed, and removal of the extra methyl groups can turn on some of these genes. Thus, DNA methylation appears to play a role in turning genes off. At least in some species, DNA methylation seems to be essential for the long-term inactivation of genes. Such modifications are a normal and necessary mechanism for the regulation of gene expression, and improper methylation can lead to problems for the organism. For example, insufficient DNA methylation can lead to abnormal embryonic development in many species.

Once methylated, genes usually stay that way through successive cell divisions in a given individual. At DNA sites where one strand is already methylated, enzymes methylate the corresponding daughter strand after each round of DNA replication. Methylation patterns are therefore passed on, and cells forming specialized tissues keep a chemical record of what occurred during embryonic development. In this way, modifications to the DNA and histones can be passed along to future generations of cells—that is, they can be inherited. Inheritance of traits transmitted by mechanisms not directly involving the nucleotide sequence is called **epigenetic inheritance**. Whereas mutations in the DNA are permanent changes, modifications to the chromatin, which do not affect the sequence of DNA itself, can be reversed by processes that are not yet fully understood.

Researchers are amassing more and more evidence for the importance of epigenetic information in the regulation of gene expression. Epigenetic variations might help explain differences in identical twins. It is often the case that one identical twin acquires a genetically influenced disease, such as schizophrenia, but the other does not, despite their identical genomes. Researchers suspect that epigenetics may be behind such differences. Alterations in normal patterns of DNA methylation are seen in some cancers, where they are associated with inappropriate gene expression. Evidently, enzymes that modify chromatin structure are integral parts of the eukaryotic cell's machinery for regulating transcription.

X Inactivation Female mammals, including humans, inherit two X chromosomes, whereas males inherit only one. So why don't females make twice as much of the proteins encoded by genes on the X chromosome compared to the amounts in males? It turns out that in female mammals, one X chromosome in each somatic (body) cell is chemically modified and highly compacted, rendering it almost entirely inactive. Inactivation of an X chromosome involves modification of the DNA (by, for example, methylation) and the histone proteins that help compact it. A specific gene on the X chromosomes ensures that one and only one of them will be inactivated. This **X chromosome inactivation** is initiated early in embryonic development, when one of the two X chromosomes in each cell is inactivated at random. As a result, the cells of females and males have the same effective dose (one copy) of these genes. The inactive X in each cell of a female condenses into a compact object called a **Barr body**.

Which X chromosome is inactivated is a matter of chance in each embryonic cell, but once an X chromosome is inactivated, all descendant cells have the same copy turned off—an example of epigenetic inheritance. Consequently, females consist of a mosaic of two types of cells: those with the active X derived from the father and those with the active X derived from the mother. If a female is heterozygous for a gene on the X chromosome (a sex-linked gene; see Module 9.21), about half her cells will express one allele, while the others will express the alternate allele.

A striking example of this mosaic phenomenon is the tortoiseshell cat, which has orange and black patches of fur (Figure 11.2B). The relevant fur-color gene is on the X chromosome, and the tortoiseshell phenotype requires the presence of two different alleles, one for orange fur and one for black fur. Normally, only females can have both alleles because only they have two X chromosomes. If a female is heterozygous for the tortoiseshell gene, she will have the tortoiseshell phenotype. Orange patches are formed by populations of cells in which the X chromosome with the orange allele is active; black patches have cells in which the X chromosome with the black allele is active.

In this module, we have seen how the physical structure of chromosomes can affect which genes are expressed in a cell. In the next module, we discuss mechanisms for regulating genes in active, unpacked chromosomes.

? If a nerve cell and a skin cell in your body have the same genes, how can the cells be so different?

● Each cell type must be expressing certain genes that are present in, but not expressed in, the other cell type.

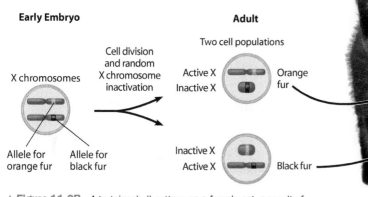

▲ **Figure 11.2B** A tortoiseshell pattern on a female cat, a result of X chromosome inactivation

Early Embryo

X chromosomes

Allele for orange fur

Allele for black fur

Cell division and random X chromosome inactivation

Adult

Two cell populations

Active X
Inactive X

Orange fur

Inactive X
Active X

Black fur

11.3 Complex assemblies of proteins control eukaryotic transcription

The packing and unpacking of chromosomal DNA provide a coarse adjustment for eukaryotic gene expression by making a region of DNA either more or less available for transcription. The fine-tuning begins with the initiation of RNA synthesis—transcription. In both prokaryotes and eukaryotes, the initiation of transcription (whether transcription starts or not) is the most important stage for regulating gene expression.

Like prokaryotes (see Module 11.1), eukaryotes employ regulatory proteins—activators and repressors—that bind to specific segments of DNA and either promote or block the binding of RNA polymerase, turning the transcription of genes on or off. However, most eukaryotic genes have individual promoters and other control sequences and are not clustered together as in operons.

The current model for the initiation of eukaryotic transcription features an intricate array of regulatory proteins that interact with DNA and with one another to turn genes on or off. In eukaryotes, activator proteins seem to be more important than repressors. That is, in multicellular eukaryotes, the "default" state for most genes seems to be "off." A typical animal or plant cell needs to turn on (transcribe) only a small percentage of its genes, those required for the cell's specialized structure and function. Housekeeping genes, those continually active in virtually all cells for routine activities such as glycolysis, may be in an "on" state by default.

In order to function, eukaryotic RNA polymerase requires the assistance of proteins called **transcription factors.** In the model depicted in **Figure 11.3**, the first step in initiating gene transcription is the binding of activator proteins ( ) to DNA control sequences called **enhancers** (   ). In contrast to the operators of prokaryotic operons, enhancers are usually far away on the chromosome from the gene they help regulate. The binding of activators to enhancers leads to bending of the DNA. Once the DNA is bent, the bound activators interact with other transcription factor proteins ( ), which then bind as a complex at the gene's promoter (   ). This large assembly of proteins facilitates the correct attachment of RNA polymerase to the promoter and the initiation of transcription. Only when the complete complex of proteins has assembled can the polymerase begin to move along the gene, producing an RNA strand. As shown in the figure, several enhancers and activators may be involved. Not shown are *repressor* proteins called **silencers** that may bind to DNA sequences and *inhibit* the start of transcription.

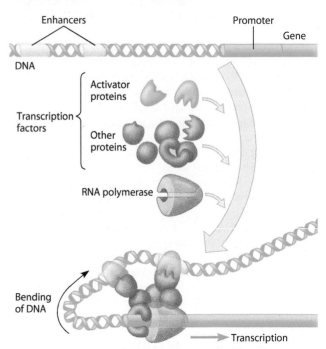

▲ **Figure 11.3** A model for the turning on of a eukaryotic gene

If eukaryotic genomes only rarely have operons, how does a eukaryotic cell deal with genes of related function that all need to be turned on or off at the same time? Making the situation even more complex, genes coding for the enzymes of a metabolic pathway are often scattered across different chromosomes. The key to coordinated gene expression in eukaryotes is often the association of a specific combination of control sequences with every gene of a particular metabolic pathway. Copies of the activators that recognize these control sequences bind to them all at once (since they are all identical), promoting simultaneous transcription of the genes, no matter where they are in the genome. In the next module, we consider another method of gene regulation that is unique to eukaryotes.

? **What must occur before RNA polymerase can bind to a promoter and transcribe a specific eukaryotic gene?**

● Enhancers must bind to transcription factors to facilitate the attachment of RNA polymerase to the promoter.

11.4 Eukaryotic RNA may be spliced in more than one way

Although regulation of transcription is the most important step in gene regulation in most cells, transcription alone does not equal gene expression. Several other points along the path from DNA to protein can be regulated. Within a eukaryotic cell, for example, RNA transcripts are processed into mRNA before moving to the cytoplasm for translation by the ribosomes.

RNA processing includes the addition of a cap and a tail, as well as the removal of any introns—noncoding DNA segments that interrupt the genetic message—and the splicing together of the remaining exons (see Module 10.10).

Some scientists think that the splicing process may help control the flow of mRNA from nucleus to cytoplasm because until splicing is completed, the RNA is attached to the molecules of the splicing machinery and cannot pass through the nuclear pores. Moreover, in some cases, the cell can carry out splicing in more than one way, generating different mRNA molecules from the same RNA transcript. Notice in **Figure 11.4**, for example, that one mRNA molecule ends up with the green exon and the other with the brown exon. With this sort of **alternative RNA splicing**, an organism can produce more than one type of polypeptide from a single gene.

One interesting example of two-way splicing is found in the fruit fly, where the differences between males and females are largely due to different patterns of RNA splicing. And as you will learn in Chapter 12, results from the Human Genome Project suggest that alternative splicing is very common in humans. Included among the many instances already known is one gene whose transcript can be spliced to encode *seven* alternative versions of a protein, each of which is made in a different type of cell.

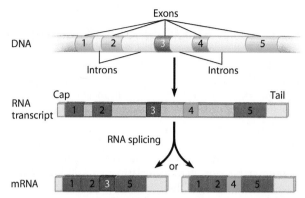

▲ **Figure 11.4** The production of two different mRNAs from the same gene

? How does alternative RNA splicing enable a single gene to encode more than one kind of polypeptide?

● Each kind of polypeptide is encoded by an mRNA molecule containing a different combination of exons.

11.5 Small RNAs play multiple roles in controlling gene expression

Recall that only 1.5% of the human genome—and a similarly small percentage of the genomes of many other multicellular eukaryotes—codes for proteins. Another very small fraction of DNA consists of genes for ribosomal RNA and transfer RNA. Until recently, most of the remaining DNA was thought to be untranscribed and therefore considered to be lacking any genetic information. However, a flood of recent data has contradicted this view. It turns out that a significant amount of the genome is transcribed into functioning but non-protein-coding RNAs, including a variety of small RNAs. While many questions about the functions of these RNAs remain unanswered, researchers are uncovering more evidence of their biological roles every day.

In 1993, researchers discovered small RNA molecules, called **microRNAs (miRNAs)**, that can bind to complementary sequences on mRNA molecules (**Figure 11.5**). Each miRNA, typically about 20 nucleotides long, ❶ forms a complex with protein. The miRNA-protein complex can ❷ bind to any mRNA molecule with the complementary sequence. Then the complex either ❸ degrades the target mRNA or ❹ blocks its translation. It has been estimated that miRNAs may regulate the expression of up to one-third of all human genes, a striking figure given that miRNAs were unknown a mere 20 years ago.

Researchers can take advantage of miRNA to artificially control gene expression. For example, injecting miRNA into a cell can turn off expression of a gene with a sequence that matches the miRNA, a procedure called **RNA interference (RNAi).** The RNAi pathway may have evolved as a natural defense against infection by certain viruses with RNA genomes (see Chapter 10). In 2006, two American researchers were awarded a Nobel Prize for their discovery and categorization of RNA interference.

Biologists are excited about these recent discoveries, which hint at a large, diverse population of RNA molecules in the cell

that play crucial roles in regulating gene expression—and have gone largely unnoticed until now. Our new understanding may lead to important clinical applications. For example, in 2009, researchers discovered a particular microRNA that is essential to the proper functioning of the pancreas. Without it, insulin-producing beta cells die off, which can lead to diabetes. Clearly, we must revise the long-standing view that because they code for proteins, messenger RNAs are the most important RNAs in terms of cellular function.

? If a gene has the sequence AATTCGCG, what would be the sequence of an miRNA that turns off the gene?

● The gene will be transcribed as the mRNA sequence UUAAGCGC; an miRNA of sequence AAUUCGCG would bind to and disable this mRNA.

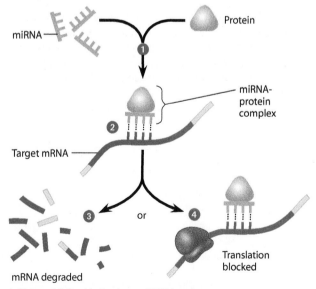

▲ **Figure 11.5** Mechanisms of RNA interference

11.6 Later stages of gene expression are also subject to regulation

Even after a eukaryotic mRNA is fully processed and transported to the cytoplasm, there are several additional opportunities for regulation. Such control points include mRNA breakdown, initiation of translation, protein activation, and protein breakdown.

Breakdown of mRNA Molecules of mRNA do not remain intact forever. Enzymes in the cytoplasm eventually break them down, and the timing of this event is an important factor regulating the amounts of various proteins that are produced in the cell. Long-lived mRNAs can be translated into many more protein molecules than short-lived ones. Prokaryotic mRNAs have very short lifetimes; they are typically degraded by enzymes within a few minutes after their synthesis. This is one reason bacteria can change their protein production so quickly in response to environmental changes. In contrast, the mRNA of eukaryotes can have lifetimes of hours or even weeks.

A striking example of long-lived mRNA is found in vertebrate red blood cells, which manufacture large quantities of the protein hemoglobin. In most species of vertebrates, the mRNAs for hemoglobin are unusually stable. They probably last as long as the red blood cells that contain them—about a month or a bit longer in reptiles, amphibians, and fishes—and are translated again and again. Mammals are an exception. When their red blood cells mature, they lose their ribosomes (along with their other organelles) and thus cease to make new hemoglobin. However, mammalian hemoglobin itself lasts about as long as the red blood cells last, around four months.

Initiation of Translation The process of translating an mRNA into a polypeptide also offers opportunities for regulation. Among the molecules involved in translation are a great many proteins that control the start of polypeptide synthesis. Red blood cells, for instance, have an inhibitory protein that prevents translation of hemoglobin mRNA unless the cell has a supply of heme, the iron-containing chemical group essential for hemoglobin function. (It is the iron atom of the heme group to which oxygen molecules actually attach.) By controlling the start of protein synthesis, cells can avoid wasting energy if the needed components are currently unavailable.

Protein Activation After translation is complete, some polypeptides require alterations before they become functional. Post-translational control mechanisms in eukaryotes often involve the cleavage (cutting) of a polypeptide to yield a smaller final product that is the active protein, able to carry out a specific function in the organism. In **Figure 11.6**, we see the example of the hormone insulin, which is a protein. Insulin is synthesized in the cells of the pancreas as one long polypeptide that has no hormonal activity. After translation is completed, the polypeptide folds up, and covalent bonds form between the sulfur (S) atoms of sulfur-containing amino acids (see Figure 3.12B, which shows S—S bonds in another protein). Two H atoms are lost as each S—S bond forms, linking together parts of the polypeptide in a specific way. Finally, a large center portion is cut away, leaving two shorter chains held together by the sulfur linkages. This combination of two shorter polypeptides is the form of insulin that functions as a hormone. By controlling the timing of such protein modifications, the rate of insulin synthesis can be fine-tuned.

Protein Breakdown The final control mechanism operating after translation is the selective breakdown of proteins. Though mammalian hemoglobin may last as long as the red blood cell housing it, the lifetimes of many other proteins are closely regulated. Some of the proteins that trigger metabolic changes in cells are broken down within a few minutes or hours. This regulation allows a cell to adjust the kinds and amounts of its proteins in response to changes in its environment. It also enables the cell to maintain its proteins in prime working order. Indeed, when proteins are damaged, they are usually broken down right away and replaced by new ones that function properly.

Over the last five modules, you have learned about several ways that eukaryotes can control gene expression. The next module summarizes all of these processes.

? Review Figure 11.6. If the enzyme responsible for cleaving inactive insulin is deactivated, what effect will this have on the form and function of insulin?

● The final molecule will have a shape different from that of active insulin and therefore will not be able to function as a hormone.

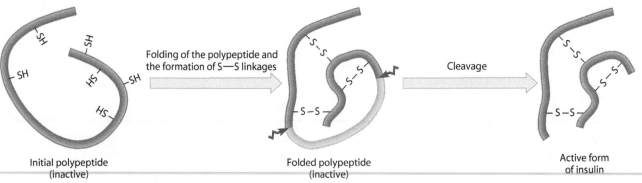

▲ Figure 11.6 Protein activation: the role of polypeptide cleavage in producing the active insulin protein

11.7 Review: Multiple mechanisms regulate gene expression in eukaryotes

Figure 11.7 provides a review of eukaryotic gene expression and highlights the multiple control points where the process can be turned on or off, speeded up, or slowed down. Picture the series of pipes that carry water from your local water supply, perhaps a reservoir, to a faucet in your home. At various points, valves control the flow of water. We use this model in the figure to illustrate the flow of genetic information from a chromosome—a reservoir of genetic information—to an active protein that has been synthesized in the cell's cytoplasm. The multiple mechanisms that control gene expression are analogous to the control valves in water pipes. In the figure, each gene expression "valve" is indicated by a control knob. Note that these knobs represent *possible* control points; for most proteins, only a few control points may be important. The most important control point, in both eukaryotes and prokaryotes, is usually the start of transcription. In the diagram, the large yellow knob represents the mechanisms that regulate the start of transcription.

Although the initiation of transcription is the most important control point, there are several other opportunities for regulation. RNA processing in the nucleus adds nucleotides to the ends of the RNA (cap and tail) and splices out introns. As we discussed in Module 11.4, a growing body of evidence suggests the importance of control at this stage. Once mRNA reaches the cytoplasm, additional stages that can be regulated include mRNA translation and eventual breakdown, possible alteration of the polypeptide to activate it, and the eventual breakdown of the protein.

Despite its numerous steps, Figure 11.7 actually oversimplifies the control of gene expression. What it does not show is the web of control that connects different genes, often through their products. We have seen examples in both prokaryotes and eukaryotes of the actions of gene products (usually proteins) on other genes or on other gene products within the same cell. The genes of operons in *E. coli*, for instance, are controlled by repressor or activator proteins encoded by regulatory genes on the same DNA molecule. In eukaryotes, many genes are controlled by proteins encoded by regulatory genes on other chromosomes. The numerous interactions of these various proteins, taken in total, result in flexible yet precise control of gene expression.

In eukaryotes, cellular differentiation results from the selective turning on and off of genes. In the next module, we examine the stage in the life cycle of a multicellular eukaryote when cellular differentiation by selective gene expression is most vital: the development of a multicellular embryo from a unicellular zygote.

? Of the nine regulatory "valves" in Figure 11.7, which five can also operate in a prokaryotic cell?

protein breakdown

control of translation; (4) control of protein activation; and (5) control of

(1) Control of transcription; (2) control of mRNA breakdown; (3)

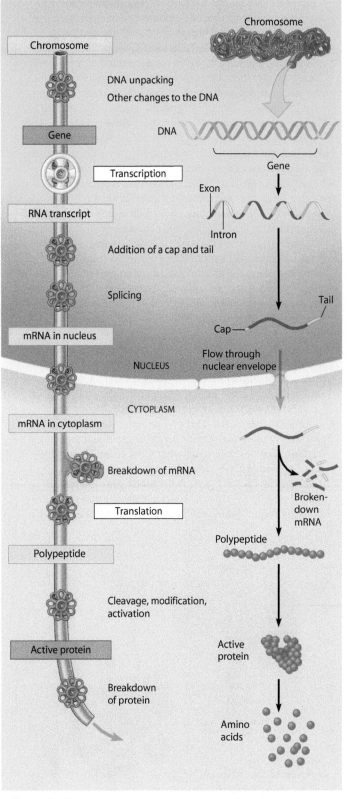

▲ **Figure 11.7** The gene expression "pipeline" in a eukaryotic cell

11.8 Cell signaling and cascades of gene expression direct animal development

Some of the first glimpses into the relationship between gene expression and embryonic development came from studies of mutants of the fruit fly *Drosophila melanogaster* (see Module 9.18). Figure 11.8A shows the heads of two fruit flies. The one on the right, a mutant, developed in a strikingly abnormal way: It has two legs where its antennae should be! Research on this and other developmental mutants has led to the identification of many of the genes that program development in the normal fly. This genetic approach has revolutionized developmental biology.

Among the earliest events in fruit fly development are ones that determine which end of the egg cell will become the head and which end will become the tail. As you can see in Figure 11.8B, ❶ these events occur in the ovaries of the mother fly and involve communication between an unfertilized egg cell and cells adjacent to it in its follicle (egg chamber). The back-and-forth signaling between the cells triggers expression of certain genes in the two cell types. ❷ One important result is the localization of a specific type of mRNA (pink) at the end of the egg where the fly's head will develop, thus defining the animal's head-to-tail axis. (Similar events lead to the positioning of the top-to-bottom and side-to-side axes.) Molecular interactions and further gene expression bring about growth of the egg.

After the egg is fertilized and laid, repeated rounds of mitosis transform the zygote into an embryo. The early embryo makes proteins that diffuse through its cell layers. Cell signaling—now among the cells of the embryo—helps drive the process. ❸ The result is the subdivision of the embryo's body into segments.

Now the finer details of the fly can take shape. Protein products of some of the axis-specifying genes and segment-forming genes activate yet another set of genes. These genes, called homeotic genes, determine what body parts will develop from each segment. A **homeotic gene** is a master control gene that regulates batteries of other genes that actually determine the anatomy of parts of the body. For example,

one set of homeotic genes in fruit flies instructs cells in the segments of the head and thorax (midbody) to form antennae and legs, respectively. Elsewhere, these homeotic genes remain turned off, while others are turned on. (See Module 27.14 for a discussion of evidence that homeotic genes evolved early in the history of animals.) ❹ The eventual outcome is an adult fly. Notice that the adult's body segments correspond to those of the embryo in step 3. It was mutation of a homeotic gene that was responsible for the abnormal fly in Figure 11.8A.

Cascades of gene expression, with the protein products of one set of genes activating other sets of genes, are a common theme in development. Next we look at how DNA technology can help elucidate gene expression in any cell.

? **What determines which end of a developing fruit fly will become the head?**

● A specific kind of mRNA localizes at the end of the unfertilized egg that will become the head.

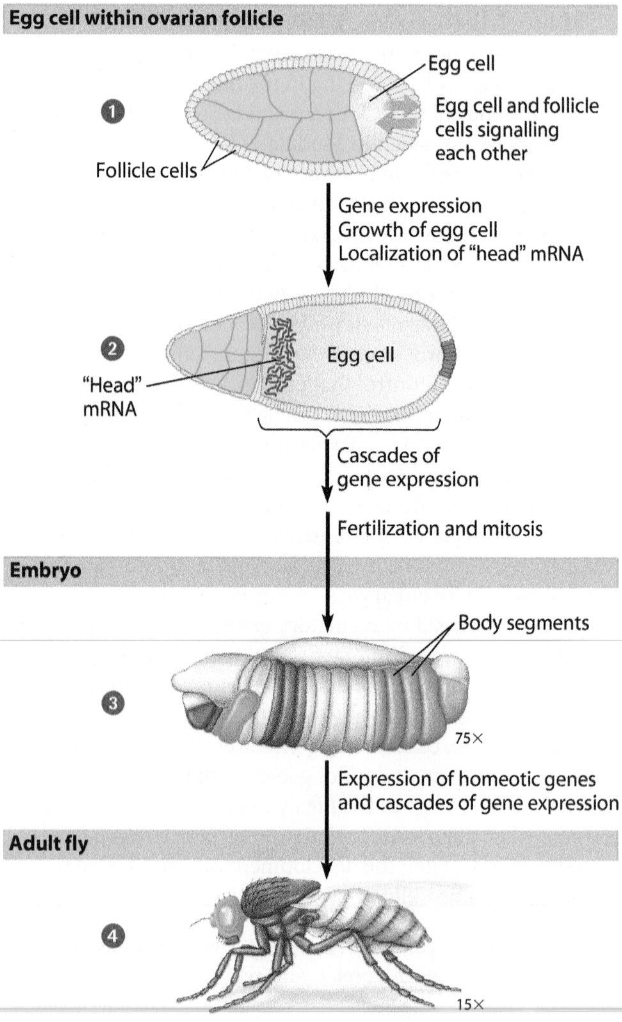

Egg cell within ovarian follicle

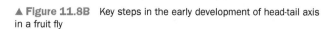

❶ Egg cell
Egg cell and follicle cells signalling each other
Follicle cells

Gene expression
Growth of egg cell
Localization of "head" mRNA

❷ Egg cell
"Head" mRNA

Cascades of gene expression

Fertilization and mitosis

Embryo

❸ Body segments
75×

Expression of homeotic genes and cascades of gene expression

Adult fly

❹ 15×

▲ Figure 11.8B   Key steps in the early development of head-tail axis in a fruit fly

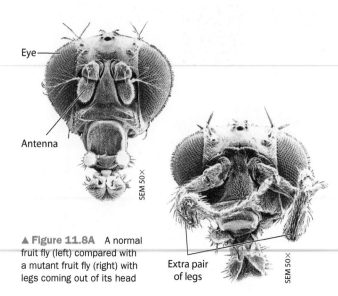

Eye

Antenna

SEM 50×

Extra pair of legs

SEM 50×

▲ Figure 11.8A   A normal fruit fly (left) compared with a mutant fruit fly (right) with legs coming out of its head

11.9 DNA microarrays test for the transcription of many genes at once

A major goal of biologists is to learn how genes act together within a functioning organism. Now that a number of whole genomes have been sequenced (see Module 12.17), it is possible to study the expression of large groups of genes. Researchers can use gene sequences as probes to investigate which genes are transcribed in different situations, such as in different tissues or at different stages of development. They also look for groups of genes that are expressed in a coordinated manner, with the aim of identifying networks of gene expression across an entire genome.

Genome-wide expression studies are made possible by DNA microarrays. A **DNA microarray** is a glass slide with tiny amounts of thousands of different kinds of single-stranded DNA fragments fixed to it in tiny wells in a tightly spaced array, or grid. (A DNA microarray is also called a DNA chip or gene chip by analogy to a computer chip.) Each fixed DNA fragment is obtained from a particular gene; a single microarray thus carries DNA from thousands of genes, perhaps even all the genes of an organism.

Figure 11.9 outlines how microarrays are used. ➊ A researcher collects all of the mRNA transcribed from genes in a particular type of cell at the current moment. ➋ This collection of mRNAs is mixed with reverse transcriptase (an enzyme that produces DNA from an RNA template; see Module 10.20) to produce a mixture of DNA fragments. These fragments are called cDNAs (complementary DNAs) because each one is complementary to one of the mRNAs. The cDNAs are produced in the presence of nucleotides that have been modified to fluoresce (glow). The fluorescent cDNA collection thus represents all of the genes that are being actively transcribed in the cell. ➌ A small amount of the fluorescently labeled cDNA mixture is added to each of the wells in the microarray. If a molecule in the cDNA

mixture is complementary to a DNA fragment at a particular location on the grid, the cDNA molecule binds to it, becoming fixed there. ➍ After unbound cDNA is rinsed away, the remaining cDNA produces a detectable glow in the microarray. The pattern of glowing spots enables the researcher to determine which genes were being transcribed in the starting cells.

DNA microarrays are a potential boon to medical research. For example, a 2002 study showed that DNA microarray data can classify different types of leukemia into specific subtypes based on the activity of 17 genes. This information can be used to predict which of several available regimens of chemotherapy is likely to be most effective. Further research suggests that many cancers have a variety of subtypes with different patterns of gene expression that can be identified with DNA microarrays. Indeed, some oncologists predict that DNA microarrays will usher in a new era where medical treatment is customized to each patient.

DNA microarrays can also reveal general profiles of gene expression over the lifetime of an organism. In one example of a global expression study using this technique, researchers performed DNA microarray experiments on more than 90% of the genes of the nematode worm *Caenorhabditis elegans* during every stage of its life cycle. The results showed that expression of nearly 60% of the *C. elegans* genes changed dramatically during development. This study supported the model held by most developmental biologists that embryonic development of multicellular eukaryotes involves a complex and elaborate program of gene expression, rather than simply the expression of a small number of important genes.

❓ **What is learned from a DNA microarray?**

● Which genes are active (transcribed) in a particular sample of cells

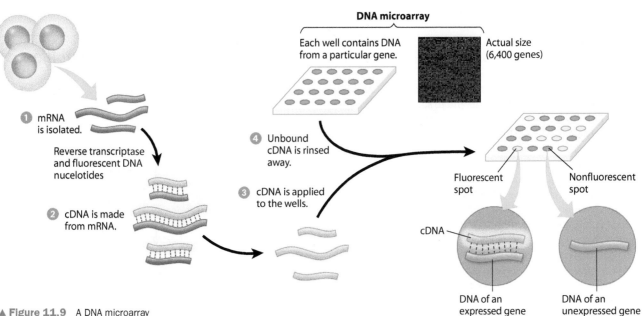

▲ Figure 11.9   A DNA microarray

11.10 Signal transduction pathways convert messages received at the cell surface to responses within the cell

Cell-to-cell signaling, with proteins or other kinds of molecules carrying messages from signaling cells to receiving (target) cells, is a key mechanism in the coordination of cellular activities. In most cases, a signaling molecule acts by binding to a receptor protein in the plasma membrane of the target cell and initiating a signal transduction pathway in the cell. A **signal transduction pathway** is a series of molecular changes that converts a signal on a target cell's surface to a specific response inside the cell.

Figure 11.10 shows the main elements of a signal transduction pathway in which the target cell's response is the expression of a gene. ❶ The signaling cell secretes a signaling molecule. ❷ This molecule binds to a receptor protein embedded in the target cell's plasma membrane. ❸ The binding activates the first in a series of relay proteins within the target cell. Each relay molecule activates another. ❹ The last relay molecule in the series activates a transcription factor that ❺ triggers transcription of a specific gene. ❻ Translation of the mRNA produces a protein.

Signal transduction pathways are crucial to many cellular functions. Throughout your study of biology, you'll see their importance again and again. We encountered them when we studied the cell cycle control system in Module 8.8; we'll revisit them when we discuss cancer later in this chapter (see, for example, Module 11.18); and we'll see how they relate to hormone function in animals (Chapter 26) and plants (Chapter 33).

? **How can a signaling molecule from one cell alter gene expression in a target cell without even entering the target cell?**

By binding to a receptor protein in the membrane of the target cell and triggering a signal transduction pathway that activates transcription factors.

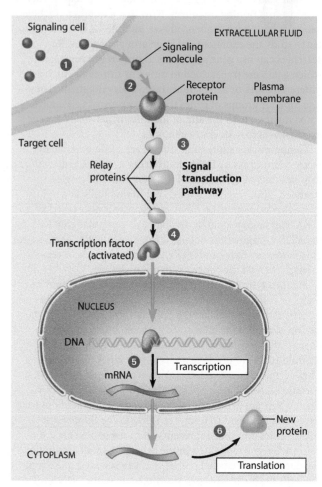

▲ Figure 11.10   A signal transduction pathway that turns on a gene

---

11.11 Cell-signaling systems appeared early in the evolution of life

As explained in Module 11.10, one cell can communicate with another by secreting molecules that bind to surface proteins on a target cell. How ancient and widespread are such signaling systems among Earth's organisms? To answer these questions, we can look at communication between microorganisms, for modern microbes are a window on the role of cell signaling in the evolution of life on Earth.

One topic of cell "conversation" is sex—at least for the yeast *Saccharomyces cerevisiae,* which people have used for millennia to make bread, wine, and beer. Researchers have learned that cells of this yeast identify their mates by chemical signaling. There are two sexes, or mating types, called **a** and **α** (Figure 11.11). Cells of mating type **a** secrete a chemical signal called **a** factor, which can bind to specific receptor proteins on nearby **α** cells. At the same time, **α** cells secrete **α** factor, which binds to receptors on **a** cells. Without actually

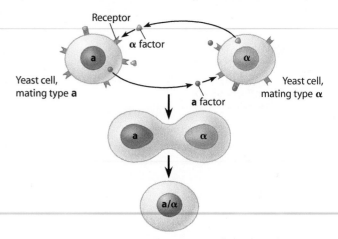

▲ Figure 11.11   Communication between mating yeast cells

entering the target cells, the two mating factors cause the cells to grow toward each other and bring about other cellular changes. The result is the fusion, or mating, of two cells of opposite type. The new **a/α** cell contains all the genes of both original cells, a combination of genetic resources that provides advantages to the cell's descendants, which arise by subsequent cell divisions.

The signal transduction pathways involved in this yeast mating system have been extensively studied, as have many other pathways in yeasts and other organisms. Amazingly, the molecular details of signal transduction in yeast and mammals are strikingly similar, even though the last common ancestor of these two groups of organisms lived over a billion years ago. These similarities—and others more recently uncovered between signaling systems in bacteria and plants—suggest that early versions of the cell-signaling mechanisms used today evolved well before the first multicellular creatures appeared on Earth. Scientists think that signaling mechanisms evolved first in ancient prokaryotes and single-celled eukaryotes and then became adapted for new uses in their multicellular descendants.

? **In what sense is the joining of yeast mating types "sex"?**

● The process results in the creation of a diploid cell that is a genetic blend of two parental haploid cells.

Cloning of Plants and Animals

11.12 Plant cloning shows that differentiated cells may retain all of their genetic potential

One of the most important "take home lessons" from this chapter is that differentiated cells express only a small percentage of their genes. So then how do we know that all the genes are still present? And if all the genes are still there, do differentiated cells retain the potential to express them?

One way to approach these questions is to see if a differentiated cell can dedifferentiate, or reverse its differentiation, and then be stimulated to generate a whole new organism. In plants, this ability is common. In fact, if you have ever grown a plant from a small cutting, you've seen evidence that a differentiated plant cell can undergo cell division and give rise to all the tissues of an adult plant. On a larger scale, the technique described in **Figure 11.12** can be used to produce hundreds or thousands of genetically identical plants from the cells of a single plant. For

example, when cells from a carrot are transferred to a culture medium, a single cell can begin dividing and eventually grow into an adult plant, a genetic replica of the parent plant. Such an organism, produced through asexual reproduction from a single parent, is called a **clone**. The fact that a mature plant cell can dedifferentiate and then give rise to all the different kinds of specialized cells of a new plant shows that differentiation does not necessarily involve irreversible changes in the plant's DNA.

Plant cloning is now used extensively in agriculture. For some plants, such as orchids, cloning is the only commercially practical means of reproducing plants. In other cases, cloning has been used to reproduce a plant with desirable traits, such as high fruit yield or the ability to resist a plant pathogen.

But is this sort of cloning possible in animals? A good indication that differentiation need not impair an animal cell's genetic potential is the natural process of **regeneration**, the regrowth of lost body parts. When a salamander loses a leg, for example, certain cells in the leg stump dedifferentiate, divide, and then redifferentiate, giving rise to a new leg. Many animals, especially among the invertebrates, can regenerate lost parts, and in a few relatively simple animals, isolated differentiated cells can dedifferentiate and then develop into an entire organism (see Module 27.1). Further evidence for the complete genetic potential of animal cells comes from cloning experiments, our next topic.

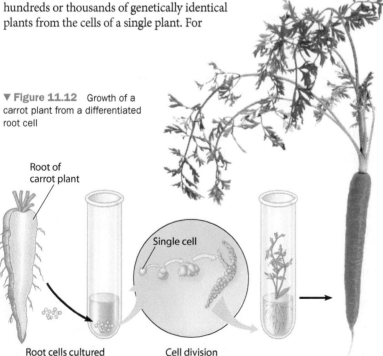

▼ **Figure 11.12** Growth of a carrot plant from a differentiated root cell

Root of carrot plant

Single cell

Root cells cultured in growth medium

Cell division in culture

Plantlet

Adult plant

? **How does the cloning of plants from differentiated cells support the view that differentiation is based on the control of gene expression rather than on irreversible changes in the genome?**

● Cloning shows that all the genes of a fully differentiated plant are still present, but some may be turned off.

11.13 Nuclear transplantation can be used to clone animals

Animal cloning can be achieved through a procedure called **nuclear transplantation** (Figure 11.13). First performed in the 1950s using cells from frog embryos, nuclear transplantation involves replacing the nucleus of an egg cell or a zygote with the nucleus of an adult somatic cell. The recipient cell may then begin to divide. By about 5 days later, repeated cell divisions have formed a blastocyst, a hollow ball of about 100 cells. At this point, the blastocyst may be used for different purposes, as indicated by the two branches in Figure 11.13.

If the animal to be cloned is a mammal, further development requires implanting the blastocyst into the uterus of a surrogate mother (Figure 11.13, upper branch). The resulting animal will be genetically identical to the donor of the nucleus—a "clone" of the donor. This type of cloning, which results in the birth of a new living individual, is called **reproductive cloning**. Scottish researcher Ian Wilmut and his colleagues used reproductive cloning to produce the world-famous sheep Dolly in 1997. The researchers used an electric shock to fuse 277 specially treated adult sheep udder cells with eggs from which they had removed the nuclei.

After several days of growth, 29 of the resulting embryos were implanted in the uteruses of surrogate mothers. One of the embryos developed into Dolly. As expected, Dolly resembled her genetic parent, the nucleus donor, not the egg donor or the surrogate mother.

In a different cloning procedure (Figure 11.13, lower branch), **embryonic stem cells (ES cells)** are harvested from the blastocyst. In nature, embryonic stem cells give rise to all the different kinds of specialized cells of the body. In the laboratory, embryonic stem cells are easily grown in culture, where, given the right conditions, they can perpetuate themselves indefinitely. When the major aim is to produce embryonic stem cells for therapeutic treatments, the process is called **therapeutic cloning**. In the next two modules, we discuss applications of reproductive and therapeutic cloning, respectively.

? **What are the intended products of reproductive cloning and therapeutic cloning?**

● Reproductive cloning is used to produce new individuals. Therapeutic cloning is used to harvest embryonic stem cells.

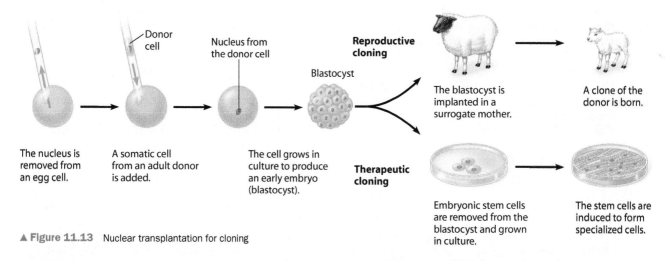

The nucleus is removed from an egg cell.

A somatic cell from an adult donor is added.

The cell grows in culture to produce an early embryo (blastocyst).

Nucleus from the donor cell

Blastocyst

Reproductive cloning

The blastocyst is implanted in a surrogate mother.

A clone of the donor is born.

Therapeutic cloning

Embryonic stem cells are removed from the blastocyst and grown in culture.

The stem cells are induced to form specialized cells.

▲ **Figure 11.13** Nuclear transplantation for cloning

CONNECTION | ## 11.14 Reproductive cloning has valuable applications, but human reproductive cloning raises ethical issues

Since Dolly's landmark birth in 1997, researchers have cloned many other mammals, including mice, cats, horses, cows, mules, pigs, rabbits, ferrets, and dogs. We have already learned much from such experiments. For example, cloned animals of the same species do not always look or behave identically. In a herd of cows cloned from the same line of cultured cells, certain cows are dominant and others are more submissive. Another example is the first cloned cat, named CC for Carbon Copy (Figure 11.14). She has a calico coat, like her single female parent, but the color and pattern are different due to random X chromosome inactivation (see Module 11.2). Moreover, CC and her lone parent behave differently; CC is playful, while her mother is more

▶ **Figure 11.14** CC, the world's first cloned cat (right), and her lone parent (left)

reserved. You've probably observed that identical human twins, which are naturally occurring "clones," are always slightly different. Clearly, environmental influences and random phenomena can play a significant role during development.

Reproductive cloning has potential for many practical applications. On an experimental basis, agricultural scientists are cloning farm animals with specific sets of desirable traits in the hope of creating high-yielding, genetically identical herds. The pharmaceutical industry is experimenting with cloning mammals for the production of potentially valuable drugs. For example, researchers have produced piglet clones that lack one of two copies of a gene for a protein that can cause immune system rejection in humans. Such pigs may one day provide organs for transplant into humans. Some wildlife biologists hope that reproductive cloning can be used to restock the populations of endangered animals. Among the rare animals that have been cloned are a wild mouflon (a small European sheep), a banteng (a Javanese cow), a gaur (an Asian ox), and gray wolves.

The successful cloning of various mammals has heightened speculation that humans could be cloned. Critics point out that there are many obstacles—both practical and ethical—to human cloning. Practically, animal cloning is extremely difficult and inefficient. Only a small percentage of cloned embryos develop normally. Ethically, the discussion about whether or not humans should be cloned—and if so, under what circumstances—is far from settled. Meanwhile, the research and the debate continue.

? **If you cloned your dog, would you expect the original and the clone to look and act exactly alike?**

● No. While cloning produces genetically identical dogs, appearance and behavior are affected by environment.

11.15 Therapeutic cloning can produce stem cells with great medical potential

Therapeutic cloning produces embryonic stem cells, cells that in the early animal embryo differentiate to give rise to all the cell types in the body. When grown in laboratory culture, embryonic stem cells can divide indefinitely (like cancer cells; see Module 8.9). Furthermore, the right conditions can induce changes in gene expression that cause differentiation into a variety of cell types (Figure 11.15).

The adult body also has stem cells, which serve to replace nonreproducing specialized cells as needed. In contrast to embryonic stem cells, **adult stem cells** are able to give rise to many but not all cell types in the organism. For example, bone marrow contains several types of stem cells, including one that can generate all the different kinds of blood cells. Although adult animals have only tiny numbers of stem cells, scientists are learning to identify and isolate these cells from various tissues and, in some cases, to grow them in culture.

Recently, researchers have discovered stem cells in human skin, hair, eyes, and oral tissues. However, the developmental potential of adult stem cells is limited to certain cell types, so embryonic stem cells are considered more promising than adult stem cells for medical applications, at least for now. In 2007, three research groups reported transforming mouse skin cells into embryonic stem cells simply by causing the skin cells to express four "stem cell" master regulatory genes. The researchers used retroviruses as vectors to introduce extra copies of these genes into the skin cells.

The ultimate aim of therapeutic cloning is to supply cells for the repair of damaged or diseased organs: for example, insulin-producing pancreatic cells for people with diabetes or certain kinds of brain cells for people with Parkinson's disease or Alzheimer's disease. Adult stem cells from donor bone marrow have long been used as a source of immune system cells in patients whose own immune systems have been destroyed by genetic disorders or radiation treatments for cancer. More

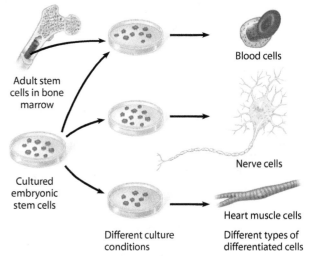

Adult stem cells in bone marrow

Cultured embryonic stem cells

Different culture conditions

Blood cells

Nerve cells

Heart muscle cells

Different types of differentiated cells

▲ **Figure 11.15** Differentiation of stem cells in culture

recently, clinical trials using bone marrow stem cells have shown slight success in promoting regeneration of heart tissue in patients whose hearts have been damaged by heart attacks. In the future, a donor nucleus from a patient with a particular disease could allow production of embryonic stem cells for treatment that match the patient and are thus not rejected by his or her immune system.

While many people believe that reproductive cloning of humans is unethical, opinions vary more widely about the morality of therapeutic cloning using embryonic stem cells. As with reproductive cloning, the research and the debate continue.

? **In nature, how do embryonic stem cells differ from adult stem cells?**

● Embryonic cells give rise to all the different kinds of cells in the body. Adult stem cells generate only a few related types of cells.

The Genetic Basis of Cancer

11.16 Cancer results from mutations in genes that control cell division

In Module 8.9, you learned that cancerous cells have escaped from the control mechanisms that normally limit their growth. Scientists have learned that such escape is often due to changes in gene expression.

The abnormal behavior of cancer cells was observed years before anything was known about the cell cycle, its control, or the role genes play in making cells cancerous. One of the earliest clues to the cancer puzzle was the discovery, in 1911, of a virus that causes cancer in chickens. Recall that viruses are simply molecules of DNA or RNA surrounded by protein and in some cases a membranous envelope. Viruses that cause cancer can become permanent residents in host cells by inserting their nucleic acid into the DNA of host chromosomes (see Module 10.17).

The genes that a cancer-causing virus inserts into a host cell can make the cell cancerous. Such a gene, which can cause cancer when present in a single copy in the cell, is called an **oncogene** (from the Greek *onkos*, tumor). Over the last century, researchers have identified a number of viruses that harbor cancer-causing genes. One example is the human papillomavirus (HPV), which is associated with several types of cancer, most frequently cervical cancer.

Proto-oncogenes In 1976, American molecular biologists J. Michael Bishop, Harold Varmus, and their colleagues made a startling discovery. They found that the cancer-causing chicken virus discovered in 1911 contains an oncogene that is an altered version of a normal gene found in chicken cells. Subsequent research has shown that the chromosomes of many animals, including humans, contain genes that can be converted to oncogenes. A normal gene that has the potential to become an oncogene is called a **proto-oncogene**. (These terms can be confusing, so they bear repeating: a *proto-oncogene* is a normal, healthy gene that, if changed, can become a cancer-causing

oncogene.) Thus, a cell can acquire an oncogene either from a virus or from the mutation of one of its own genes.

The cancer research conducted by Bishop and Varmus focused on proto-oncogenes. Searching for the normal role of these genes, researchers found that many proto-oncogenes code for growth factors—proteins that stimulate cell division—or for other proteins that somehow affect growth factor function or some other aspect of the cell cycle. When all these proteins are functioning normally, in the right amounts at the right times, they help properly control cell division and cellular differentiation.

How might a proto-oncogene—a gene that has an essential function in normal cells—become an oncogene, a cancer-causing gene? In general, an oncogene arises from a genetic change that leads to an increase either in the amount of the proto-oncogene's protein product or in the activity of each protein molecule. **Figure 11.16A** illustrates three kinds of changes in DNA that can produce oncogenes. Let's assume that the starting proto-oncogene codes for a protein that stimulates cell division. On the left in the figure, a mutation (green) in the proto-oncogene itself creates an oncogene that codes for a hyperactive protein, which is produced in the usual amount but whose stimulating effect is stronger than normal. In the center, an error in DNA replication or recombination generates multiple copies of the gene, which are all transcribed and translated; the result is an excess of the normal stimulatory protein. On the right, the proto-oncogene has been moved from its normal location in the cell's DNA to another location. At its new site, the gene is under the control of a different promoter, one that causes it to be transcribed more often than normal; the normal protein is again made in excess. So in all three cases, normal gene expression is changed, and the cell is stimulated to divide excessively.

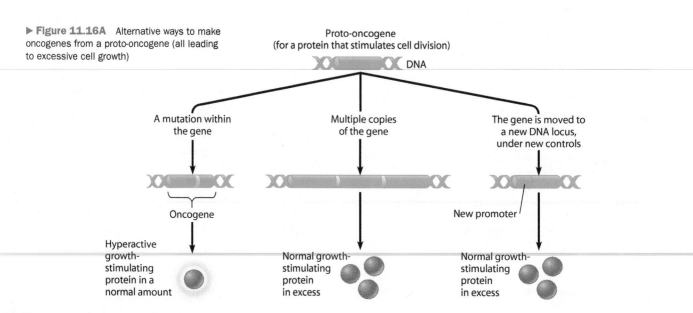

▶ **Figure 11.16A** Alternative ways to make oncogenes from a proto-oncogene (all leading to excessive cell growth)

Proto-oncogene
(for a protein that stimulates cell division)

DNA

A mutation within the gene

Multiple copies of the gene

The gene is moved to a new DNA locus, under new controls

Oncogene

New promoter

Hyperactive growth-stimulating protein in a normal amount

Normal growth-stimulating protein in excess

Normal growth-stimulating protein in excess

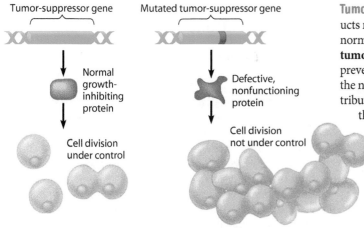

Tumor-suppressor gene   Mutated tumor-suppressor gene

Normal growth-inhibiting protein

Defective, nonfunctioning protein

Cell division under control

Cell division not under control

▲ **Figure 11.16B**   The effect of a mutation in a tumor-suppressor gene

Tumor-Suppressor Genes   In addition to genes whose products normally *promote* cell division, cells contain genes whose normal products *inhibit* cell division. Such genes are called **tumor-suppressor genes** because the proteins they encode help prevent uncontrolled cell growth. Any mutation that decreases the normal activity of a tumor-suppressor protein may contribute to the onset of cancer, in effect stimulating growth through the absence of suppression (Figure 11.16B). Scientists have also discovered a class of tumor-suppressor genes that function in the repair of damaged DNA. When these genes are mutated, other cancer-causing mutations are more likely to accumulate.

?   **How do proto-oncogenes relate to oncogenes?**

● A proto-oncogene is a normal gene that, if mutated, can become a cancer-causing oncogene.

11.17   Multiple genetic changes underlie the development of cancer

Nearly 150,000 Americans will be stricken by cancer of the colon (the main part of the large intestine) this year. One of the best-understood types of human cancer, colon cancer illustrates an important principle about how cancer develops: More than one somatic mutation is needed to produce a full-fledged cancer cell. As in many cancers, the development of malignant (spreading) colon cancer is gradual. (See Module 8.9 to review cancer terms.)

Figure 11.17A illustrates this idea using colon cancer as an example. ❶ Colon cancer begins when an oncogene arises or is activated through mutation, causing unusually frequent division of apparently normal cells in the colon lining. ❷ Later, one or more additional DNA mutations, such as the inactivation of a tumor-suppressor gene, cause the growth of a small benign tumor (a polyp) in the colon wall. ❸ Still more mutations eventually lead to formation of a malignant tumor, a tumor that has the potential to metastasize (spread). The requirement for several mutations—the actual number is usually four or more—explains why cancers can take a long time to develop.

Thus, the development of a malignant tumor is paralleled by a gradual accumulation of mutations that convert proto-oncogenes to oncogenes and knock out tumor-suppressor genes. Multiple changes must occur at the DNA level for a cell to become fully cancerous. Such changes usually include the appearance of at least

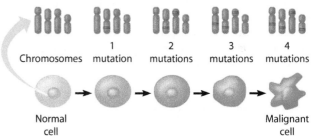

Chromosomes   1 mutation   2 mutations   3 mutations   4 mutations

Normal cell

Malignant cell

▲ **Figure 11.17B**   Accumulation of mutations in the development of a cancer cell

one active oncogene and the mutation or loss of several tumor-suppressor genes. In Figure 11.17B, colors distinguish the normal cell (tan) from cells with one or more mutations leading to increased cell division and cancer (red). Once a cancer-promoting mutation occurs (the red band on the chromosome), it is passed to all the descendants of the cell carrying it.

The fact that more than one somatic mutation is generally needed to produce a full-fledged cancer cell may help explain why the incidence of cancer increases with age. If cancer results from an accumulation of mutations that occur throughout life, then the longer we live, the more likely we are to develop cancer. Cancer researchers hope to learn about mutations that cause cancer through the Cancer Genome Project, a 10-year effort to map all human cancer-causing genes.

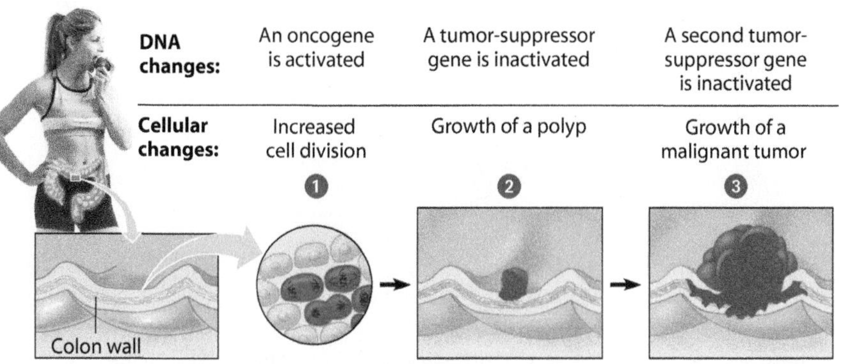

?   **Epithelial cells, those that line body cavities, are frequently replaced and so divide more often than most other types of body cells. Will epithelial cells become cancerous more or less frequently than other types of body cells?**

● More frequent cell divisions will result in more frequent mutation and thus a greater chance of cancer.

DNA changes:	An oncogene is activated	A tumor-suppressor gene is inactivated	A second tumor-suppressor gene is inactivated
Cellular changes:	Increased cell division	Growth of a polyp	Growth of a malignant tumor
	❶	❷	❸

Colon wall

▲ **Figure 11.17A**   Stepwise development of a typical colon cancer

11.18 Faulty proteins can interfere with normal signal transduction pathways

To understand how oncogenes and defective tumor-suppressor genes can contribute to uncontrolled cell growth, we need to look more closely at the normal functions of proto-oncogenes and tumor-suppressor genes. Genes in both categories often code for proteins involved in signal transduction pathways leading to gene expression (see Module 11.10).

The figures below (excluding, for the moment, the white boxes) illustrate two types of signal transduction pathways leading to the synthesis of proteins that influence the cell cycle. In **Figure 11.18A**, the pathway leads to the stimulation of cell division. The initial signal is a growth factor (●), and the target cell's ultimate response is the production of a protein that stimulates the cell to divide. By contrast, **Figure 11.18B** shows an inhibitory pathway, in which a growth-*inhibiting* factor (▽) causes the target cell to make a protein that inhibits cell division. In both cases, the newly made proteins function by interacting with components of the cell cycle control system (see Module 8.8), although the figures here do not show these interactions.

Now, let's see what can happen when the target cell undergoes a cancer-causing mutation. The white box in Figure 11.18A shows the protein product of an oncogene resulting from mutation of a proto-oncogene called *ras*. The normal product of *ras* is a relay protein. Ordinarily, a stimulatory pathway like this will not operate unless the growth factor is available. However, an oncogene protein that is a hyperactive

version of a protein in the pathway may trigger the pathway even in the absence of a growth factor. In this example, the oncogene protein is a hyperactive version of the *ras* relay protein that issues signals on its own. In fact, abnormal versions or amounts of any of the pathway's components—from the growth factor itself to the transcription factor—could have the same final effect: overstimulation of cell division.

The white box in Figure 11.18B indicates how a mutant tumor-suppressor protein can affect cell division. In this case, the mutation affects a gene called *p53*, which codes for an essential transcription factor. This mutation leads to the production of a faulty transcription factor, one that the signal transduction pathway cannot activate. As a result, the gene for the inhibitory protein at the bottom of the figure remains turned off, and excessive cell division may occur.

Mutations of the *ras* and *p53* genes have been implicated in many kinds of cancer. In fact, mutations in *ras* occur in about 30% of human cancers, and mutations in *p53* occur in more than 50%. As we see next, carcinogens are responsible for many mutations that lead to cancer.

? **Contrast the action of an oncogene with that of a cancer-causing mutation in a tumor-suppressor gene.**

● An oncogene encodes an abnormal protein that stimulates cell division via a signal transduction pathway; a mutant tumor-suppressor gene encodes a defective protein unable to function in a pathway that normally inhibits cell division.

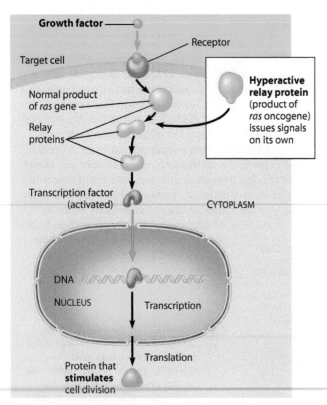

▲ **Figure 11.18A** A stimulatory signal transduction pathway and the effect of an oncogene protein

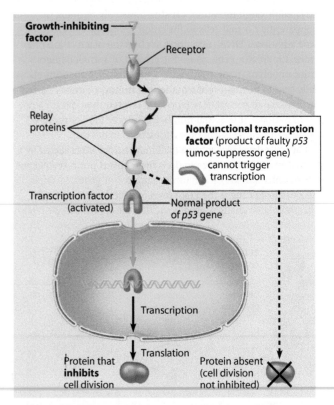

▲ **Figure 11.18B** An inhibitory signal transduction pathway and the effect of a faulty tumor-suppressor protein

Cancer is the second-leading cause of death in most industrialized nations, after heart disease. Death rates due to certain forms of cancer—including stomach, cervical, and uterine cancers—have decreased in recent years, but the overall cancer death rate is on the rise, currently increasing at about 1% per decade. Table 11.19 lists the most common cancers in the United States and associated risk factors for each.

The fact that multiple genetic changes are required to produce a cancer cell helps explain the observation that cancers can run in families. An individual inheriting an oncogene or a mutant allele of a tumor-suppressor gene is one step closer to accumulating the necessary mutations for cancer to develop than an individual without any such mutations.

But the majority of cancers are not associated with a mutation that is passed from parent to offspring; they arise from new mutations caused by environmental factors. Cancer-causing agents, factors that alter DNA and make cells cancerous, are called **carcinogens**. Most mutagens, substances that cause mutations, are carcinogens. Two of the most potent mutagens are X-rays and ultraviolet radiation in sunlight. X-rays are a significant cause of leukemia and brain cancer. Exposure to UV radiation from the sun is known to cause skin cancer, including a deadly type called melanoma.

The one substance known to cause more cases and types of cancer than any other single agent is tobacco. More people die of lung cancer (nearly 160,000 Americans in 2010) than any other form of cancer. Most tobacco-related cancers come from smoking, but the passive inhalation of secondhand smoke is also a risk. As Table 11.19 indicates, tobacco use, sometimes in combination with alcohol consumption, causes a number of other types of cancer in addition to lung cancer. In nearly all cases, cigarettes are the main culprit, but smokeless tobacco products, such as snuff and chewing tobacco, are linked to cancer of the mouth and throat.

How do carcinogens cause cancer? In many cases, the genetic changes that cause cancer result from decades of exposure to the mutagenic effects of carcinogens. Carcinogens can also produce their effect by promoting cell division. Generally, the higher the rate of cell division, the greater the chance for mutations resulting from errors in DNA replication or recombination. Some carcinogens seem to have both effects. For instance, the hormones linked to breast and uterine cancers promote cell division and may also cause genetic changes that lead to cancer. In other cases, several different agents, such as viruses and one or more carcinogens, may together produce cancer.

Avoiding carcinogens is not the whole story, for there is growing evidence that some food choices significantly reduce cancer risk. For instance, eating 20–30 grams (g) of plant fiber daily—roughly equal to the amount of fiber in four slices of whole-grain bread, 1 cup of bran flakes, one apple, and 1/2 cup of carrots combined—and at the same time reducing animal fat intake may help prevent colon cancer. There is also evidence that other substances in fruits and vegetables, including vitamins C and E and certain compounds related to vitamin A, may offer protection against a variety

of cancers. Cabbage and its relatives, such as broccoli and cauliflower (see Figure 13.2), are thought to be especially rich in substances that help prevent cancer, although the identities of these substances are not yet established. Determining how diet influences cancer has become a major research goal.

The battle against cancer is being waged on many fronts, and there is reason for optimism in the progress being made. It is especially encouraging that we can help reduce our risk of acquiring and increase our chance of surviving some of the most common forms of cancer by the choices we make in our daily life. Not smoking, exercising adequately, avoiding overexposure to the sun, and eating a high-fiber, low-fat diet can all help prevent cancer. Furthermore, seven types of cancer can be easily detected: cancers of the skin and oral cavity (via physical exam), breast (via self-exams and mammograms for higher-risk women), prostate (via rectal exam), cervix (via Pap smear), testes (via self-exam), and colon (via colonoscopy). Regular visits to the doctor can help identify tumors early, thereby significantly increasing the possibility of successful treatment.

? Which of the most common cancers affect primarily males? Which affect primarily females?

 Males: prostate; females: breast, uterus, cervix

TABLE 11.19 | CANCER IN THE UNITED STATES

Cancer	Risk Factors	Estimated Number of Cases in 2010
Lung	Tobacco smoke	222,520
Prostate	African heritage; possibly dietary fat	217,730
Breast	Estrogen	209,060
Colon, rectum	High dietary fat; tobacco smoke; alcohol	142,570
Lymphomas	Viruses (for some types)	74,030
Urinary bladder	Tobacco smoke	70,530
Melanoma of the skin	Ultraviolet light	68,130
Kidney	Tobacco smoke	58,240
Uterus	Estrogen	43,470
Pancreas	Tobacco smoke; obesity	43,140
Leukemias	X-rays; benzene; virus (for one type)	43,050
Oral cavity	Tobacco in various forms; alcohol	36,540
Liver	Alcohol; hepatitis viruses	24,120
Brain and nerve	Trauma; X-rays	22,020
Ovary	Obesity; many ovulation cycles	21,880
Stomach	Table salt; tobacco smoke	21,000
Cervix	Sexually transmitted viruses; tobacco smoke	12,200
All others		199,330

For Practice Quizzes, BioFlix, MP3 Tutors, and Activities, go to www.masteringbiology.com.

Reviewing the Concepts

Control of Gene Expression (11.1–11.11)

11.1 Proteins interacting with DNA turn prokaryotic genes on or off in response to environmental changes. In prokaryotes, genes for related enzymes are often controlled together in units called operons. Regulatory proteins bind to control sequences in the DNA and turn operons on or off in response to environmental changes.

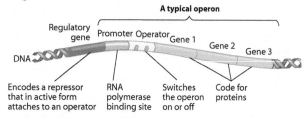

A typical operon

Regulatory gene — Encodes a repressor that in active form attaches to an operator

Promoter — RNA polymerase binding site

Operator — Switches the operon on or off

Gene 1, Gene 2, Gene 3 — Code for proteins

DNA

11.2 Chromosome structure and chemical modifications can affect gene expression. In multicellular eukaryotes, different types of cells make different proteins because different combinations of genes are active in each type. A chromosome contains DNA wound around clusters of histone proteins, forming a string of beadlike nucleosomes. DNA packing tends to block gene expression by preventing access of transcription proteins to the DNA. One example of DNA packing is X chromosome inactivation in the cells of female mammals. Chemical modification of DNA bases or histone proteins can result in epigenetic inheritance.

11.3 Complex assemblies of proteins control eukaryotic transcription. A variety of regulatory proteins interact with DNA and with each other to turn the transcription of eukaryotic genes on or off.

11.4 Eukaryotic RNA may be spliced in more than one way. After transcription, alternative RNA splicing may generate two or more types of mRNA from the same transcript.

11.5 Small RNAs play multiple roles in controlling gene expression. MicroRNAs, bound to proteins, can prevent gene expression by forming complexes with mRNA molecules.

11.6 Later stages of gene expression are also subject to regulation. The lifetime of an mRNA molecule helps determine how much protein is made, as do factors involved in translation. A protein may need to be activated in some way, and eventually the cell will break it down.

11.7 Review: Multiple mechanisms regulate gene expression in eukaryotes. Figure 11.7 reviews the multiple stages of eukaryotic gene expression, each stage offering opportunities for regulation.

11.8 Cell signaling and cascades of gene expression direct animal development. A series of RNAs and proteins produced in the embryo control the development of an animal from a fertilized egg.

11.9 DNA microarrays test for the transcription of many genes at once. Scientists can use a DNA microarray to gather data about which genes are turned on or off in a particular cell.

11.10 Signal transduction pathways convert messages received at the cell surface to responses within the cell. A glass slide containing DNA fragments from thousands of genes can be used to test which of those genes are being produced in a particular cell type.

11.11 Cell-signaling systems appeared early in the evolution of life. Similarities among organisms suggest that signal transduction pathways evolved early in the history of life on Earth.

Cloning of Plants and Animals (11.12–11.15)

11.12 Plant cloning shows that differentiated cells may retain all of their genetic potential. A clone is an individual created by asexual reproduction and thus genetically identical to a single parent.

11.13 Nuclear transplantation can be used to clone animals. Inserting DNA from a host cell into a nucleus-free egg can result in an early embryo that is a clone of the DNA donor. Implanting a blastocyst into a surrogate mother allows for the birth of a cloned mammal.

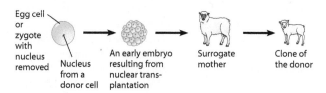

Egg cell or zygote with nucleus removed → Nucleus from a donor cell → An early embryo resulting from nuclear transplantation → Surrogate mother → Clone of the donor

11.14 Reproductive cloning has valuable applications, but human reproductive cloning raises ethical issues.

11.15 Therapeutic cloning can produce stem cells with great medical potential. The goal of therapeutic cloning is to produce embryonic stem cells. Such cells may eventually be used for a variety of therapeutic purposes. Like embryonic stem cells, adult stem cells can both perpetuate themselves in culture and give rise to differentiated cells. Unlike embryonic stem cells, adult stem cells normally give rise to only a limited range of cell types.

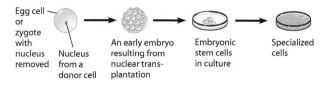

Egg cell or zygote with nucleus removed → Nucleus from a donor cell → An early embryo resulting from nuclear transplantation → Embryonic stem cells in culture → Specialized cells

The Genetic Basis of Cancer (11.16–11.19)

11.16 Cancer results from mutations in genes that control cell division. Cancer cells, which divide uncontrollably, result from mutations in genes whose protein products affect the cell cycle. A mutation can change a proto-oncogene, a normal gene that helps control cell division, into an oncogene, which causes cells to divide excessively. Mutations that inactivate tumor-suppressor genes have similar effects.

11.17 Multiple genetic changes underlie the development of cancer. Cancers result from a series of genetic changes.

11.18 Faulty proteins can interfere with normal signal transduction pathways. Many proto-oncogenes and tumor-suppressor genes code for proteins active in signal transduction pathways regulating cell division.

11.19 Lifestyle choices can reduce the risk of cancer. Reducing exposure to carcinogens, which induce cancer-causing mutations, and making other lifestyle choices can help reduce cancer risk.

Connecting the Concepts

1. Complete the following concept map to test your knowledge of gene regulation.

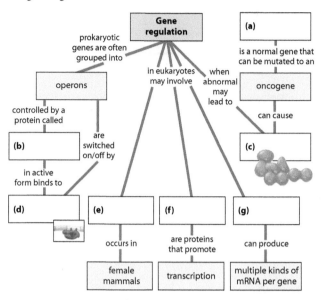

Testing Your Knowledge

Multiple Choice

2. The control of gene expression is more complex in multicellular eukaryotes than in prokaryotes because _____. (*Explain your answer.*)
   a. eukaryotic cells are much smaller
   b. in a multicellular eukaryote, different cells are specialized for different functions
   c. prokaryotes are restricted to stable environments
   d. eukaryotes have fewer genes, so each gene must do several jobs
   e. eukaryotic genes code for proteins

3. Your bone cells, muscle cells, and skin cells look different because
   a. each cell contains different kinds of genes.
   b. they are present in different organs.
   c. different genes are active in each kind of cell.
   d. they contain different numbers of genes.
   e. each cell has different mutations.

4. Which of the following methods of gene regulation do eukaryotes and prokaryotes have in common?
   a. elaborate packing of DNA in chromosomes
   b. activator and repressor proteins, which attach to DNA
   c. the addition of a cap and tail to mRNA after transcription
   d. *lac* and *trp* operons
   e. the removal of noncoding portions of RNA

5. A homeotic gene does which of the following?
   a. It serves as the ultimate control for prokaryotic operons.
   b. It regulates the expression of groups of other genes during development.
   c. It represses the histone proteins in eukaryotic chromosomes.
   d. It helps splice mRNA after transcription.
   e. It inactivates one of the X chromosomes in a female mammal.

6. All your cells contain proto-oncogenes, which can change into cancer-causing genes. Why do cells possess such potential time bombs?
   a. Viruses infect cells with proto-oncogenes.
   b. Proto-oncogenes are genetic "junk" with no known function.
   c. Proto-oncogenes are unavoidable environmental carcinogens.
   d. Cells produce proto-oncogenes as a by-product of mitosis.
   e. Proto-oncogenes normally control cell division.

7. Which of the following is a valid difference between embryonic stem cells and the stem cells found in adult tissues?
   a. In laboratory culture, only adult stem cells are immortal.
   b. In nature, only embryonic stem cells give rise to all the different types of cells in the organism.
   c. Only adult stem cells can differentiate in culture.
   d. Embryonic stem cells are generally more difficult to grow in culture than adult stem cells.
   e. Only embryonic stem cells are found in every tissue of the adult body.

Describing, Comparing, and Explaining

8. A mutation in a single gene may cause a major change in the body of a fruit fly, such as an extra pair of legs or wings. Yet it probably takes the combined action of hundreds or thousands of genes to produce a wing or leg. How can a change in just one gene cause such a big change in the body?

Applying the Concepts

9. You obtain an egg cell from the ovary of a white mouse and remove the nucleus from it. You then obtain a nucleus from a liver cell from an adult black mouse. You use the methods of nuclear transplantation to insert the nucleus into the empty egg. After some prompting, the new zygote divides into an early embryo, which you then implant into the uterus of a brown mouse. A few weeks later, a litter of mice is born. What color will they be? Why?

10. Mutations can alter the function of the *lac* operon (see Module 11.1). Predict how the following mutations would affect the function of the operon in the presence and absence of lactose:
    a. Mutation of regulatory gene; repressor cannot bind to lactose.
    b. Mutation of operator; repressor will not bind to operator.
    c. Mutation of regulatory gene; repressor will not bind to operator.
    d. Mutation of promoter; RNA polymerase will not attach to promoter.

11. A chemical called dioxin is produced as a by-product of some chemical manufacturing processes. This substance was present in Agent Orange, a defoliant sprayed on vegetation during the Vietnam War. There has been a continuing controversy over its effects on soldiers exposed to it during the war. Animal tests have suggested that dioxin can be lethal and can cause birth defects, cancer, organ damage, and immune system suppression. But its effects on humans are unclear, and even animal tests are inconclusive. Researchers have discovered that dioxin enters a cell and binds to a protein that in turn attaches to the cell's DNA. How might this mechanism help explain the variety of dioxin's effects? How might you determine whether a particular individual became ill as a result of exposure to dioxin?

Answers to all questions can be found in Appendix 4.

CHAPTER 12

DNA Technology and Genomics

BIG IDEAS

Gene Cloning
(12.1–12.5)

A variety of laboratory
techniques can be used to copy
and combine DNA molecules.

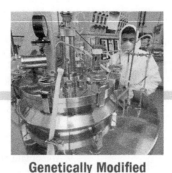

Genetically Modified
Organisms
(12.6–12.10)

Transgenic cells, plants, and
animals are used in agriculture
and medicine.

DNA Profiling
(12.11–12.16)

Genetic markers can be used to
definitively match a DNA
sample to an individual.

Genomics
(12.17–12.21)

The study of complete DNA
sets helps us learn about
evolutionary history.

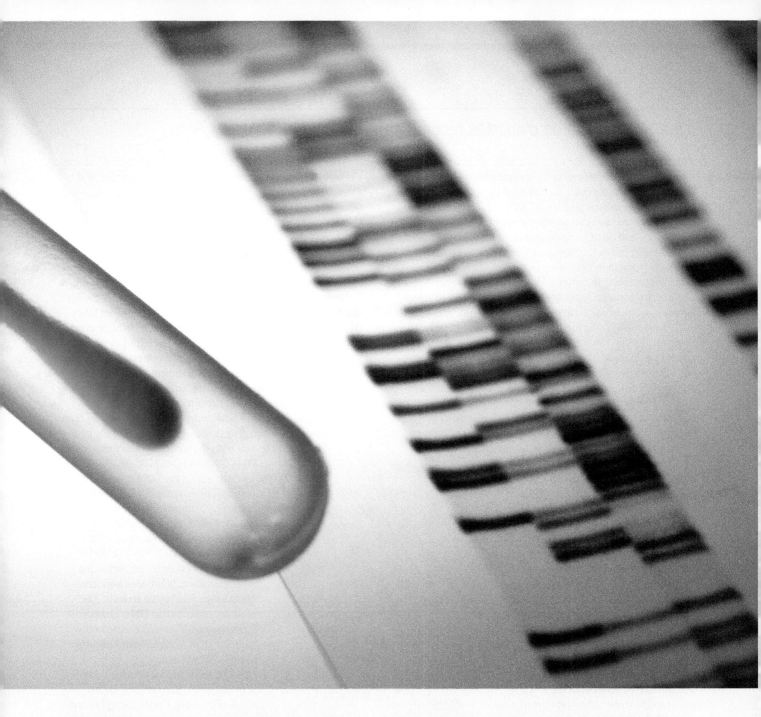

DNA technology—a set of methods for studying and manipulating genetic material—has rapidly revolutionized the field of forensics, the scientific analysis of evidence for legal investigations. Since its introduction, DNA analysis has become a standard law enforcement tool. The photograph above shows a swab containing DNA for analysis. The data on the printout beneath it is part of a DNA profile. Because the DNA sequence of every person is unique (except for identical twins), DNA profiling can be used to determine with near certainty whether two DNA samples are from the same individual. And due to its unbiased nature—a DNA profile is able to prove innocence as well as guilt—DNA profiling has provided crucial evidence in many famous cases.

You will learn in this chapter that DNA technology has many practical applications beyond the courtroom. In fact,

DNA technology has led to some of the most remarkable scientific advances in recent years. Applications of DNA technology include the use of gene cloning to produce medical and industrial products, such as human insulin made by bacteria; the development of genetically modified organisms for agriculture, such as crop plants that produce their own insecticide; and even the investigation of historical questions, such as famous mysteries of paternity, from Thomas Jefferson to the modern day. Equally important, DNA technology is invaluable in many areas of biological research, including cancer and evolution.

As we discuss these various applications throughout this chapter, we'll consider the specific techniques involved, how they are applied, and some of the social, legal, and ethical issues that are raised by the new technologies.

Gene Cloning

12.1 Genes can be cloned in recombinant plasmids

Although it may seem like a modern field, **biotechnology**, the manipulation of organisms or their components to make useful products, actually dates back to the dawn of civilization. Consider such ancient practices as the use of microbes to make beer, wine, and cheese, and the selective breeding of livestock, dogs, and other animals. But when people use the term *biotechnology* today, they are usually referring to **DNA technology**, modern laboratory techniques for studying and manipulating genetic material. Using these techniques, scientists can, for instance, modify specific genes and move them between organisms as different as bacteria, plants, and animals.

The field of DNA technology grew out of discoveries made about 60 years ago by American geneticists Joshua Lederberg and Edward Tatum. They performed a series of experiments with *Escherichia coli* (*E. coli*) that demonstrated that two individual bacteria can combine genes—a phenomenon that was previously thought to be limited to sexually reproducing eukaryotic organisms. With this work, they pioneered bacterial genetics, a field that within 20 years made *E. coli* the most thoroughly studied and understood organism at the molecular level.

In the 1970s, the field of biotechnology exploded with the invention of methods for making recombinant DNA in a test tube. **Recombinant DNA** is formed when scientists combine nucleotide sequences (pieces of DNA) from two different sources—often different species—to form a single DNA molecule. Today, recombinant DNA technology is widely used in the field of **genetic engineering**, the direct manipulation of genes for practical purposes. Scientists have genetically engineered bacteria to mass-produce a variety of useful chemicals, from cancer drugs to pesticides. Scientists have also transferred genes from bacteria into plants and from one animal species into another (Figure 12.1A).

▲ **Figure 12.1A** Glowing fish produced by transferring a gene originally obtained from a jelly (cnidarian)

To manipulate genes in the laboratory, biologists often use bacterial **plasmids**, which are small, circular DNA molecules that replicate (duplicate) separately from the much larger bacterial chromosome (see Module 10.23). Because plasmids can carry virtually any gene and are passed from one generation of bacteria to the next, they are key tools for **gene cloning**, the production of multiple identical copies of a gene-carrying piece of DNA. Gene-cloning methods are central to the production of useful products via genetic engineering.

Consider a typical genetic engineering challenge: A molecular biologist at a pharmaceutical company has identified a gene that codes for a valuable product, a hypothetical substance called protein V. The biologist wants to manufacture large amounts of protein V. Figure 12.1B illustrates how the techniques of gene cloning can be used to accomplish this goal.

To begin, the biologist isolates two kinds of DNA: ❶ a bacterial plasmid that will serve as the **vector**, or gene carrier, and ❷ the DNA containing the gene of interest—in this case, gene *V* (shown in red in the figure)—along with other, unwanted genes. Often, the plasmid comes from the bacterium *E. coli*. The DNA containing gene *V* could come from a variety of sources, such as a different bacterium, a plant, a nonhuman animal, or even human tissue cells growing in laboratory culture.

The researcher treats both the plasmid and the gene *V* source DNA with an enzyme that cuts DNA. ❸ An enzyme is chosen that cleaves the plasmid in only one place. ❹ The other DNA, which is usually much longer in sequence, may be cut into many fragments, one of which carries gene *V*. The figure shows the processing of just one DNA fragment and one plasmid, but actually, millions of plasmids and DNA fragments, most of which do not contain gene *V*, are treated simultaneously. The cuts leave single-stranded ends, as we'll explain in Module 12.2.

❺ The cut DNA from both sources—the plasmid and target gene—are mixed. The single-stranded ends of the plasmid base-pair with the complementary ends of the target DNA fragment (see Module 10.4 if you need a refresher on the DNA base-pairing rules). ❻ The enzyme **DNA ligase** joins the two DNA molecules by covalent bonds. This enzyme, which the cell normally uses in DNA replication (see Module 10.5), is a "DNA pasting" enzyme that catalyzes the formation of covalent bonds between adjacent nucleotides, joining the strands. The result is a recombinant DNA plasmid containing gene *V*, as well as many other recombinant DNA plasmids carrying other genes not shown here.

❼ The recombinant plasmid containing the targeted gene is mixed with a culture of bacteria. Under the right conditions, a bacterium takes up the plasmid DNA by transformation (see Module 10.22). ❽ This recombinant bacterium then reproduces to form a **clone** of cells, a group of identical cells descended from a single ancestral cell, each carrying a copy of gene *V*. This step is the actual gene cloning. In our example, the biologist will eventually grow a cell clone large enough to produce protein V in marketable quantities.

❾ Gene cloning can be used to produce a variety of desirable products. Copies of the gene itself can be the immediate product, to be used in further genetic engineering projects. For example, a pest-resistance gene present in one plant species might be cloned and transferred into plants of another species. Other times, the protein product of the cloned gene is harvested and used. For example, an enzyme that creates a faded look in blue jeans can be harvested in large quantities from

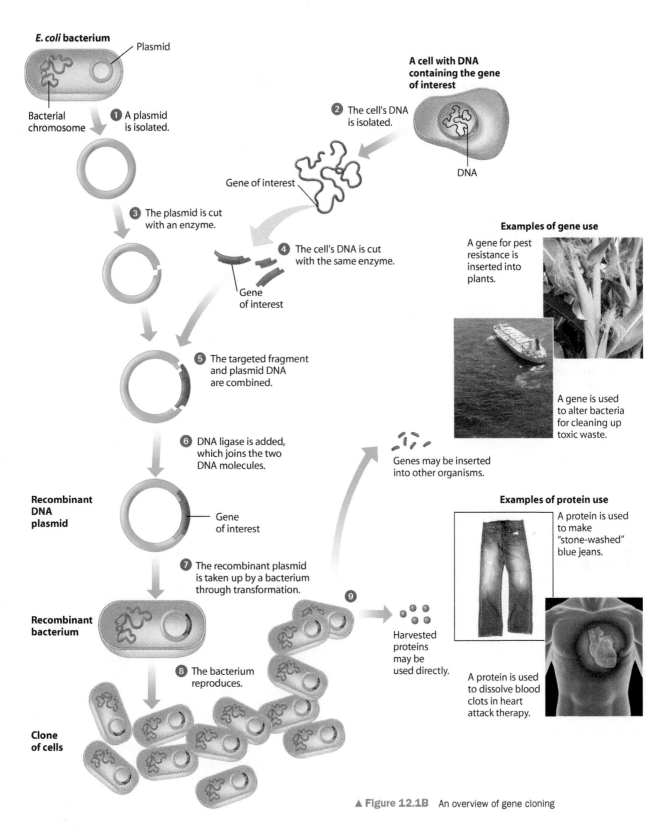

E. coli bacterium — Plasmid

Bacterial chromosome

1 A plasmid is isolated.

A cell with DNA containing the gene of interest

2 The cell's DNA is isolated.

DNA

Gene of interest

3 The plasmid is cut with an enzyme.

4 The cell's DNA is cut with the same enzyme.

Gene of interest

5 The targeted fragment and plasmid DNA are combined.

6 DNA ligase is added, which joins the two DNA molecules.

Recombinant DNA plasmid

Gene of interest

7 The recombinant plasmid is taken up by a bacterium through transformation.

Recombinant bacterium

8 The bacterium reproduces.

Clone of cells

9

Genes may be inserted into other organisms.

Harvested proteins may be used directly.

Examples of gene use

A gene for pest resistance is inserted into plants.

A gene is used to alter bacteria for cleaning up toxic waste.

Examples of protein use

A protein is used to make "stone-washed" blue jeans.

A protein is used to dissolve blood clots in heart attack therapy.

▲ **Figure 12.1B**   An overview of gene cloning

bacteria carrying the cloned gene (that's right: No stones are used to make stone-washed jeans!).

In the next four modules, we discuss the methods outlined in Figure 12.1B. You may find it useful to turn back to this summary figure as each technique is discussed.

? **Why does the rapid reproduction of bacteria make them a good choice for cloning a foreign gene?**

● A foreign gene located within plasmid DNA inside a bacterium is replicated each time the cell divides, resulting in rapid accumulation of many copies of the gene.

12.2 Enzymes are used to "cut and paste" DNA

In the gene-cloning procedure outlined in Figure 12.1B, a recombinant DNA molecule is created by combining two ingredients: a bacterial plasmid and the gene of interest. To understand how these DNA molecules are spliced together, you need to learn how enzymes cut and paste DNA. The cutting tools are bacterial enzymes called **restriction enzymes**. In nature, these enzymes protect bacterial cells against intruding DNA from other organisms or viruses. They work by chopping up the foreign DNA, a process that restricts the ability of the invader to do harm to the bacterium. (The bacterial cell's own DNA is protected from restriction enzymes through chemical modification by other enzymes.)

Biologists have identified hundreds of different restriction enzymes. Each restriction enzyme is specific, recognizing a particular short DNA sequence, usually four to eight nucleotides long. For example, a restriction enzyme called *Eco*RI (found naturally in *E. coli*) only recognizes the DNA sequence GAATTC, whereas the enzyme called *Bam*HI only recognizes GGATCC. The DNA sequence recognized by a particular restriction enzyme is called a **restriction site**. Once a restriction site is recognized, the restriction enzyme cuts both strands of the DNA at specific points within the sequence. All copies of a particular DNA molecule always yield the same set of DNA fragments when exposed to the same restriction enzyme. In other words, a restriction enzyme cuts a DNA molecule in a precise, reproducible way.

Figure 12.2 ❶ shows a piece of DNA containing one recognition sequence for the restriction enzyme *Eco*RI. In this case, the restriction enzyme cuts each DNA strand between the bases A and G within the sequence, producing pieces of DNA called **restriction fragments**. ❷ Notice that the DNA is cut unevenly; the staggered cuts yield two double-stranded DNA fragments with single-stranded ends, called "sticky ends." Sticky ends are the key to joining DNA restriction fragments originating from different sources because these short extensions can form hydrogen-bonded base pairs with complementary single-stranded stretches of DNA.

❸ A piece of DNA (gray, with the red area showing the gene of interest) from another source is now added. Notice that the gray DNA has single-stranded ends identical in base sequence to the sticky ends on the blue DNA. The gray, "foreign" DNA has ends with this particular base sequence because it was cut from a larger molecule by the same restriction enzyme used to cut the blue DNA. ❹ The complementary ends on the blue and gray fragments allow them to stick together by base pairing. (The hydrogen bonds are not shown in the figure.) This union between the blue and gray DNA fragments is temporary; it can be made permanent by the "pasting" enzyme DNA ligase. ❺ The final outcome is a stable molecule of recombinant DNA.

The ability to cut DNA with restriction enzymes and then paste it back together with DNA ligase is the key to the gene-cloning procedure outlined in Figure 12.1B and most other modern genetic engineering methods. This particular cloning procedure, which uses a mixture of fragments from the entire

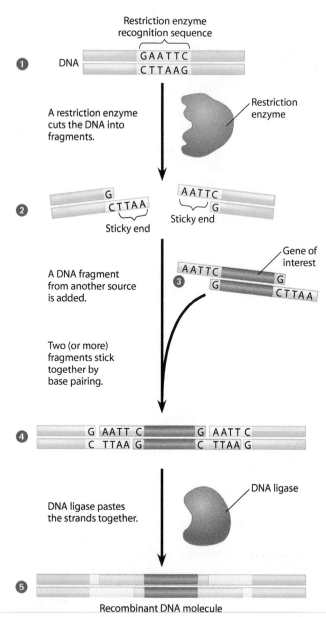

▲ Figure 12.2 Creating recombinant DNA using a restriction enzyme and DNA ligase

genome of an organism, is called a "shotgun" approach. Thousands of different recombinant plasmids are produced, and a clone of each is made. The complete set of plasmid clones, each carrying copies of a particular segment from the initial genome, is a type of library. The next three modules discuss such libraries in more detail.

? What are "sticky ends"?

● Single-stranded regions whose unpaired bases can hydrogen-bond to the complementary sticky ends of other fragments created by the same restriction enzyme

12.3 Cloned genes can be stored in genomic libraries

Each bacterial clone from the procedure in Figure 12.1B consists of identical cells with plasmids carrying one particular fragment of target DNA. The entire collection of all the cloned DNA fragments from a genome is called a **genomic library**. On the left side of **Figure 12.3**, the red, yellow, and green DNA

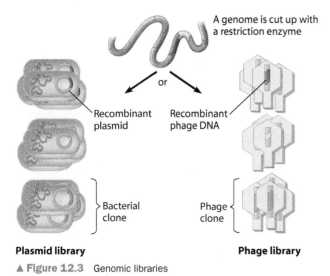

Plasmid library   **Phage library**

▲ **Figure 12.3**   Genomic libraries

segments represent three of the thousands of different library "books" that are "shelved" in plasmids inside bacterial cells. A typical cloned DNA fragment is big enough to carry one or a few genes, and together, the fragments include the entire genome of the organism from which the DNA was derived.

Bacteriophages (also called phages)—viruses that infect bacteria—can also serve as vectors when cloning genes (Figure 12.3, right). When a phage is used, the DNA fragments are inserted into phage DNA molecules. The recombinant phage DNA can then be introduced into a bacterial cell through the normal infection process (see Figure 10.22B). Inside the cell, phage DNA is replicated, producing new phage particles, each carrying the foreign DNA. Another type of vector commonly used in library construction is a bacterial artificial chromosome (BAC). BACs are essentially large plasmids containing only the genes necessary to ensure replication. The primary advantage of BACs is that they can carry more foreign DNA than other vectors. In the next module, we look at another source of DNA for cloning: eukaryotic mRNA.

> **?** In what sense does a genomic library have multiple copies of each "book"?

Each "book"—a piece of DNA from the genome that was the source of the library—is present in every recombinant bacterium or phage in a clone.

12.4 Reverse transcriptase can help make genes for cloning

Rather than starting with an entire eukaryotic genome, a researcher can focus on the genes expressed in a particular kind of cell by using its mRNA as the starting material for cloning. As shown in **Figure 12.4**, ❶ the chosen cells transcribe their genes and ❷ process the transcripts, removing introns and splicing exons together, producing mRNA. ❸ The researcher isolates the mRNA and makes single-stranded DNA transcripts from it using the enzyme **reverse transcriptase** (gold in the figure; see Module 10.20). ❹ Another enzyme is added to break down the mRNA, and ❺ DNA polymerase (the enzyme that replicates DNA; see Module 10.5) is used to synthesize a second DNA strand.

The double-stranded DNA that results from such a procedure, called **complementary DNA (cDNA)**, represents only the subset of genes that had been transcribed into mRNA in the starting cells. Among other purposes, such a cDNA library is useful for studying the genes responsible for the specialized functions of a particular cell type, such as brain or liver cells. Because cDNAs lack introns, they are shorter than the full versions of the genes and therefore easier to work with.

In the next module, you will learn how to find one particular piece of DNA from among the thousands that are stored in a genomic or cDNA library.

> **?** Why is a cDNA gene made using reverse transcriptase often shorter than the natural form of the gene?

Because cDNAs are made from spliced mRNAs, which lack introns

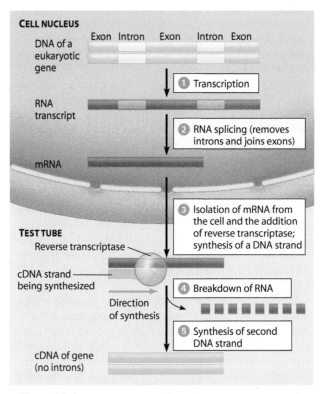

▲ **Figure 12.4**   Making an intron-lacking gene from eukaryotic mRNA

12.5 Nucleic acid probes identify clones carrying specific genes

Often, the most difficult task in gene cloning is finding the right "books" in a genomic library—that is, identifying clones containing a desired gene from among all those created. For example, a researcher might want to pull out just the clone of bacteria carrying the red gene in Figure 12.3. If bacterial clones containing a specific gene actually translate the gene into protein, they can be identified by testing for the protein product. However, not every desired gene produces detectable proteins. In such cases, researchers can also test directly for the gene itself.

Methods for detecting a gene directly depend on base pairing between the gene and a complementary sequence on another nucleic acid molecule, either DNA or RNA. When at least part of the nucleotide sequence of a gene is known, this information can be used to a researcher's advantage. Taking a simplified example, if we know that a hypothetical gene contains the sequence TAGGCT, a biochemist can synthesize a short single strand of DNA with the complementary sequence (ATCCGA) and label it with a radioactive isotope or fluorescent tag. This labeled, complementary molecule is called a **nucleic acid probe** because it is used to find a specific gene or other nucleotide sequence within a mass of DNA. (In practice, probe molecules are usually considerably longer than six nucleotides.)

Figure 12.5 shows how a probe works. The DNA sample to be tested is treated with heat or chemicals to separate the DNA strands. When the radioactive DNA probe is added to these strands, it tags the correct molecules—that is, it finds the correct books in the genomic library—by hydrogen-bonding to the complementary sequence in the gene of interest. Such a probe can be simultaneously applied to many bacterial clones to screen all of them at once for a desired gene.

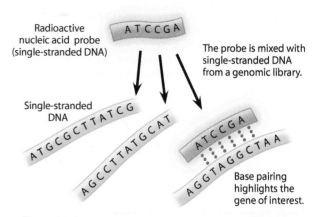

Radioactive nucleic acid probe (single-stranded DNA)

The probe is mixed with single-stranded DNA from a genomic library.

Single-stranded DNA

Base pairing highlights the gene of interest.

▲ **Figure 12.5**　How a DNA probe tags a gene by base pairing

In one technique, a piece of filter paper is pressed against bacterial colonies (clones) growing on a petri dish. The filter paper picks up cells from each colony. A chemical treatment is used to break open the cells and separate the DNA strands. The DNA strands are then soaked in probe solution. Any bacterial colonies carrying the gene of interest will be tagged on the filter paper, marking them for easy identification. Once the researcher identifies a colony carrying the desired gene, the cells can be grown further, and the gene of interest, or its protein product, can be collected in large amounts.

?　How does a probe consisting of radioactive DNA or RNA enable a researcher to find the bacterial clones carrying a particular gene?

● The probe molecules bind to and label DNA only from the cells containing the gene of interest, which has a complementary DNA sequence.

Genetically Modified Organisms

12.6 Recombinant cells and organisms can mass-produce gene products

Recombinant cells and organisms constructed by DNA technology are used to manufacture many useful products, chiefly proteins (Table 12.6, on the facing page). By transferring the gene for a desired protein into a bacterium, yeast, or other kind of cell that is easy to grow in culture, a genetic engineer can produce large quantities of proteins that are otherwise difficult to obtain.

Bacteria are often the best organisms for manufacturing a protein product. Major advantages of bacteria include the plasmids and phages available for use as gene-cloning vectors and the fact that bacteria can be grown rapidly and cheaply in large tanks. Furthermore, bacteria can be engineered to produce large amounts of particular proteins and, in some cases, to secrete the proteins directly into their growth medium,

simplifying the task of collecting and purifying the products. As Table 12.6 shows, a number of proteins of importance in human medicine and agriculture are being produced in the bacterium *Escherichia coli*.

Despite the advantages of using bacteria, it is sometimes desirable or necessary to use eukaryotic cells to produce a protein product. Often, the first-choice eukaryotic organism for protein production is the yeast used in making bread and beer, *Saccharomyces cerevisiae*. As bakers and brewers have recognized for centuries, yeast cells are easy to grow. And like *E. coli*, yeast cells can take up foreign DNA and integrate it into their genomes. Yeast cells also have plasmids that can be used as gene vectors, and yeast is often better than bacteria at synthesizing and secreting eukaryotic proteins.

TABLE 12.6 | SOME PROTEIN PRODUCTS OF RECOMBINANT DNA TECHNOLOGY

Product	Made In	Use
Human insulin	*E. coli*	Treatment for diabetes
Human growth hormone (HGH)	*E. coli*	Treatment for growth defects
Epidermal growth factor (EGF)	*E. coli*	Treatment for burns, ulcers
Interleukin-2 (IL-2)	*E. coli*	Possible treatment for cancer
Bovine growth hormone (BGH)	*E. coli*	Improving weight gain in cattle
Cellulase	*E. coli*	Breaking down cellulose for animal feeds
Taxol	*E. coli*	Treatment for ovarian cancer
Interferons (alpha and gamma)	*S. cerevisiae,* *E. coli*	Possible treatment for cancer and viral infections
Hepatitis B vaccine	*S. cerevisiae*	Prevention of viral hepatitis
Erythropoietin (EPO)	Mammalian cells	Treatment for anemia
Factor VIII	Mammalian cells	Treatment for hemophilia
Tissue plasminogen activator (TPA)	Mammalian cells	Treatment for heart attacks and some strokes

S. cerevisiae is currently used to produce a number of proteins. In certain cases, the same product—for example, interferons used in cancer research—can be made in either yeast or bacteria. In other cases, such as the hepatitis B vaccine, yeast alone is used.

The cells of choice for making some gene products come from mammals. Many proteins that mammalian cells normally secrete are glycoproteins, proteins with chains of sugars attached. Because only mammalian cells can attach the sugars correctly, mammalian cells must be used for making these products. For example, recombinant mammalian cells growing in laboratory cultures are currently used to produce human erythropoietin (EPO), a hormone that stimulates the production of red blood cells. EPO is used as a treatment for anemia, but the drug is also abused by some athletes who seek the advantage of artificially high levels of oxygen-carrying red blood cells (called "blood doping"; see Module 23.13).

Recently, pharmaceutical researchers have been exploring the mass production of gene products by whole animals or plants rather than cultured cells. Genetic engineers have used recombinant DNA technology to insert genes for desired human proteins into other mammals, where the protein encoded by the recombinant gene may secreted in the animal's milk. For example, a gene for antithrombin—a human protein that helps prevent inappropriate blood clotting—has been inserted into the genome of a goat (**Figure 12.6A**); isolated from the milk, the protein can be administered to patients with a rare hereditary disorder in which this protein is lacking. The pig in **Figure 12.6B** has been genetically modified

▲ Figure 12.6A A goat carrying a gene for a human blood protein that is secreted in the milk

to produce human hemoglobin; this vital blood protein can be supplied to patients via blood transfusion.

However, genetically engineered animals are difficult and costly to produce. Typically, a biotechnology company starts by injecting the desired DNA into a large number of embryos, which are then implanted into surrogate mothers. With luck, one or a few recombinant animals may result; success rates for such procedures are very low. Once a recombinant organism is successfully produced, it may be cloned. The result can be a genetically identical herd—a grazing pharmaceutical "factory" of "pharm" animals that produce otherwise rare biological substances for medical use.

We continue an exploration of the medical applications of DNA technology in the next module.

? **Why can't glycoproteins be mass-produced by engineered bacteria or yeast cells?**

● Because bacteria and yeast cells cannot correctly attach the sugar groups to the protein of glycoproteins

▲ Figure 12.6B A pig that has been genetically modified to produce a useful human protein

12.7 DNA technology has changed the pharmaceutical industry and medicine

DNA technology, and gene cloning in particular, is widely used to produce medicines and to diagnose diseases.

Therapeutic Hormones   Consider the first two products in Table 12.6 on the previous page—human insulin and human growth hormone. About 2 million people with diabetes in the United States depend on insulin treatment. Before 1982, the main sources of this hormone were slaughtered pigs and cattle. Insulin extracted from these animals is chemically similar, but not identical, to human insulin, and it causes harmful side effects in some people. Genetic engineering has largely solved this problem by developing bacteria that synthesize and secrete the human form of insulin. In 1982, Humulin (Figure 12.7A)—human insulin produced by bacteria—became the first recombinant DNA drug approved by the U.S. Food and Drug Administration.

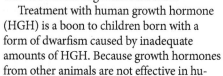

▲ **Figure 12.7A** Human insulin produced by bacteria

Treatment with human growth hormone (HGH) is a boon to children born with a form of dwarfism caused by inadequate amounts of HGH. Because growth hormones from other animals are not effective in humans, children with HGH deficiency historically have had to rely on scarce supplies from human cadavers or else face dwarfism. In 1985, however, molecular biologists made an artificial gene for HGH by joining a human DNA fragment to a chemically synthesized piece of DNA; using this gene, they were able to produce HGH in *E. coli*. HGH from recombinant bacteria is now widely used.

Another important pharmaceutical product produced by genetic engineering is tissue plasminogen activator (TPA). If administered soon after a heart attack, this protein helps dissolve blood clots and reduces the risk of subsequent heart attacks.

Diagnosis of Disease   DNA technology is being used increasingly to diagnose disease. Among the hundreds of genes for human diseases that have been identified are those for sickle-cell disease, hemophilia, cystic fibrosis, and Huntington's disease. Affected individuals with such diseases often can be identified before the onset of symptoms, even before birth. It is also possible to identify symptomless carriers of potentially harmful recessive alleles (see Module 9.9). Additionally, DNA technology can pinpoint infections. For example, DNA analysis can help track down and identify elusive viruses such as HIV, the virus that causes AIDS.

Vaccines   DNA technology is also helping medical researchers develop vaccines. A **vaccine** is a harmless variant (mutant) or derivative of a pathogen—usually a bacterium or virus—that is used to stimulate the immune system to mount a lasting defense against that pathogen (see Module 24.4). For many viral diseases, prevention by vaccination is the only medical way to prevent illness.

Genetic engineering can be used in several ways to make vaccines. One approach is to use genetically engineered cells or organisms to produce large amounts of a protein molecule that is found on the pathogen's outside surface. This method has been used to make the vaccine against the hepatitis B virus. Hepatitis is a disabling and sometimes fatal liver disease, and the hepatitis B virus may also cause liver cancer. Figure 12.7B shows a tank for growing yeast cells that have been engineered to carry the gene for the virus's surface protein. Made by the yeast, this protein will be the main ingredient of the vaccine.

Another way to use DNA technology in vaccine development is to make a harmless artificial mutant of the pathogen by altering one or more of its genes. When a harmless mutant is used as a so-called "live vaccine," it multiplies in the body and may trigger a strong immune response. Artificial-mutant vaccines may cause fewer side effects than vaccines that have traditionally been made from natural mutants.

Yet another method for making vaccines employs a virus related to the one that causes smallpox. Smallpox was once a dreaded human disease, but it was eradicated worldwide in the 1970s by widespread vaccination with a harmless variant of the smallpox virus. Using this harmless virus, genetic engineers could replace some of the genes encoding proteins that induce immunity to smallpox with genes that induce immunity to other diseases. In fact, the virus could be engineered to carry genes needed to vaccinate against several diseases simultaneously. In the future, one inoculation may prevent a dozen diseases.

Genetic engineering rapidly transformed the field of medicine and continues to do so today. But genetically modified organisms affect our lives in other ways, as we'll see next.

? **Human growth hormone and insulin produced by DNA technology are used in the treatment of _____ and _____, respectively.**

● dwarfism . . . diabetes

▲ **Figure 12.7B**   Equipment used in the production of a vaccine against hepatitis B

12.8 Genetically modified organisms are transforming agriculture

Since ancient times, people have selectively bred agricultural crops to make them more useful. Today, DNA technology is quickly replacing traditional breeding programs as scientists work to improve the productivity of agriculturally important plants and animals. Genetic engineers have produced many varieties of **genetically modified (GM) organisms**, organisms that have acquired one or more genes by artificial means. If the newly acquired gene is from another organism, typically of another species, the recombinant organism is called a **transgenic organism**.

The most common vector used to introduce new genes into plant cells is a plasmid from the soil bacterium *Agrobacterium tumefaciens* called the **Ti plasmid** (Figure 12.8A). ❶ With the help of a restriction enzyme and DNA ligase, the gene for the desired trait (indicated in red in the figure) is inserted into a modified version of the plasmid. ❷ Then the recombinant plasmid is put into a plant cell, where the DNA carrying the new gene integrates into the plant chromosome. ❸ Finally, the recombinant cell is cultured and grown into a plant.

With an estimated 1 billion people facing malnutrition, GM crops may be able to help a great many hungry people by improving food production, pest resistance, and the nutritional value of crops. For example, in India, the insertion of a salinity-resistance gene has enabled new varieties of rice to grow in water three times as salty as seawater. Similar research is under way in Australia to help improve wheat yields in salty soil. In Hawaii, the ring spot virus seemed poised to devastate the papaya industry until a GM variety resistant to the virus was introduced in 1992. Golden Rice, a transgenic variety created in 2000 with a few daffodil genes, produces yellow grains containing beta-carotene, which our body uses to make vitamin A. A new strain (Golden Rice 2) uses corn genes to boost beta-carotene levels even higher (Figure 12.8B). This rice could help prevent vitamin A deficiency—and the resulting blindness—among the half of the world's people who depend on rice as their staple food.

In addition to agricultural applications, genetic engineers are now creating plants that make human proteins for medical use. A recently developed transgenic rice strain harbors genes for milk proteins that can be used in rehydration formulas to treat infant diarrhea, a serious problem in developing countries. Other pharmaceutical trials currently under way involve using modified corn to treat cystic fibrosis, safflower to treat diabetes, and duckweed to treat hepatitis. Although these trials seem promising, no plant-made drugs intended for use by humans have yet to be approved or sold.

Agricultural researchers are also producing transgenic animals, as mentioned in Module 12.6. To do this, scientists remove egg cells from a female and fertilize them. They then inject a previously cloned gene directly into the nuclei of the fertilized eggs. Some of the cells integrate the foreign DNA into their genomes. The engineered embryos are then surgically implanted in a surrogate mother. If an embryo develops successfully, the result is an animal containing a gene from a third "parent," which may even be of another species.

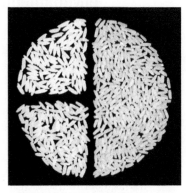

▲ Figure 12.8B   A mix of conventional rice (white), the original Golden Rice (light gold), and Golden Rice 2 (dark gold)

The goals in creating a transgenic animal are often the same as the goals of traditional breeding—for instance, to make a sheep with better quality wool or a cow that will mature in less time. In 2006, researchers succeeded in transferring a fat metabolism gene from a roundworm into a pig. Meat from the resulting swine had levels of healthy omega-3 fatty acids—which are believed to reduce the risk of heart disease—four to five times higher than meat from normal pigs. Atlantic salmon have been genetically modified by the addition of a more active growth hormone gene from Chinook salmon. Such fish can grow to market size in about half the time of conventional salmon. As of 2010, the FDA was considering whether to grant approval for the modified salmon to be sold as food. To date, the vast majority of the GM organisms that contribute to our food supply are not animals, but crop plants. As we'll discuss next, some people question whether such genetically modified organisms are beneficial to our society.

? **What is the function of the Ti plasmid in the creation of transgenic plants?**

● It is used as the vector for introducing foreign genes into a plant cell.

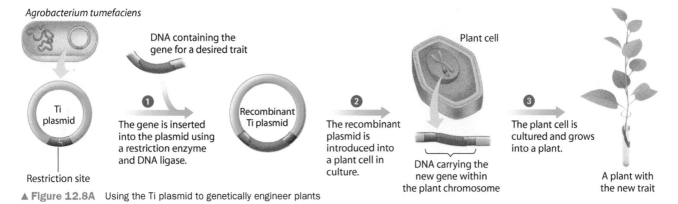

Agrobacterium tumefaciens

DNA containing the gene for a desired trait

Ti plasmid

Restriction site

❶ The gene is inserted into the plasmid using a restriction enzyme and DNA ligase.

Recombinant Ti plasmid

❷ The recombinant plasmid is introduced into a plant cell in culture.

Plant cell

DNA carrying the new gene within the plant chromosome

❸ The plant cell is cultured and grows into a plant.

A plant with the new trait

▲ **Figure 12.8A**   Using the Ti plasmid to genetically engineer plants

12.9 Genetically modified organisms raise concerns about human and environmental health

As soon as scientists realized the power of DNA technology, they began to worry about potential dangers. Early concerns focused on the possibility that recombinant DNA technology might create new pathogens. What might happen, for instance, if cancer cell genes were transferred into infectious bacteria or viruses? To guard against such rogue microbes, scientists developed a set of guidelines that were adopted as formal government regulations in the United States and some other countries. One safety measure is a set of strict laboratory procedures designed to protect researchers from infection by engineered microbes and to prevent the microbes from accidentally leaving the laboratory (Figure 12.9A). In addition, strains of microorganisms to be used in recombinant DNA experiments are genetically crippled to ensure that they cannot survive outside the laboratory. Finally, certain obviously dangerous experiments have been banned.

Today, most public concern about possible hazards centers not on recombinant microbes but on genetically modified organisms (GMOs) used for food. Some fear that crops carrying genes from other species might be hazardous to human health or the environment. Others fear that the protein products of transplanted genes might lead to allergic reactions.

About a decade ago, negotiators from 130 countries, including the United States, agreed on a Biosafety Protocol that requires all exporters to identify GM organisms present in bulk food shipments and allows importing countries to decide whether they pose environmental or health risks. Although the majority of several staple crops grown in the United States—including corn and soybeans—are genetically modified, products made from GMOs are not required to be labeled in any way. Chances are, you eat a food containing GMOs nearly every day, but the lack of labeling means there is little chance that you would be able to say for certain. However, labeling of foods containing more than trace amounts of GMOs is required in Europe, Japan, Australia, and some other countries. Critics of GM crops point out that labeling would allow consumers to decide for themselves whether or not they wish to be exposed to GM foods. Some biotechnology advocates, however, respond that similar demands were not made when "transgenic" crop plants produced by traditional breeding techniques were put on the market. For example, triticale was created decades ago by combining the genomes of wheat and rye—two plants that do not interbreed in nature. Triticale is now grown worldwide.

Advocates of a cautious approach toward GM crops also fear that transgenic plants might pass their new genes to close relatives in nearby wild areas (Figure 12.9B). We know that lawn and crop grasses, for example, commonly exchange genes with wild relatives via pollen transfer. If crop plants carrying genes for resistance to herbicides, diseases, or insect pests pollinated wild ones, the offspring might become "superweeds" that would be very difficult to control. In 2003, the U.S. Department of Agriculture imposed multimillion-dollar fines and tightened rules for tests involving GM plants after leftover corn plants engineered to make a pig vaccine popped up in a soybean field in Nebraska. Concern has also been raised that the widespread use of GM seeds may reduce natural genetic diversity, leaving crops susceptible to catastrophic die-offs in the event of a sudden change to the environment or introduction of a new pest.

▲ Figure 12.9B Genetically engineered crop plants growing near their wild relatives

Today, governments and regulatory agencies throughout the world are grappling with how to facilitate the use of biotechnology in agriculture, industry, and medicine while ensuring that new products and procedures are safe. In the United States, such applications of biotechnology are evaluated for potential risks by multiple government agencies. Meanwhile, these same agencies and the public must consider the ethical implications of biotechnology.

In the case of GM plants and certain other applications of DNA technology, zero risk is probably unattainable. Scientists and the public need to weigh the possible benefits versus risks on a case-by-case basis. The best scenario would be for us to proceed with caution, basing our decisions on sound scientific information rather than on either irrational fear or blind optimism.

? What is one of the concerns about engineering crop plants by adding genes for herbicide resistance?

● The possibility that the genes could escape via cross-pollination to weeds that are closely related to the crop species

▶ Figure 12.9A A maximum-security laboratory at the Pasteur Institute in Paris

In this chapter, we have discussed transgenic viruses, bacteria, yeast, plants, and animals. What about transgenic humans? Why would anyone want to insert genes into a living person?

One reason to tamper with the human genome is the potential for treating a variety of diseases by **gene therapy**—alteration of an afflicted individual's genes for therapeutic purposes. In people with disorders traceable to a single defective gene, it might be possible to replace or supplement the defective gene by inserting a normal allele into cells of the tissue affected by the disorder. Once there, the normal allele may be expressed, potentially curing the disease after just a single treatment.

For gene therapy to be permanent, the normal allele would have to be transferred to cells that multiply throughout a person's life. Bone marrow cells, which include the stem cells that give rise to all the cells of the blood and immune system, are prime candidates (see Modules 11.15 and 23.15). Figure 12.10 outlines one possible procedure for gene therapy. ❶ The normal gene is cloned, converted to an RNA version, and then inserted into the RNA genome of a harmless retrovirus vector. ❷ Bone marrow cells are taken from the patient and infected with the virus. ❸ The virus inserts a DNA version of its genome, including the normal human gene, into the cells' DNA (see Module 10.20). ❹ The engineered

cells are then injected back into the patient. If the procedure succeeds, the cells will multiply throughout the patient's life and produce a steady supply of the missing protein, curing the patient.

The first successful human gene therapy trial, begun in 2000, used this method to treat 10 young children with severe combined immunodeficiency disease (SCID), a disorder in which the patient lacks a functional immune system (see Module 24.16). Nine of these patients showed significant improvement, providing the first definitive success of gene therapy. However, three of the patients subsequently developed leukemia, a cancer of the blood cells, and one died. Researchers discovered that in two of the cases, the inserted DNA appeared to disrupt a gene involved in proliferation and development of blood cells. This insertion somehow caused the leukemia. Active research into treating SCID continues with new, tougher safety guidelines.

A 2009 gene therapy trial involved a disease called Leber's congenital amaurosis (LCA). People with one form of LCA have a defective version of a gene needed to produce rhodopsin, a pigment that enables the eye to detect light. In such people, photoreceptor cells gradually die, causing progressive blindness. An international research team found that a single injection—containing a virus carrying the normal gene—into one eye of affected children improved vision in that eye, sometimes enough to allow normal functioning.

The use of gene therapy raises several technical questions. For example, how can researchers build in gene control mechanisms to ensure that cells with the transferred gene make appropriate amounts of the gene product at the right time and in the right parts of the body? And how can they be sure that the gene's insertion does not harm the cell's normal function?

In addition to technical challenges, gene therapy raises difficult ethical questions. Some critics suggest that tampering with human genes in any way will inevitably lead to the practice of eugenics, the deliberate effort to control the genetic makeup of human populations. Other observers see no fundamental difference between the transplantation of genes into somatic cells and the transplantation of organs.

The implications of genetically manipulating gamete-forming cells or zygotes (already accomplished in lab animals) are more problematic. This possibility raises the most difficult ethical questions of all: Should we try to eliminate genetic defects in our children and their descendants? Should we interfere with evolution in this way? From a biological perspective, the elimination of unwanted alleles from the gene pool could backfire. Genetic variety is a necessary ingredient for the survival of a species as environmental conditions change with time. Genes that are damaging under some conditions may be advantageous under others (one example is the sickle-cell allele; see Module 9.13). Are we willing to risk making genetic changes that could be detrimental to our species in the future? We may have to face this question soon.

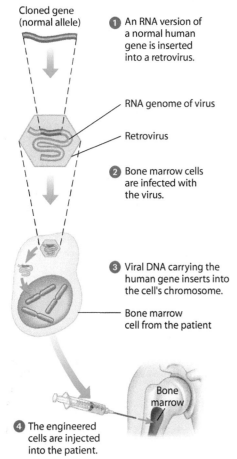

Cloned gene
(normal allele)

❶ An RNA version of a normal human gene is inserted into a retrovirus.

RNA genome of virus

Retrovirus

❷ Bone marrow cells are infected with the virus.

❸ Viral DNA carrying the human gene inserts into the cell's chromosome.

Bone marrow cell from the patient

Bone marrow

❹ The engineered cells are injected into the patient.

▲ Figure 12.10 One type of gene therapy procedure

? **What characteristic of bone marrow makes those cells good targets for gene therapy?**

● They multiply throughout a person's life.

DNA Profiling

12.11 The analysis of genetic markers can produce a DNA profile

Modern DNA technology methods have rapidly transformed the field of **forensics**, the scientific analysis of evidence for crime scene investigations and other legal proceedings. The most important application to forensics is **DNA profiling**, the analysis of DNA samples to determine whether they came from the same individual.

How do you prove that two samples of DNA come from the same person? You could compare the entire genomes found in the two samples, but such an approach would be extremely impractical, requiring a lot of time and money. Instead, scientists compare genetic markers, sequences in the genome that vary from person to person. Like a gene, which is one type of genetic marker, a genetic marker within a noncoding stretch of DNA is more likely to be a match between relatives than between unrelated individuals.

Figure 12.11 summarizes the basic steps in creating a DNA profile. ❶ First, DNA samples are isolated from the crime scene, suspects, victims, or stored evidence. ❷ Next, selected markers from each DNA sample are amplified (copied many times), producing an adequate supply for testing. ❸ Finally, the amplified DNA markers are compared, proving which samples were derived from the same individual. In the next four modules, we'll explore the methods behind these steps in detail.

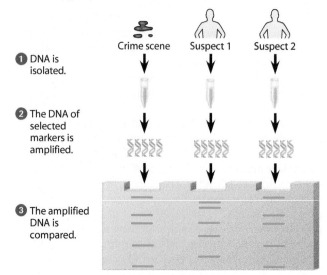

❶ DNA is isolated.

❷ The DNA of selected markers is amplified.

❸ The amplified DNA is compared.

▲ **Figure 12.11**   An overview of DNA profiling

? **According to the data presented in Figure 12.11, which suspect left DNA at the crime scene?**

● Suspect 2; notice that the number and location of the DNA markers match between suspect 2's DNA and the crime scene DNA.

12.12 The PCR method is used to amplify DNA sequences

Cloning DNA in host cells is often the best method for preparing large quantities of DNA from a particular gene (see Module 12.1). However, when the source of DNA is scant or impure, the polymerase chain reaction is a much better method. The **polymerase chain reaction (PCR)** is a technique by which a specific segment of a DNA molecule can be targeted and quickly amplified in the laboratory. Starting with a minute sample of blood or other tissue, automated PCR can generate billions of copies of a DNA segment in just a few hours, producing enough DNA to allow a DNA profile to be constructed.

In principle, PCR is fairly simple (**Figure 12.12**). A repeated, three-step cycle brings about a chain reaction that doubles the population of identical DNA molecules during each round. The key to amplifying one particular segment of DNA and no others

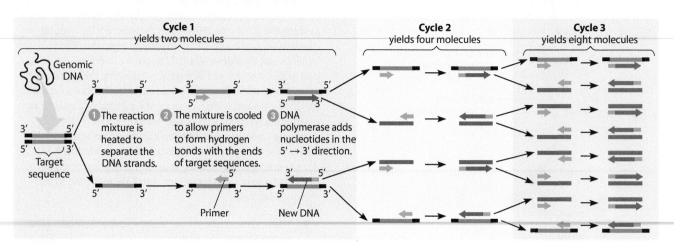

▲ **Figure 12.12**   DNA amplification by PCR

is the use of **primers**, short (usually 15 to 20 nucleotides long), chemically synthesized single-stranded DNA molecules with sequences that are complementary to sequences at each end of the target sequence. One primer is complementary to one strand at one end of the target sequence; the second primer is complementary to the other strand at the other end of the sequence. The primers thus bind to sequences that flank the target sequence, marking the start and end points for the segment of DNA being amplified.

❶ In the first step of each PCR cycle, the reaction mixture is heated to separate the strands of the DNA double helices. ❷ Next, the strands are cooled. As they cool, primer molecules hydrogen-bond to their target sequences on the DNA. ❸ In the third step, a heat-stable DNA polymerase builds new DNA strands by extending the primers in the $5' \to 3'$ direction. These three steps are repeated over and over, doubling the amount of DNA after each three-step cycle. A key prerequisite for automating PCR was the discovery of an unusual DNA polymerase, first isolated from a bacterium living in hot springs, that could withstand the heat at the start of each cycle. Without such a heat-stable polymerase, PCR would not be possible because standard DNA

polymerases would denature (unfold) during the heating step of each cycle.

Just as impressive as the speed of PCR is its sensitivity. Only minute amounts of DNA need to be present in the starting material, and this DNA can even be in a partially degraded state. The key to the high sensitivity is the primers. Because the primers only bind the sequences associated with the target, the DNA polymerase duplicates only the desired segments of DNA. Other DNA will not be bound by primers and thus not copied by the DNA polymerase.

Devised in 1985, PCR has had a major impact on biological research and biotechnology. PCR has been used to amplify DNA from a wide variety of sources: fragments of ancient DNA from a mummified human, a 40,000-year-old frozen woolly mammoth, and a 30-million-year-old plant fossil; DNA from fingerprints or from tiny amounts of blood, tissue, or semen found at crime scenes; DNA from single embryonic cells for rapid prenatal diagnosis of genetic disorders; and DNA of viral genes from cells infected with viruses that are difficult to detect, such as HIV.

❓ **Why is amplification of DNA from a crime scene often necessary?**

The DNA from a crime scene is often scant and impure. ◉

12.13 Gel electrophoresis sorts DNA molecules by size

Many approaches for studying DNA molecules in the lab make use of **gel electrophoresis**. A gel is a thin slab of jellylike material often made from agarose, a carbohydrate polymer extracted from seaweed. Because agarose contains a dense tangle of cable-like threads (similar to the structure of fiberglass, and resembling a jungle dense with vines), it can act as a molecular sieve that separates macromolecules—usually proteins or nucleic acids—on the basis of size, electrical charge, or other physical properties.

Figure 12.13 outlines how gel electrophoresis can be used to separate mixtures of DNA fragments obtained from three different sources. A DNA sample from each source is placed in a separate well (or hole) at one end of a flat, rectangular gel. A negatively charged electrode from a power supply is attached near the end of the gel containing the DNA, and a positive electrode is attached near the other end. Because all nucleic acid molecules carry negative charges on their phosphate groups (PO_4^-; see Module 10.2), the DNA molecules all travel through the gel toward the positive

pole. However, longer DNA fragments are held back by the thicket of polymer fibers within the gel, so they move more slowly than the shorter fragments. Over time, shorter molecules move farther through the gel than longer fragments. Gel electrophoresis thus separates DNA fragments by length, with shorter molecules migrating toward the bottom faster than longer molecules.

When the current is turned off, a series of bands is left in each "lane" of the gel. Each band is a collection of DNA fragments of the same length. The bands can be made visible by staining, by exposure onto photographic film (if the DNA is radioactively labeled), or by measuring fluorescence (if the DNA is labeled with a fluorescent dye).

❓ **What causes DNA molecules to move toward the positive pole during electrophoresis? Why do large molecules move more slowly than smaller ones?**

The negatively charged phosphate groups of the DNA are attracted to the positive pole; the gel restricts the movement of longer fragments more. ◉

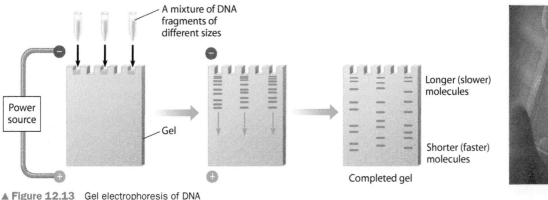

▲ **Figure 12.13** Gel electrophoresis of DNA

A mixture of DNA fragments of different sizes

Power source

Gel

Longer (slower) molecules

Shorter (faster) molecules

Completed gel

12.14 STR analysis is commonly used for DNA profiling

If you take another look at the overview of DNA profiling in Figure 12.11, you will see that we have learned about DNA amplification by PCR (step 2) and gel electrophoresis (step 3). Now, let's put them together to see how a DNA profile is made.

To create a DNA profile, a forensic scientist must compare genetic markers from two or more DNA samples. The genetic markers most often used in DNA profiling are inherited variations in the lengths of repetitive DNA segments. **Repetitive DNA** consists of nucleotide sequences that are present in multiple copies in the genome; much of the DNA that lies between genes in humans is of this type. Some regions of repetitive DNA vary considerably from one individual to the next.

For DNA profiling, the relevant type of repetitive DNA consists of short sequences repeated many times in a row; such a series of repeats is called a **short tandem repeat (STR)**. For example, one person might have the sequence AGAT repeated 12 times in a row at one place in the genome, the sequence GATA repeated 45 times in a row at a second place, and so on. Another person is likely to have the same sequences at the same places but with different numbers of repeats. These stretches of repetitive DNA, like any genetic marker, are more likely to be an exact match between relatives than between unrelated individuals.

STR analysis is a method of DNA profiling that compares the lengths of STR sequences at specific sites in the genome. Most commonly, STR analysis compares the number of repeats of specific four-nucleotide DNA sequences at 13 sites scattered throughout the genome. Each of these repeat sites, which typically contain from 3 to 50 four-nucleotide repeats in a row, vary widely from person to person. In fact, some of the short tandem repeats used in the standard procedure can be found in up to 80 different variations in the human population.

Consider the two samples of DNA shown in **Figure 12.14A**, where the top DNA was obtained at a crime scene and the bottom DNA from a suspect's blood. The two segments have the same number of repeats at the first site: 7 repeats of the four-nucleotide DNA sequence AGAT (shown in orange). Notice, however, that they differ in the number of repeats at

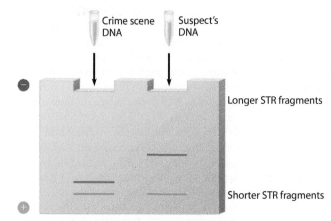

▲ **Figure 12.14B**　DNA profiles generated from the STRs in Figure 12.14A

the second site: 8 repeats of GATA (shown in purple) in the crime scene DNA, compared with 13 repeats in the suspect's DNA. To create a DNA profile, a scientist uses PCR to specifically amplify the regions of DNA that include these STR sites. This can be done by using primers matching nucleotide sequences known to flank the STR sites. The resulting DNA molecules are then compared by gel electrophoresis.

Figure 12.14B shows a gel that could have resulted from the STR fragments in Figure 12.14A. The differences in the locations of the bands reflect the different lengths of the DNA fragments. (A gel from an actual DNA profile would typically contain more than just two bands in each lane.) This gel would provide evidence that the crime scene DNA did not come from the suspect. Notice that electrophoresis allows us to see similarities as well as differences between mixtures of DNA molecules. Thus, data from DNA profiling can provide evidence of either innocence or guilt.

Although other methods have been used in the past, STR analysis of 13 predetermined STR sites is the current standard for DNA profiling in forensic and legal systems. Once determined, the number of repeats at each of these sites can be entered into the Combined DNA Index System (CODIS) database, administered by the Federal Bureau of Investigation. Within the human population, so much variation exists within the 13 standard sites that a DNA profile made from them can definitely identify a single person from within the entire human population. In the next module, we'll examine several real-world examples of how this technology has been used.

? **What are STRs? What is STR analysis?**

STRs are regions of the genome that contain varying numbers of in-a-row repeats of a short nucleotide sequence; STR analysis is a technique for determining whether two DNA samples have identical STRs.

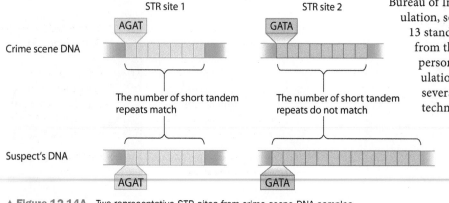

▲ **Figure 12.14A**　Two representative STR sites from crime scene DNA samples

12.15 DNA profiling has provided evidence in many forensic investigations

When a violent crime is committed, body fluids or small pieces of tissue may be left at the crime scene or on the clothes of the victim or assailant. If rape has occurred, semen may be recovered from the victim. DNA profiling can match such samples to the person they came from with a high degree of certainty because the DNA sequence of every person is unique, except for identical twins. And with PCR amplification of DNA, a tissue sample as small as 20 cells can be sufficient for testing.

Since its introduction in 1986, DNA profiling has become a standard tool of forensics and has provided crucial evidence in many famous cases. In the O. J. Simpson murder trial, DNA analysis proved that blood in Simpson's car belonged to the victims and that blood at the crime scene belonged to Simpson. (The jury in this case did not find the DNA evidence alone to be sufficient and Simpson was found not guilty.) During the investigation that led to his impeachment, President Bill Clinton repeatedly denied having sexual relations with Monica Lewinsky—until DNA profiling proved that his semen was on her dress.

Of course, DNA evidence can prove innocence as well as guilt. The Innocence Project, a nonprofit organization dedicated to overturning wrongful convictions, has used DNA technology and legal work to exonerate over 260 convicted criminals since 1989, including 15 on death row (Figure 12.15A). In more than a third of these cases, DNA profiling also identified the true perpetrators.

The use of DNA profiling extends beyond crimes. For instance, a comparison of the DNA of a child and the purported father can conclusively settle a question of paternity. Sometimes, paternity is of historical interest: DNA profiling proved that Thomas Jefferson or a close male relative fathered a child with his slave Sally Hemings.

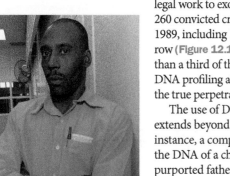

▲ Figure 12.15A STR analysis proved that convicted murderer Earl Washington was innocent, freeing him after 17 years in prison.

Going back much further, one of the strangest cases of DNA profiling is that of Cheddar Man, a 9,000-year-old skeleton found in a cave near Cheddar, England (Figure 12.15B). DNA was extracted from his tooth and analyzed. The DNA profile showed that Cheddar Man was a direct ancestor—through approximately 300 generations—of a present-day schoolteacher who lived only a half mile from the cave!

DNA profiling can also be used to identify victims. The largest such effort in history occurred after the World Trade Center attack of September 11, 2001. Forensic scientists, under the coordination of the Office of the Chief Medical Examiner of New York City, worked for years to identify over 20,000 samples of victims' remains. DNA profiles of tissue samples from the

▲ Figure 12.15B Cheddar Man and one of his modern-day descendants

disaster site were matched to DNA profiles from tissue known to be from the victims. If no sample of a victim's DNA was available, blood samples from close relatives were used to confirm identity through near matches. Over half of the identified victims at the World Trade Center site were identified solely by DNA evidence, providing closure to many grieving families.

Just how reliable is DNA profiling? When the standard CODIS set of 13 STR sites (see Module 12.14) is used, the probability of finding the same DNA profile in randomly selected, unrelated individuals is less than one in 10 billion. Put another way, a standard DNA profile can provide a statistical match of a particular DNA sample to just one living human. For this reason, DNA analyses are now accepted as compelling evidence by legal experts and scientists alike. In fact, DNA analysis on stored forensic samples has provided the evidence needed to solve many "cold cases" in recent years.

DNA analysis has also been used to probe the origin of non-human materials. In 1998, the U.S. Fish and Wildlife Service began testing the DNA in caviar to determine if the fish eggs originated from the species claimed on the label. By conclusively proving the origin of contraband animal products, DNA profiling could help protect endangered species. In another example, a 2005 study determined that DNA extracted from a 27,000-year-old Siberian mammoth was 98.6% identical to DNA from modern African elephants.

Although DNA profiling has provided definitive evidence in many investigations, the method is far from foolproof. Problems can arise from insufficient data, human error, or flawed evidence. While the science behind DNA profiling is irrefutable, the human element remains a possible confounding factor.

 In what way is DNA profiling valuable for determining innocence as well as guilt?

provide evidence in support of guilt or innocence.
does not come from a particular individual. DNA profiling therefore can
● A DNA profile can prove with near certainty that a sample of DNA does or

12.16 RFLPs can be used to detect differences in DNA sequences

Recall that a genetic marker is a DNA sequence that varies in a population. Like different alleles of a gene, the DNA sequence at a specific place on a chromosome may exhibit small nucleotide differences, or polymorphisms (from the Greek for "many forms"). Geneticists have cataloged many single-base-pair variations in the genome. Such a variation found in at least 1% of the population is called a **single nucleotide polymorphism** (**SNP**, pronounced "snip"). SNPs occur on average about once in 100 to 300 base pairs in the human genome either in the coding sequence of a gene or in a noncoding sequence.

SNPs may alter a restriction site—the sequence recognized by a restriction enzyme. Such alterations change the lengths of the restriction fragments formed by that enzyme when it cuts the DNA. A sequence variation of this type is called a **restriction fragment length polymorphism (RFLP**, pronounced "rif-lip"). Thus, RFLPs can serve as genetic markers for particular loci in the genome. RFLPs have many uses. For example, disease-causing alleles can be diagnosed with reasonable accuracy if a closely linked RFLP marker has been found. Alleles for a number of genetic diseases were first detected by means of RFLPs in this indirect way.

Restriction fragment analysis involves two of the methods you have learned about: DNA fragments produced by restriction enzymes (see Module 12.2) are sorted by gel electrophoresis (see Module 12.13). The number of restriction fragments and their sizes reflect the specific sequence of nucleotides in the starting DNA.

At the top of Figure 12.16, you can see corresponding segments of DNA from two DNA samples prepared from human tissue. Notice that the DNA sequences differ by a single base pair (highlighted in gold). In this case, the restriction enzyme cuts DNA between two cytosine (C) bases in the sequence CCGG and in its complement, GGCC. Because DNA from the first sample has two recognition sequences for the restriction enzyme, it is cleaved in two places, yielding three restriction fragments (labeled *w*, *x*, and *y*). DNA from the second sample, however, has only one recognition sequence and yields only two restriction fragments (*z* and *y*). Notice that the lengths of restriction fragments, as well as the number of fragments, differ, depending on the exact sequence of bases in the DNA.

To detect the differences between the collections of restriction fragments, we need to separate the restriction fragments in the two mixtures and compare their lengths. This process, called RFLP analysis, is accomplished through gel electrophoresis. As shown in the bottom of the figure, the three kinds of restriction fragments from sample 1 separate into three bands in the gel, while those from sample 2 separate into only two bands. Notice that the shortest fragment from sample 1 (*y*) produces a band at the same location as the identical short fragment from the sample 2. So you can see that electrophoresis allows us to see similarities as well as differences between mixtures of restriction fragments—and similarities as well as differences between the base sequences in DNA from two individuals. The restriction fragment analysis in Figure 12.16 clearly shows that

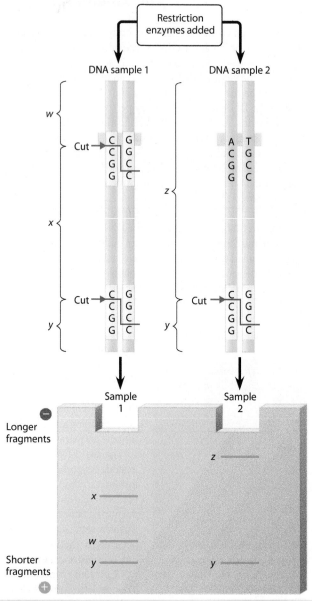

▲ **Figure 12.16** RFLP analysis

the two DNA samples differ in sequence. While RFLP analysis is rarely used today for identification, this method was vital in some of the earliest discoveries of disease-causing genes. For example, the gene for Huntington's disease was found after researchers used RFLPs to track a genetic marker that was closely associated with the disorder.

? You use a restriction enzyme to cut a DNA molecule that has three copies of the enzyme's recognition sequence clustered near one end. When you separate the restriction fragments by gel electrophoresis, how do you expect the bands to look?

● Three bands near the positive pole at the bottom of the gel (small fragments) and one band near the negative pole at the top of the gel (large fragment)

Genomics

12.17 Genomics is the scientific study of whole genomes

By the 1980s, biologists were using RFLPs to help map important genes in humans and some other organisms. But it didn't take long for biologists to think on a larger scale. In 1995, a team of scientists announced that they had determined the nucleotide sequence of the entire genome of *Haemophilus influenzae*, a bacterium that can cause several human diseases, including pneumonia and meningitis. **Genomics**, the science of studying a complete set of genes (a genome) and their interactions, was born.

Since 1995, researchers have used the tools and techniques of DNA technology to develop more and more detailed maps of the genomes of a number of species. The first targets of genomics research were bacteria, which have relatively little DNA. The genome of *H. influenzae*, for example, contains only 1.8 million nucleotides and 1,709 genes. But soon, the attention of genomics researchers turned toward more complex organisms with much larger genomes. As of 2009, the genomes of over 1,000 species have been published, and thousands more are in progress. Table 12.17 lists some of the completed genomes; for diploids, the size refers to the haploid genome. The vast majority of genomes under study are from prokaryotes, including *Escherichia coli* and several hundred other bacteria (some of medical importance), and a few dozen archaea. Over 100 eukaryotic species have been sequenced, including vertebrates, invertebrates, fungi, and plants.

Baker's yeast (*Saccharomyces cerevisiae*) was the first eukaryote to have its full sequence determined, and the roundworm *Caenorhabditis elegans* was the first multicellular organism. Other sequenced animals include the fruit fly (*Drosophila melanogaster*) and the lab mouse (*Mus musculus*), both model organisms for genetics. Plants, such as one type of mustard (*Arabidopsis thaliana*, an important

research organism) and rice (*Oryza sativa*, one of the world's most economically important crops), have also been completed. Other recently completed eukaryotic genomes include sorghum (another important commercial crop) and the honeybee, dog, chicken, and sea urchin.

In 2005, researchers completed the genome sequence for our closest living relative on the evolutionary tree of life, the chimpanzee (*Pan troglodytes*). Comparisons with human DNA revealed that we share 96% of our genome with our closest animal relative. As you will see in Module 12.21, genomic scientists are currently finding and studying the important differences, shedding scientific light on the age-old question of what makes us human.

Why map so many genomes? Not only are all genomes of interest in their own right, but comparative analysis provides invaluable insights into the evolutionary relationships among organisms. Also, having maps of a variety of genomes helps scientists interpret the human genome. For example, when scientists find a nucleotide sequence in the human genome similar to a yeast gene whose function is known, they have a valuable clue to the function of the human sequence. Indeed, several yeast protein-coding genes are so similar to certain human disease-causing genes that researchers have figured out the functions of the disease genes by studying their normal yeast counterparts. Many genes of disparate organisms are turning out to be astonishingly similar, to the point that one researcher has joked that he now views fruit flies as "little people with wings."

? Why is it useful to sequence nonhuman genomes?

● Besides their value in understanding evolution, comparative analysis of nonhuman genes helps scientists interpret human data.

TABLE 12.17 | SOME IMPORTANT COMPLETED GENOMES

Organism	Year Completed	Size of Haploid Genome (in Base Pairs)	Approximate Number of Genes
Haemophilus influenzae (bacterium)	1995	1.8 million	1,700
Saccharomyces cerevisiae (yeast)	1996	12 million	6,300
Escherichia coli (bacterium)	1997	4.6 million	4,400
Caenorhabditis elegans (nematode)	1998	100 million	20,100
Drosophila melanogaster (fruit fly)	2000	165 million	13,700
Arabidopsis thaliana (mustard plant)	2000	120 million	27,000
Mus musculus (mouse)	2001	2.6 billion	22,000
Oryza sativa (rice)	2002	430 million	42,000
Homo sapiens (humans)	2003	3.0 billion	21,000
Rattus norvegius (lab rat)	2004	2.8 billion	25,000
Pan troglodytes (chimpanzee)	2005	3.1 billion	22,000
Macaca mulatta (macaque)	2007	2.9 billion	22,000
Xenopus tropicalis (frog)	2010	1.7 billion	20,000

12.18 The Human Genome Project revealed that most of the human genome does not consist of genes

The **Human Genome Project (HGP)** had the goals of determining the nucleotide sequence of all DNA in the human genome and identifying the location and sequence of every gene. The HGP began in 1990 at 20 government-funded research centers in six countries. Several years into the project, private companies, chiefly Celera Genomics, in the United States, joined the effort. At the completion of the final draft of the sequence, over 99% of the genome had been determined to 99.999% accuracy. (There remain a few hundred gaps of unknown sequences within the human genome that will require special methods to figure out.) The DNA sequences determined by the HGP have been deposited in a publicly available database called Genbank.

The chromosomes in the human genome—22 autosomes plus the X and Y sex chromosomes—contain approximately 3.0 billion nucleotide pairs of DNA. To try to get a sense of this much DNA, imagine that its nucleotide sequence is printed in letters (A, T, C, and G) like the letters in this book. At this size, the sequence would fill a stack of books 18 stories high! The biggest surprise from the HGP is the small number of human genes. The current estimate is about 21,000 genes—very close to the number found in a nematode worm. How, then, do we account for human complexity? Part of the answer may lie in alternative RNA splicing (see Module 11.4); scientists think that a typical human gene specifies several polypeptides.

In humans, as in most complex eukaryotes, only a small amount of our total DNA (about 1.5%) is contained in genes that code for proteins, tRNAs, or rRNAs (Figure 12.18). Most multicellular eukaryotes have a huge amount of noncoding DNA; about 98.5% of human DNA is of this type. About one-quarter of our DNA consists of introns and gene control sequences such as promoters and enhancers (see Modules 11.1 and 11.3). The remaining noncoding DNA has been dubbed "junk DNA," a tongue-in-cheek way of saying that scientists don't fully understand its functions.

Much of the DNA between genes consists of repetitive DNA, nucleotide sequences present in many copies in the genome. The repeated units of some of this DNA, such as the STRs used in DNA profiling, are short (see Module 12.14). Stretches of DNA with thousands of short repetitions are also prominent at the centromeres and ends of chromosomes—called **telomeres**—suggesting that this DNA plays a role in chromosome structure.

In the second main type of repetitive DNA, each repeated unit is hundreds of nucleotides long, and the copies are scattered around the genome. Most of these sequences seem to be associated with **transposable elements** ("jumping genes"), DNA segments that can move or be copied from one location to another in a chromosome and even between chromosomes. Researchers believe that transposable elements, through their copy-and-paste mechanism, are responsible for the proliferation of dispersed repetitive DNA in the human genome.

The potential benefits of having a complete map of the human genome are enormous, especially to medicine. For instance, hundreds of disease-associated genes have already been identified. One example is the gene that is mutated in an inherited type of Parkinson's disease, a debilitating brain disorder that causes motor problems of increasing severity. Until recently, Parkinson's disease was not known to have a hereditary component. But data from the Human Genome Project mapped a small number of cases of Parkinson's disease to a specific gene. Interestingly, an altered version of the protein encoded by this gene has also been tied to Alzheimer's disease, suggesting a previously unknown link between these two brain disorders. Moreover, the same gene is also found in rats, where it plays a role in the sense of smell, and in zebra finches, where it is thought to be involved in song learning. Cross-species comparisons such as these may uncover clues about the role played by the normal version of the protein in the human brain. And such knowledge could eventually lead to treatment for the half a million Americans with Parkinson's disease.

One interesting question about the Human Genome Project is: Whose genome was sequenced? The human genome sequenced by the public consortium was actually a reference genome compiled from a group of individuals. The genome sequenced by Celera consisted primarily of DNA sampled from the company's president. These representative sequences will serve as standards so that comparisons of individual differences and similarities can be made. Starting in 2007, the genomes of a number of other individuals—the first was James Watson, codiscoverer of the structure of DNA—have also been sequenced. These sequences are part of a larger effort to collect information on all of the genetic variations that affect human characteristics. As the amount of sequence data multiplies, the small differences that account for individual variation within our species will come to light.

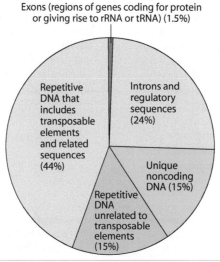

▲ Figure 12.18   Composition of the human genome

? The haploid human genome consists of about _____ base pairs and _____ genes spread over _____ different chromosomes (provide three numbers).

3 billion . . . 21,000 . . . 24 (22 autosomes plus 2 sex chromosomes)

12.19 The whole-genome shotgun method of sequencing a genome can provide a wealth of data quickly

Sequencing an entire genome is a complex task that requires careful work. The Human Genome Project proceeded through three stages that provided progressively more detailed views of the human genome. First, geneticists combined pedigree analyses of large families to map over 5,000 genetic markers (mostly RFLPs) spaced throughout all of the chromosomes. The resulting low-resolution *linkage map* (see Module 9.19) provided a framework for mapping other markers and for arranging later, more detailed maps of particular regions. Next, researchers determined the number of base pairs between the markers in the linkage map. These data helped them construct a *physical map* of the human genome. Finally came the most arduous part of the project: determining the nucleotide sequences of the set of DNA fragments that had been mapped. Advances in automated DNA sequencing were crucial to this endeavor.

This three-stage approach is logical and thorough. However, in 1992, molecular biologist J. Craig Venter proposed an alternative strategy called the **whole-genome shotgun method** and set up the company Celera Genomics to implement it. His idea was essentially to skip the genetic and physical mapping stages and start directly with the sequencing step. In the whole-genome shotgun method, an entire genome is chopped by restriction enzymes into fragments that are cloned and sequenced in just one stage (**Figure 12.19**). High-performance computers running specialized mapping software can assemble the millions of overlapping short sequences into a single continuous sequence for every chromosome—an entire genome.

Today, the whole-genome shotgun approach is the method of choice for genomic researchers because it is fast and relatively inexpensive. However, recent research has revealed some limitations of this method, such as difficulties with

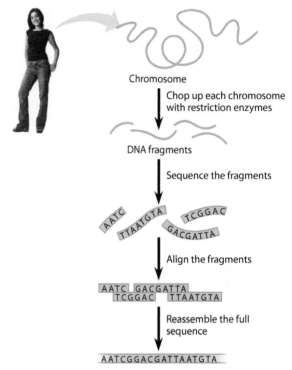

▲ **Figure 12.19** The whole-genome shotgun method

repetitive sequences, suggesting that a hybrid approach that combines whole-genome shotgunning with physical or genetic maps may prove to be the most useful method in the long run.

? **What are the primary advantages of the whole-genome shotgun method?**

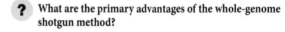
● It is faster and cheaper than the three-stage method of genome sequencing.

12.20 Proteomics is the scientific study of the full set of proteins encoded by a genome

The successes in the field of genomics have encouraged scientists to attempt a similar systematic study of the full protein sets (proteomes) encoded by genomes, an approach called **proteomics**. The number of different proteins in humans far exceeds the number of genes—about 100,000 proteins versus about 21,000 genes. And since proteins, not genes, actually carry out most of the activities of the cell, scientists must study when and where proteins are produced in an organism and how they interact in order to understand the functioning of cells and organisms. Given the huge number of proteins and the myriad ways that their production can be controlled, assembling and analyzing proteomes pose many experimental challenges. Ongoing advances are beginning to provide the tools to meet those challenges.

Genomics and proteomics are enabling biologists to approach the study of life from an increasingly holistic perspective. Biologists are now in a position to compile complete catalogs of genes and proteins—that is, a full listing of all the "parts" that contribute to the operation of cells, tissues, and organisms. With such catalogs in hand, researchers are shifting their attention from the individual parts to how they function together in biological systems.

? **If every protein is encoded by a gene, how can humans have many more proteins than genes?** *Hint*: See Module 11.4.

● The RNA transcribed from one gene may be spliced several different ways to produce different mRNAs that are translated into different proteins.

12.21 Genomes hold clues to human evolution

Comparisons of genome sequences from different species allow geneticists to evaluate the evolutionary relationships between those species. The more similar in sequence the same gene is in two species, the more closely related those species are in their evolutionary history. Comparing genes of closely related species sheds light on recent evolutionary events, whereas comparing those of distantly related species helps us understand more ancient evolutionary history.

The small number of genetic differences between closely related species makes it easier to correlate phenotypic differences between the species with particular genetic differences. The completion of the chimpanzee genome in 2005 has allowed us to compare our genome with that of our primate cousins. Such an analysis revealed that these two genomes differ by 1.2% in single-base substitutions. Researchers were surprised when they found a further 2.7% difference due to insertions or deletions of larger regions in the genome of one or the other species, with many of the insertions being duplications or other repetitive DNA. In fact, a third of the human duplications are not present in the chimpanzee genome, and some of these duplications contain regions associated with human diseases. All of these observations provide clues to the forces that might have swept the two genomes along different paths, but we don't have a complete picture yet.

What about specific genes and types of genes that differ between humans and chimpanzees? Using evolutionary analyses, biologists have identified a number of genes that have evolved faster in humans. Among them are genes involved in defense against malaria and tuberculosis and a gene regulating brain size. One gene that changed rapidly in the human lineage is *FOXP2*, a gene implicated in speech and vocalization. Differences between the *FOXP2* gene in humans and chimpanzees may play a role in the ability of humans, but not chimpanzees, to communicate by speech.

Neanderthals (*Homo neanderthalensis*) were humans' closest relatives (Figure 12.21). First appearing at least 300,000 year ago, Neanderthals lived in Europe and Asia until suddenly going extinct a mere 30,000 years ago. Modern humans (*Homo sapiens*) first appeared in Africa around 200,000 years ago and spread into Europe and Asia around 50,000 years ago (see Module 19.14)—meaning that modern humans and Neanderthals most likely comingled for some time.

A 2009 rough draft of a 60%-complete Neanderthal genome has, for the first time, allowed detailed genomic comparisons between two species in the genus *Homo*. Using 38,000-year-old thigh bone fossils of two *Homo neanderthalensis* females discovered in a Croatian cave, genomic analysis confirmed Neanderthals as a separate species and as our closest relatives (much closer than chimpanzees). Further comparisons, completed in 2010, suggested that Neanderthals and some *H. sapiens* probably did interbreed. Analysis of the sequence of the *FOXP2* gene showed that Neanderthals had the same allele as modern humans, hinting that Neanderthals may have had the same ability to speak as we do. Other genetic analyses of less complete Neanderthal genomes revealed one male to have an unusual allele for a pigment gene that would have given him pale skin and red hair. And, interestingly, analysis of the lactase gene suggests that Neanderthals, like the majority of modern humans, were lactose intolerant as adults.

▲ Figure 12.21
Reconstruction of a Neanderthal female, based on a 36,000-year-old skull

Comparisons with Neanderthals and chimpanzees are part of a larger effort to learn more about the human genome. Other research efforts are extending genomic studies to many more species. These studies will advance our understanding of all aspects of biology, including health, ecology, and evolution. In fact, comparisons of the completed genome sequences of bacteria, archaea, and eukaryotes supported the theory that these are the three fundamental domains of life—a topic we discuss further in the next unit.

 How can cross-species comparisons of the nucleotide sequences of a gene provide insight into evolution?

Similarities in gene sequences correlate with evolutionary relatedness; greater genetic similarities reflect a more recent shared ancestry.

C H A P T E R   1 2   R E V I E W

 For Practice Quizzes, BioFlix, MP3 Tutors, and Activities, go to www.masteringbiology.com.

Reviewing the Concepts

Gene Cloning (12.1–12.5)

12.1 Genes can be cloned in recombinant plasmids. Gene cloning is one application of biotechnology, the manipulation of organisms or their components to make useful products. Researchers can create plasmids containing recombinant DNA and insert those plasmids into bacteria. If the recombinant bacteria multiply into a clone, the foreign genes are also duplicated and copies of the gene or its protein product can be harvested.

12.2 Enzymes are used to "cut and paste" DNA. Restriction enzymes cut DNA at specific sequences, forming restriction fragments. DNA ligase "pastes" DNA fragments together.

12.3 Cloned genes can be stored in genomic libraries. Genomic libraries, sets of DNA fragments containing all of an organism's genes, can be constructed and stored using cloned bacterial plasmids, phages, or bacterial artificial chromosomes (BACs).

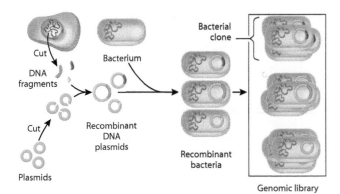

Bacterial clone

Cut

DNA fragments

Bacterium

Cut

Recombinant DNA plasmids

Plasmids

Recombinant bacteria

Genomic library

12.4 Reverse transcriptase can help make genes for cloning. cDNA libraries contain only the genes that are transcribed by a particular type of cell.

12.5 Nucleic acid probes identify clones carrying specific genes. A short, single-stranded molecule of labeled DNA or RNA can tag a desired gene in a library.

Genetically Modified Organisms (12.6–12.10)

12.6 Recombinant cells and organisms can mass-produce gene products. Bacteria, yeast, cell cultures, and whole animals can be used to make products for medical and other uses.

12.7 DNA technology has changed the pharmaceutical industry and medicine. Researchers use gene cloning to produce hormones, diagnose diseases, and produce vaccines.

12.8 Genetically modified organisms are transforming agriculture. A number of important crop plants are genetically modified.

12.9 Genetically modified organisms raise concerns about human and environmental health. Genetic engineering involves risks, such as ecological damage from GM crops.

12.10 Gene therapy may someday help treat a variety of diseases.

DNA Profiling (12.11–12.16)

12.11 The analysis of genetic markers can produce a DNA profile. DNA technology—methods for studying and manipulating genetic material—has revolutionized the field of forensics. DNA profiling—the analysis of DNA fragments—can determine whether two samples of DNA come from the same individual.

12.12 The PCR method is used to amplify DNA sequences. The polymerase chain reaction (PCR) can be used to amplify a DNA sample. The use of specific primers that flank the desired sequence ensures that only a particular subset of the DNA sample will be copied.

12.13 Gel electrophoresis sorts DNA molecules by size.

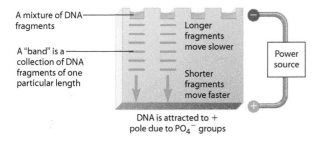

A mixture of DNA fragments

Longer fragments move slower

A "band" is a collection of DNA fragments of one particular length

Shorter fragments move faster

Power source

DNA is attracted to + pole due to PO_4^- groups

12.14 STR analysis is commonly used for DNA profiling. Short tandem repeats (STRs) are stretches of DNA that contain short nucleotide sequences repeated many times in a row. DNA profiling by STR analysis involves amplifying a set of 13 STRs.

12.15 DNA profiling has provided evidence in many forensic investigations. The applications of DNA profiling include helping to solve crimes and establishing paternity.

12.16 RFLPs can be used to detect differences in DNA sequences. Restriction fragment length polymorphisms (RFLPs) reflect differences in the sequences of DNA samples.

Genomics (12.17–12.21)

12.17 Genomics is the scientific study of whole genomes. Genomics researchers have sequenced many prokaryotic and eukaryotic genomes. Besides being of interest in their own right, nonhuman genomes can be compared with the human genome.

12.18 The Human Genome Project revealed that most of the human genome does not consist of genes. Data from the Human Genome Project (HGP) revealed that the human genome contains about 21,000 genes and a huge amount of noncoding DNA, much of which consists of repetitive nucleotide sequences and transposable elements that can move about within the genome.

12.19 The whole-genome shotgun method of sequencing a genome can provide a wealth of data quickly. The HGP uses genetic and physical mapping of chromosomes followed by DNA sequencing. Modern genomic analysis often uses the faster whole-genome shotgun method.

12.20 Proteomics is the scientific study of the full set of proteins encoded by a genome.

12.21 Genomes hold clues to human evolution.

Connecting the Concepts

1. Imagine you have found a small quantity of DNA. Fill in the following diagram, which outlines a series of DNA technology experiments you could perform to study this DNA.

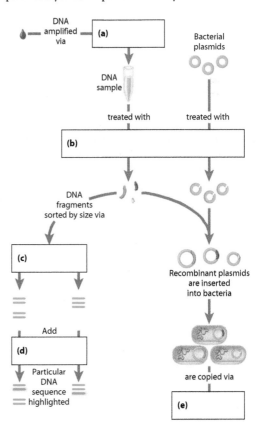

DNA amplified via **(a)**

Bacterial plasmids

DNA sample

treated with

treated with

(b)

DNA fragments sorted by size via

(c)

Recombinant plasmids are inserted into bacteria

Add

(d)

Particular DNA sequence highlighted

are copied via

(e)

Testing Your Knowledge

Multiple Choice

2. Which of the following would be considered a transgenic organism?
   a. a bacterium that has received genes via conjugation
   b. a human given a corrected human blood-clotting gene
   c. a fern grown in cell culture from a single fern root cell
   d. a rat with rabbit hemoglobin genes
   e. a human treated with insulin produced by bacteria

3. When a typical restriction enzyme cuts a DNA molecule, the cuts are uneven, giving the DNA fragments single-stranded ends. These ends are useful in recombinant DNA work because
   a. they enable a cell to recognize fragments produced by the enzyme.
   b. they serve as starting points for DNA replication.
   c. the fragments will bond to other fragments with complementary ends.
   d. they enable researchers to use the fragments as molecular probes.
   e. only single-stranded DNA segments can code for proteins.

4. The DNA profiles used as evidence in a murder trial look something like supermarket bar codes. The pattern of bars in a DNA profile shows
   a. the order of bases in a particular gene.
   b. the presence of various-sized fragments of DNA.
   c. the presence of dominant or recessive alleles for particular traits.
   d. the order of genes along particular chromosomes.
   e. the exact location of a specific gene in a genomic library.

5. A biologist isolated a gene from a human cell, attached it to a plasmid, and inserted the plasmid into a bacterium. The bacterium made a new protein, but it was nothing like the protein normally produced in a human cell. Why? (*Explain your answer.*)
   a. The bacterium had undergone transformation.
   b. The gene did not have sticky ends.
   c. The gene contained introns.
   d. The gene did not come from a genomic library.
   e. The biologist should have cloned the gene first.

6. A paleontologist has recovered a tiny bit of organic material from the 400-year-old preserved skin of an extinct dodo. She would like to compare DNA from the sample with DNA from living birds. Which of the following would be most useful for increasing the amount of DNA available for testing?
   a. restriction fragment analysis
   b. polymerase chain reaction
   c. molecular probe analysis
   d. electrophoresis
   e. Ti plasmid technology

7. How many genes are there in a human sperm cell?
   a. 23   d. about 21,000
   b. 46   e. about 3 billion
   c. 5,000–10,000

Describing, Comparing, and Explaining

8. Why does DNA profiling rely on comparing specific genetic markers rather than the entire genome?

9. Explain how you might engineer *E. coli* to produce human growth hormone (HGH) using the following: *E. coli* containing a plasmid, DNA carrying the gene for HGH, DNA ligase, a restriction enzyme, equipment for manipulating and growing bacteria, a method for extracting and purifying the hormone, an appropriate DNA probe. (Assume that the human HGH gene lacks introns.)

10. Recombinant DNA techniques are used to custom-build bacteria for two main purposes: to obtain multiple copies of certain genes and to obtain useful proteins produced by certain genes. Give an example of each of these applications in medicine and agriculture.

Applying the Concepts

11. A biochemist hopes to find a gene in human liver cells that codes for an important blood-clotting protein. She knows that the nucleotide sequence of a small part of the blood-clotting gene is CTGGACTGACA. Briefly outline a possible method she might use to isolate the desired gene.

12. What is left for genetic researchers to do now that the Human Genome Project has determined nearly complete nucleotide sequences for all of the human chromosomes? Explain.

13. Today, it is fairly easy to make transgenic plants and animals. What are some important safety and ethical issues raised by this use of recombinant DNA technology? What are some of the possible dangers of introducing genetically engineered organisms into the environment? What are some reasons for and against leaving decisions in these areas to scientists? To business owners and executives? What are some reasons for and against more public involvement? How might these decisions affect you? How do you think these decisions should be made?

14. In the not-too-distant future, gene therapy may be an option for the treatment and cure of some inherited disorders. What do you think are the most serious ethical issues that must be dealt with before human gene therapy is used on a large scale? Why do you think these issues are important?

15. The possibility of extensive genetic testing raises questions about how personal genetic information should be used. For example, should employers or potential employers have access to such information? Why or why not? Should the information be available to insurance companies? Why or why not? Is there any reason for the government to keep genetic files? Is there any obligation to warn relatives who might share a defective gene? Might some people avoid being tested for fear of being labeled genetic outcasts? Or might they be compelled to be tested against their wishes? Can you think of other reasons to proceed with caution?

Answers to all questions can be found in Appendix 4.

Metric Conversion Table

Measurement	Unit and Abbreviation	Metric Equivalent	Approximate Metric-to-English Conversion Factor	Approximate English-to-Metric Conversion Factor
Length	1 kilometer (km)	= 1,000 (10^3) meters	1 km = 0.6 mile	1 mile = 1.6 km
	1 meter (m)	= 100 (10^2) centimeters	1 m = 1.1 yards	1 yard = 0.9 m
		= 1,000 millimeters	1 m = 3.3 feet	1 foot = 0.3 m
			1 m = 39.4 inches	
	1 centimeter (cm)	= 0.01 (10^{-2}) meter	1 cm = 0.4 inch	1 foot = 30.5 cm
				1 inch = 2.5 cm
	1 millimeter (mm)	= 0.001 (10^{-3}) meter	1 mm = 0.04 inch	
	1 micrometer (μm)	= 10^{-6} meter (10^{-3} μm)		
	1 nanometer (nm)	= 10^{-9} meter (10^{-3} μm)		
	1 angstrom (Å)	= 10^{-10} meter (10^{-4} μm)		
Area	1 hectare (ha)	= 10,000 square meters	1 ha = 2.5 acres	1 acre = 0.4 ha
	1 square meter (m^2)	= 10,000 square centimeters	1 m^2 = 1.2 square yards	1 square yard = 0.8 m^2
			1 m^2 = 10.8 square feet	1 square foot = 0.09 m^2
	1 square centimeter (cm^2)	= 100 square millimeters	1 cm^2 = 0.16 square inch	1 square inch = 6.5 cm^2
Mass	1 metric ton (t)	= 1,000 kilograms	1 t = 1.1 tons	1 ton = 0.91 t
	1 kilogram (kg)	= 1,000 grams	1 kg = 2.2 pounds	1 pound = 0.45 kg
	1 gram (g)	= 1,000 milligrams	1 g = 0.04 ounce	1 ounce = 28.35 g
			1 g = 15.4 grains	
	1 milligram (mg)	= 10^{-3} gram	1 mg = 0.02 grain	
	1 microgram (μg)	= 10^{-6} gram		
Volume (Solids)	1 cubic meter (m^3)	= 1,000,000 cubic centimeters	1 m^3 = 1.3 cubic yards	1 cubic yard = 0.8 m^3
			1 m^3 = 35.3 cubic feet	1 cubic foot = 0.03 m^3
	1 cubic centimeter (cm^3 or cc)	= 10^{-6} cubic meter	1 cm^3 = 0.06 cubic inch	1 cubic inch = 16.4 cm^3
	1 cubic millimeter (mm^3)	= 10^{-9} cubic meter (10^{-3} cubic centimeter)		
Volume (Liquids and Gases)	1 kiloliter (kL or kl)	= 1,000 liters	1 kL = 264.2 gallons	
	1 liter (L or l)	= 1,000 milliliters	1 L = 0.26 gallon	1 gallon = 3.79 L
			1 L = 1.06 quarts	1 quart = 0.95 L
	1 milliliter (mL or ml)	= 10^{-3} liter	1 mL = 0.03 fluid ounce	1 quart = 946 mL
		= 1 cubic centimeter	1 mL = $\frac{1}{4}$ teaspoon	1 pint = 473 mL
			1 mL = 15–16 drops	1 fluid ounce = 29.6 mL
				1 teaspoon = 5 mL
	1 microliter (μL or μl)	= 10^{-6} liter (10^{-3} milliliters)		
Time	1 second (s)	= $\frac{1}{60}$ minute		
	1 millisecond (ms)	= 10^{-3} second		
Temperature	Degrees Celsius (°C)		°F = $\frac{9}{5}$ °C − 32	°C = $\frac{5}{9}$(°F − 32)

The Periodic Table

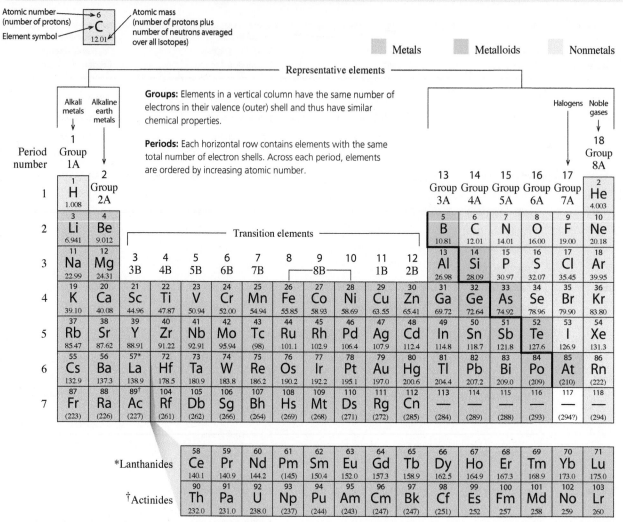

Name (Symbol)	Atomic Number	Name (Symbol)	Atomic Number	Name (Symbol)	Atomic Number	Name (Symbol)	Atomic Number	Name (Symbol)	Atomic Number
Actinium (Ac)	89	Copernicium (Cn)	112	Iridium (Ir)	77	Palladium (Pd)	46	Sodium (Na)	11
Aluminum (Al)	13	Copper (Cu)	29	Iron (Fe)	26	Phosphorus (P)	15	Strontium (Sr)	38
Americium (Am)	95	Curium (Cm)	96	Krypton (Kr)	36	Platinum (Pt)	78	Sulfur (S)	16
Antimony (Sb)	51	Darmstadtium (Ds)	110	Lanthanum (La)	57	Plutonium (Pu)	94	Tantalum (Ta)	73
Argon (Ar)	18	Dubnium (Db)	105	Lawrencium (Lr)	103	Polonium (Po)	84	Technetium (Tc)	43
Arsenic (As)	33	Dysprosium (Dy)	66	Lead (Pb)	82	Potassium (K)	19	Tellurium (Te)	52
Astatine (At)	85	Einsteinium (Es)	99	Lithium (Li)	3	Praseodymium (Pr)	59	Terbium (Tb)	65
Barium (Ba)	56	Erbium (Er)	68	Lutetium (Lu)	71	Promethium (Pm)	61	Thallium (Tl)	81
Berkelium (Bk)	97	Europium (Eu)	63	Magnesium (Mg)	12	Protactinium (Pa)	91	Thorium (Th)	90
Beryllium (Be)	4	Fermium (Fm)	100	Manganese (Mn)	25	Radium (Ra)	88	Thulium (Tm)	69
Bismuth (Bi)	83	Fluorine (F)	9	Meitnerium (Mt)	109	Radon (Rn)	86	Tin (Sn)	50
Bohrium (Bh)	107	Francium (Fr)	87	Mendelevium (Md)	101	Rhenium (Re)	75	Titanium (Ti)	22
Boron (B)	5	Gadolinium (Gd)	64	Mercury (Hg)	80	Rhodium (Rh)	45	Tungsten (W)	74
Bromine (Br)	35	Gallium (Ga)	31	Molybdenum (Mo)	42	Roentgenium (Rg)	111	Uranium (U)	92
Cadmium (Cd)	48	Germanium (Ge)	32	Neodymium (Nd)	60	Rubidium (Rb)	37	Vanadium (V)	23
Calcium (Ca)	20	Gold (Au)	79	Neon (Ne)	10	Ruthenium (Ru)	44	Xenon (Xe)	54
Californium (Cf)	98	Hafnium (Hf)	72	Neptunium (Np)	93	Rutherfordium (Rf)	104	Ytterbium (Yb)	70
Carbon (C)	6	Hassium (Hs)	108	Nickel (Ni)	28	Samarium (Sm)	62	Yttrium (Y)	39
Cerium (Ce)	58	Helium (He)	2	Niobium (Nb)	41	Scandium (Sc)	21	Zinc (Zn)	30
Cesium (Cs)	55	Holmium (Ho)	67	Nitrogen (N)	7	Seaborgium (Sg)	106	Zirconium (Zr)	40
Chlorine (Cl)	17	Hydrogen (H)	1	Nobelium (No)	102	Selenium (Se)	34		
Chromium (Cr)	24	Indium (In)	49	Osmium (Os)	76	Silicon (Si)	14		
Cobalt (Co)	27	Iodine (I)	53	Oxygen (O)	8	Silver (Ag)	47		

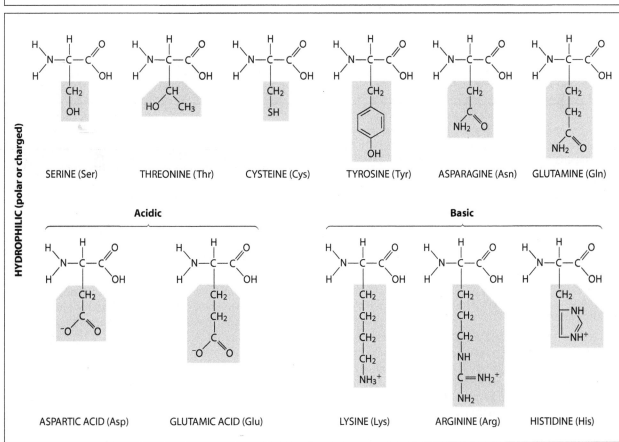

HYDROPHOBIC (Nonpolar)

GLYCINE (Gly) ALANINE (Ala) VALINE (Val) LEUCINE (Leu) ISOLEUCINE (Ile)

METHIONINE (Met) PHENYLALANINE (Phe) TRYPTOPHAN (Trp) PROLINE (Pro)

HYDROPHILIC (polar or charged)

SERINE (Ser) THREONINE (Thr) CYSTEINE (Cys) TYROSINE (Tyr) ASPARAGINE (Asn) GLUTAMINE (Gln)

Acidic

Basic

ASPARTIC ACID (Asp) GLUTAMIC ACID (Glu) LYSINE (Lys) ARGININE (Arg) HISTIDINE (His)

Chapter Review Answers

Chapter 1

1. The vertical scale of biology refers to the hierarchy of biological organization: from molecules to organelles, cells, tissues, organs, organ systems, organisms, populations, communities, ecosystems, and the biosphere. At each level, emergent properties arise from the interaction and organization of component parts. The horizontal scale of biology refers to the incredible diversity of living organisms, past and present, including the 1.8 million species that have been named so far. Biologists divide these species into three domains—Bacteria, Archaea, and Eukarya—and organize them into kingdoms and other groups that attempt to reflect evolutionary relationships.

2. a. life; b. evolution; c. natural selection; d. unity of life; e. three domains (or numerous kingdoms; 1.8 million species)

3. d 4. c 5. e (You may have been tempted to choose b, the molecular level. However, protists may have chemical communication or interactions with other protists. No protists, however, have organs.) 6. d 7. c 8. b 9. d

10. Both energy and chemical nutrients are passed through an ecosystem from producers to consumers to decomposers. But energy enters an ecosystem as sunlight and leaves as heat. Chemical nutrients are recycled from the soil or atmosphere through plants, consumers, and decomposers and returned to the air, soil, and water.

11. Darwin described how natural selection operates in populations whose individuals have varied traits that are inherited. When natural selection favors the reproductive success of certain individuals in a population more than others, the proportions of heritable variations change over the generations, gradually adapting a population to its environment.

12. In pursuit of answers to questions about nature, a scientist uses a logical thought process involving these key elements: observations about natural phenomena, questions derived from observations, hypotheses posed as tentative explanations of observations, logical predictions of the outcome of tests if the hypotheses are correct, and actual tests of hypotheses. Scientific research is not a rigid method because a scientist must adapt these processes to the set of conditions particular to each study. Intuition, chance, and luck are also part of science.

13. Technology is the application of scientific knowledge. For example, the use of solar power to run a calculator or heat a home is an application of our knowledge, derived by the scientific process, of the nature of light as a type of energy and how light energy can be converted to other forms of energy. Another example is the use of DNA to insert new genes into crop plants. This process, often called genetic engineering, stems from decades of scientific research on the structure and function of DNA from many kinds of organisms.

14. Natural selection screens (edits) heritable variations by favoring the reproductive success of some individuals over others. It can only select from the variations that are present in the population; it does not create new genes or variations.

15. a. Hypothesis: Giving rewards to mice will improve their learning. Prediction: If mice are rewarded with food, they will learn to run a maze faster.
    b. The control group was the mice that were not rewarded. Without them, it would be impossible to know if the mice that were rewarded decreased their time running the maze only because of practice.
    c. Both groups of mice should not have run the maze before and should be about the same age. Both experiments should be run at the same time of day and under the same conditions.
    d. Yes, the results fail to falsify the hypothesis because data show that the rewarded mice began to run the maze faster by day 3 and improved their performance (ran faster than the control mice) each day thereafter.

16. The researcher needed to compare the number of attacks on artificial king snakes with attacks on artificial brown snakes. It may be that there were simply more predators in the coral snake areas or that the predators were hungrier than the predators in the other areas. The experiment needed a control and proper data analysis.

17. If these cell division control genes are involved in producing the larger tomato, they may have similar effects if transferred to other fruits or vegetables. Cancer is a result of uncontrolled cell division. One could see if there are similarities between the tomato genes and any human genes that could be related to human development or disease. The control of cell division is a fundamental process in growth, repair, and asexual reproduction—all important topics in biology.

18. Virtually any news report or magazine contains stories that are mainly about biology or at least have biological connections. How about biological connections in advertisements?

Chapter 2

1. a. protons; b. neutrons; c. electrons; d. different isotopes; e. covalent bonds; f. ionic bonds; g. polar covalent bonds; h. hydrogen bonding

2.

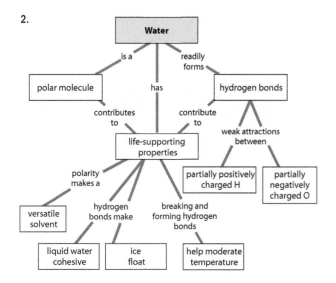

3. c 4. b 5. c 6. e 7. a (It needs to share 2 more electrons for a full outer shell of 8.) 8. a 9. c 10. d 11. F (Only salt and water are compounds; carbon is an element.) 12. F (The smallest unit of an element is an atom.) 13. T 14. T 15. F (Water molecules in ice are farther apart.) 16. T 17. F (Most acid precipitation results from burning fossil fuels.) 18. T

19. For a diagram, see Figure 2.8. Water molecules form hydrogen bonds because their slightly negative O atoms are attracted to the slightly positive H atoms of neighboring molecules. The unique properties of water that result from hydrogen bonding are cohesion, adhesion, surface tension, the ability to absorb and store large amounts of heat and to release heat as water cools, a solid form (ice) that is less dense than liquid water, and solvent properties.

20. First: Because increasing the temperature of water (the average speed of its molecules) requires breaking hydrogen bonds, a process that absorbs heat, a large amount of heat can be added to water before the water's temperature starts to rise. Conversely, when the surrounding temperature falls, new hydrogen bonds form in water, with the release of heat that slows the cooling process. Second: When the body becomes overheated, water evaporating from its surface decreases the body's temperature (evaporative cooling) because the hotter water molecules leave.

21. A covalent bond forms when atoms complete their outer shells by sharing electrons. Atoms can also complete their outer shells by gaining or losing electrons. This leaves the atoms as ions, with + or – charges. The oppositely charged ions are attracted to each other, forming an ionic bond.

22. An acid is a compound that donates hydrogen ions (H$^+$) to a solution. A base is a compound that accepts hydrogen ions and removes them from solution. Acidity is described by the pH scale, which measures H$^+$ concentration on a scale of 0 (most acidic) to 14 (most basic).

23. Fluorine needs 1 electron for a full outer shell of 8, and if potassium loses 1 electron, its outer shell will have 8. Potas-

sium will lose an electron (becoming a + ion), and fluorine will pick it up (becoming a – ion). The ions can form an ionic bond.

24. The elements in a row all have the same number of electron shells. In a column, all the elements have the same number of electrons in their outer shell.

25. These extreme environments may be similar to those found on other planets. The fact that life may have evolved and continues to flourish in such extreme environments here on Earth suggests that some form of life may have evolved on other planets. Astrobiologists would want to study these extreme habitats and the adaptations to such challenging conditions that have evolved in extremophiles. In addition to seeking evidence for the past or current presence of water on Mars or other planets, scientists now know to search in environments that previously would have been thought incapable of supporting life.

Chapter 3

1. Carbon forms four covalent bonds, either with other carbon atoms, producing chains or rings of various lengths and shapes, or with other atoms, such as characteristic chemical groups that confer specific properties on a molecule. This is the basis for the incredible diversity of organic compounds. Organisms can link a small number of monomers into different arrangements to produce a huge variety of polymers.

2. a. glucose; b. energy storage; c. cellulose; d. fats; e. cell membrane component; f. steroids; g. amino group; h. carboxyl group; i. R group; j. enzyme; k. structural protein; l. movement; m. hemoglobin; n. defense; o. phosphate group; p. nitrogenous base; q. ribose or deoxyribose; r. DNA; s. code for proteins

3. d (The second kind of molecule is a polymer of the first.) 4. c 5. d 6. c 7. a 8. b 9. e 10. d

11. Fats (triglycerides)—energy storage. Phospholipids—major components of membranes. Steroids—cholesterol is a component of animal cell membranes; other steroids function as hormones.

12. Weak bonds that stabilize the three-dimensional structure of a protein are disrupted, and the protein unfolds. Function depends on shape, so if the protein is the wrong shape, it won't function properly.

13. Proteins are made of 20 amino acids arranged in many different sequences into chains of many different lengths. Genes, defined stretches of DNA, dictate the amino acid sequences of proteins in the cell.

14. Proteins function as enzymes, which catalyze chemical reactions. They also function in structure, movement, transport, defense, signaling, signal reception, and storage of amino acids (see Module 3.12).

15. The sequence of nucleotides in DNA is transcribed into a sequence of nucleotides in RNA, which determines the sequence of amino acids that will be used to build a polypeptide.

Proteins mediate all the activities of a cell; thus, by coding for proteins, DNA controls the functions of a cell.

16. This is a hydrolysis reaction, which consumes water. It is essentially the reverse of the diagram in Figure 3.5, except that fructose has a different shape than glucose.

17. Circle NH_2, an amino group; COOH, a carboxyl group; and OH, a hydroxyl group on the R group. This is an amino acid, a monomer of proteins. The OH group makes it a polar amino acid.

18. a. A: at about 37°C; B: at about 78°C.
    b. A: from humans (human body temperature is about 37°C); B: from thermophilic bacteria.
    c. Above 40°C, the human enzyme denatures and loses its shape and thus its function. The increased thermal energy disrupts the weak bonds that maintain secondary and tertiary structure in an enzyme.

19. Silicon has four electrons in its outer electron shell, as does carbon. One would predict that silicon could thus form complex molecules by binding with four partners. Neon has a filled outer shell and is nonreactive. Sulfur can only form two covalent bonds and thus would not have the versatility of carbon or silicon.

Chapter 4

1. a. nucleus; b. nucleolus; c. ribosomes; d. Golgi apparatus; e. plasma membrane; f. mitochondrion; g. cytoskeleton; h. peroxisome; i. centriole; j. lysosome; k. rough endoplasmic reticulum; l. smooth endoplasmic reticulum. For functions, see Table 4.22.

2. flagellum or cilia (some plant sperm cells have flagella), lysosome, centriole (involved with microtubule formation)

3. chloroplast, central vacuole, cell wall

4. d 5. c (Small cells have a greater ratio of surface area to volume.) 6. b 7. d 8. e 9. a 10. c 11. b 12. d 13. c 14. d

15. DNA as genetic material, ribosomes, plasma membrane, and cytoplasm

16. Tight junctions form leakproof sheets of cells. Anchoring junctions link cells to each other; they form strong sheets of cells. Gap junctions are channels through which small molecules can move from cell to cell.

17. Both process energy. A chloroplast converts light energy to chemical energy (sugar molecules). A mitochondrion converts chemical energy (food molecules) to another form of chemical energy (ATP).

18. Different conditions and conflicting processes can occur simultaneously within separate, membrane-enclosed compartments. Also, there is increased area for membrane-attached enzymes that carry out metabolic processes.

19. Cilia may propel a cell through its environment or sweep a fluid environment past the cell.

20. A protein inside the ER is packaged inside transport vesicles that bud off the ER and then join to the Golgi apparatus. A transport vesicle containing the finished protein product then buds off the Golgi and travels to and joins with the plasma membrane, expelling the protein from the cell.

21. Part true, part false. All animal and plant cells have mitochondria; plant cells but not animal cells have chloroplasts.

22. The plasma membrane is a phospholipid bilayer with the hydrophilic heads facing the aqueous environment on both sides and the hydrophobic fatty acid tails mingling in the center of the membrane. Proteins are embedded in and attached to this membrane. Microfilaments form a three-dimensional network just inside the plasma membrane. The extracellular matrix outside the membrane is composed largely of glycoproteins, which may be attached to membrane proteins called integrins. Integrins can transmit information from the ECM to microfilaments on the other side of the membrane.

23. Cell 1: $S = 1,256$ μm^2; $V = 4,187$ μm^3; $S/V = 0.3$. Cell 2: $S = 5,024$ μm^2; $V = 33,493$ μm^3; $S/V = 0.15$. The smaller cell has a larger surface area relative to volume for absorbing food and oxygen and excreting waste. Small cells thus perform these activities more efficiently.

24. Individuals with PCD have nonfunctional cilia and flagella due to a lack of dynein motor proteins. This defect would also mean that the cilia involved in left-right pattern formation in the embryo would not be able to set up the fluid flow that initiates the normal arrangement of organs.

25. A single layer of phospholipids surrounding the oil droplet would have their hydrophobic fatty acid tails associated with the hydrophobic oil and their hydrophilic heads facing the aqueous environment of the cell outside the droplet.

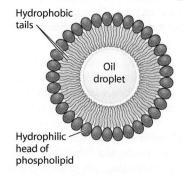

Hydrophobic tails

Oil droplet

Hydrophilic head of phospholipid

26. Some issues and questions to consider: Were the cells the patient's property, a gift, or just surplus? Was he asked to donate the cells? Was he informed about how the cells might be used? Is it important to ask permission or inform the patient in such a case? How much did the researchers modify the cells? What did they have to do to them to sell the product? Do the researchers and the university have a right to make money from patients' cells? Is the fact that they saved the patient's life a factor? Does the patient have the right to sell his cells? Would he have been able to sell the cells without the researchers' help?

Chapter 5

1. a. active transport; b. concentration gradient; c. small nonpolar molecules; d. facilitated diffusion; e. transport proteins

2. a. enzyme; b. active site of enzyme; c. substrate; d. substrate in active site; induced fit strains substrate bonds; e. substrate

converted to products; f. product molecules released; enzyme is ready for next catalytic cycle

3. b 4. d 5. e 6. c (Only active transport can move solute against a concentration gradient.) 7. d 8. b

9. Aquaporins are water transport channels that allow for very rapid diffusion of water through a cell membrane. They are found in cells that have high water transport needs, such as blood cells, kidney cells, and plant cells.

10. Energy is neither created nor destroyed but can be transferred and transformed. Plants transform the energy of sunlight into chemical energy stored in organic molecules. Almost all organisms rely on the products of photosynthesis for the source of their energy. In every energy transfer or transformation, disorder increases as some energy is lost to the random motion of heat.

11. The work of cells falls into three main categories: mechanical, chemical, and transport. ATP provides the energy for cellular work by transferring a phosphate group to a protein (movement and transport) or to a substrate (chemical).

12. Energy is stored in the chemical bonds of organic molecules. The barrier of E_A prevents these molecules from spontaneously breaking down and releasing that energy. When a substrate fits into an enzyme's active site with an induced fit, its bonds may be strained and thus easier to break, or the active site may orient two substrates in such a way as to facilitate the reaction.

13. Cell membranes are composed of a phospholipid bilayer with embedded proteins. The bilayer creates the hydrophobic boundary between cells and their surroundings (or between organelles and the cytoplasm). The proteins perform the many functions of membranes, such as enzyme action, transport, attachment, and signaling.

14. Inhibitors that are toxins or poisons irreversibly inhibit key cellular enzymes. Inhibitors that are designed as drugs are beneficial, such as when they interfere with the enzymes of bacterial or viral invaders or cancer cells. Cells use feedback inhibition of enzymes in metabolic pathways as important mechanisms that conserve resources.

15. Heating, pickling, and salting denature enzymes, changing their shapes so they do not fit substrates. Freezing decreases the kinetic energy of molecules, so enzymes are less likely to interact with their substrates.

16. a. The more enzyme present, the faster the rate of reaction, because it is more likely that enzyme and substrate molecules will meet.

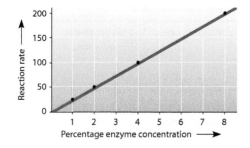

b. The more substrate present, the faster the reaction, for the same reason, but only up to a point. An enzyme molecule can work only so fast; once it is saturated (working at top speed), more substrate does not increase the rate.

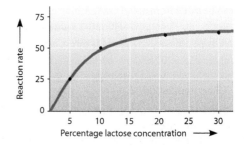

17. The black curve on the left would correspond to the stomach enzyme pepsin, which has a lower optimal pH, as is found in the stomach; the red curve on the right would correspond to trypsin, which has a higher optimal pH. The curve for a lysosomal enzyme should have an optimal pH at 4.5.

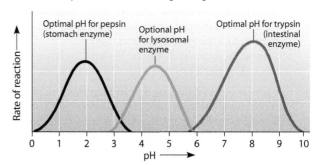

18. Some issues and questions to consider: Is improving crop yields of paramount importance in a world where many people can't get enough food? Does the fact that these compounds rapidly break down indicate that the risk to humans is low? How about the risks to people who work in agriculture or to other organisms, such as bees and other pollinating insects, birds, and small mammals? Might there be negative effects on ecosystems that are impossible to predict?

Chapter 6

1. a. glycolysis; b. citric acid cycle; c. oxidative phosphorylation; d. oxygen; e. electron transport chain; f. CO_2; g. H_2O

2. e 3. c (NAD^+ and FAD, which are recycled by electron transport, are in limited supply in a cell.) 4. e 5. d 6. c 7. b (at the same time NADH is oxidized to NAD^+) 8. a

9. Glycolysis is considered the most ancient because it occurs in all living cells and doesn't require oxygen or membrane-enclosed organelles.

10. Oxygen picks up electrons from the oxidation of glucose at the end of the electron transport chain. Carbon dioxide results from the oxidation of glucose. It is released in the oxidation of pyruvate and in the citric acid cycle.

11. In lactic acid fermentation (in muscle cells), pyruvate is reduced by NADH to form lactate, and NAD^+ is recycled. In alcohol fermentation, pyruvate is broken down to CO_2 and ethanol as NADH is oxidized to NAD^+. Both types of

fermentation allow glycolysis to continue to produce 2 ATP per glucose by recycling NAD$^+$.

12. As carbohydrates are broken down in glycolysis and the oxidation of pyruvate, glycerol can be made from G3P and fatty acids can be made from acetyl CoA. Amino groups, containing N atoms, must be supplied to various intermediates of glycolysis and the citric acid cycle to produce amino acids.

13. 100 kcal per day is 700 kcal per week. On the basis of Figure 6.4, walking 3 mph would require $\frac{700}{245}$ = about 2.8 hr; swimming, 1.7 hr; running, 0.7 hr.

14. NAD$^+$ and FAD are coenzymes that are not used up during the oxidation of glucose. NAD$^+$ and FAD are recycled when NADH and FADH$_2$ pass the electrons they are carrying to the electron transport chain. We need a small additional supply to replace those that are damaged.

15. a. No, this shows the blue color getting more intense. The reaction decolorizes the blue dye.
    b. No, this shows the dye being decolorized, but it also shows the three mixtures with different initial color intensities. The intensities should have started out the same, since all mixtures used the same concentration of dye.
    c. Correct. The mixtures all start out the same, and then the ones with more succinate (reactant) decolorize faster.

16. The presence of ATP synthase enzymes in prokaryotic plasma membranes and the inner membrane of mitochondria provides support for the theory of endosymbiosis—that mitochondria evolved from an engulfed prokaryote that used aerobic respiration (see Module 4.15).

17. Some issues and questions to consider: Is your customer aware of the danger? Do you have an obligation to protect the customer, even against her wishes? Does your employer have the right to dismiss you for informing the customer? For refusing to serve the customer? Could you or the restaurant later be held liable for injury to the fetus? Or is the mother responsible for willfully disregarding warnings about drinking?

Chapter 7

1. a. electron transport chain; b. ATP synthase; c. thylakoid space; d. stroma; e. ATP. The higher H$^+$ concentration is found in the intermembrane space of the mitochondrion and in the thylakoid space of the chloroplast.

2. In mitochondria: a. Electrons come from food molecules. b. Electrons have high potential energy in the bonds in organic molecules. c. Electrons are passed to oxygen, which picks up H$^+$ and forms water.

   In chloroplasts: a. Electrons come from splitting of water. b. Light energy excites the electrons to a higher energy level. c. Electrons flow from water to the reaction-center chlorophyll in photosystem II to the reaction-center chlorophyll in photosystem I to NADP$^+$, reducing it to NADPH.

   In both processes: d. Energy released by redox reactions in the electron transport chain is used to transport H$^+$ across a membrane. The flow of H$^+$ down its concentration gradient back through ATP synthase drives the phosphorylation of ADP to make ATP.

3. a. light energy; b. light reactions; c. Calvin cycle; d. O$_2$ released; e. electron transport chain; f. NADPH; g. ATP; h. 3-PGA is reduced.

4. c 5. c 6. a 7. c (NADPH and ATP from the light reactions are required by the Calvin cycle.) 8. d 9. e 10. b 11. c

12. Light reactions: Light and water are inputs; ATP, NADPH, and O$_2$ are outputs. Calvin cycle: CO$_2$, ATP, and NADPH are inputs; G3P is the output. Also, ADP and NADP$^+$ are inputs to the light reactions and outputs of the Calvin cycle.

13. The light reactions require ADP and NADP$^+$, which are not recycled from ATP and NADPH when the Calvin cycle stops.

14. Plants can break down the sugar for energy in cellular respiration or use the sugar as a raw material for making other organic molecules. Excess sugar is stored as starch.

15. Some issues and questions to consider: What are the risks that we take and costs we must pay if global warming continues? How certain do we have to be that warming is caused by human activities before we act? What can we do to reduce CO$_2$ emissions? Is it possible that the costs and sacrifices of reducing CO$_2$ emissions might actually improve our lifestyle?

16. Some issues and questions to consider: How much land would be required for large-scale conversion to biofuel production, and would that detract from land needed to produce food? Are there fertilizer needs and waste disposal issues with biofuel production? Is there a difference in net input and output of CO$_2$ between production and use of fossil fuels and production and use of biofuels? Which one offers a more long-term solution to energy needs? How do other alternative energy sources compare in cost, potential problems and pollution, and benefit?

Chapter 8

1.

	Mitosis	Meiosis
Number of chromosomal duplications	1	1
Number of cell divisions	1	2
Number of daughter cells produced	2	4
Number of chromosomes in the daughter cells	Diploid (2n)	Haploid (n)
How the chromosomes line up during metaphase	Singly	In tetrads (metaphase I), then singly (metaphase II)
Genetic relationship of the daughter cells to the parent cell	Genetically identical	Genetically unique
Functions performed in the human body	Growth, development, and repair	Production of gametes

2. c 3. a 4. b 5. c 6. e (A diploid cell would have an even number of chromosomes; the odd number suggests that meiosis I has been completed. Sister chromatids are together only in prophase and metaphase of meiosis II.) 7. c 8. b 9. c 10. b 11. d

12. Mitosis without cytokinesis would result in a single cell with two nuclei. Multiple rounds of cell division like this could produce such a "megacell."

13. Various orientations of chromosomes at metaphase I of meiosis lead to different combinations of chromosomes in gametes. Crossing over during prophase I results in an exchange of chromosome segments and new combinations of genes. Random fertilization of eggs by sperm further increases possibilities for variation in offspring.

14. In culture, normal cells usually divide only when they are in contact with a surface but not touching other cells on all sides (the cells usually grow to form only a single layer). The density-dependent inhibition of cell division apparently results from local depletion of substances called growth factors. Growth factors are proteins secreted by certain cells that stimulate other cells to divide; they act via signal transduction pathways to signal the cell cycle control system of the affected cell to proceed past its checkpoints. The cell cycle control systems of cancer cells do not function properly. Cancer cells generally do not require externally supplied growth factors to complete the cell cycle, and they divide indefinitely (in contrast to normal mammalian cells, which stop dividing after 20 to 50 generations)—two reasons why they are relatively easy to grow in the lab. Furthermore, cancer cells can often grow without contacting a solid surface, making it possible to culture them in suspension in a liquid medium.

15. Interphase (for example, third column from left in micrograph, third cell from top): Growth; metabolic activity; DNA synthesis. Prophase (for example, second column, cell at bottom): Chromosomes shorten and thicken; mitotic spindle forms. Metaphase (for example, first column, middle cell): Chromosomes line up on a plane going through the cell's equator. Anaphase (for example, third column, second cell from top): Sister chromatids separate and move to the poles of the cell. Telophase (for example, fourth column, fourth complete cell from top): Daughter nuclei form around chromosomes; cytokinesis usually occurs.

16. A ring of microfilaments pinches an animal cell in two, a process called cleavage. In a plant cell, membranous vesicles form a disk called the cell plate at the midline of the parent cell, cell plate membranes fuse with the plasma membrane, and a cell wall grows in the space, separating the daughter cells.

17. See Figures 8.20A and 8.20B.

18. a. No. For this to happen, the chromosomes of the two gametes that fused would have to represent, together, a complete set of the donor's maternal chromosomes (the ones that originally came from the donor's mother) and a complete set of the donor's paternal chromosomes (from the donor's father). It is much more likely that the zygote would be missing one or more maternal chromosomes and would have an excess of paternal chromosomes, or vice versa.

    b. Correct. Consider what would have to happen to produce a zygote genetically identical to the gamete donor: The zygote would have to have a complete set of the donor's maternal chromosomes and a complete set of the donor's paternal chromosomes. The first gamete in this union could contain any mixture of maternal and paternal chromosomes, but once that first gamete was "chosen," the second one would have to have one particular combination of chromosomes—the combination that supplies whatever the first gamete did not supply. So, for example, if the first three chromosomes of the first gamete were maternal, maternal, and paternal, the first three of the second gamete would have to be paternal, paternal, and maternal. The chance that all 23 chromosome pairs would be complementary in this way is only one in 22^3 (that is, one in 8,388,608). Because of independent assortment, it is much more likely that the zygote would have an unpredictable combination of chromosomes from the donor's father and mother.

    c. No. First, the zygote could not be genetically identical to the gamete donor (see b). Second, the zygote could not be identical to either of the gamete donor's parents because the donor only has half the genetic material of each of his or her parents. For example, even if the zygote were formed by two gametes containing only paternal chromosomes, the combined set of chromosomes could not be identical to that of the donor's father because it would still be missing half of the father's chromosomes.

    d. No. See answer c.

19. Some possible hypotheses: The replication of the DNA of the bacterial chromosome takes less time than the replication of the DNA in a eukaryotic cell. The time required for a growing bacterium to roughly double its cytoplasm is much less than for a eukaryotic cell. Bacteria have a cell cycle control system much simpler than that of eukaryotes.

20. 1 cm^3 = 1,000 mm^3, so 5,000 mm^3 of blood contains 5,000 × 1,000 × 5,000,000 = 25,000,000,000,000, or 2.5 × 10^{13}, red blood cells. The number of cells replaced each day = 2.5 × 10^{13}/120 = 2.1 × 10^{11} cells. There are 24 × 60 × 60 = 86,400 seconds in a day. Therefore, the number of cells replaced each second = 2.1 × 10^{11}/86,400 = about 2 × 10^6, or 2 million. Thus, about 2 million cell divisions must occur each second to replace red blood cells that are lost.

21. Each chromosome is on its own in mitosis; chromosome replication and the separation of sister chromatids occur independently for each horse or donkey chromosome. Therefore, mitotic divisions, starting with the zygote, are not impaired. In meiosis, however, homologous chromosomes must pair in prophase I. This process of synapsis cannot occur properly because horse and donkey chromosomes do not match in number or content.

Chapter 9

1. a. alleles; b. loci; c. homozygous; d. dominant; e. recessive; f. incomplete dominance

2. c 3. d 4. d (Neither parent is ruby-eyed, but some offspring are, so it is recessive. Different ratios among male and female offspring show that it is sex-linked.) 5. e

6. Genes on the single X chromosome in males are always expressed because there are no corresponding genes on the Y

chromosome to mask them. A male needs only one recessive colorblindness allele (from his mother) to show the trait; a female must inherit the allele from both parents, which is less likely.

7. The parental gametes are *WS* and *ws*. Recombinant gametes are *Ws* and *wS*, produced by crossing over.

8. Height appears to be a quantitative trait resulting from polygenic inheritance, like human skin color. See Module 9.14.

9. The trait of freckles is dominant, so Tim and Jan must both be heterozygous. There is a $\frac{3}{4}$ chance that they will produce a child with freckles and a $\frac{1}{4}$ chance that they will produce a child without freckles. The probability that the next two children will have freckles is $\frac{3}{4} \times \frac{3}{4} = \frac{9}{16}$.

10. As in problem 9, both Tim and Jan are heterozygous, and Mike is homozygous recessive. The probability of the next child having freckles is $\frac{3}{4}$. The probability of the next child having a straight hairline is $\frac{1}{4}$. The probability that the next child will have freckles and a straight hairline is $\frac{3}{4} \times \frac{1}{4} = \frac{3}{16}$.

11. The genotype of the black short-haired parent rabbit is *BBSS*. The genotype of the brown long-haired parent rabbit is *bbss*. The F$_1$ rabbits will all be black and short-haired, *BbSs*. The F$_2$ rabbits will be $\frac{9}{16}$ black short-haired, $\frac{3}{16}$ black long-haired, $\frac{3}{16}$ brown short-haired, and $\frac{1}{16}$ brown long-haired.

12. If the genes are not linked, the proportions among the offspring will be 25% gray red, 25% gray purple, 25% black red, 25% black purple. The actual percentages show that the genes are linked. The recombination frequency is 6%.

13. The recombination frequencies are black dumpy 36%, purple dumpy 41%, and black purple 6% (see problem 12). Since these recombination frequencies reflect distances between the genes, the sequence must be purple-black-dumpy (or dumpy-black-purple).

14. $\frac{1}{4}$ will be boys suffering from hemophilia, and $\frac{1}{4}$ will be female carriers. (The mother is a heterozygous carrier, and the father is normal.)

15. For a woman to be colorblind, she must inherit X chromosomes bearing the colorblindness allele from both parents. Her father has only one X chromosome, which he passes on to all his daughters, so he must be colorblind. A male need only inherit the colorblindness allele from a carrier mother; both his parents are usually phenotypically normal.

16. Start out by breeding the cat to get a population to work with. If the curl allele is recessive, two curl cats can have only curl kittens. If the allele is dominant, curl cats can have "normal" kittens. If the curl allele is sex-linked, ratios will differ in male and female offspring of some crosses. If the curl allele is autosomal, the same ratios will be seen among males and females. Once you have established that the curl allele is dominant and autosomal, you can determine if a particular curl cat is true-breeding (homozygous) by doing a testcross with a normal cat. If the curl cat is homozygous, all offspring of the testcross will be curl; if heterozygous, half of the offspring will be curl and half normal.

Chapter 10

1. a. nucleotides; b. transcription; c. RNA polymerase; d. mRNA; e. rRNA; f. tRNA; g. translation; h. ribosomes; i. amino acids

2. e (Only the phage DNA enters a host cell; lambda DNA determines both DNA and protein.) **3.** e **4.** b **5.** c

6. Ingredients: Original DNA, nucleotides, several enzymes and other proteins, including DNA polymerase and DNA ligase. Steps: Original DNA strands separate at a specific site (origin of replication), free nucleotides hydrogen-bond to each strand according to base-pairing rules, and DNA covalently bonds the nucleotides to form new strands. New nucleotides are added only to the 3' end of a growing strand. One new strand is made in one continuous piece; the other new strand is made in a series of short pieces that are then joined by DNA ligase. Product: Two identical DNA molecules, each with one old strand and one new strand.

7. A gene is the polynucleotide sequence with information for making one polypeptide. Each codon—a triplet of bases in DNA or RNA—codes for one amino acid. Transcription occurs when RNA polymerase produces RNA using one strand of DNA as a template. In prokaryotic cells, the RNA transcript may immediately serve as mRNA. In eukaryotic cells, the RNA is processed: A cap and tail are added, and RNA splicing removes introns and links exons together to form a continuous coding sequence. A ribosome is the site of translation, or polypeptide synthesis, and tRNA molecules serve as interpreters of the genetic code. Each folded tRNA molecule has an amino acid attached at one end and a three-base anticodon at the other end. Beginning at the start codon, mRNA is moved relative to the ribosome a codon at a time. A tRNA with a complementary anticodon pairs with each codon, adding its amino acid to the polypeptide chain. The amino acids are linked by peptide bonds. Translation stops at a stop codon, and the finished polypeptide is released. The polypeptide folds to form a functional protein, sometimes in combination with other polypeptides.

8.

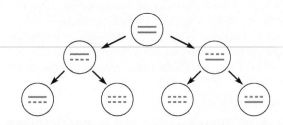

9. mRNA: GAUGCGAUCCGCUAACUGA. Amino acids: Met-Arg-Ser-Ala-Asn.

10. Some issues and questions to consider: Is it fair to issue a patent for a gene or gene product that occurs naturally in every human being? Or should a patent be issued only for something new that is invented rather than found? Suppose another scientist slightly modifies the gene or protein. How different does the gene or protein have to be to avoid patent infringement? Might patents encourage secrecy and interfere

with the free flow of scientific information? What are the benefits to the holder of a patent? When research discoveries cannot be patented, what are the scientists' incentives for doing the research? What are the incentives for the institution or company that is providing financial support?

Chapter 11

1. a. proto-oncogene; b. repressor (or activator); c. cancer; d. operator; e. X inactivation; f. transcription factors; g. alternative RNA splicing

2. b (Different genes are active in different kinds of cells.) **3.** c **4.** b **5.** b **6.** e **7.** b

8. A mutation in a single gene can influence the actions of many other genes if the mutated gene is a control gene, such as a homeotic gene. A single control gene may encode a protein that affects (activates or represses) the expression of a number of other genes. In addition, some of the affected genes may themselves be control genes that in turn affect other batteries of genes. Cascades of gene expression are common in embryonic development.

9. Black, because the DNA of the cell was obtained from a black mouse.

10. a. If the mutated repressor could still bind to the operator on the DNA, it would continuously repress the operon; enzymes for lactose utilization would not be made, whether or not lactose was present.
    b. The *lac* genes would continue to be transcribed and the enzymes made, whether or not lactose was present.
    c. Same predicted result as for b.
    d. RNA polymerase would not be able to transcribe the genes; no proteins would be made, whether or not lactose was present.

11. The protein to which dioxin binds in the cell is probably a transcription factor that regulates multiple genes (see Module 11.3). If the binding of dioxin influences the activity of this transcription factor—either activating or inactivating it—dioxin could thereby affect multiple genes and thus have a variety of effects on the body. The differing effects in different animals might be explained by differing genetic details in the different species. It would be extremely difficult to demonstrate conclusively that dioxin exposure was the cause of illness in a particular individual, even if dioxin had been shown to be present in the person's tissues. However, if you had detailed information about how dioxin affects patterns of gene expression in humans and were able to show dioxin-specific abnormal patterns in the patient (perhaps using DNA microarrays; see Module 11.9), you might be able to establish a strong link between dioxin and the illness.

Chapter 12

1. a. PCR; b. a restriction enzyme; c. gel electrophoresis; d. nucleic acid probe; e. cloning

2. d **3.** c **4.** b **5.** c (Bacteria lack the RNA-splicing machinery needed to delete eukaryotic introns.) **6.** b **7.** d

8. Because it would be too expensive and time consuming to compare whole genomes. By choosing STR sites that vary

considerably from person to person, investigators can get the necessary degree of specificity without sequencing DNA.

9. Isolate plasmids from a culture of *E. coli*. Cut the plasmids and the human DNA containing the HGH gene with the restriction enzyme to produce molecules with sticky ends. Join the plasmids and the fragments of human DNA with ligase. Allow *E. coli* to take up recombinant plasmids. Bacteria will then replicate plasmids and multiply, producing clones of bacterial cells. Identify a clone carrying and expressing the HGH gene using a nucleic acid probe. Grow large amounts of the bacteria and extract and purify HGH from the culture.

10. Medicine: Genes can be used to produce transgenic lab animals for AIDS research or for research related to human gene therapy. Proteins can be hormones, enzymes, blood-clotting factor, or the active ingredient of vaccines. Agriculture: Foreign genes can be inserted into plant cells or animal eggs to produce transgenic crop plants or farm animals. Animal growth hormones are examples of agriculturally useful proteins that can be made using recombinant DNA technology.

11. She could start with DNA isolated from liver cells (the entire genome) and carry out the procedure outlined in Module 12.1 to produce a collection of recombinant bacterial clones, each carrying a small piece of liver cell DNA. To find the clone with the desired gene, she could then make a probe of radioactive RNA with a nucleotide sequence complementary to part of the gene: GACCUGACUGU. This probe would bind to the gene, labeling it and identifying the clone that carries it. Alternatively, the biochemist could start with mRNA isolated from liver cells and use it as a template to make cDNA (using reverse transcriptase). Cloning this DNA rather than the entire genome would yield a smaller library of genes to be screened—only those active in liver cells. Furthermore, the genes would lack introns, making the desired gene easier to manipulate after isolation.

12. Determining the nucleotide sequences is just the first step. Once researchers have written out the DNA "book," they will have to try to figure out what it means—what the nucleotide sequences code for and how they work.

13. Some issues and questions to consider: What are some of the unknowns in recombinant DNA experiments? Do we know enough to anticipate and deal with possible unforeseen and negative consequences? Do we want this kind of power over evolution? Who should make these decisions? If scientists doing the research were to make the decisions about guidelines, what factors might shape their judgment? What might shape the judgment of business executives in the decision-making process? Does the public have a right to a voice in the direction of scientific research? Does the public know enough about biology to get involved in this decision-making process? Who represents "the public," anyway?

14. Some issues and questions to consider: What kinds of impact will gene therapy have on the individuals who are treated? On society? Who will decide what patients and diseases will be

treated? What costs will be involved, and who will pay them? How do we draw the line between treating disorders and "improving" the human species?

15. Some issues and questions to consider: Should genetic testing be mandatory or voluntary? Under what circumstances? Why might employers and insurance companies be interested in genetic data? Since genetic characteristics differ among ethnic groups and between the sexes, might such information be used to discriminate? Which of these questions do you think is most important? Which issues are likely to be the most serious in the future?

Chapter 13

1. According to Darwin's theory of descent with modification, all life has descended from a common ancestral form as a result of natural selection. Individuals in a population have hereditary variations. The overproduction of offspring in the face of limited resources leads to a struggle for existence. Individuals that are well suited to their environment tend to leave more offspring than other individuals, leading to the gradual accumulation of adaptations to the local environment in the population.

2. a. genetic drift; b. gene flow; c. natural selection; d. small population; e. founder effect; f. bottleneck effect; g. unequal reproductive success

3. e 4. a 5. e 6. b (Erratic rainfall and unequal reproductive success would ensure that a mixture of both forms remained in the population.) 7. c 8. e 9. b (All of these provide evidence of evolution, but DNA and the nearly universal genetic code are best able to connect all of life's diverse forms through common ancestry.) 10. d 11. c

12. Your paragraph should include such evidence as fossils and the fossil record, biogeography, comparative anatomy, comparative embryology, DNA and protein comparisons, artificial selection, and examples of natural selection.

13. If $q^2 = 0.0025$, $q = 0.05$. Since $p + q = 1$, $p = 1 − q = 0.95$. The proportion of heterozygotes is $2pq = 2 \times 0.95 \times 0.05 = 0.095$. About 9.5% of African Americans are carriers.

14. Genetic variation is retained in a population by diploidy and balanced selection. Recessive alleles are hidden from selection when in the heterozygote; thus, less adaptive or even harmful alleles are maintained in the gene pool and are available should environmental conditions change. Both heterozygote advantage and frequency-dependent selection tend to maintain alternate alleles in a population.

15. The unstriped snails appear to be better adapted. Striped snails make up 47% of the living population but 56% of the broken shells. Assuming that all the broken shells result from the meals of birds, we would predict that bird predation would reduce the frequency of striped snails and the frequency of unstriped individuals would increase.

16. Some issues and questions to consider: Who should decide curriculum, scientific experts in a field or members of the community? Are these alternative versions scientific ideas? Who judges what is scientific? If it is fairer to consider

alternatives, should the door be open to all alternatives? Are constitutional issues (separation of church and state) involved here? Can a teacher be compelled to teach an idea he or she disagrees with? Should a student be required to learn an idea he or she thinks is wrong?

Chapter 14

1. a. Allopatric speciation: Reproductive barriers may evolve between these two geographically separated populations as a by-product of the genetic changes associated with each population's adaptation to its own environment or as a result of genetic drift or mutation.
   b. Sympatric speciation: Some change, perhaps in resource use or female mate choice, may lead to a reproductive barrier that isolates the gene pools of these two populations, which are not separated geographically. Once the gene pools are separated, each species may go down its own evolutionary path. If speciation occurs by polyploidy—which is common in plants but unusual in animals—then the new species is instantly isolated from the parent species.

2. a. hybrid zone; b. reinforcement; c. fusion; d. stability; e. strengthened; f. weakened or eliminated

3. c 4. b 5. b 6. d 7. c 8. b 9. c 10. a 11. d 12. e

13. Different physical appearances may indicate that organisms belong in different species; but they may just be physical differences within a species. Isolated populations may or may not be able to interbreed; breeding experiments would need to be performed to determine this. Organisms that reproduce only asexually and fossil organisms do not have the potential to interbreed and produce fertile offspring; therefore, the biological species concept cannot apply to them.

14. There is more chance for gene flow between populations on a mainland and nearby island. This interbreeding would make it more difficult for reproductive isolation to develop and separate the two populations.

15. The term *punctuated equilibria* refers to a common pattern seen in the fossil record, in which most species diverge relatively quickly as they arise from an ancestral species and then remain fairly unchanged for the rest of their existence as a species.

16. Yes. Factors such as polyploidy, sexual selection, and habitat specialization can lead to reproductive barriers that would separate the gene pools of allopatric as well as sympatric populations.

17. A broad hypothesis would be that cultivated American cotton arose from a sequence of hybridization, mistakes in cell division, and self-fertilization. We can divide this broad statement into at least three hypotheses. *Hypothesis 1*: The first step in the origin of cultivated American cotton was hybridization between a wild American cotton plant (with 13 pairs of small chromosomes) and an Old World cotton plant (with 13 pairs of large chromosomes). If this hypothesis is correct, we would predict that the hybrid offspring would have had 13 small chromosomes and 13 large chromosomes. *Hypothesis 2*: The second step in the origin of cultivated

American cotton was a failure of cell division in the hybrid offspring, such that all chromosomes were duplicated (now 26 small and 26 large). If this hypothesis is true, we would expect the resulting gametes to each have had 13 large chromosomes and 13 small chromosomes. *Hypothesis 3*: The third step in the origin of cultivated American cotton was self-fertilization of these gametes. If this hypothesis is true, we would expect the outcome of self-fertilization to be a hybrid plant with 52 chromosomes: 13 pairs of large ones and 13 pairs of small ones. Indeed, this is the genetic makeup of cultivated American cotton.

18. By decreasing the ability of females to distinguish males of their own species, the polluted turbid waters have increased the frequency of mating between members of species that had been reproductively isolated from one another. As the number of hybrid fish increase, the parent species' gene pools may fuse, resulting in a loss of the two separate parent species and the formation of a new hybrid species. Future speciation events in Lake Victoria cichlids are less likely to occur in turbid water because females are less able to base mate choice on male breeding color. Reducing the pollution in the lake may help reverse this trend.

19. Some issues and questions to consider: One could look at this question in two ways: If the biological species concept is followed strictly, one could argue that red wolves and coyotes are the same species, since they can interbreed. Because coyotes are not rare, this line of argument would suggest that red wolves should not be protected. On the other hand, because red wolves and coyotes differ in many ways, they can be viewed as distinct species by other species concepts. Protecting the remaining red wolves from hybridizing with coyotes can preserve their distinct species status. The rationale behind protecting all endangered groups is the desire to preserve genetic diversity. Questions for society in general are: What is the value of any particular species and its genetically distinct subgroups? And how far are we willing to go to preserve a rare and distinct group of organisms? How should the costs of preserving genetic diversity compare with the costs of other public projects?

Chapter 15

1. a. Abiotic synthesis of important molecules from simpler chemicals in atmosphere, with lightning or UV radiation as energy source
   b. Polymerization of monomers, perhaps on hot rocks
   c. Enclosure within a lipid membrane, which maintained a distinct internal environment
   d. Beginnings of heredity as RNA molecules replicated themselves. Natural selection could have acted on protocells that enclosed self-replicating RNA.

2. a. phylogeny; b. homologies; c. morphology; d. analogies; e. phylogenetic tree; f. outgroup; g. shared derived characters

3. c 4. b 5. e 6. c 7. e 8. a 9. d 10. b

11. Microevolution is the change in the gene pool of a population from one generation to the next. Macroevolution involves the pattern of evolutionary changes over large time spans and includes the origin of new groups and evolutionary novelties as well as mass extinctions.

12. The latter are more likely to be closely related, because even small genetic changes can produce divergent physical appearances. But if genes have diverged greatly, it implies that lineages have been separate for some time, and the similar appearances may be analogous, not homologous.

13. Complex structures can evolve by the gradual refinement of earlier versions of those structures, all of which served a useful function in each ancestor.

14. Where and when key developmental genes are expressed in a developing embryo can greatly affect the final form and arrangement of body parts. The regulation of gene expression allows these genes to continue to be expressed in some areas, turned off in other areas, and/or expressed at different times during development.

15. The ribosomal RNA genes, which specify the RNA parts of ribosomes, have evolved so slowly that homologies between even distantly related organisms can still be detected. Analysis of other homologous genes is also used.

16. 22,920 years old, a result of four half-life reductions

17.

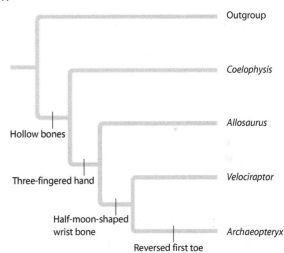

18. Some issues and questions to consider: Whereas previous mass extinctions have resulted from catastrophic events, such as asteroid collisions or volcanism, a sixth mass extinction would be caused by a single species—the result of human-caused environmental alteration. Mass extinctions can reduce complex ecological communities to much simpler ones. It can take millions of years for diversity to recover from a mass extinction. Do we have an ethical responsibility to preserve other species? By disrupting ecological communities throughout the world, a sixth mass extinction would have great consequences for all species alive today—including humans.

Chapter 16

1. Cell wall: maintains cell shape; provides physical protection; prevents cell from bursting in a hypotonic environment

Capsule: enables cell to stick to substrate or to other individuals in a colony; shields pathogens from host's defensive cells

Flagella: provide motility, enabling cell to respond to chemical or physical signals in the environment that lead to nutrients or other members of their species and away from toxic substances

Fimbriae: allow cells to attach to surfaces, including host cells, or to each other

Endospores: withstand harsh conditions

2. a. Archaeplastids; b. Charophytes; c. Unikonts; d. Fungi; e. Choanoflagellates; f. Animals

3. d (Algae are autotrophs; slime molds are heterotrophs.) 4. e
5. c 6. d 7. b 8. d 9. b

10. Rapid rate of reproduction enables prokaryotes to colonize favorable habitats quickly. The production of large numbers of cells by binary fission results in a great deal of genetic variation, making it more likely that some individuals will survive—and be able to recolonize the habitat—if the environment changes again.

11. Small, free-living prokaryotes were probably engulfed by a larger cell and took up residence inside. A symbiotic relationship developed between the host cell and engulfed cells, which became mitochondria. By a similar process, heterotrophic eukaryotic cells engulfed cyanobacteria, which became chloroplasts. Lineages of these autotrophic cells diverged into red and green algae. Secondary endosymbiosis of eukaryotic cells by red and green algae gave rise to diverse lineages of protists.

12. *Chlamydomonas* is a eukaryotic cell, much more complex than a prokaryotic bacterium. It is autotrophic, while amoebas are heterotrophic. It is unicellular, unlike multicellular sea lettuce.

13. Multicellular organisms have a greater extent of cellular specialization and more interdependence of cells. New organisms are produced from a single cell, either an egg or an asexual spore.

14. Not a good idea; all life depends on bacteria. You could predict that eliminating all bacteria from an environment would result in a buildup of toxic wastes and dead organisms (both of which bacteria decompose), a shutdown of all chemical cycling, and the consequent death of all organisms.

15. Some issues and questions to consider: Could we determine beforehand whether the iron would really have the desired effect? How? Would the "fertilization" need to be repeated? Could it be a cure for the problem, or would it merely treat the symptoms? Might the iron treatment have side effects? What might they be?

Chapter 17

1. a. bryophytes (nonvascular plants); b. seedless vascular plants (ferns and relatives); c. gymnosperms; d. angiosperms; 1. apical meristems and embryos retained in the parent plant; 2. lignin-hardened vascular tissue; 3. seeds that protect and disperse embryos

2. a. This is a cloud of pollen being released from a pollen cone of a pine tree. In pollen cones, spores produce millions of the male gametophytes—the pollen grains.

b. This is a cloud of haploid spores produced by a puffball fungus. Each spore may germinate to produce a haploid mycelium.

3. b 4. c (It is the only gametophyte among the possible answers.) 5. a 6. e 7. b 8. e 9. c 10. d

11. The alga is surrounded and supported by water, and it has no supporting tissues, vascular system, or special adaptations for obtaining or conserving water. Its whole body is photosynthetic, and its gametes and embryos are dispersed into the water. The seed plant has lignified vascular tissues that support it against gravity and carry food and water. The seed plant also has specialized organs that absorb water and minerals (roots), provide support (stems and roots), and photosynthesize (leaves and stems). It is covered by a waterproof cuticle and has stomata for gas exchange. Its sperm are carried by pollen grains, and embryos develop on the parent plant and are then protected and provided for by seeds.

12. Animals carry pollen from flower to flower and thus help fertilize the plants' eggs. They also disperse seeds by consuming fruit or carrying fruit that clings to their fur. In return, they get food (nectar, pollen, fruit).

13. Plants are autotrophs; they have chlorophyll and make their own food by photosynthesis. Fungi are heterotrophs that digest food externally and absorb nutrient molecules. There are also many structural differences; for example, the threadlike fungal mycelium is different from the plant body, and their cell walls are made of different substances. Plants evolved from green algae, which belong to the protist supergroup Archaeplastida; the ancestor of fungi was in the protist supergroup Unikonta. Molecular evidence indicates that fungi are more closely related to animals than to plants.

14. Antibiotics probably kill off bacteria that compete with fungi for food. Similarly, bad tastes and odors deter animals that eat or compete with fungi. Those fungi that produce antibiotics or bad-smelling and bad-tasting chemicals would survive and reproduce more successfully than fungi unable to inhibit competitors. Animals that could recognize the smells and tastes also would survive and reproduce better than their competitors. Thus, natural selection would favor fungi that produce the chemicals and, to some extent, the competitors deterred by them.

15. Moss gametophytes, the dominant stage in the moss life cycle, are haploid plants. The diploid (sporophyte) generation is dominant in most other plants. Recessive mutations are not expressed in a diploid organism unless both homologous chromosomes carry the mutation. In haploid organisms, recessive mutations are apparent in the phenotype of the organism because haploid organisms have only one set of chromosomes. Some factors to consider in designing your experiment: What are the advantages/disadvantages of performing the experiment in the laboratory? In the field? What variables would be important to control? How many potted plants should you use? At what distances from the radiation source should you place them? What would serve as a control group for the experiment? What age of plants should you use?

Chapter 18

1. Sponges: sessile, saclike body with pores, suspension feeder; sponges

   Cnidarians: radial symmetry, gastrovascular cavity, cnidocytes, polyp or medusa body form; hydras, sea anemones, jellies, corals

   Flatworms: bilateral symmetry, gastrovascular cavity, no body cavity; free-living planarians, flukes, tapeworms

   Nematodes: pseudocoelom, covered with cuticle, complete digestive tract, ubiquitous, free-living and parasitic; roundworms, heartworms, hookworms, trichinosis worms

   Molluscs: muscular foot, mantle, visceral mass, circulatory system, many with shells, radula in some; snails and slugs, bivalves, cephalopods (squids and octopuses)

   Annelids: segmented worms, closed circulatory system, many organs repeated in each segment; earthworms, polychaetes, leeches

   Arthropods: exoskeleton, jointed appendages, segmentation, open circulatory system; chelicerates (spiders), crustaceans (lobsters, crabs), millipedes and centipedes, insects

   Echinoderms: radial symmetry as adult, water vascular system with tube feet, endoskeleton, spiny skin; sea stars, sea urchins

   Chordates: (1) notochord, (2) dorsal, hollow nerve cord, (3) pharyngeal slits, (4) post-anal tail; tunicates, lancelets, hagfish, and all the vertebrates (lampreys, sharks, ray-finned fishes, lobe-fins, amphibians, reptiles (including birds), mammals

2. c 3. d 4. a (The invertebrates include all animals except the vertebrates.) 5. d 6. c 7. i 8. f 9. e 10. c 11. a 12. d 13. h 14. b 15. g

16. The gastrovascular cavity of a flatworm is an incomplete digestive tract; the worm takes in food and expels waste through the same opening. An earthworm has a complete digestive tract; food travels one way, and different areas are specialized for different functions. The flatworm's body is solid and unsegmented. The earthworm has a coelom, allowing its internal organs to grow and move independently of its outer body wall. Fluid in the coelom cushions internal organs, acts as a skeleton, and aids circulation. Segmentation of the earthworm, including its coelom, allows for greater flexibility and mobility.

17. Cnidarians and most adult echinoderms are radially symmetric, while most other animals, such as arthropods and chordates, are bilaterally symmetric. Most radially symmetric animals stay in one spot or float passively. Most bilateral animals are more active and move headfirst through their environment.

18. For example, the legs of a horseshoe crab are used for walking, while the antennae of a grasshopper have a sensory function. Some appendages on the abdomen of a lobster are used for swimming, while the scorpion catches prey with its pincers. (Note that the scorpion stinger and insect wings are not considered jointed appendages.)

19. Both trees agree on the early branching of eumetazoans into two groups based on body symmetry and the number of cell layers formed in gastrulation. Both trees recognize deuterostomes as a clade of bilaterians. In the morphological tree, protostomes are a second clade of bilaterians. The molecular tree distinguishes two clades within the protostomes, lophotrochozoans and ecdysozoans.

20. Important characteristics include symmetry, the presence and type of body cavity, segmentation, type of digestive tract, type of skeleton, and appendages.

Chapter 19

1. a. Old World monkeys; b. gibbons; c. orangutans; d. gorillas; e. chimpanzees. All are anthropoids; gibbons, orangutans, gorillas, chimpanzees, and humans are apes.

2. a. brain; b. head; c. vertebral column; d. jaws; e. lungs or lung derivatives; f. lobed fins; g. legs; h. amniotic egg; i. milk

3. c 4. c 5. b 6. b 7. c 8. c 9. a

10. Amphibians have four limbs adapted for locomotion on land, a skeletal structure that supports the body in a nonbuoyant medium, and lungs. However, most amphibians are tied to water because they obtain some of their oxygen through thin, moist skin and they require water for fertilization and development. Reptiles are completely adapted to life on land. They have amniotic eggs that contain food and water for the developing embryo and a shell to protect it from dehydration. Reptiles are covered by waterproof scales that enable them to resist dehydration (more efficient lungs eliminate the need for gas exchange through the skin).

11. Fossil evidence supports the evolution of birds from a small, bipedal, feathered dinosaur, which was probably endothermic. The last common ancestor that birds and mammals shared was the ancestral amniote. The four-chambered hearts of birds and mammals must have evolved independently.

12. Several primate characteristics make it easy for us to make and use tools—mobile digits, opposable fingers and thumb, and great sensitivity of touch. Primates also have forward-facing eyes, which enhances depth perception and eye-hand coordination, and a relatively large brain.

13. UV radiation is most intense in tropical regions and decreases farther north. Skin pigmentation is darkest in people indigenous to tropical regions and much lighter in northern latitudes. Scientists hypothesize that depigmentation was an adaptation to permit sufficient exposure to UV radiation, which catalyzes the production of vitamin D, a vitamin that permits the calcium absorption needed for both maternal and fetal bones. Dark pigmentation is hypothesized to protect against degradation of folate, a vitamin essential to normal embryonic development.

14. The paleontologists who discovered *Tiktaalik* hypothesized the existence of transitional forms between fishlike tetrapods such as *Panderichthys* and tetrapod-like fish such as *Acanthostega*. From the available evidence, they knew the time periods when fishlike tetrapods and tetrapod-like fish lived. From the rocks in which the fossils had been found, they knew the geographic region and the type of habitat these creatures occupied. With this knowledge, they predicted the type of rock formation where transitional fossils might be found.

15. Our intelligence and culture—accumulated and transmitted knowledge, beliefs, arts, and products—have enabled us to overcome our physical limitations and alter the environment to fit our needs and desires.

16. Most anthropologists think that humans and chimpanzees diverged from a common ancestor 5–7 million years ago. Primate fossils 4–8 million years old might help us understand how the human lineage first evolved.

Chapter 20

1. a. epithelial tissue; b. connective tissue; c. smooth muscle tissue; d. connective tissue; e. epithelial tissue

   The structure of the specialized cells in each type of tissue fits their function. For example, columnar epithelial cells are specialized for absorption and secretion; the fibers and cells of connective tissue provide support and connect the tissues. The hierarchy from cell to tissue to organ is evident in this diagram. The functional properties of a tissue or organ emerge from the structural organization and coordination of its component parts. The many projections of the lining of the small intestine greatly increase the surface area for absorption of nutrients.

2. c 3. e 4. a 5. d (Expelling salt opposes the increase in blood salt concentration, thereby maintaining a constant internal environment.) 6. d 7. c 8. a 9. d 10. a 11. c 12. b 13. d 14. b

15. Stratified squamous epithelium consists of many cell layers. The outer cells are flattened, filled with the protein keratin, and dead, providing a protective, waterproof covering for the body. Neurons are cells with long extensions that conduct signals to other cells, making multiple connections in the brain. Simple squamous epithelium is a single, thin layer of cells that allows for diffusion of gases across the lining of the lung. Bone cells are surrounded by a matrix that consists of fibers and mineral salts, forming a hard protective covering around the brain.

16. Extensive exchange surfaces are often located within the body. The surfaces of the intestine, urinary system, and lungs are highly folded and divided, increasing their surface area for exchange. These surfaces interface with many blood capillaries. Not all animals have such extensive exchange surfaces. Animals with small, simple bodies or thin, flat bodies have a greater surface-to-volume ratio, and their cells are closer to the surface, enabling direct exchange between cells and the outside environment.

17. The ice water would cool the blood in your head, which would then circulate throughout your body. This effect would accelerate the return to a normal body temperature. If, however, the ice water cooled the blood vessel that supplies the thermostat in your brain so that it sensed a decrease in temperature, this control center would respond by inhibiting sweating and constricting blood vessels in the skin, thereby slowing the cooling of your body.

18. Some issues and questions to consider: Should a doctor's prescription be required for a whole-body CT scan? Should such scans be available only to those who can pay for them? Are CT scan machines calibrated so that they expose children or small adults to less radiation? Have there been research studies to test the effect of repeated exposures to radiation from CT scans? Whose responsibility is it to perform such studies and then publicize the results?

Chapter 21

1. a. oral cavity—ingests and chews food; b. salivary glands—produce saliva; c. liver—produces bile and processes nutrient-laden blood from intestines; d. gallbladder—stores bile; e. pancreas—produces digestive enzymes and bicarbonate; f. rectum—stores feces before elimination; g. pharynx—site of openings into esophagus and trachea; h. esophagus—transports bolus to stomach by peristalsis; i. stomach—stores food, mixes food with acid, begins digestion of proteins; j. small intestine—digestion and absorption; k. large intestine—absorbs water, compacts feces; l. anus—eliminates feces

2. a. fuel, chemical energy; b. raw materials, monomers; c. essential nutrients; d. overnutrition or obesity; e. vitamins and minerals; f. essential amino acids; g. malnutrition

3. e 4. e 5. b 6. d 7. e

8. You ingest the sandwich one bite at a time. In the oral cavity, chewing begins mechanical digestion, and salivary amylase action on starch begins chemical digestion. When you swallow, food passes through the pharynx and esophagus to the stomach. Mechanical and chemical digestion continues in the stomach, where HCl in gastric juice breaks apart food cells and pepsin begins protein digestion. In the small intestine, enzymes from the pancreas and intestinal wall break down starch, protein, and nucleic acids to monomers. Bile from the liver and gallbladder emulsifies fat droplets for attack by enzymes. Most nutrients are absorbed into the bloodstream through the villi of the small intestine. Fats travel through lymph vessels. In the large intestine, absorption of water is completed, and undigested material and intestinal bacteria are compacted into feces, which are eliminated through the anus.

9. Our craving for fatty foods may have evolved from the feast-and-famine existence of our ancestors. Natural selection may have favored individuals who gorged on and stored high-energy molecules, as they were more likely to survive famines.

10. a. 58% (110/190)
    b. Based on a 2,000-Calorie diet, this product supplies about 9.5% of daily Calories, and it supplies 10% of vitamin A and calcium. If all food consumed supplied a similar quantity, the daily requirement for these two nutrients would be met.
    c. The 8 g of saturated fat in this product represents 40% of the daily value. Thus, the daily value must be 20 g (8/0.4 = 20). This represents 180 Calories from saturated fat per day.

11. Sodas, chips, cookies, and candy provide many calories (high energy) but few vitamins, minerals, proteins, or other nutrients. Unprocessed, fresh foods such as fruits and vegetables are considered nutrient dense; they provide substantial amounts of vitamins, minerals, and other nutrients and relatively few calories.

12. Some issues and questions to consider: What are the roles of family, school, advertising, media, and government in

providing nutritional information? How might the available information be improved? What types of scientific studies form the foundation of various nutritional claims?

13. Some issues and questions to consider: In wealthy countries, what are the factors that make it difficult for some people to get enough food? In your community, what types of help exist to feed hungry people? Think of two recent food crises in other countries and what caused them. Did other countries or international organizations provide aid? Which ones, and how did they help? Did that aid address the underlying causes of malnutrition and starvation in the stricken area or only provide temporary relief? How might that aid be changed to offer more permanent solutions to food shortages?

Chapter 22

1. a. respiratory surface; b. circulatory system; c. lungs; d. hemoglobin; e. cellular respiration; f. negative pressure breathing; g. O_2

2. a. nasal cavity; b. pharynx; c. larynx; d. trachea; e. right lung; f. bronchus; g. bronchiole; h. diaphragm

3. c 4. b 5. d 6. a 7. e 8. d 9. c

10. Advantages of breathing air: It has a higher concentration of O_2 than water and is easier to move over the respiratory surface. Disadvantage of breathing air: Living cells on the respiratory surface must remain moist, but breathing air dries out this surface.

11. Nasal cavity, pharynx, larynx, trachea, bronchus, bronchiole, alveolus, through wall of alveolus into blood vessel, blood plasma, into red blood cell, attaches to hemoglobin, carried by blood through heart, blood vessel in muscle, dropped off by hemoglobin, out of red blood cell, into blood plasma, through capillary wall, through interstitial fluid, and into muscle cell.

12. Both these effects of carbon monoxide interfere with cellular respiration and the production of ATP. By binding more tightly to hemoglobin, CO would decrease the amount of O_2 picked up in the lungs and delivered to body cells. Without sufficient O_2 to act as the final electron acceptor, cellular respiration would slow. And by blocking electron flow in the electron transport chain, cellular respiration and ATP production would cease. Without ATP, cellular work stops and cells and organisms die.

13. Llama hemoglobin has a higher affinity for O_2 than does human hemoglobin. The dissociation curve shows that its hemoglobin becomes saturated with O_2 at the lower P_{O_2} of the high altitudes to which llamas are adapted. At that P_{O_2}, human hemoglobin is only 80% saturated.

14. The athlete's body would respond to training at high altitudes or sleeping in an artificial atmosphere with lower P_{O_2} by producing more red blood cells. Thus, the athlete's blood would carry more O_2, and this increase in aerobic capacity may improve endurance and performance.

15. Insects have a tracheal system for gas exchange. To provide O_2 to all the body cells in such a huge moth, the tracheal tubes would have to be wider (to provide enough ventilation across longer distances) and very extensive (to service large flight muscles and other tissues), thus presenting problems of water loss and increased weight. Both the tracheal system and the weight of the exoskeleton limit the size of insects.

16. Some issues and questions to consider: Would a total ban on advertising decrease the number of cigarette smokers? If cigarettes are legal, can the right of cigarette manufacturers to advertise their product be restricted in this manner? Have similar bans on advertising of other legal but potentially deadly products (such as alcohol) been tried? How have they worked? Do health concerns outweigh commercial concerns? If cigarettes are so bad, should they be declared illegal?

Chapter 23

1. a. capillaries of head, chest, and arms; b. aorta; c. pulmonary artery; d. capillaries of left lung; e. pulmonary vein; f. left atrium; g. left ventricle; h. aorta; i. capillaries of abdominal region and legs; j. inferior vena cava; k. right ventricle; l. right atrium; m. pulmonary vein; n. capillaries of right lung; o. pulmonary artery; p. superior vena cava

See text Figure 23.3A for numbers and red vessels that carry oxygen-rich blood.

2. b 3. d (The second sound is the closing of the semilunar valves as the ventricles relax.) 4. c 5. c 6. a 7. e 8. b 9. a

10. Pulmonary vein, left atrium, left ventricle, aorta, artery, arteriole, body tissue capillary bed, venule, vein, vena cava, right atrium, right ventricle, pulmonary artery, capillary bed in lung, pulmonary vein

11. Capillaries are very numerous, producing a large surface area for exchange close to body cells. The capillary wall is only one epithelial cell thick. Pores in the wall and clefts between epithelial cells allow fluid with small solutes to move out of the capillary.

12. a. Plasma (the straw-colored fluid) would contain water, inorganic salts (ions such as sodium, potassium, calcium, magnesium, chloride, and bicarbonate), plasma proteins such as fibrinogen and immunoglobulins (antibodies), and substances transported by blood, such as nutrients (for example, glucose, amino acids, vitamins), waste products of metabolism, respiratory gases (O_2 and CO_2), and hormones.
    b. The red portion would contain erythrocytes (red blood cells), leukocytes (white blood cells—basophils, eosinophils, neutrophils, lymphocytes, and monocytes), and platelets.

13. Oxygen content is reduced as oxygen-poor blood returning to the right ventricle from the systemic circuit mixes with oxygen-rich blood of the left ventricle.

14. Proteins are important solutes in blood, accounting for much of the osmotic pressure that counters the flow of fluid out of a capillary. If protein concentration is reduced, the inward pull of osmotic pressure will fail to balance the outward push of blood pressure, and more fluid will leave the capillary and accumulate in the tissues.

15. Some issues and questions to consider: Is it ethical to have a child to save the life of another? Is it right to conceive a child as a means to an end—to produce a tissue or organ? Is this a less acceptable reason than most reasons parents have for bearing children? Do parents even need a reason for conceiving a child? Do parents have the right to make decisions like this for their young children? How will the donor (and recipient) feel about this when the donor is old enough to know what happened?

16. With a three-chambered heart, there is some mixing of oxygen-rich blood returning from the lungs with oxygen-poor blood returning from the systemic circulation. Thus, the blood of a dinosaur might not have supplied enough O_2 to support the higher metabolism and strong cardiac muscle contractions needed to generate such a high systolic blood pressure. Also, with a single ventricle pumping simultaneously to both pulmonary and systemic circuits, the blood pumped to the lungs would be at such a high pressure that it would damage the lungs.

Chapter 24

1. a. innate immunity; b. adaptive immunity; c. B cells; d. T cells; e. antibodies; f. helper T cells

2. e 3. b 4. b 5. d 6. a 7. b 8. f 9. d 10. e 11. a 12. g 13. c

14. AIDS is mainly transmitted in blood and semen. It enters the body through slight wounds during sexual contact or via needles contaminated with infected blood. AIDS is deadly because it infects helper T cells, crippling both the humoral and cell-mediated immune responses and leaving the body vulnerable to other infections. The most effective way to avoid HIV transmission is to prevent contact with body fluids by practicing safe sex and avoiding intravenous drugs.

15. Inflammation is triggered by tissue injury. Damaged cells release histamine and other chemicals, which cause nearby blood vessels to dilate and become leakier. Blood plasma leaves vessels, and phagocytes are attracted to the site of injury. An increase in blood flow, fluid accumulation, and increased cell population cause redness, heat, and swelling. Inflammation disinfects and cleans the area and curtails the spread of infection from the injured area. Inflammation is considered part of the innate immune response because similar defenses are presented in response to any infection.

16. One hypothesis is that your roommate's previous bee stings caused her to become sensitized to the allergens in bee venom. During sensitization, antibodies to allergens attach to receptor proteins on mast cells. During this sensitization stage, she would not have experienced allergy symptoms. When she was exposed to the bee venom again at a later time, the bee venom allergens bound to the mast cells, which triggered her allergic reaction.

17. There is no correct answer to this question. Some issues and questions to consider: Possible directions include the idea that if the donor felt strongly about the process, then his or her wishes should be respected. The opposite direction would be that the next of kin should be able to approve or deny the procedure. Other considerations may be appropriate, including religious beliefs.

18. Some issues and questions to consider: How important is it to protect students from HIV? Is this a function of schools? Do schools serve other such "noneducational" purposes? Should parents or citizens' and church groups—on either side of the issue—have a say in this, or is it a matter between the school and the student? Does the distribution of condoms condone or sanction sexual activity or promiscuity? Is a school legally liable if a school-issued condom fails to protect a student? Are there alternative measures, such as education, that might be as effective for slowing the spread of HIV?

19. Some issues and questions to consider: How much do people in various nations stand to gain by the development of new drugs, in terms of both lives saved and profits made? How can oversight be used to ensure that drug companies are acting in the best interests of all their patients, and not purely for profit? Can studies be modified so as to maximize the potential benefits to HIV-infected people while minimizing the risks to study participants? Or is such a trade-off impossible? Should studies on humans be banned altogether?

Chapter 25

1. a. thermoregulation; b. osmoregulation; c. excretion; d. ectotherm; e.–g. ammonia, urea, uric acid; h. behavioral responses; i. environment

2. a. filtration: water; NaCl, HCO_3^-, H^+, urea, glucose, amino acids, some drugs; b. reabsorption: nutrients, NaCl, water, HCO_3^-, urea; c. secretion: some drugs and toxins, H^+, K^+; d. excretion: urine containing water, urea, and excess ions

3. c 4. c 5. c 6. a 7. e 8. d 9. c 10. b 11. c 12. c 13. b 14. d 15. b 16. a

17. In salt water, the fish loses water by osmosis. It drinks salt water and disposes of salts through its gills. Its kidneys conserve water and excrete excess ions. In fresh water, it gains water by osmosis. Its kidneys excrete a lot of dilute urine. Its gills take up salt, and some ions are ingested with food.

18. Yes. Ectotherms that live in very stable environments, such as tropical seas or deep oceans, have stable body temperatures. And terrestrial ectotherms can maintain relatively stable temperatures by behavioral means.

19. a. An endotherm would produce more nitrogenous wastes because it must eat more food to maintain its higher metabolic rate.
    b. A carnivore, because it eats more protein and thus produces more breakdown products of protein digestion—nitrogenous wastes.

20. You could take it back to the laboratory and measure its body temperature under different ambient temperatures.

21. A countercurrent heat exchange in the birds' legs reduces the loss of heat from the body. You would expect the temperature of blood flowing back to the body from the legs to be only slightly cooler than the blood flowing from the body to the legs.

22. Some issues and questions to consider: Could drug use endanger the safety of the employee or others? Is drug testing relevant to jobs where safety is not a factor? Is drug testing an

APPENDIX 4

invasion of privacy, interfering in the private life of an employee? Is an employer justified in banning drug use off the job if it does not affect safety or ability to do the job? Do the same criteria apply to employers requiring the test? Could an employer use a drug test to regulate other employee behavior that is legal, such as smoking?

23. Some issues and questions to consider: Should human organs be sold? If the donor is poor, he or she may also not be in the best of health. What are the health risks to the donor? Will the recipient be assured of buying a healthy organ? How much does the organ broker make from this transaction? Both parties in such a transaction are extremely desperate. Should regulations be in place when people may not be able to make reasoned decisions? Or do people have a right to sell parts of their bodies, just as they can now sell other possessions or their labor?

Chapter 26

1. Testes: 3, d
   Pineal gland: 5, f
   Parathyroid gland: 7, g
   Adrenal medulla: 2, c
   Hypothalamus: 8, h
   Pancreas: 4, a
   Anterior pituitary: 6, b
   Thyroid gland: 1, e

9. d 10. e 11. a 12. b (Negative feedback: When thyroxine increases, it inhibits TSH, which reduces thyroxine secretion.) 13. d

14. The hypothalamus secretes releasing hormones and inhibiting hormones, which are carried by the blood to the anterior pituitary. In response to these signals from the hypothalamus, the anterior pituitary increases or decreases its secretion of a variety of hormones that directly affect body activities or influence other glands. Neurosecretory cells that extend from the hypothalamus into the posterior pituitary secrete hormones that are stored in the posterior pituitary until they are released into the blood.

15. Only cells with the proper receptors will respond to a hormone. For a steroid hormone, the presence (or absence) and types of receptor proteins inside the cell determine the hormone's effect. For a nonsteroid hormone, the types of receptors on the cell's plasma membrane are key, and the proteins of the signal transduction pathway may have different effects inside different cells.

16. a. No. Blood sugar level goes too low. Diabetes would tend to make the blood sugar level go too high after a meal.
    b. No. Insulin is working, as seen by the homeostatic blood sugar response to feeding.
    c. Correct. Without glucagon, exercise and fasting lower blood sugar, the cells cannot mobilize any sugar reserves, and blood sugar level drops. Insulin (which lowers blood sugar) has no effect.
    d. No. If this were true, blood sugar level would increase too much after a meal.

17. If cells within a male embryo do not secrete testosterone at the proper time during development, the embryo will develop into a female despite being genetically male.

Chapter 27

1. A. FSH; B. estrogen; C. LH; D. progesterone; P. menstruation; Q. growth of follicle; R. ovulation; S. development of corpus luteum

   If pregnancy occurs, the embryo produces human chorionic gonadotrophin (hCG), which maintains the corpus luteum, keeping levels of estrogen and progesterone high.

2. c 3. c (The outer layer in a gastrula is the ectoderm; of the choices given, only the brain develops from ectoderm.) 4. a 5. d 6. e 7. g 8. d 9. h 10. f 11. a 12. b 13. c

14. Both produce haploid gametes. Spermatogenesis produces four small sperm; oogenesis produces one large egg. In humans, the ovary contains all the primary oocytes at birth, while testes can keep making primary spermatocytes throughout life. Oogenesis is not complete until fertilization, but sperm mature without eggs.

15. The extraembryonic membranes provide a moist environment for the embryos of terrestrial vertebrates and enable the embryos to absorb food and oxygen and dispose of wastes. Such membranes are not needed when an embryo is surrounded by water, as are those of fishes and amphibians.

16. The nerve cells may follow chemical trails to the muscle cells and identify and attach to them by means of specific surface proteins.

17. The researcher might find out whether chemicals from the notochord stimulate the nearby ectoderm to become the neural tube, a process called induction. Transplanted notochord tissue might cause ectoderm anywhere in the embryo to become neural tissue. Control: Transplant non-notochord tissue under the ectoderm of the belly area.

18. Some issues and questions to consider: What characteristics might parents like to select for? If parents had the right to choose embryos based on these characteristics, what are some of the possible benefits? What are potential pitfalls? Could an imbalance of the population result?

Chapter 28

1. (a) sensory receptor; (b) sensory neuron; (c) synapse; (d) spinal cord; (e) interneuron; (f) motor neuron; (g) effector cells; (h) CNS; (i) PNS

2. b 3. a 4. Both a and c would prevent action potentials from occurring; b could actually increase the generation of action potentials.

5. At the point where the action potential is triggered, sodium ions rush into the neuron. They diffuse laterally and cause sodium gates to open in the adjacent part of the membrane, triggering another action potential. The moving wave of action potentials, each triggering the next, is a moving nerve signal. Behind the action potential, sodium gates are temporarily inactivated, so the action potential can only go forward. At a synapse, the transmitting cell releases a chemical neurotransmitter, which binds to receptors on the receiving cell and may trigger a nerve signal in the receiving cell.

6. The results show the cumulative effect of all incoming signals on neuron D. Comparing experiments 1 and 2, we see that the more nerve signals D receives from C, the more it sends; C is excitatory. Because neuron A is not varied here, its action is unknown; it may be either excitatory or mildly inhibitory. Comparing experiments 2 and 3, we see that neuron B must release a strongly inhibitory neurotransmitter, because when B is transmitting, D stops.

7. Some issues and questions to consider: Some people might be against the use of embryonic stem cells for any disorder. This may be related to religious or moral beliefs. Potentially, some people may not be aware of the source of these stem cells and may be against their use because they believe that the cells come from elective abortions. Other people may agree with the use of stem cell research because of the potential to cure diseases that are currently fatal. Some people who may have a neutral opinion on the issue might be swayed by the thought of a loved one who might be helped by stem cell therapy.

8. Some issues and questions to consider: What is the role of alcohol in crime? What are its effects on families and in the workplace? In what ways is the individual responsible for alcohol abuse? The family? Society? Who is affected by alcohol abuse? How effective are treatment and punishment in curbing alcohol abuse? Who pays for alcohol abuse and consequent treatment or punishment? Is it possible to enjoy alcohol without abusing it?

Chapter 29

1. a. mechanoreceptors; b. chemoreceptors; c. electricity, magnetism, light; d. hair cells; e. photoreceptors

2. d (He could hear the tuning fork against his skull, so the cochlea, nerve, and brain are OK. Apparently, sounds are not being transmitted to the cochlea; therefore, the bones are the problem.) 3. b 4. a 5. b 6. e 7. a

8. Louder sounds create pressure waves with greater amplitude, moving hair cells more and generating a greater frequency of action potentials. Different pitches affect different parts of the basilar membrane; different hair cells stimulate different sensory neurons that transmit action potentials to different parts of the brain.

9. Sensation is the detection of stimuli (light) by the photoreceptors of the retina and transmission of action potentials to the brain. Perception is the interpretation of these nerve signals—sorting out the patterns of light and dark and determining their meaning.

10. Taste is used to sample food and determine its quality. Smell is used for many functions—communicating territories (scent marking), navigating (salmon), locating mates (moths), sensing danger (predators, fires), and finding food.

11. Some possible hypotheses: Paired sensory receptors enable an animal to determine the direction from which stimuli come. Paired receptors enable comparison of the intensity of stimuli on either side. Paired receptors enable comparison of slightly different images seen by the eyes or sounds heard by the ears (thus enabling the brain to perceive depth and distance).

12. Do the turtles hear the surf? Plug the ears of some turtles and not others. If turtles without earplugs head for the water and turtles with earplugs get lost, they probably hear the ocean. Or do they smell the water? Plug their nostrils and follow the same process.

13. Some issues and questions to consider: Assuming that the sound is loud enough to impair hearing, how long an exposure is necessary for this to occur? Does exposure have to occur all at once, or is damage cumulative? Who is responsible, concert promoters or listeners? Should there be regulations regarding sound exposure at concerts (as there are for job-related noise)? Are young people sufficiently mature and aware to heed such warnings?

Chapter 30

1. a. skeleton; b. muscles; c. exoskeleton; d. sarcomeres; e. bone and cartilage

2. c 3. d 4. a (Water supports aquatic animals, reducing the effects of gravity.) 5. c 6. d 7. e 8. a 9. a (Each neuron controls a smaller number of muscle fibers.) 10. e

11. Advantages of an insect exoskeleton include strength, good protection for the body, flexibility at joints, and protection from water loss. The major disadvantage is that the exoskeleton must be shed periodically as the insect grows, leaving the insect temporarily weak and vulnerable.

12. The bird's wings are airfoils, with convex upper surfaces and flat or concave lower surfaces. As the wings beat, air passing over them travels farther than air beneath. Air molecules above the wings are more spread out, lowering pressure. Higher pressure beneath the wings pushes them up.

13. Calcium is needed for healthy bone development. It strengthens bones and makes them less susceptible to stress fractures.

14. Action potentials from the brain travel down the spinal cord and along a motor neuron to the muscle. The neuron releases a neurotransmitter, which triggers action potentials in a muscle fiber membrane. These action potentials initiate the release of calcium ions from the ER of the cell. Calcium enables myosin heads of the thick filaments to bind with the actin of the thin filaments. ATP provides energy for the movement of myosin heads, which causes the thick and thin filaments to slide along one another, shortening the muscle fiber. The shortening of muscle fibers pulls on bones, bending the arm. If more motor units are activated, the contraction is stronger.

15. The fundamental vertebrate body plan includes an axial skeleton (skull, backbone, and rib cage) and an appendicular skeleton (bones of the appendages). Species vary in the numbers of vertebrae and the numbers of different types of vertebrae they possess. For example, pythons have no cervical vertebrae. Almost all mammals have seven cervical vertebrae but may have different numbers of other types. For example, human coccygeal vertebrae are small and fused together, but horses and other animals with long tails have many coccygeal vertebrae. Limb bones have been modified into a variety of appendages, such as wings, fins, and limbs. Snakes have no appendages.

16. Chemical A would work better, because acetylcholine triggers contraction. Blocking it would prevent contraction. Chemical B would actually increase contraction, because Ca^{2+} allows contraction to occur.

17. Circular muscles in the earthworm body wall decrease the diameter of each segment, squeezing internal fluid and lengthening the segment. Longitudinal muscles shorten and thicken each segment. Different parts of the earthworm can lengthen while others shorten, producing a crawling motion. The whole roundworm body moves at once because of a lack of segmentation. The body can only shorten or bend, not lengthen, because of a lack of circular muscles. Roundworms simply thrash from side to side.

18. The binding of calcium ions causes the regulatory protein tropomyosin to move out of the way, enabling myosin heads to bind to actin. This results in muscle contraction. ATP causes the myosin heads of the thick filaments to detach from the thin filaments (Figure 30.9B, step 1). If there is no ATP present, the myosin heads remain attached to the thin filaments, and the muscle fiber remains fixed in position.

19. Some issues and questions to consider: Are the places where you live, work, or attend class accessible to a person in a wheelchair? If you were in a wheelchair, would you have trouble with doors, stairs, drinking fountains, toilet facilities, and eating facilities? What kinds of transportation would be available to you, and how convenient would they be? What activities would you have to forgo? How might your disability alter your relationships with your friends and family? How well would you manage on your own?

Chapter 31

1. Here is one possible concept map:

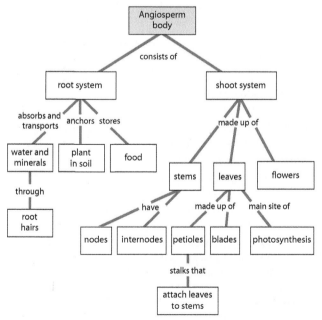

2. d (The vascular cambium forms to the outside of the primary xylem. The secondary xylem forms between primary xylem and the vascular cambium. The secondary phloem and pri-

mary phloem are outside the vascular cambium.) **3.** b **4.** e **5.** e **6.** f **7.** b **8.** e **9.** a **10.** c **11.** d

12. Pollen is deposited on the stigma of a carpel, and a pollen tube grows to the ovary at the base of the carpel. Sperm travel down the pollen tube and fertilize egg cells in ovules. The ovules grow into seeds, and the ovary grows into the flesh of the fruit. As the seeds mature, the fruit ripens and falls (or is picked).

13. Fragmentation of bulbs and sprouting from roots are examples of asexual reproduction. Asexual reproduction is less wasteful and costly than sexual reproduction and less hazardous for young plants. The primary disadvantage of asexual reproduction is that it produces genetically identical offspring, decreasing genetic variability that can help a species survive times of environmental change.

14. Celery stalk: leaf stalk (petiole); peanut: seed (ovule); strawberry: fruit (ripened ovary); lettuce: leaf blades; beet: root

15. Modern methods of plant breeding and propagation have increased crop yields but have decreased genetic variability, so plants have become more vulnerable to epidemics. Primitive varieties of crop plants could contribute to gene banks and be used for breeding new strains.

Chapter 32

1. a. roots; b. xylem; c. sugar source; d. phloem; e. transpiration; f. sugar sink

2. d **3.** d **4.** e **5.** b

6. If the plant starts to dry out, K^+ is pumped out of the guard cells. Water follows by osmosis, the guard cells become flaccid, and the stomata close. This prevents wilting, but it keeps leaves from taking in carbon dioxide, which is needed for photosynthesis.

7. Hypothesis: The hydrogen ions in acid precipitation displace positively charged nutrient ions from negatively charged clay particles. Test: In the laboratory, place equal amounts and types of soil in separate filters. The pore size of the filter must not allow any undissolved soil particles to pass through. Spray (to simulate rain) soil samples in the filters with solutions of different pH (for example, pH 5, 6, 7, 8, 9). Determine the concentration of nutrient ions in the solutions. (The only variable in the solutions should be the hydrogen ion concentration. Ideally, the solutions would contain no dissolved nutrient ions.) Collect fluid that drips through soil samples and filters. Determine the hydrogen ion concentration and the nutrient ion concentration in each sample of fluid. Prediction: If the hypothesis is correct, the fluid collected from the soil samples exposed to pH lower than 5.6 (acid rain) will contain the highest concentration of positively charged nutrient ions.

8. Hypothesis: When fixed nitrogen levels increase to a certain level in the soil, it slows the metabolism of (or otherwise harms or kills) the nitrogen-fixing bacteria that provide usable nitrogen to the crops. Test: Expose cultures of nitrogen-fixing bacteria (symbiotic and nonsymbiotic ones found in soil) to solutions of different concentrations of fixed nitrogen (that is,

NO_3^- and NH_4^+). Determine the concentrations of nitrogen-fixing enzymes produced by the surviving bacteria in each sample. Prediction: If your hypothesis is correct and the fixed nitrogen concentration is high enough to cause harm in some of the samples, you would expect the enzyme concentration to be measurably lower in samples whose fixed nitrogen concentration is above the level that causes harm.

9. The hypothesis is supported if transpiration varies with light intensity when humidity and temperature are about the same. These conditions are seen at two places in the table; at hours 11 and 12, recordings for temperature and humidity are about the same, but light intensity increased markedly from 11 to 12, as did the transpiration rate. The recordings made at hours 3 and 4 show the same effects. Also, the recordings made at hours 1 and 2 generally support the hypothesis. Here, both temperature and humidity decreased, so you might expect the transpiration rate to stay about the same or perhaps increase because the temperature decrease is small; however, the transpiration rate dropped, as did the light intensity.

10. Some issues and questions to consider: How were the farmers assigned or sold "rights" to the water? How is the price established when a farmer buys or sells water rights? Is there enough water for everyone who "owns" it? What kinds of crops are these farmers growing? What will the water be used for in the city? Are there other users with no rights, such as wildlife? Is any effort being made to curb urban growth and conserve water? Should millions of people be living in what is essentially a desert? What are the reasons for farming desert land?

Chapter 33

1. a. auxin; b. gibberellin; c. auxin; d. cytokinin; e. auxin; f. ethylene; g. gibberellin; h. abscisic acid

2. b 3. c 4. b 5. a 6. d 7. b 8. b 9. f 10. e 11. d 12. a 13. b 14. g 15. c

16. Fruits produce ethylene gas, which triggers the ripening and aging of the fruit. Ventilation prevents a buildup of ethylene and delays its effects.

17. The terminal bud produces auxins, which counter the effects of cytokinins from the roots and inhibit the growth of axillary buds. If the terminal bud is removed, the cytokinins predominate, and lateral growth occurs at the axillary buds.

18. The red wavelengths in the room's lights quickly convert the phytochrome in the chrysanthemums to the P_{fr} form, which inhibits flowering in a long-night plant. The chrysanthemums will not flower unless the security guard can set up some far-red lights. Exposure to a burst of far-red light would convert the phytochrome to the P_r form, allowing flowering to occur.

19. The biologist could remove leaves at different stages of being eaten to see how long it takes for changes to occur in nearby leaves. The "hormone" could be captured in an agar block, as in the phototropism experiments in Module 33.1, and applied to an undamaged plant. Another experiment would be to block "hormone" movement out of a damaged leaf or into a nearby leaf.

20. Some issues and questions to consider: Is the hormone safe for human consumption? What are its effects in the environment? Could its production produce impurities or wastes that might be harmful? What kinds of tests need to be done to demonstrate its safety? How much does it cost to make and use? Are the benefits worth the costs and risks? Is it worth using an artificial chemical on food simply to improve its appearance?

   A scientist could seek answers by studying the stability of the hormone in a variety of laboratory simulations of natural conditions. The toxicity of the hormone, the materials used to produce it, and its breakdown products could be determined in laboratory tests.

Chapter 34

1. a. The shape of Earth results in uneven heating, such that the tropics are warm and polar regions are cold.
   b. The seasonal differences of winter and summer in temperate and polar regions are produced as Earth tips toward or away from the sun during its orbit around the sun.
   c. Intense solar radiation in the tropics evaporates moisture; warm air rises, cools, and drops its moisture as rain; air circulates, cools, and drops around 30°N and S, warming as it descends and evaporating moisture from land, which creates arid regions.

2. a. All three areas have plenty of sunlight and nutrients.
   b. The addition of nitrogen or phosphorus "fertilizes" the algae living in ponds and lakes, leading to explosive population growth. (These nutrients are typically in short supply in aquatic ecosystems.) The effects are harmful to the ecosystem. Algae cover the surface, reducing light penetration. When the algae die, bacterial decomposition of the large amount of biomass can deplete the oxygen available in the pond or lake, which may adversely affect the animal community.

3. f 4. g 5. d 6. a 7. c 8. b 9. e 10. a 11. e 12. d 13. a 14. c 15. b 16. e

17. Tropical rain forests have a warm, moist climate, with favorable growing conditions year-round. The diverse plant growth provides various habitats for other organisms.

18. After identifying your biome by looking at the map in Figure 34.8, review Module 34.5 on climate and the module that describes your biome (Modules 34.9–34.17).

19. a. desert; b. grassland; c. tropical forest; d. temperate forest; e. coniferous forest; f. arctic tundra. Areas of overlap have to do with seasonal variations in temperature and precipitation.

20. Through convergent evolution, these unrelated animals adapted in similar ways to similar environments—temperate grasslands and savanna.

Chapter 35

1. a. genes; b. fixed action pattern (FAP); c. imprinting; d. spatial learning; e. associative learning; f. social learning

2. d 3. c 4. d 5. a

6. Main advantage: Flies do not live long. Innate behaviors can be performed the first time without learning, enabling flies to find food, mates, and so on without practice. Main disadvantage: Innate behaviors are rigid; flies cannot learn to adapt to specific situations.

7. In a stressful environment, for example, where predators are abundant, rats that behave cautiously are more likely to survive long enough to reproduce.

8. Courtship behaviors reduce aggression between potential mates and confirm their species, sex, and physical condition. Environmental changes such as rainfall, temperature, and day length probably lead frogs to start calling, so these would be the proximate causes. The ultimate cause relates to evolution. Fitness (reproductive success) is enhanced for frogs that engage in courtship behaviors.

9. a. Yes. The experimenter found that 5 m provided the most food for the least energy because the total flight height (number of drops × height per drop) was the lowest. Crows appear to be using an optimal foraging strategy.
   b. An experiment could measure the average drop height for juvenile and adult birds, or it could trace individual birds during a time span from juvenile to adult and see if their drop height changed.

10. One likely hypothesis is that the helper is closely related to one or both of the birds in the mated pair. Because closely related birds share relatively many genes, the helper bird is indirectly enhancing its own fitness by helping its relatives raise their young. (In other words, this behavior evolved by kin selection.) The easiest way to test the hypothesis would be to determine the relatedness of the birds by DNA analysis. If birds are closely related, their DNA should be more similar than those of more distantly related or unrelated birds.

11. Identical twins are genetically the same, so any differences between them are due to environment. Thus, the study of identical twins enables researchers to sort out the effects of "nature" and "nurture" on human behavior. The data suggest that many aspects of human behavior are inborn. Some people find these studies disturbing because they seem to leave less room for free will and self-improvement than we would like. Results of such studies may be carelessly cited in support of a particular social agenda.

12. Animals are used in experiments for various reasons. A particular species of animal may have features that make it well suited to answer an important biological question. Squids, for example, have a giant nerve fiber that made possible the discovery of how all nerve cells function. Animal experiments play a major role in medical research. Many vaccines that protect humans against deadly diseases, as well as drugs that can cure diseases, have been developed using animal experiments. Animals also benefit, as vaccines and drugs are developed for combating their own pathogens. Some researchers point out that the number of animals used in research is a small fraction of those killed as strays by animal shelters and a minuscule fraction of those killed for human food. They also maintain that modern research facilities are models of responsible and considerate treatment of animals. Whether or not this is true,

the possibility that at least some kinds of animals used in research suffer physical pain as a result, and perhaps mental anguish as well, raises serious ethical issues. Some questions to consider: What are some medical treatments or products that have undergone testing in animals? Have you benefited from any of them? Are there alternatives to using animals in experiments? Would alternatives put humans at risk? Are all kinds of animal experiments equally valuable? In your opinion, what kinds of experiments are acceptable, and what kinds are unnecessary? What kinds of treatment are humane, and what kinds are inhumane?

Chapter 36

1. a. The x-axis is time; the y-axis is the number of individuals (N). The blue curve represents exponential growth; red is logistic growth.
   b. $G = rN$
   c. The carrying capacity of the environment (K)
   d. In exponential growth, population growth continues to increase as the population size increases. In logistic growth, the population grows fastest when the population is about $\frac{1}{2}$ the carrying capacity—when N is large enough so that rN produces a large increase, but the expression $(K - N)/K$ has not yet slowed growth as much as it will as N gets closer to K.
   e. Exponential growth curve, although the worldwide growth rate is slowing

2. a. The blue line is birth rate; the red line is death rate.
   b. I. Both birth and death rates are high. II. Birth rate remains high; death rate decreases, perhaps as a result of increased sanitation and health care. III. Birth rate declines, often coupled with increased opportunities for women and access to birth control; death rates are low. IV. Both birth and death rates are low.
   c. I and IV
   d. II, when death rate has fallen but birth rate remains high

3. d 4. a 5. c 6. c 7. e 8. b 9. d

10. Food and resource limitation, such as food or nesting sites; accumulation of toxic wastes; disease; increase in predation; stress responses, such as seen in some rodents

11. Survivorship is the fraction of individuals in a given age interval that survive to the next interval. It is a measure of the probability of surviving at any given age. A survivorship curve shows the fraction of individuals in a population surviving at each age interval during the life span. Oysters produce large numbers of offspring, most of which die young, with a few living a full life span. Few humans die young; most live out a full life span and die of old age. Squirrels have approximately constant mortality and about an equal chance of surviving at all ages.

12. Clumped is the most common dispersion pattern, usually associated with unevenly distributed resources or social grouping. Uniform dispersion may be related to territories or inhibitory interactions between plants. A random dispersion is least common and may occur when other factors do not influence the distribution of organisms.

13. Populations with *K*-selected life history traits tend to live in fairly stable environments held near carrying capacity by density-dependent limiting factors. They reproduce later and have fewer offspring than species with *r*-selected traits. Their lower reproductive rate makes it hard for them to recover from human-caused disruption of their habitat. We would expect species with *K*-selected life histories to have a Type I survivorship curve (see Module 36.3).

14. The largest population segment, the baby boomers, is currently in the workforce in their peak earning years, paying into the Social Security system. However, they are approaching the end of their contributing years, and the smaller working numbers following them will provide less money, driving the fund into a deficit.

15. Some issues and questions to consider: How does population growth in developing countries relate to food supply, pollution, and the use of natural resources such as fossil fuels? How are these things affected by population growth in developed countries? Which of these factors are most critical to our survival? Are they affected more by the growth of developing or developed countries? What will happen as developing countries become more developed? Will it be possible for everyone to live at the level of the developed world?

Chapter 37

1.

Interspecific Interaction	Effect on Species 1	Effect on Species 2	Example (many other answers possible)
Predation	+	−	Crocodile/fish
Competition	−	−	Squirrel/black bear
Herbivory	+	−	Caterpillar/leaves
Parasites and pathogens	+	−	Heartworn/dog; *Salmonella*/person
Mutualism	+	+	Plant/mycorrhizae

2.

	Carbon	Phosphorus	Nitrogen
Main abiotic reservoir(s)	Atmosphere	Rocks	Atmosphere, soil
Form in abiotic reservoir	Carbon dioxide (CO_2)	Phosphate (PO_4^{3-}) bound with other minerals in rock	N_2 in atmosphere; ammonium (NH_4^+) or nitrate (NO_3^-) in soil
Form used by producers	Carbon dioxide (CO_2)	Phosphate (PO_4^{3-})	NH_4^+ or NO_3^-
Human activities that alter cycle	Burning wood and fossil fuels	Agriculture (fertilizers, feedlots, pesticides, soil erosion)	Agriculture (fertilizers, feedlots, soil erosion); combustion of fossil fuels; manufacture of nitrogen fertilizer
Effects of altering cycle	Global warming	Eutrophication of aquatic ecosystem; nutrient-depleted soils	Eutrophication of aquatic ecosystems; nutrient-depleted soils; global warming; smog; depletion of ozone layer; acid precipitation

3. e 4. d 5. c 6. c 7. c

8. Plants benefit by having their seeds distributed away from the parent. Animals benefit when the seeds contains food, as in fleshy fruits.

9. Rapid eutrophication occurs when bodies of water receive nutrient pollution (for example, from agricultural runoff) that results in blooms of cyanobacteria and algae. Respiration from these organisms and their decomposers depletes oxygen levels, leading to fish kills. Reducing this type of pollution will require controlling the sources of excess inorganic nutrients, for example, runoff from feedlots and fertilizers.

10. The abiotic reservoir of the first three nutrients is the soil. Carbon is available as carbon dioxide in the atmosphere.

11. These animals are secondary or tertiary consumers, at the top of the production pyramid. Stepwise energy loss means not much energy is left for them; thus, they are rare and require large territories in which to hunt.

12. Chemicals with a gaseous form in the atmosphere, such as carbon and nitrogen, have a global biogeochemical cycle.

13. Nitrogen fixation of atmospheric N_2 into ammonium; decomposition of detritus into ammonium; nitrification of ammonium into nitrate; denitrification (by denitrifiers) of nitrates into N_2

14. Hypothesis: The kangaroo rat is a keystone species in the desert. (Apparently, herbivory by the rats kept the one plant from outcompeting the others; removing the rats reduced plant diversity.) Additional supporting evidence: Observations of the rats preferentially eating dominant plants; finding that the dominant plant recovers from herbivore damage faster.

15. Some issues and questions to consider: What relationships (predators, competitors, parasites) might exist in the mussels' native habitat that are altered in the Great Lakes? How might the mussels compete with Great Lakes organisms? Might the Great Lakes species adapt in some way? Might the mussels adapt? Could possible solutions present problems of their own?

Chapter 38

1. a. species at risk of extinction; b. restoration ecology; c. bioremediation; d. zoned reserves

2. c 3. d 4. a 5. e 6. b 7. d 8. a

9. Genetic, species, and ecosystem diversity. As populations become smaller, genetic diversity is usually reduced. Genetic diversity is also threatened when local populations of a species are extirpated owing to habitat destruction or other assaults or when entire species are lost. Many human activities have led to the extinction of species. The greatest threats include habitat loss, invasive species, and overharvesting. Species extinction or population extirpation may alter the structure of whole communities. Pollution and other widespread disruptions may lead to the loss of entire ecosystems.

10. Greenhouse gases in the atmosphere, including carbon dioxide, methane, and nitrous oxide, absorb infrared radiation and thus slow the escape of heat from Earth. This is called the greenhouse effect (see Module 7.13). Without greenhouse gases in the atmosphere, the temperature at the surface of Earth would be much colder and less hospitable for life.

11. Fossil fuel consumption, industry, and agriculture are increasing the quantity of greenhouse gases—such as CO_2, methane, and nitrous oxide—in the atmosphere. These gases are trapping more heat and raising atmospheric temperatures. Increases of 2–5°C are projected over the next century. Logging and the clearing of forests for farming contribute to global warming by reducing the uptake of CO_2 by plants (and adding CO_2 to the air when trees are burned). Global warming is having numerous effects already, including melting polar ice, permafrost, and glaciers, shifting patterns of precipitation, causing spring temperatures to arrive earlier, and reducing the number of cold days and nights. Future consequences include rising sea levels and the extinction of many plants and animals. Global warming is an international problem; air and climate do not recognize international boundaries. Greenhouse gases are primarily produced by industrialized nations. Cooperation and commitment to reduce use of fossil fuels and to reduce deforestation will be necessary if the problem of global warming is to be solved.

12. These birds might be affected by pesticides while in their wintering grounds in Central and South America, where such chemicals may still be in use. The birds are also affected by deforestation throughout their range.

13. About 1.8 million species have been named and described. Assume that 80% of all living things (not just plants and animals) live in tropical rain forests. This means that there are 1.44 million species there. If half the species survive, this means that 0.72 million species will be extinct in 100 years, or 7,400 per year. This means that 19+ species will disappear per day, or almost one per hour. If there are 30 million species on Earth, 24 million live in the tropics, and 12 million will disappear in the next century. This is 120,000 per year, 329 per day, or 14 per hour.

14. Some issues and questions to consider: How does the use of fossil fuels affect the environment? What about oil spills? Disruption of wildlife habitat for construction of oil fields and pipelines? Burning of fossil fuels and possible climate change and flooding from global warming? Pollution of lakes and destruction of property by acid precipitation? Health effects of polluted air on humans? How are we paying for these "side effects" of fossil fuel use? In taxes? In health insurance premiums? Do we pay a nonfinancial price in terms of poorer health and quality of life? Could oil companies be required to pick up the tab for environmental effects of fossil fuel use? Could these costs be covered by an oil tax? How would this change the price of oil? How would a change in the price of oil change our pattern of energy use, our lifestyle, and our environment?

15. Data on carbon emissions can be found at a number of websites, including the United Nations Statistics Division (http://unstats.un.org/unsd/default.htm) and the World Resources Institute (http://www.wri.org/climate/). The per capita rankings of the United States and Canada are generally very high, along with other developed nations. Transportation and energy use are the major contributors to the carbon footprint. Any actions you can take to reduce these will help. For example, if you have a car, you can try to minimize the number of miles you drive by consolidating errands into fewer trips and using an alternative means of transportation (public transportation, walking, biking) whenever possible. To reduce energy consumption, be aware of the energy you use: Turn off lights, disconnect electronics that draw power when on standby, do laundry in cold water, for example. Websites such as http://www.ucsusa.org/ (Union of Concerned Scientists) and http://climatecrisis.net offer simple suggestions such as changing to energy-efficient lightbulbs. A Web search will turn up plenty of sites.

16. Some issues and questions to consider: How do population growth, resource consumption, pollution, and reduction in biodiversity relate to sustainability? How do poverty, economic growth and development, and political issues relate to sustainability? Why might developed and developing nations take different views of a sustainable society? What would life be like in a sustainable society? Have any steps toward sustainability been taken in your community? What are the obstacles to sustainability in your community? What steps have you taken toward a sustainable lifestyle? How old will you be in 2030? What do you think life will be like then?

APPENDIX 5 Credits

Photo Credits

Detailed Table of Contents, page xxii–xxxvii

Cyril Ruoso/Photolibrary; Fotosearch/age fotostock; M.I. Walker/Photo Researchers; Fiona Rogers/naturepl.com; M. I. Walker/Photo Researchers; Dr. Yorgos Nikas/Photo Researchers; Charles Orrico/SuperStock; Health Protection Agency Centre for Infections/Photo Researchers; Pat Sullivan/Associated Press; Hank Morgan/Photo Researchers; tbkmedia.de/Alamy; Neg./Transparency no.5789. Courtesy Dept. of Library Services, American Museum of Natural History; Steve Gschmeissner/Photo Researchers; ARCO/H Reinhard/AGE fotostock; Jurgen Freund/Nature Picture Library; Dave Watts/Alamy; Martin Harvey/Photolibrary; Jennette van Dyk/Getty Images; Ingram Publishing/Photolibrary; Science Photo Library/Alamy; Four Oaks/Shutterstock; Jonathan Blair/CORBIS; Dr. Yorgos Nikas/Photo Researchers; John Mitchell/Photo Researchers; Christopher Nuzzaco/iStockphoto; Eric J. Simon; Mario Verin/Photolibrary; Martin Shields/Photo Researchers; Vincent Munier/naturepl.com; AlexeyVis/iStockphoto; David Jay Zimmerman/Corbis; William E. Townsend/Photo Researchers; Tom Murphy/WWI/Peter Arnold, Inc./PhotoLibrary

Unit Openers: Unit 1 David Becker/Photo Researchers. **Unit 2** suravid/Shutterstock. **Unit 3** Vaughan Fleming/Photo Researchers. **Unit 4** Wild Wonders of Europe/Lundgren/Nature Picture Library. **Unit 5** Martin Harvey/Corbis. **Unit 6** John Warburton-Lee Photography/Alamy. **Unit 7** Petra Wegner/Alamy.

Chapter 1: opposite the Chapter Opener top left Image State Media Partners Limited. **opposite the Chapter Opener top right** Neg./Transparency no. 326668. Courtesy Dept. of Library Services, American Museum of Natural History. **opposite the Chapter Opener bottom left** E. R. Degginger/Photo Researchers. **opposite the Chapter Opener bottom right** National Geographic. **Chapter Opener** Cyril Ruoso/Photolibrary. **1.1.1** Image State Media Partners Limited. **1.1.2** Frans Lanting/Corbis. **1.1.3** Frans Lanting/Corbis. **1.1.4** Michael De Young/Corbis. **1.1.5** Kim Taylor and Jane Burton/Dorling Kindersley. **1.1.6** Chris Mattison/Photolibrary. **1.1.7** Frans Lanting/DanitaDelimont.com. **1.2. top to bottom** NASA/Johnson Space Center; Alain Mafart-Renodier/Photolibrary; Martin Harvey/Photolibrary. **1.3 left** Steve Gschmeissner/Photo Researchers. **1.3 right** S. C. Holt/Biological Photo Service. **1.4** Dave Stamboulis/age fotostock. **1.6 top** Oliver Meckes/Nicole Ottawa/Photo Researchers. **1.6 center** Eye of Science/Photo Researchers. **1.6 center left** D. P. Wilson/Photo Researchers. **1.6 center right** Florapix/Alamy. **1.6 bottom left** Frank Young/ Papilio/Corbis. **1.6 bottom right** Michael and Patricia Fogden/Corbis. **1.7A** Seelevel.com. **1.7B** Neg./Transparency no. 326668. Courtesy Dept. of Library Services, American Museum of Natural History. **1.7D top** Photoshot Holdings Ltd/Alamy. **1.7D bottom** Fred Felleman/Stone/Getty Images. **1.8** Colin Radford. **1.9B** E. R. Degginger/Photo Researchers. **1.9C** Steve Kaufman/Photolibrary. **1.9D** David Pfennig. **1.10** National Geographic. **p.13** Dave Stamboulis/age fotostock.

Chapter 2: Chapter Opener NASA. **2.1 left** Chip Clark. **2.2A** Alison Wright/Photo Researchers. **2.2B** Anton Prado/Alamy. **2.2C** Kristin Piljay. **2.4A** Will & Deni McIntyre/Photo Researchers. **2.4B** W. E. Klunk and C. A. Mathis, University of Pittsburgh. **2.10** Herman Eisenbeiss/Photo Researchers. **2.11** Novastock/Photolibrary. **2.12** thp73/iStockphoto. **2.14 top to bottom** Jakub Semeniuk/iStockphoto; VR Photos/Shutterstock; VBeth Van Trees/Shutterstock. **2.15** Shutterstock. **2.16** NASA.

Chapter 3: p.32 top Alexandru Magurean/iStockphoto. **p.32 bottom** Fotosearch/age fotostock. **3.2 left** Miki Verebes/Shutterstock. **3.2 right** Herbert Kratky/iStockphoto. **3.4A** Alexandru Magurean/iStockphoto. **3.6** Kristin Piljay. **3.7 clockwise from top left** Dougal Waters/Getty Images; Biophoto Associates/Photo Researchers; Courtesy of Dr. L. M. Beidler; Biophoto Associates/Photo Researchers. **3.8A** Tony Hamblin/Frank Lane Picture

Agency/Corbis. **p.41** Shutterstock. **3.12A** Fotosearch/age fotostock. **p.44** Peter Zaharov/iStockphoto. **3.16** Serge de Sazo/Photo Researchers.

Chapter 4: p.50 top M.I. Walker/Photo Researchers. **p.50 bottom** Dr. Frank Solomon. **Chapter Opener** James King-Holmes/Photo Researchers. **4.1A** Michael Abbey/Photo Researchers. **4.1C** Andrew Syred/Photo Researchers. **4.1D** Dr. Klaus Boller/Photo Researchers. **4.1E** M.I. Walker/Photo Researchers. **4.3** S. C. Holt, University of Texas Health Center/Biological Photo Service. **4.5** Courtesy of Richard Rodewald/Biological Photo Service. **4.6** D. W. Fawcett/Photo Researchers. **4.8A** R. Bolender, D. Fawcett/Photo Researchers. **4.9** Don W. Fawcett/Photo Researchers. **4.11A** Roland Birke/Peter Arnold, Inc./PhotoLibrary. **4.11B** Biophoto Associates/Photo Researchers. **4.13** Nicolae Simionescu. **4.14** E.H. Newcomb & W.P. Wergin/Biological Photo Service. **4.16 left to right** Dr. Frank Solomon; Mark S. Ladinsky and J. Richard McIntosh, University of Colorado; Dr. Mary Osborn. **4.17A** Science Photo Library/Photo Researchers. **4.17B** Eye of Science/Photo Researchers. **4.17C** W. L. Dentler/Biological Photo Service. **4.18** Bjorn Afzelius.

Chapter 5: Chapter Opener Dante Fenolio/Photo Researchers. **5.2** Peter B. Armstrong. **5.7** "This water permeation through aquaporin was made by Drs. Emad Tajkhorshid and Klaus Schulten using VMD and is owned by the Theoretical and Computational Biophysics Group, NIH Resource for Macromolecular Modeling and Bioinformatics, at the Beckman Institute, University of Illinois at Urbana-Champaign." **5.9 top to bottom** Oxford Scientific/Photolibrary; D.W. Fawcett/Science Source/Photo Researchers; M.M. Perry. **5.16** Krista Kennell/Newscom.

Chapter 6: p.88 left StockLite/Shutterstock. **p.88 right** Fiona Rogers/naturepl.com. **Chapter Opener** Wolfgang Kaehler/Alamy. **6.1** Cyril Ruoso/Photolibrary. **6.2** UpperCut Images/Alamy. **6.4** Corbis RF/Getty Images. **6.13C top** StockLite/Shutterstock. **6.13C bottom** Sean Lower. **6.15** Simon Smith/Dorling Kindersley. **6.16** Fiona Rogers/naturepl.com.

Chapter 7: p.106 rodho/Shutterstock. **Chapter Opener** M. I. Walker/Photo Researchers. **7.1A** Theresa de Salis/Peter Arnold, Inc./Photo Library. **7.1B** M. I. Walker/Photo Researchers. **7.1C** Jeff Rotman/Nature Picture Library. **7.1D** Susan M. Barns, Ph.D. **7.2 top to bottom** rodho/Shutterstock; Graham Kent; E.H. Newcomb & W.P. Wergin/Biological Photo Service. **7.3A** Martin Shields/Alamy. **7.6B** loriklaszlo/Shutterstock. **7.7A** Christine Case. **7.11 left** Dinodia/Pixtal/AGE Fotostock. **7.11 right** ImageDJ/Jupiter Images/Getty Images. **7.13A** Doug Martin/Photo Researchers. **7.14A** NASA. **7.14B** NOAA.

Chapter 8: p.124 top left Dr. Yorgos Nikas/Photo Researchers. **p.124 bottom right** Michelle Gilders/Alamy. **Chapter Opener** SPL/Photo Researchers. **8.1A** London School of Hygiene & Tropical Medicine/Photo Researchers. **8.1B** Roger Steene/Image Quest Marine. **8.1C** Eric J. Simon. **8.1D** Bob Thomas/Photographers Choice/Getty Images. **8.1E** Dr. Yorgos Nikas/Photo Researchers. **8.1F** Dr. Torsten Wittmann/Photo Researchers. **8.2B** Lee D. Simon/Photo Researchers. **8.3A** Andrew S. Bajer. **8.3B** Biophoto/Photo Researchers. **8.5** Conly L. Rieder, Ph.D. **8.6A** Don W. Fawcett/Photo Researchers. **8.6B** Eldon H. Newcomb. **8.10A left to right** Garcia/photocuisine/Corbis; Joseph F. Gennaro Jr./Photo Researchers; Brian Capon. **8.10B** Biophoto/Science Source/ Photo Researchers. **8.10C** Biophoto/Science Source/Photo Researchers. **8.12A** Ron Chapple Stock/Alamy. **8.13** Ed Reschke/Peter Arnold, Inc./PhotoLibrary. **8.16 top** F. Schussler/Getty Images. **8.16 bottom** Chris Collins/Bettmann/Corbis. **8.17A** Mark Petronczki and Maria Siomos. **8.18.4** Veronique Burger/Phanie Agency/ Photo Researchers. **8.18.5** CNRI/SPL/Photo Researchers. **8.19A left** SPL/Photo Researchers. **8.19A right** George Doyle/Getty Images. **8.22** Michelle Gilders/Alamy. **p.151** USDA/ARS/Agricultural Research Service.

Chapter 9: **p.152 top left** Hulton Archive/Getty Images. **p.152 top right** Eric J. Simon. **p.152 bottom right** Andrew Syred/Photo Researchers. **Chapter Opener** Charles Orrico/SuperStock. **9.1** frog-traveller/Shutterstock. **9.2A** Hulton Archive/Getty Images. **9.8A top left** Liza McCorkle/iStockphoto. **9.8A top right** Westend61/Getty Images. **9.8A center left** PhotoDisc/Getty Images. **9.8A center right** PhotoDisc/Getty Images. **9.8A bottom left** Aleksandr S. Khachunts/Shutterstock. **9.8A bottom right** Michael Fernahl/iStockphoto. **9.8B left** Michael Fernahl/iStockphoto. **9.8B right** Aleksandr S. Khachunts/Shutterstock. **9.9B** Michael Ciesielski Photography. **9.10A** Science Source/Photo Researchers. **9.10B top left** Gusto/Photo Researchers. **9.10B bottom right** Eric J. Simon. **9.13A** Eye of Science/Photo Researchers. **9.13B** Eye of Science/Photo Researchers. **9.15A** Eric J. Simon. **9.15B** Eric J. Simon. **9.18B** Graphic Science/Alamy. **9.20A** Andrew Syred/Photo Researchers. **9.20B** Jose Luis Pelaez, Inc./Getty Images. **9.20C** Tomasz Zachariasz/iStockphoto. **9.20D** kosam/Shutterstock. **9.20E** Tomasz Zachariasz/iStockphoto. **9.21A** From: "Learning to Fly: Phenotypic Markers in Drosophila." A poster of common phenotypic markers used in Drosophila genetics. Jennifer Childress, Richard Behringer, and Georg Halder. 2005. Genesis 43(1). Cover illustration. **9.22** Taxi/Getty Images. **9.23** Dschingis Khan und seine Erben (exhibition catalogue), München 2005, p. 304. **p.179** Norma Jubinville.

Chapter 10: **Chapter Opener** Eye of Science/Photo Researchers. **10.1A** Robley C. Williams, University of California Berkeley/Biological Photo Services. **10.3A left** Courtesy of the Library of Congress. **10.3A right** From the Double Helix: by James D. Watson, Atheneum Press, N. Y., 1968, p. 215. (c) 1968. Courtesy CSHL Archive. **10.3B** National Institute of Health. **10.6B** Kevin McCluskey. **10.8C** Dr. Masaru Okabe, Research Institute for Microbial Diseases. **10.12A** Joachim Frank. **p.200** Russell Kightley/SPL/Photo Researchers. **p.201** Hazel Appleton, Centre for Infections/Health Protection Agency/Photo Researchers. **10.19 left** Health Protection Agency Centre for Infections/Photo Researchers, Inc. **10.19 right** Mario Guzman/epa/Corbis. **10.23C** Huntington Potter, University of South Florida College of Medicine.

Chapter 11: **p.208 left** Martin Oeggerli/Photo Researchers. **p.208 right** Pat Sullivan/Associated Press. **Chapter Opener** Lee Jae Won/Reuters. **11.1A** Martin Oeggerli/Photo Researchers. **11.2A left** S. C. Holt/Biological Photo Service. **11.2A right** Biophoto/Photo Researchers. **11.2B** Eric Isselée/Shutterstock. **11.8A** F. Rudolf Turner. **11.9** American Association for the Advancement of Science. **11.12** Robyn Mackenzie/Shutterstock. **11.14** Pat Sullivan/Associated Press.

Chapter 12: **p.230 top left** AP Wide World Photos. **p.230 top right** Hank Morgan/Photo Researchers. **p.230 bottom left** Steve Helber/AP Wide World Photos. **p.230 bottom right** Philippe Plailly & Atelier Daynes/Photo Researchers. **Chapter Opener** Tek Image/Photo Researchers. **12.1A** AP Wide World Photos. **12.1B top to bottom** Smileus/Dreamstime; UPI/A.J. Sisco/Newscom; Kadroff/Shutterstock; Max Delson Martins Santos/iStockphoto. **12.6A** Brad DeCecco Photography. **12.6B** DNX/Photolibrary. **12.7A** Eli Lilly and Company. Used with permission. **12.7B** Hank Morgan/Photo Researchers. **12.8A** Vladimir Nikitin/Shutterstock. **12.8B** Syngenta Corporate Communications. **12.9A** Ocean/Corbis. **12.9B** Dave Porter/Alamy. **12.13** Repligen Corporation. **12.15A** Steve Helber/AP Wide World Photos. **12.15B** South West News Service, Bristol, England. **12.19** Rubberball/Getty Images. **12.21** Philippe Plailly & Atelier Daynes/Photo Researchers.

Chapter 13: **p.254 top left** ARCHIV/Photo Researchers. **Chapter Opener** tbkmedia.de/Alamy. **13.1A** Gerry Ellis/Getty Images. **13.1B** Brandon Cole/Photolibrary. **13.1C left** ARCHIV/Photo Researchers. **13.1C right** National Maritime Museum Picture Library, London, England. **13.2 clockwise from bottom left** Robert Sarno/iStockphoto; Paul Rapson/Alamy; Izaokas Sapiro/Shutterstock; YinYang/iStockphoto; floricica buzlea/iStockphoto; Karin Lau/Alamy. **13.3A top** Edward S. Ross. **13.3A bottom** Michael & Patricia Fogden/Corbis. **13.3B** Corbis. **13.4A** Colin Keates/Dorling Kindersley. **13.4B** Chip Clark. **13.4C** Martin Lockley. **13.4D** Manfred Kage/Peter Arnold, Inc./PhotoLibrary. **13.4E** Alfred Pasieka/SPL/Photo Researchers. **13.4F** Hanny Paul/ZUMA Press – Gamma. **13.4G** Albo/Shutterstock. **13.5B left** Dr. Keith Wheeler/Photo Researchers. **13.5B right** Lennart Nilsson/Scanpix. **13.7** Earth Imaging/Getty Images. **13.8 left** Laura Jesse, Extension Entomologist, Iowa State University. **13.8 right** Edmund D. Brodie III. **13.10** Anne Dowie. **13.11B** William Ervin/Photo Researchers. **13.12** Tom Brakefield/Corbis. **13.14A** Dave Blackey/PhotoLibrary. **13.14B** George D. Lepp/Corbis. **13.15C** Barry Mansell/Nature Picture Library. **13.15** Scott Camazine/Photo Researchers.

Chapter 14: **p.276** Wolfgang Kaehler/Corbis. **Chapter Opener** David Hosking/FLPA. **14.1** AKrieger/Photolibrary. **14.2A left** Malcolm Schuyl/Alamy. **14.2A right** David Kjaer/Nature Picture Library. **14.2B left to right** Robert Kneschke/iStockphoto; Justin Horrocks/iStockphoto; Photodisc/Getty Images; Photos.com; Phil Date/Shutterstock; Masterfile. **14.2C top to bottom** Boris Karpinski/Alamy; janprchal/Shutterstock; Troy Maben/AP Images. **14.3B left** Joe McDonald/Photoshot Holdings Ltd./Bruce Coleman. **14.3B right** Joe McDonald/Corbis. **14.3C top** USDA/APHIS Animal and Plant Health Inspection Service. **14.2C bottom** Stephen Krasemann/Photo Researchers. **14.3D** Wolfgang Kaehler/Corbis. **14.3E** Ueshima R, Asami T. Evolution: single-gene speciation by left-right reversal. Nature. 2003 Oct 16;425(6959):679; Fig. 1. **14.3F** Joseph Dovala/Image Quest Marine. **14.3G top left** photosbyjohn/Shutterstock. **14.3G top right** Photodisc/Getty Images. **14.3G bottom** DawnYL/Fotolia. **14.4A main** Corbis. **14.4A left** John Shaw/Photoshot Holdings Ltd./Bruce Coleman. **14.4A right** Michael Fogden/Photoshot Holdings Ltd./Bruce Coleman. **14.4B** Arthur Anker. **14.5B** Douglas W. Schemske. **14.7** photobank.kiev.ua/Shutterstock. **14.8 top to bottom** INTERFOTO/Alamy; Mary Plage/Photolibrary; Frans Lanting/DanitaDelimont.com. **14.9** Peter Grant. **14.10B left** Melvin Grey/Photoshot/NHPA. **14.10B right** Juan Martin Simon. **14.10C** Ole Seehausen.

Chapter 15: **Chapter Opener 1 left** Joe Tucciarone/Photo Researchers. **Chapter Opener 2 top right** Theo Allofs/CorbisS. **Chapter Opener 2 bottom right** BIOS Huguet Pierre/Peter Arnold, Inc./PhotoLibrary. **15.1 main** Peter Sawyer/Chip Clark. **15.1 inset** Francois Gohier/Photo Researchers. **15.3A** Fred M. Menger and Kurt Gabrielson, Emory University. **15.7D** Wildlife/D.Harms/Still Pictures/ Specialiststock.com. **15.8** Tom Bean/Alamy. **15.11A** Stephen Dalton/Photo Researchers. **15.11B** Jean Kern. **15.11C** Dr. William A. Cresko. **15.12 left to right** Hal Beral/V & W/Image Quest Marine; Christophe Courteau/Biosphoto/Photo Researchers; Reinhard Dirscherl/Photolibrary; Jim Greenfield/Image Quest Marine; Image Quest Marine. **15.15A** PhotoDisc/Getty Images. **15.16C** Neg./Transparency no.5789. Courtesy Dept. of Library Services, American Museum of Natural History.

Chapter 16: **p.318 left** Dr. Tony Brain/David Parker/Science Photo Library/Photo Researchers, Inc. **p.318 right** Manfred Kage/Peter Arnold/PhotoLibrary. **Chapter Opener** Andre Seale/AGE fotostock. **16.1** Dr. Tony Brain/David Parker/Science Photo Library/Photo Researchers. **16.2A left to right** Eye of Science/Photo Researchers; David McCarthy/Photo Researchers; Stem Jems/Photo Researchers. **16.2B** L. Brent Selinger. **16.2C** Dr. Immo Rantala/SPL/Photo Researchers. **16.2D** Eye of Science/Photo Researchers. **16.3A** Huntington Potter, Byrd Alzheimer's Institute and University of South Florida, David Dressler, Oxford University and Balliol College. **16.3B** H.S. Pankratz, T.C. Beaman/Biological Photo Service. **16.4 top left** Sinclair Stammers/Photo Researchers. **16.4 top right** T. Stevens & P. McKinley, PNNL/Photo Researchers. **16.4 bottom left** Pasieka/SPL/Photo Researchers. **16.4 bottom right** Alfred Pasieka/Peter Arnold/Photolibrary. **16.5** Garry Palmateer. **16.6A** Photo Researchers. **16.6B** ExxonMobil Corporation. **16.8A** Jack Dykinga/Stone/Getty Images. **16.8B** Jim West/Alamy. **16.9A** National Library of Medicine. **16.9B** David Scharf/Photo Researchers. **16.9C** Susan M. Barns, Ph.D. **16.9D** Moredon Animal Health/SPL/Photo Researchers. **16.9E** Science Source/Photo Researchers. **16.10** David M. Phillips/Photo Researchers. **16.11** Anders Wiklund/Scanpix/Reuters. **16.12** Centers for Disease Control and Prevention. **16.13A left to right** Carol Buchanan/AGE fotostock; Eye of Science/Photo Researchers; Alex Rakosy/Custom Medical Stock Photo. **16.13B top left** Kevin Carpenter and Patrick Keeling. **16.13B right** Eric V. Grave/Photo Researchers. **16.15A** Steve Gschmeissner/Photo Researchers. **16.15B** Miriam Godfrey, NIWA. **16.15C** Georgie Holland/AGE fotostock. **16.15D** Fred Rhoades. **16.15E** Steve Gscheissner/Photo Researchers.

Type/iStockphoto; Magnet Creative/iStockphoto; Motorolka/Shutterstock; NatUlrick/Shutterstock. **21.20A** Susumu Nishinaga/SPL/Photo Researchers. **21.20B** Photo courtesy of The Jackson Laboratory, Bar Harbor, Maine. **21.21** Clynt Garnham Lifestyle/Alamy. **21.22** Steve Allen/Brand X Pictures/Jupiter Images. **p.450** GeoM/Shutterstock.

Chapter 22: p.452 Douglas Pulsipher/Alamy. **Chapter Opener** John Holmes/FLPA. **22.1** Corbis/AGE fotostock. **22.4A** Thomas Eisner. **22.4B** Paulo De Oliveira/Photolibrary. **22.5** Ted Daeschler/AFP/Getty Images. **22.6A** Douglas Pulsipher/Alamy. **22.6B** Motta & Macchiarelli/Anatomy Dept./Univ. "LA Sapienza", Rome/Photo Researchers. **22.7** Martin M. Rotker. **p.464** Douglas Pulsipher/Alamy.

Chapter 23: Chapter Opener Frank Stober/Photolibrary. **23.2A** George Peters/iStockphoto. **23.2B** Matt Antonino/Shutterstock. **23.2C** Chris Mattison/Alamy. **23.5B** Gustoimages/Photo Researchers. **23.6B left** Ed Reschke. **23.6B right** J & L Weber/Photolibrary. **23.7A** Lennart Nilsson/Scanpix. **23.11A** D. W. Fawcett/Photo Researchers. **23.13** Ingram Publishing/Photolibrary. **23.14B** Courtesy, The Gillette Company.

Chapter 24: p.484 top David McNew/Getty Images. **p.484 bottom** Salisbury District Hospital/Photo Researchers. **Chapter Opener** SPL/Photo Researchers. **24.2** Photodisc/Getty Images. **24.3** Ryan McVay/Getty Images. **24.4 main** David McNew/Getty Images. **24.4 inset** Science Source/Photo Researchers. **24.5B left** Science Photo Library/Alamy. **24.5B right** NIBSC/Photo Researchers. **24.10** Raimund Koch/Photonica Amana America, Inc./Getty Images. **24.11** Biology Media/Science Source/Photo Researchers. **24.13** Lennart Nilsson/Scanpix. **24.14** Impact Visuals/Newscom. **24.16** Salisbury District Hospital/Photo Researchers. **p.501** Author series Dey L. P. Pharmaceuticals.

Chapter 25: p.504 top Four Oaks/Shutterstock. **p.504 bottom** George Peters/iStockphoto. **Chapter Opener** Lynn Rogers/Peter Arnold, Inc./PhotoLibrary. **25.2** Mike Wilkes/naturepl.com. **p.506** Cherkas/Shutterstock. **25.3A** Four Oaks/Shutterstock. **25.3B left** Jeff Lepore/Photo Researchers. **25.3B right** O. Alamany & E. Vicens/Corbis. **25.4A** George Peters/iStockphoto. **25.4B** holbox/Shutterstock. **p.508** Zig Leszczynski/AA/PhotoLibrary. **25.5 left to right** George Peters/iStockphoto; Eric Isselée/iStockphoto; Maksym Gorpenyuk/Shutterstock. **25.6A** Yuri Arcurs/Shutterstock. **25.10** Phanie/Photo Researchers.

Chapter 26: p.516 Jonathan Blair/Corbis. **Chapter Opener** Mitch Reardon/Lonely Planet Images. **26.3** Rolf Bruderer/Blend Images/Corbis. **26.4D** AP Wide World Photos. **26.5A top** Chris Howes/Wild Places Photography/Alamy. **26.5A bottom** John M. Burnley/Photo Researchers. **26.8A left** Ian Hooton/Photo Researchers. **26.8A right** Edward Kinsman/Photo Researchers. **26.9** Steve Cady/iStockphoto. **26.10** Jonathan Blair/Corbis. **26.11** Corbis.

Chapter 27: p.532 top left John R. Finnerty. **p.532 top right** C. Edelman/La Vilette/Photo Researchers. **p.532 bottom left** David Barlow. **p.532 bottom right** Eric J. Simon. **Chapter Opener** Picture Partners/Photo Researchers. **27.1A** Oxford Scientific/PhotoLibrary. **27.1B** David Wrobel. **27.2A** John R. Finnerty. **27.2B** Hans Pfletschinger/Peter Arnold, Inc./PhotoLibrary. **27.2C** John Cancalosi/Nature Picture Library. **27.3B** C. Edelman/La Vilette/Photo Researchers. **27.8** Gusto/Photo Researchers. **27.9A** D. Phillips/Photo Researchers. **27.12A** Huw Williams. **27.12C** Thomas Poole. **27.12D** G.I. Bernard/Photo Researchers. **27.13** David Barlow. **27.16A-D** Lennart Nilsson/Scanpix. **27.16E** Eric J. Simon. **27.18** Dr. Yorgos Nikas/Photo Researchers.

Chapter 28: p.562 top left Manfred Kage/Peter Arnold, Inc./PhotoLibrary. **p.562 top right** Edwin R. Lewis, Professor Emeritus. **p.562 bottom** WDCN/Univ. College London/Photo Researchers. **Chapter Opener** Lester Lefkowitz/Corbis. **28.2** Manfred Kage/Peter Arnold, Inc./PhotoLibrary. **28.7** Edwin R. Lewis, Professor Emeritus. **28.9 left** Steve Gorton/Dorling Kindersley. **28.9 right** PhotoDisc/Getty Images. **28.16A** The Dornsife Neuroscience Imaging Center. **28.26B** Johns Hopkins University. **28.17** Robert W. Haley, M.D. **28.20A** WDCN/Univ. College London/Photo Researchers. **28.20B** Jonathan Nourak/Stone/Getty Images. **28.20C** Douglas Graham/Roll Call/Sygma/Corbis.

Chapter 29: p.586 John Mitchell/Photo Researchers. **Chapter Opener** Dietmar Nill/Photolibrary. **29.1** Andre Seale/Photolibrary. **29.2A** Fuse/Getty Images. **29.3C top** John Mitchell/Photo Researchers. **29.3C bottom** Dr. R.A. Steinbrecht. **29.3D** James Gerholdt/Photolibrary. **29.4E** Keith Publicover/Shutterstock. **29.7A** Tom E. Adams/Photolibrary. **29.7B** Thomas Eisner. **29.9A-B** Corbis. **29.11** szefei/Shutterstock. **29.12** RubberBall/Alamy.

Chapter 30: p.602 Photodisc/PhotoLibrary. **Chapter Opener** Manfred Grebler/Alamy. **30.1A** Danita Delimont/Alamy. **30.1B** Tamara Bauer/iStockphoto. **30.1C** Dave Watts/NHPA/Photo Researchers. **30.1D** JUNIORS BILDARCHIV/AGE fotostock. **30.1E** Photodisc/Photolibrary. **30.2A left** Natural Visions/Alamy. **30.2A right** Laguna Design/Photolibrary. **30.2B** Tony Florio/Photo Researchers. **30.2C** Carlos Villoch/Image Quest Marine. **30.2D left** Darrell Gulin/Corbis. **30.2D right** Kaj R. Svensson/Photo Researchers. **30.2E** alle/Shutterstock. **30.5A** Jochen Tack Alamy. **30.5B** Professor P. Motta, Department of Anatomy, University 'la Sapienza" Rome/Photo Researchers, Inc. **30.8** Professor Clara Franzini-Armstrong. **30.11** Christopher Nuzzaco/iStockphoto. **p.617 clockwise from top left** Photodisc/Photolibrary; Tamara Bauer/iStockphoto; Danita Delimont/Alamy; Dave Watts/NHPA/Photo Researchers.

Chapter 31: p.620 zhuda/Shutterstock. **Chapter Opener** Michael Nichols/National Geographic Stock. **31.1** ARCO/Diez, O/AGE fotostock. **31.3** Adam Hart-Davis/SPL/Photo Researchers. **31.4A** Eric J. Simon. **31.4B left** Rosemary Mayer/FLPA. **31.4B top right** Donald Gregory Clever. **31.4B bottom right** FhF Greenmedia/AGE fotostock. **31.4C left** Scott Camazine/Photo Researchers. **31.4C right** Corbis. **31.6B** Ed Reschke/Photolibrary. **31.6C** Graham Kent. **31.6D** Graham Kent. **31.6E** N.C. Brown Center for Ultrastructure Studies, SUNY-Environmental Science & Forestry, Syracuse, NY. **31.6F** Graham Kent. **31.7B top** Viktor Kitaykin/iStockphoto. **31.7B bottom** Ed Reschke/Photolibrary. **31.7C** Ed Reschke. **31.8B** Don Mason/Corbis. **31.8C** California Historical Society Collection (CHS-1177), University of Southern California on behalf of the USC Specialized Libraries and Archival Collections. **31.9A clockwise from top left** Ostanina Ekaterina/Shutterstock; alohaspirit/iStockphoto; Alex James Bramwell/Shutterstock; zhuda/Shutterstock. **31.12A** Walter H. Hodge/Peter Arnold, Inc./PhotoLibrary. **31.12C top** Andrey Armyagov/Shutterstock. **31.12C center left** Corbis. **31.12C center right** Rolf Klebsattel/Shutterstock. **31.12C bottom** Elena Schweitzer/Shutterstock. **31.14A** Tim Hill/Alamy. **31.14B** Frank Balthis. **31.14C** Dan Suzio/SPL/Photo Researchers. **31.14D** Dennis Frates/Alamy. **31.14E** Rosenfeld Images Ltd/Photo Researchers. **31.15** David Welling/Nature Picture Library.

Chapter 32: p.642 top Brian Capon. **p.642 bottom** R. L. Peterson/Biological Photo Service. **Chapter Opener** Igor Plotnikov/Shutterstock. **32.1B** Mario Verin/Photolibrary. **32.2A** Brian Capon. **32.4 left** Frank Greenaway/Dorling Kindersley. **32.4 center, right** Jeremy Bur/Photo Researchers. **32.5A** Ray F. Evert. **32.5B** Lezh/iStockphoto. **32.5C top left** Nigel Cattlin/FLPA. **32.5C others** P. B. Tomlinson. **32.7B** Paul Rapson/Photo Researchers. **32.8A** Agricultural Research Service/USDA. **32.9A** U.S. Geological Survey, Denver. **32.9B** NOAA. **32.9C** Kevin Horan/Stone/Getty Images. **32.10** Ralf-Finn Hestoft/Corbis. **32.11** Louisiana State University Press. **32.13A** R. L. Peterson/Biological Photo Service. **32.13B main** Scimat/Photo Researchers. **32.13B inset** E. H. Newcomb and S. R. Tandon/Biological Photo Service. **32.14A** Clay Perry/Photolibrary. **32.14B** Kevin Schafer/CorbisS. **32.14C** ARCO/H. Reinhard/AGE fotostock. **32.14D** Jean-Philippe Delobelle/Photolibrary. **32.14E** James H. Robinson/Photo Researchers.

Chapter 33: p.660 top Kristin Piljay. **p.660 bottom** Martin Shields/Photo Researchers. **Chapter Opener** Brian Leatart/Getty Images. **33.1A** Dorling Kindersley. **33.3A** William M.Gray. **33.4** Chandoha Photography. **33.5A** Alan Crozier. **33.5B** Kristin Piljay. **33.5C** Fred Jensen. **33.6** Design Pics Inc./Alamy. **33.7A** Kristin Piljay. **33.7B left** Yuri Shirokov/iStockphoto. **33.7B right** Ed Reschke. **p.669** Rudolf Madár/Shutterstock. **33.8** Stockbyte. **33.9A** Michael Evans. **33.9B** Martin Shields/Photo Researchers. **33.10** Malcolm B. Wilkins. **33.13A** USDA/Nature Source/Photo Researchers.

Chapter 34: p.678 top left franzfoto.com/Alamy. **p.678 top right** James Randklev/Image Bank/Getty Images. **p.678 bottom** Dennis Frates/Workbook Stock/Getty Images. **Chapter Opener** Garry Weare/Lonely Planet Images. **34.2A** Rich Reid/NGS Image Collection. **34.2B** Alfred Eisenstaedt/Time Life Pictures/Getty Images. **34.3A** Peter Batson/Imagequest Marine. **34.3B** Vincent Munier/naturepl.com. **34.4** franzfoto.com/Alamy. **34.6B** Digital Vision/Getty Images. **34.6C** SOC/Image Quest Marine. **34.6D** James Randklev/Image Bank/Getty Images. **34.7B** Don Fink/Shutterstock. **34.7C** Jean Dickey. **34.9** Frans Lanting/Corbis. **34.10** Eric Isselée/Shutterstock. **34.11** Dennis Frates/Workbook Stock/Getty Images. **34.12** Michel Gunther/Mau/Photolibrary. **34.13** Mike Grandmaison/PhotoLibrary. **34.14** Kennan Ward/Corbis. **34.15** Jorma Luhta/Nature Picture Library. **34.16** Darrell Gulin/Corbis. **34.17** Gordon Wiltsie/National Geographic Image Collection.

Chapter 35: p.698 top left Theo Allofs/Danita Delimont. **p.698 top right** John Cancalosi/Photolibrary. **p.698 bottom left** Carol Walker/Nature Picture Library. **p.698 bottom right** Rupert Barrington/Nature Picture Library. **Chapter Opener** AlexeyVis/iStockphoto. **35.2B** Theo Allofs/Danita Delimont. **35.5A** Thomas McAvoy/Time & Life Pictures/Getty Images. **35.5B** Frank Lane Picture Agency/Corbis. **35.6A** USGS. **35.6B** Star Banner, Doug Engle/AP Photo. **35.7A** pzAxe/Shutterstock. **35.7B** James Watt/Photolibrary. **35.8** Jonathan Blair/Woodfin Camp & Associates, Inc. **35.9** John Cancalosi/Photolibrary. **35.10 main** Righard Wrangham. **35.10 inset** Alissa Crandall/Corbis. **35.11A** Clive Bromhall/Photolibrary. **35.11B** Bernd Heinrich. **35.12A** Jose B. Ruiz/Nature Picture Library. **35.12B** Michael Hutchinson/Nature Picture Library. **35.13A** J.P. Varin/Jacana/Photo Researchers. **35.14A** Steve Bloom Images/Alamy. **35.14C** Carol Walker/Nature Picture Library. **35.15** Image Quest Marine. **35.16B** Mike W. Howell. **35.18A** Wolfgang Kaehler/Corbis. **35.18B** C & M Denis-Huot/Peter Arnold, Inc./PhotoLibrary. **35.19** Rupert Barrington/Nature Picture Library. **35.20** Renne Lynn. **35.21A** Jennifer Jarvis. **35.21B** Stephen Kraseman/Peter Arnold, Inc./PhotoLibrary. **35.22A** Michael Nichols/National Geographic Stock. **35.22B** Martin Harvey/Photolibrary. **35.23A** Dominic Chan/WENN.com/Newscom. **35.23B** Janet Mayer/Splash News/Newscom.

Chapter 36: p.722 David Jay Zimmerman/Corbis. **Chapter Opener** Antoine Dervaux/Photolibrary. **36.2A** Matthew Banks/Alamy. **36.2B** David Jay Zimmerman/Corbis. **36.2C** mashe/Shutterstock. **36.3 left to right** Roger Phillips/Dorling Kindersley; Jane Burton/Dorling Kindersley; Yuri Arcurs/Shutterstock. **36.4A** Wild Dales Photography - Simon Phillpotts/Alamy. **36.4B** Roy Corral/Corbis. **36.4C left** Joshua Lewis/Shutterstock. **36.4C right** WizData/Shutterstock. **36.5A** Marcin Perkowski/Shutterstock. **36.5B** Nigel Cattlin/Alamy. **36.5C** Meul/ARCO/Nature Picture Library. **36.6** Alan Carey/Photo Researchers. **36.11A left** Peter Ginter. **36.11A right** Peter Menzel Photography.

Chapter 37: Chapter Opener Chad Ehlers/Photolibrary. **37.3A** Doug Backlund. **37.3B** Tim Zurowski/All Canada Photos/Alamy. **37.4** Jurgen Freund/Nature Picture Library. **37.5A** S.J. Krasemann/Photolibrary. **37.5B** Jean Dickey. **37.6** Lawrence E. Gilbert/Biological Photo Service. **37.7** Joel Sartore/Photolibrary. **37.11B** William E. Townsend/Photo Researchers. **37.11C** Aletta Yniguez, National Center for Coral Reef Research (NCORE). **37.11D** Reinhard Dirscherl/Alamy. **37.12A** Jean Dickey. **37.13B** Embassy of Australia. **37.13C** Ace Stock Limited/Alamy. **37.22A** Michael Marten/SPL/Photo Researchers. **37.22B** NASA/Goddard Space Flight Center. **37.23A** Fang xinwu/Newscom. **37.23B** Thony Belizaire/AFP/Getty Images.

Chapter 38: p.760 top Charlie Riedel/AP Photo. **p.760 bottom** Rick & Nora Bowers/Alamy. **Chapter Opener** Arco Images GmbH/Alamy. **38.1A** Mike Dobel/Alamy. **38.1C** Jeff March/Alamy. **38.1D** James King-Holmes/Photo Researchers. **38.2A** Corbis/SuperStock. **38.2B** David M Dennis/Photolibrary. **38.2C** Ho New/Reuters. **38.2D** Charlie Riedel/AP Photo. **38.3B left to right** National Parks Service; U.S. Geological Survey, Denver; U.S. Geological Survey, Denver. **38.5A** Greg Cortopassi/dailycamera.com. **38.5B** Tom Murphy/WWI/Peter Arnold, Inc./PhotoLibrary. **38.6A** William Osborn/Nature Picture Library. **38.6B** Paul McCormick/Getty Images. **38.7A** Rick & Nora Bowers/Alamy. **38.7B** DLILLC/Corbis. **38.8A** Yann Arthus-Bertrand/Corbis. **38.8B** Calvin Larsen/Photo Researchers. **38.8C** Joel Sartore/National Geographic Image Collection. **38.9B** Roger Kirkpatrick/V&W/Image Quest Marine. **p.772** Neo Edmund/Shutterstock. **38.10B** Chris Fredriksson/Alamy. **38.11B** NPS Photo. **38.11C** Corbis/Fotolia. **38.12B** South Florida Water Management District (WPB). **38.13** Inaki Relanzon/Nature Picture Library.

Illustration and Text Credits

4.2B is adapted from W. M. Becker, J. B. Reece, and M. F. Poenie, *The World of the Cell,* 3rd ed. Copyright © 1996 Pearson Education, Inc., publishing as Pearson Benjamin Cummings.

The following figures are adapted from Elaine N. Marieb, *Human Anatomy and Physiology,* 5th ed. Copyright © 2001 Pearson Education, Inc., publishing as Pearson Benjamin Cummings: **4.4A, 4.5, 4.8A,** and **EOC UN4.5.**

The following figures are adapted from Elaine N. Marieb, *Human Anatomy and Physiology,* 4th ed. Copyright © 1998 Pearson Education, Inc., publishing as Pearson Benjamin Cummings: **22.10, 22.12, 25.8, 27.3A, 27.3C, 27.4B, 27.17B, 29.5, 29.9A, 29.9B, 30.4, 30.8, 30.10A.**

The following figures are adapted from Gerard J. Tortora, Berdell R. Funke, and Christine L. Case, *Microbiology: An Introduction,* 9th ed. Copyright © 2007 Pearson Education, Inc., publishing as Pearson Benjamin Cummings: **16.6A, 24.8B,** and **Table 27.7.**

The following figures are adapted from Lawrence G. Mitchell, John A. Mutchmor, and Warren D. Dolphin, *Zoology.* Copyright © 1988 Pearson Education, Inc., publishing as Pearson Benjamin Cummings: **18.1B, 18.14B, 21.10B, 25.5, 30.2E,** and **35.7C.**

Chapter 1: 1.9E: Data in graph based on D. W. Pfennig et al. 2001. Frequency-dependent Batesian mimicry. *Nature* 410: 323.

Chapter 3: Figures 3.12B: Adapted from D. W. Heinz et al. 1993. How amino-acid insertions are allowed in an alpha-helix of T4 lysozyme. *Nature* 361: 561. **Unnumbered figure of collagen, page 44:** Illustration of collagen structure by Irving Geis. Image from Irving Geis Collection, HHMI. Rights owned by Howard Hughes Medical Institute (HHMI). Not to be reproduced without permission. **Figure 3.13C/D:** PDB ID 3GS0: Palaninathan, S.K., Mohamedmohaideen, N.N., Orlandini, E., Ortore, G., Nencetti, S., Lapucci, A., Rossello, A., Freundlich, J.S., Sacchettini, J.C. 2009. Novel transthyretin amyloid fibril formation inhibitors: synthesis, biological evaluation, and X-ray structural analysis. *Public Library of Science One* 4: e6290-e6290.

Chapter 5: Module 5.7: Scientific Discovery: Adapted from an interview in Neil Campbell and Jane Reece, *Biology* 7th ed. Copyright © 2005 Pearson Education, Inc., publishing as Pearson Benjamin Cummings.

Chapter 6: Figure 6.4: Data from C. M. Taylor and G. M. McLeod, *Rose's Laboratory Handbook for Dietetics,* 5th ed. (New York: Macmillan, 1949), p. 18; J. V. G. A. Durnin and R. Passmore, *Energy and Protein Requirements in FAO/WHO Technical Report* No. 522, 1973; W. D. McArdle, F. I. Katch, and V. L. Katch, *Exercise Physiology* (Philadelphia, PA: Lea & Feibiger, 1981); R. Passmore and J. V. G. A. Durnin, *Physiological Reviews* vol. 35, pp. 801–840 (1955). **Figure 6.5** From *Molecular Biology of the Cell,* 4th edition, by Bruce Alberts et al., fig. 2.69, p. 92. Copyright © 2002 by Bruce Alberts, Alexander Johnson, Julian Lewis, Martin Raff, Keith Roberts, and Peter Walter. Used by permission.

Chapter 7: 7.8B: Adapted from Richard and David Walker. *Energy, Plants and Man,* fig. 4.1, p. 69. Sheffield: University of Sheffield. © Richard Walker. Used courtesy of Oxygraphics.

Chapter 11: 11.2A: Adapted from C. K. Mathews and K. E. van Holde, *Biochemistry,* 2nd ed. Copyright © 1996 Pearson Education, Inc., publishing as Pearson Benjamin Cummings. **11.12:** Adapted from W. H. Becker, *The World of the Cell,* p. 592. Copyright © 1986 Pearson Education, Inc., publishing as Pearson Benjamin Cummings. **Table 11.19:** Data from *American Cancer Society. Cancer Facts & Figures 2010.* Atlanta: American Cancer Society; 2010.

Chapter 13: 13.4Ha: Reprinted by permission from Macmillan Publishers Ltd.: *Nature.* From J. G. M. Thewissen et al. 2001. Skeletons of terrestrial cetaceans and the relationship of whales to artiodactyls. Vol. 413: 277-281, fig. 2a, copyright 2001. **13.4Hb:** Adapted from P. D. Gingerich et al. 2001. Origin of whales from early artiodactyls: Hands and feet of eocene protocetidae from Pakistan. *Science* 293: 2239-2242, fig. 3. Copyright © 2001 American Association for the Advancement of Science. Reprinted with permission from AAAS. **13.4Hc and d:** Reprinted by permission from Macmillan Publishers Ltd.: *Nature.* From C. de Muizon. 2001. Walking with whales. Vol. 413: 259-260, fig. 1, copyright 2001. **13.16:** From M. Hori. 1993. Frequency-dependent natural selection in the handedness of scale-eating Cichlid fish. *Science* 260: 216-219, fig. 2a. Copyright ©1993 American Association for the Advancement of Science. Reprinted with permission from AAAS.

Chapter 14: 14.5A: Adapted from D. M. B. Dodd, *Evolution,* vol. 11, pp. 1308-1311. Reprinted by permission of the Society for the Study of Evolution. **Module 14.9:** Scientific Discovery: Adapted from an interview in Neil Campbell and Jane Reece, *Biology,* 6th ed. Copyright © 2002 Pearson Education, Inc., publishing as Pearson Benjamin Cummings. **14.9:** From P. R. Grant et al. 2006. Evolution of character displacement in Darwin's finches, *Science, 313,* 224-226, fig. 2. Copyright ©2006 American Association for the Advancement of Science. Reprinted with permission from AAAS.

Chapter 15: Module 15.2: Scientific Discovery: Adapted from an interview in Neil Campbell, *Biology,* 2nd ed. Copyright © 1990 Pearson Education, Inc. publishing as Pearson Benjamin Cummings. **15.7A:** Map adapted from http://geology.er. usgs.gov/eastern/plates.html. **15.7D:** Adapted from W. K. Purves and G. H. Orians, *Life: The Science of Biology,* 2nd ed., fig. 16.5c, p. 1180 (New York: Sinauer Associates, 1987). Used with permission. **15.18:** Adapted from B. Korber et al. 2000. Timing the ancestor of the HIV-1 pandemic strains. *Science* 288: 1789-1796, fig. 1b. Copyright © 2000 American Association for the Advancement of Science. Reprinted with permission from AAAS. **15.19A:** Adapted from S. Blair Hedges. The origin and evolution of model organisms. *Nature Reviews Genetics* 3: 838-848, fig. 1, p. 840.

Chapter 16: 16.14: From Archibald and Keeling, "Recycled Plastids," *Trends in Genetics,* Vol. 18, No. 11, 2002. Copyright © 2002, with permission from Elsevier.

Chapter 19: 19.4A: Adapted from B. Holmes. Sept. 9, 2006. Meet your ancestor – the fish that crawled. *New Scientist,* issue 2568: 35-39. By permission of *New Scientist* magazine. **19.4B:** From C. Zimmer. *At the Water's Edge.* Free Press, Simon & Schuster, p. 90. Copyright © 1999 by Carl Zimmer. Reprinted by permission. **19.11:** Drawn from photos of fossils: *A. ramidus* adapted from www.age-of-the-sage.org/evolution/ardi_fossilized_skeleton.htm. *A. anamensis* and *H. neanderthalensis* adapted from *The Human Evolution Coloring Book.* *K. platyops* drawn from photo in Meave Leakey et al., New hominid genus from eastern Africa shows diverse middle Pliocene lineages, *Nature,* March 22, 2001, 410:433. *P. boisei* drawn from a photo by David Bill. *H. ergaster* drawn from a photo at www.inhandmuseum.com. *S. tchadensis* drawn from a photo in Michel Brunet et al., A new hominid from the Upper Miocene of Chad, Central Africa, *Nature,* July 11, 2002, 418:147, fig. 1b. **19.12A:** Adapted from Douglas Palmer, *The Origins of Man,* p. 158. New Holland Publishers, London, © 2007. Reprinted by permission of the publisher. **19.13B:** Adapted from D. Jones. Nov. 11, 2006. Blueprint for a Neanderthal. *New Scientist,* issue 2577. By permission of *New Scientist* magazine. **19.14:** Reprinted by permission from Macmillan Publishers Ltd.: *Nature Genetics.* From L. Luca Cavalli-Sforza and M. W. Feldman. 2003. The application of molecular genetic approaches to the study of human evolution. Vol. 33: 266-275, fig. 3, copyright 2003.

Chapter 21: 21.4: Figure 22-1 from Rhoades and Pflanzer, *Human Physiology,* 3e. © 1996 Brooks/Cole, a part of Cengage Learning, Inc. Repro-

duced by permission. www.cengage.com/permissions. **21.16:** Adapted from Murray W. Nabors, *Introduction to Botany.* Copyright © 2004 Pearson Education, Inc., publishing as Pearson Benjamin Cummings. **Table 21.17A:** Data from RDA Subcommittee, *Recommended Dietary Allowances* (Washington, D. C.: National Academy Press, 1989); M. E. Shils and V. R. Young, *Modern Nutrition in Health and Disease* (Philadelphia, PA: Lea & Feibiger, 1988). **Table 21.17B:** Data from (1) M. E. Shils, "Magnesium," in M. E. Shiels and V. R. Young, eds. *Modern Nutrition in Health and Disease* (Philadelphia, PA: Lea & Feibiger, 1988); (2) V. F. Fairbanks and E. Beutler, "Iron" [same as 1]; (3) N. W. Solomons, "Zinc and Copper" [same as 1]; (4) RDA Subcommittee, *Recommended Dietary Allowances* (Washington, D. C.: National Academy Press, 1989); (5) E. J. Underwood, *Trace Elements in Human and Animal Nutrition* (New York: Academic Press, 1977). **21.21:** Data adapted from *Clinical Guidelines on the Identification, Evaluation, and Treatment of Overweight and Obesity in Adults: The Evidence Report.* Data found at the National Heart, Lung, and Blood Institute: http://www.nhlbi.nih.gov/guidelines/obesity/bmi_tbl.htm.

Chapter 22: 22.11: Illustration by Irving Geis. Rights owned by Howard Hughes Medical Institute. Not to be reproduced without permission.

Chapter 26: 26.8B: Data from C. J. Bryne, D. F. Saxton, et al., *Laboratory Tests: Implications for Nursing Care,* 2nd ed. Copyright © 1986 Pearson Education, Inc., publishing as Pearson Benjamin Cummings, 1301 Sansome St., San Francisco, CA 94111.

Chapter 27: 27.4C: Adapted from Robert Crooks and Karla Baur, *Our Sexuality,* 5th ed. (Redwood City, CA: Benjamin Cummings, 1993). Copyright © 1993 The Benjamin Cummings Publishing Company. **27.14B:** Adapted from an illustration by William McGinnis in Peter Radetsky, "The homeobox: Something very precious that we share with flies, from egg to adult." Bethesda, MD: Howard Hughes Medical Institute, 1992, p. 92. Reprinted by permission of William McGinnis. **Table 27.8:** Data from R. Hatcher et al., *Contraceptive Technology: 1990-1992,* p. 134 (New York: Irvington, 1990).

Chapter 28: 28.4: Adapted from G. Matthews, 2003. *Cellular Physiology of Nerve and Muscle,* 4th edition, fig. 6-2d, p. 61. Cambridge, MA: Blackwell Scientific Publications. Reprinted by permission of Wiley Blackwell. **28.6:** Adapted from Becker, Kleinsmith, and Hardin, *The World of the Cell,* 6th ed. Copyright © 2006 Pearson Education, Inc., publishing as Pearson Benjamin Cummings.

Chapter 30: 30.12: Adapted from J. L. Andersen, et al. 2000. Muscles, genes, and athletic performance, illustrated by Jennifer Johansen. *Scientific American,* September, 2000, p. 49. Reprinted by permission of Jennifer Johansen Hutton.

Chapter 33: 33.13A: Adapted from E. Farmer. 1997. Plant biology: New fatty acid-based signals: A lesson from the plant world, *Science* 276: 912. Copyright © 1997 American Association for the Advancement of Science. Reprinted with permission from AAAS.

Chapter 34: Module 34.2: Text quotation from Rachel Carson, *Silent Spring* (New York: Houghton Mifflin, 1962). **34.8:** Adapted from Heinrich Walter and Siegmar-Walter Breckle. 2003. *Walter's Vegetation of the Earth,* fig. 16, p. 36. Springer-Verlag, © 2003.

Chapter 35: 35.5B: Courtesy of Masakazu Konishi. **35.9 (top):** Adapted from *Animal Navigation,* p. 109, by Talbot H. Waterman. Copyright © 1989 by Scientific American Books, Inc. Used with permission by W. H. Freeman and Company. **35.12C:** Graph from N. B. Davies. 1977. Prey selection and social behaviour in wagtails (Aves: Motacillidae). *Journal of Animal Ecology* 46: 37-57, fig. 9. Reproduced with permission of Blackwell Publishing Ltd. **35.12D:** Graph adapted from N. B. Davies. 1977. Prey selection and social behaviour in wagtails (Aves: Motacillidae). *Journal of Animal Ecology* 46: 37-57, fig. 8. Reproduced with permission of Blackwell Publishing Ltd. **35.14B:** From *The Common Loon: Spirit of Northern Lakes* by Judith W. McIntyre, drawings by Anne Olson, p. 97. (Minneapolis, MN: University Minnesota Press, 1988). Copyright © 1988 by University of Minnesota Press. Used by permission of the publisher. **35.16A:** Map adapted from W. M. Howell et al. 1980. Abnormal expression of secondary sex characteristics in a population of mosquitofish, *Gambusia affinis holbrooki*: Evidence for environmentally-induced masculinization. *Copeia* 4, 676-681, fig. 5. Used with permission. **Module 35.22:** Scientific Discovery: Adapted from an interview in Neil Campbell, Biology, 3rd ed. Copyright © 1993 Pearson Education, Inc., publishing as Pearson Benjamin Cummings.

Chapter 36: **Table 36.3:** Data from Center for Health Statistics, 2004 CDC. **36.8:** Data from Fisheries and Oceans, Canada, 1999. **Table 36.9:** Data from United Nations, the World at Six Billion, 2007. **36.9A:** Data from United Nations, the World at Six Billion, 2007. **36.9B:** Data from Population Reference Bureau, 2000 and U. S. Census Bureau International Data Base, 2003. **36.9C and 36.10:** Data from U. S. Census Bureau, International Data Base. **36.11B:** From *The Ecological Footprint Atlas* 2009 by B. Ewing et al., p. 31, Map 2. © 2009 Global Footprint Network. All rights reserved. Used by permission.

Chapter 37: **37.9:** From Robert Leo Smith, *Ecology and Field Biology,* 4th ed. Copyright © 1990 by Robert Leo Smith. Reprinted by permission of Addison Wesley Longman, Inc. **37.13A:** Source: www.dest.gov.au/archive/Science/pmsec/14meet/rcd1.html.

Chapter 38: **38.1B:** Created from data from The IUCN Red List of Threatened Species™ at iucnredlist.org. **38.3A:** Graph from J. Hansen et al. 2006. Global temperature change. *PNAS 103:* 14288-14293, fig. 1B. Copyright 2006 National Academy of Sciences, U.S.A. Used with permission. **38.4A:** From Climate Change 2007: The Physical Science Basis. Working Group I Contribution to the Fourth Assessment Report of the Intergovernmental Panel on Climate Change, FAQ 2.1, Figure 1. Cambridge University Press. Reprinted by permission of IPCC, c/o World Meteorological Organization. **38.9A:** Reprinted by permission from Macmillan Publishers Ltd.: *Nature.* From N. Myers et al. 2000. Biodiversity hotspots for conservation priorities. Vol. 403: 853, copyright 2000. **38.10A:** Adapted from http://disc.sci.gsfc.nasa.gov/oceancolor/additional/science-focus/images/central_america_topo.jpg. **38.11A:** From Yellowstone to Yukon Conservation Initiative climate change fact sheet. Used with permission of Yellowstone to Yukon Conservation Initiative, Bozeman, MT (www.y2y.net). **38.12A:** Map by Patterson Clark, June 23, 2002. Copyright © 2002, The Washington Post.

Glossary

A

A site One of two of a ribosome's binding sites for tRNA during translation. The A site holds the tRNA that carries the next amino acid in the polypeptide chain. (A stands for aminoacyl tRNA.)

abiotic factor (ā′-bī-ot′-ik) A nonliving component of an ecosystem, such as air, water, or temperature.

abiotic reservoir The part of an ecosystem where a chemical, such as carbon or nitrogen, accumulates or is stockpiled outside of living organisms.

ABO blood groups Genetically determined classes of human blood that are based on the presence or absence of carbohydrates A and B on the surface of red blood cells. The ABO blood group phenotypes, also called blood types, are A, B, AB, and O.

abscisic acid (ABA) (ab-sis′-ik) A plant hormone that inhibits cell division, promotes dormancy, and interacts with gibberellins in regulating seed germination.

absorption The uptake of small nutrient molecules by an organism's own body; the third main stage of food processing, following digestion.

acetyl CoA (a-sē′-til-kō′a′) (acetyl coenzyme A) The entry compound for the citric acid cycle in cellular respiration; formed from a fragment of pyruvate attached to a coenzyme.

acetylcholine (a-sē′-til-kō′lēn) A nitrogen-containing neurotransmitter. Among other effects, it slows the heart rate and makes skeletal muscles contract.

achondroplasia (uh-kon′-druh-plā′-zhuh) A form of human dwarfism caused by a single dominant allele; the homozygous condition is lethal.

acid A substance that increases the hydrogen ion (H⁺) concentration in a solution.

acid A substance that increases the hydrogen ion (H^+) concentration in a solution.

acid precipitation Rain, snow, or fog that is more acidic than pH 5.2.

acrosome (ak′-ruh-som) A membrane-enclosed sac at the tip of a sperm. The acrosome contains enzymes that help the sperm penetrate an egg.

actin A globular protein that links into chains, two of which twist helically around each other, forming microfilaments in muscle cells.

action potential A change in membrane voltage that transmits a nerve signal along an axon.

activation energy The amount of energy that reactants must absorb before a chemical reaction will start.

activator A protein that switches on a gene or group of genes.

active immunity Immunity conferred by recovering from an infectious disease or by receiving a vaccine.

active site The part of an enzyme molecule where a substrate molecule attaches (by means of weak chemical bonds); typically, a pocket or groove on the enzyme's surface.

active transport The movement of a substance across a biological membrane against its concentration gradient, aided by specific transport proteins and requiring an input of energy (often as ATP).

adaptation An inherited characteristic that enhances an organism's ability to survive and reproduce in a particular environment.

adaptive immunity A vertebrate-specific defense that is activated only after exposure to an antigen and is mediated by lymphocytes. It exhibits specificity, memory, and self–nonself recognition. Also called acquired immunity.

adaptive radiation Period of evolutionary change in which groups of organisms form many new species whose adaptations allow them to fill new or vacant ecological roles in their communities.

adenine (A) (ad′-uh-nēn) A double-ring nitrogenous base found in DNA and RNA.

adhesion The attraction between different kinds of molecules.

adipose tissue A type of connective tissue whose cells contain fat.

adrenal cortex (uh-drē′-nul) The outer portion of an adrenal gland, controlled by ACTH from the anterior pituitary; secretes hormones called glucocorticoids and mineralocorticoids.

adrenal gland One of a pair of endocrine glands, located atop each kidney in mammals, composed of an outer cortex and a central medulla.

adrenal medulla (uh-drē′-nul muh-dul′-uh) The central portion of an adrenal gland, controlled by nerve signals; secretes the fight-or-flight hormones epinephrine and norepinephrine.

adrenocorticotropic hormone (ACTH) (uh-drē′-nō-cōr′-ti-kō-trop′-ik) A protein hormone secreted by the anterior pituitary that stimulates the adrenal cortex to secrete corticosteroids.

adult stem cell A cell present in adult tissues that generates replacements for nondividing differentiated cells. Adult stem cells are capable of differentiating into multiple cell types, but they are not as developmentally flexible as embryonic stem cells.

age structure The relative number of individuals of each age in a population.

agonistic behavior (a′-gō-nis′-tik) Confrontational behavior involving a contest waged by threats, displays, or actual combat that settles disputes over limited resources, such as food or mates.

AIDS (acquired immunodeficiency syndrome) The late stages of HIV infection, characterized by a reduced number of T cells and the appearance of characteristic opportunistic infections.

alcohol fermentation Glycolysis followed by the reduction of pyruvate to ethyl alcohol, regenerating NAD⁺ and releasing carbon dioxide.

alga (al′-guh) (plural, **algae**) A protist that produces its food by photosynthesis.

alimentary canal (al′-uh-men′-tuh-rē) A complete digestive tract consisting of a tube running between a mouth and an anus.

allantois (al′-an-tō′-is) In animals, an extraembryonic membrane that develops from the yolk sac. The allantois helps dispose of the embryo's nitrogenous wastes and forms part of the umbilical cord in mammals.

allele (uh-lē′-ul) An alternative version of a gene.

allergen (al′-er-jen) An antigen that causes an allergy.

allergy A disorder of the immune system caused by an abnormally high sensitivity to an antigen. Symptoms are triggered by histamines released from mast cells.

allopatric speciation The formation of new species in populations that are geographically isolated from one another.

alternation of generations A life cycle in which there is both a multicellular diploid form, the sporophyte, and a multicellular haploid form, the gametophyte; a characteristic of plants and multicellular green algae.

alternative RNA splicing A type of regulation at the RNA-processing level in which different mRNA molecules are produced from the same primary transcript, depending on which RNA segments are treated as exons and which as introns.

altruism (al′-trū-iz-um) Behavior that reduces an individual's fitness while increasing the fitness of another individual.

alveolus (al-vē′-oh-lus) (plural, **alveoli**) One of the dead-end air sacs within the mammalian lung where gas exchange occurs.

Alzheimer's disease (AD) An age-related dementia (mental deterioration) characterized by confusion, memory loss, and other symptoms.

amino acid (uh-mēn′-ō) An organic molecule containing a carboxyl group and an amino group; serves as the monomer of proteins.

amino-acid-derived hormone A regulatory chemical consisting of a protein, peptide (a short polypeptide), or amine (modified amino acids). Amino-acid-derived hormones are water soluble (but not lipid soluble).

amino group A chemical group consisting of a nitrogen atom bonded to two hydrogen atoms.

ammonia NH_3; A small and very toxic nitrogenous waste produced by metabolism.

amniocentesis (am'-nē-ō-sen-tē'-sis) A technique for diagnosing genetic defects while a fetus is in the uterus. A sample of amniotic fluid, obtained by a needle inserted into the uterus, is analyzed for telltale chemicals and defective fetal cells.

amnion (am'-nē-on) In vertebrate animals, the extraembryonic membrane that encloses the fluid-filled amniotic sac containing the embryo.

amniote Member of a clade of tetrapods that have an amniotic egg containing specialized membranes that protect the embryo. Amniotes include mammals and birds and other reptiles.

amniotic egg (am'-nē-ot'-ik) A shelled egg in which an embryo develops within a fluid-filled amniotic sac and is nourished by yolk. Produced by reptiles (including birds) and egg-laying mammals, the amniotic egg enables them to complete their life cycles on dry land.

amoeba (uh-mē'-buh) A general term for a protist that moves and feeds by means of pseudopodia.

amoebocyte (uh-mē'-buh-sīt) An amoeba-like cell that moves by pseudopodia and is found in most animals; depending on the species, may digest and distribute food, dispose of wastes, form skeletal fibers, fight infections, and change into other cell types.

amoebozoan A member of a clade of protists in the supergroup Unikonta that includes amoebas and slime molds and is characterized by lobe-shaped pseudopodia.

amphibian Member of a clade of tetrapods that includes frogs, toads, salamanders, and cecilians.

amygdala (uh-mig'-duh-la) An integrative center of the cerebrum; functionally, the part of the limbic system that seems central in recognizing the emotional content of facial expressions and laying down emotional memories.

anabolic steroid (an'-uh-bol'-ik ster'-oyd) A synthetic variant of the male hormone testosterone that mimics some of its effects.

analogy The similarity between two species that is due to convergent evolution rather than to descent from a common ancestor with the same trait.

anaphase The fourth stage of mitosis, beginning when sister chromatids separate from each other and ending when a complete set of daughter chromosomes arrives at each of the two poles of the cell.

anatomy The study of the structures of an organism.

anchorage dependence The requirement that to divide, a cell must be attached to a solid surface.

androgen (an'-drō-jen) A steroid sex hormone secreted by the gonads that promotes the development and maintenance of the male reproductive system and male body features.

anemia (uh-nē'-me-ah) A condition in which an abnormally low amount of hemoglobin or a low number of red blood cells results in the body cells receiving too little oxygen.

angiosperm (an'-jē-ō-sperm) A flowering plant, which forms seeds inside a protective chamber called an ovary.

annelid (uh-nel'-id) A segmented worm. Annelids include earthworms, polychaetes, and leeches.

annual A plant that completes its life cycle in a single year or growing season.

antagonistic hormones Two hormones that have opposite effects.

anterior Pertaining to the front, or head, of a bilaterally symmetric animal.

anterior pituitary (puh-tū'-uh-tār-ē) An endocrine gland, adjacent to the hypothalamus and the posterior pituitary, that synthesizes several hormones, including some that control the activity of other endocrine glands.

anther A sac located at the tip of a flower's stamen; contains male sporangia in which meiosis occurs to produce spores that form the male gametophytes, or pollen grains.

anthropoid (an'-thruh-poyd) A member of a primate group made up of the apes (gibbons, orangutans, gorillas, chimpanzees, bonobos, and humans) and monkeys.

antibody (an'-tih-bod'-ē) A protein dissolved in blood plasma that attaches to a specific kind of antigen and helps counter its effects.

anticodon (an'-tī-kō'-don) On a tRNA molecule, a specific sequence of three nucleotides that is complementary to a codon triplet on mRNA.

antidiuretic hormone (ADH) (an'-tē-dī'-yū-ret'-ik) A hormone made by the hypothalamus and secreted by the posterior pituitary that promotes water retention by the kidneys.

antigen (an'-tuh-jen) A foreign (nonself) molecule that elicits an adaptive immune response.

antigen receptor A transmembrane version of an antibody molecule that B cells and T cells use to recognize specific antigens; also called a membrane antibody.

antigen-binding site A region of the antibody molecule responsible for the antibody's recognition and binding function.

antigenic determinant A region on the surface of an antigen molecule to which an antibody binds.

antigen-presenting cell (APC) One of a family of white blood cells (for example, a macrophage) that ingests a foreign substance or a microbe and attaches antigenic portions of the ingested material to its own surface, thereby displaying the antigens to a helper T cell.

antihistamine (an'-tē-his'-tuh-mēn) A drug that interferes with the action of histamine, providing temporary relief from an allergic reaction.

anus The opening through which undigested materials are expelled.

aorta (ā-or'-tuh) A large artery that conveys blood directly from the left ventricle of the heart to other arteries.

aphotic zone (ā-fō'-tik) The region of an aquatic ecosystem beneath the photic zone, where light does not penetrate enough for photosynthesis to take place.

apical dominance (ā'-pik-ul) In a plant, the hormonal inhibition of axillary buds by a terminal bud.

apical meristem (ā'-pik-ul mer'-uh-stem) Plant tissue made up of undifferentiated cells located at the tip of a plant root or in the terminal or axillary bud of a shoot. Apical meristems enable roots and shoots to grow in length.

apoptosis (ā-puh-tō'-sus) The timely and tidy suicide of cells; also called programmed cell death.

appendicular skeleton (ap'-en-dik'-yū-ler) Components of the skeletal system that support the fins of a fish or the arms and legs of a land vertebrate; in land vertebrates, the cartilage and bones of the shoulder girdle, pelvic girdle, forelimbs, and hind limbs. See also axial skeleton.

appendix (uh-pen'-dix) A small, finger-like extension of the vertebrate cecum; contains a mass of white blood cells that contribute to immunity.

aquaporin A transport protein in the plasma membrane of some plant or animal cells that facilitates the diffusion of water across the membrane (osmosis).

aqueous humor (ā'-kwē-us hyū'-mer) Plasma-like liquid in the space between the lens and the cornea in the vertebrate eye; helps maintain the shape of the eye, supplies nutrients and oxygen to its tissues, and disposes of its wastes.

aqueous solution (ā'-kwā-us) A solution in which water is the solvent.

arachnid A member of a major arthropod group (chelicerates) that includes spiders, scorpions, ticks, and mites.

Archaea (ar'-kē-uh) One of two prokaryotic domains of life, the other being Bacteria.

Archaeplastida One of five supergroups proposed in a current hypothesis of the evolutionary history of eukaryotes. The other four supergroups are Chromalveolata, Rhizaria, Excavata, and Unikonta.

arteriole (ar-ter'-ē-ōl) A vessel that conveys blood between an artery and a capillary bed.

artery A vessel that carries blood away from the heart to other parts of the body.

arthropod (ar'-thrō-pod) A member of the most diverse phylum in the animal kingdom. Arthropods include the horseshoe crab, arachnids (for example, spiders, ticks, scorpions, and mites), crustaceans (for example, crayfish, lobsters, crabs, and barnacles), millipedes, centipedes, and insects. Arthropods are characterized by a chitinous exoskeleton, molting, jointed appendages, and a body formed of distinct groups of segments.

artificial selection The selective breeding of domesticated plants and animals to promote the occurrence of desirable traits.

ascomycete Member of a group of fungi characterized by saclike structures called asci that produce spores in sexual reproduction.

asexual reproduction The creation of genetically identical offspring by a single parent, without the participation of sperm and egg.

assisted reproductive technology Procedure that involves surgically removing eggs from a woman's ovaries, fertilizing them, and then returning them to the woman's body. *See also in vitro* fertilization.

association areas Sites of higher mental activities, making up most of the cerebral cortex.

associative learning Learning that a particular stimulus or response is linked to a reward or punishment; includes classical conditioning and trial-and-error learning.

astigmatism (uh-stig´-muh-tizm) Blurred vision caused by a misshapen lens or cornea.

atherosclerosis (ath´-uh-rō´-skluh-rō´-sis) A cardiovascular disease in which fatty deposits called plaques develop on the inner walls of the arteries, narrowing their inner diameters.

atom The smallest unit of matter that retains the properties of an element.

atomic mass The total mass of an atom; also called atomic weight. Given as a whole number, the atomic mass approximately equals the mass number.

atomic number The number of protons in each atom of a particular element.

ATP Adenosine triphosphate, the main energy source for cells.

ATP synthase A cluster of several membrane proteins that function in chemiosmosis with adjacent electron transport chains, using the energy of a hydrogen ion concentration gradient to make ATP.

atrium (ā´-trē-um) (plural, **atria**) A heart chamber that receives blood from the veins.

auditory canal Part of the vertebrate outer ear that channels sound waves from the pinna or outer body surface to the eardrum.

autoimmune disease An immunological disorder in which the immune system attacks the body's own molecules.

autonomic nervous system (ot´-ō-nom´-ik) The component of the vertebrate peripheral nervous system that regulates the internal environment; made up of sympathetic and parasympathetic subdivisions. Most actions of the autonomic nervous system are involuntary.

autosome A chromosome not directly involved in determining the sex of an organism; in mammals, for example, any chromosome other than X or Y.

autotroph (ot´-ō-trōf) An organism that makes its own food (often by photosynthesis), thereby sustaining itself without eating other organisms or their molecules. Plants, algae, and numerous bacteria are autotrophs.

auxin (ok´-sin) A plant hormone (indoleacetic acid or a related compound) whose chief effect is to promote seedling elongation.

AV (atrioventricular) node A region of specialized heart muscle tissue between the left and right atria where electrical impulses are delayed for about 0.1 second before spreading to both ventricles and causing them to contract.

axial skeleton (ak´-sē-ul) Components of the skeletal system that support the central trunk of the body: the skull, backbone, and rib cage in a vertebrate. *See also* appendicular skeleton.

axillary bud (ak´-sil-ār-ē) An embryonic shoot present in the angle formed by a leaf and stem.

axon (ak´-son) A neuron extension that conducts signals to another neuron or to an effector cell. A neuron has one long axon.

B

B cell A type of lymphocyte that matures in the bone marrow and later produces antibodies. B cells are responsible for the humoral immune response.

bacillus (buh-sil´-us) (plural, **bacilli**) A rod-shaped prokaryotic cell.

Bacteria One of two prokaryotic domains of life, the other being Archaea.

bacteriophage (bak-tēr´-ē-ō-fāj) A virus that infects bacteria; also called a phage.

balancing selection Natural selection that maintains stable frequencies of two or more phenotypic forms in a population.

ball-and-socket joint A joint that allows rotation and movement in several planes. Examples in humans are the hip and shoulder joints.

bark All the tissues external to the vascular cambium in a plant that is growing in thickness. Bark is made up of secondary phloem, cork cambium, and cork.

Barr body A dense body formed from a deactivated X chromosome found in the nuclei of female mammalian cells.

basal metabolic rate (BMR) The number of kilocalories a resting animal requires to fuel its essential body processes for a given time.

basal nuclei (bā´-sul nū´-klē-ī) Clusters of nerve cell bodies located deep within the cerebrum that are important in motor coordination.

base A substance that decreases the hydrogen ion (H^+) concentration in a solution.

basidiomycete (buh-sid´-ē-ō-mī´sēt) Member of a group of fungi characterized by club-shaped, spore-producing structures called basidia.

basilar membrane The floor of the middle canal of the inner ear.

behavior Individually, an action carried out by the muscles or glands under control of the nervous system in response to a stimulus; collectively, the sum of an animal's responses to external and internal stimuli.

behavioral ecology The study of behavior in an evolutionary context.

benign tumor An abnormal mass of cells that remains at its original site in the body.

benthic realm A seafloor, or the bottom of a freshwater lake, pond, river, or stream.

biennial A plant that completes its life cycle in two years.

bilateral symmetry An arrangement of body parts such that an organism can be divided equally by a single cut passing longitudinally through it. A bilaterally symmetric organism has mirror-image right and left sides.

bilaterian Member of the clade Bilateria, animals exhibiting bilateral symmetry.

bile A mixture of substances that is produced by the liver and stored in the gallbladder. Bile emulsifies fats and aids in their digestion.

binary fission A means of asexual reproduction in which a parent organism, often a single cell, divides into two genetically identical individuals of about equal size.

binomial A two-part, latinized name of a species; for example, *Homo sapiens*.

biodiversity hot spot A small geographic area with an exceptional concentration of endangered and threatened species, especially endemic species (those found nowhere else).

biofilm A surface-coating colony of prokaryotes that engage in metabolic cooperation.

biogenic amine A neurotransmitter derived from an amino acid. Examples of biogenic amines are epinephrine and dopamine.

biogeochemical cycle Any of the various chemical circuits that involve both biotic and abiotic components of an ecosystem.

biogeography The study of the past and present distribution of organisms.

biological clock An internal timekeeper that controls an organism's biological rhythms, marking time with or without environmental cues but often requiring signals from the environment to remain tuned to an appropriate period. *See also* circadian rhythm.

biological control The intentional release of a natural enemy to attack a pest population.

biological magnification The accumulation of harmful chemicals that are retained in the living tissues of consumers in food chains.

biological species concept Definition of a species as a group of populations whose members have the potential to interbreed in nature and produce viable, fertile offspring, but do not produce viable, fertile offspring with members of other such populations.

biomass The amount, or mass, of organic material in an ecosystem.

biome (bī´-ōm) A major type of ecological association that occupies a broad geographic region of land or water and is characterized by organisms adapted to the particular environment.

bioremediation The use of living organisms to detoxify and restore polluted and degraded ecosystems.

biosphere The entire portion of Earth inhabited by life; the sum of all the planet's ecosystems.

biotechnology The manipulation of living organisms or their components to make useful products.

biotic factor (bī-o'-tik) A living component of a biological community; an organism, or a factor pertaining to one or more organisms.

bipolar disorder Depressive mental illness characterized by extreme mood swings; also called manic-depressive disorder.

birds Members of a clade of reptiles that have feathers and adaptations for flight.

birth control pill A chemical contraceptive that contains synthetic estrogen and/or progesterone (or a synthetic progesterone-like hormone called progestin) and prevents the release of eggs.

bivalve A member of a group of molluscs that includes clams, mussels, scallops, and oysters.

blastocoel (blas'-tuh-sēl) In a developing animal, a central, fluid-filled cavity in a blastula.

blastocyst (blas'-tō-sist) A mammalian embryo (equivalent to an amphibian blastula) made up of a hollow ball of cells that results from cleavage and that implants in the mother's endometrium.

blastula (blas'-tyū-luh) An embryonic stage that marks the end of cleavage during animal development; a hollow ball of cells in many species.

blood A type of connective tissue with a fluid matrix called plasma in which red blood cells, white blood cells, and platelets are suspended.

blood pressure The force that blood exerts against the walls of blood vessels.

blood-brain barrier A system of capillaries in the brain that restricts passage of most substances into the brain, thereby preventing large fluctuations in the brain's environment.

body cavity A fluid-containing space between the digestive tract and the body wall.

bolus A lubricated ball of chewed food.

bone A type of connective tissue consisting of living cells held in a rigid matrix of collagen fibers embedded in calcium salts.

bottleneck effect Genetic drift resulting from a drastic reduction in population size. Typically, the surviving population is no longer genetically representative of the original population.

Bowman's capsule A cup-shaped swelling at the receiving end of a nephron in the vertebrate kidney; collects the filtrate from the blood.

brain The master control center of the nervous system, involved in regulating and controlling body activity and interpreting information from the senses transmitted through the nervous system.

brainstem A functional unit of the vertebrate brain, composed of the midbrain, the medulla oblongata, and the pons; serves mainly as a sensory filter, selecting which information reaches higher brain centers.

breathing Ventilation of the lungs through alternating inhalation and exhalation.

breathing control center The part of the medulla in the brain that directs the activity of organs involved in breathing.

bronchiole (bron'-kē-ōl) A fine branch of the bronchi that transports air to alveoli.

bronchus (bron'-kus) (plural, **bronchi**) One of a pair of breathing tubes that branch from the trachea into the lungs.

brown alga One of a group of marine, multicellular, autotrophic protists belonging to the supergroup Chromalveolata; the most common and largest type of seaweed. Brown algae include the kelps.

bryophyte (brī'-uh-fīt) A plant that lacks xylem and phloem; a seedless nonvascular plant. Bryophytes include mosses, liverworts, and hornworts.

budding A means of asexual reproduction whereby a new individual develops from an outgrowth of a parent. The new individual eventually splits off and lives independently.

buffer A chemical substance that resists changes in pH by accepting hydrogen ions from or donating hydrogen ions to solutions.

bulbourethral gland (bul'-bō-yū-rē'-thrul) One of a pair of glands near the base of the penis in the human male that secrete a clear alkaline mucus.

bulk feeder An animal that eats relatively large pieces of food.

C

C_3 plant A plant that uses the Calvin cycle for the initial steps that incorporate CO_2 into organic material, forming a three-carbon compound as the first stable intermediate.

C_4 plant A plant that prefaces the Calvin cycle with reactions that incorporate CO_2 into four-carbon compounds, the end product of which supplies CO_2 for the Calvin cycle.

calcitonin (kal'-sih-tōn'-in) A peptide hormone secreted by the thyroid gland that lowers the blood calcium level.

Calvin cycle The second of two stages of photosynthesis; a cyclic series of chemical reactions that occur in the stroma of a chloroplast, using the carbon in CO_2 and the ATP and NADPH produced by the light reactions to make the energy-rich sugar molecule G3P.

CAM plant A plant that uses an adaptation for photosynthesis in arid conditions in which carbon dioxide entering open stomata during the night is converted to organic acids, which release CO_2 for the Calvin cycle during the day, when stomata are closed.

cancer A disease characterized by the presence of malignant tumors (rapidly growing and spreading masses of abnormal body cells) in the body.

capillary (kap'-il-er-ē) A microscopic blood vessel that conveys blood between an arteriole and a venule; enables the exchange of nutrients and dissolved gases between the blood and interstitial fluid.

capillary bed A network of capillaries in a tissue or organ.

capsid The protein shell that encloses a viral genome.

carbohydrate (kar'-bō-hi'-drāt) Member of the class of biological molecules consisting of single-monomer sugars (monosaccharides), two-monomer sugars (disaccharides), and polymers (polysaccharides).

carbon fixation The incorporation of carbon from atmospheric CO_2 into the carbon in organic compounds. During photosynthesis in a C_3 plant, carbon is fixed into a three-carbon sugar as it enters the Calvin cycle. In C_4 and CAM plants, carbon is fixed into a four-carbon sugar.

carbon skeleton The chain of carbon atoms that forms the structural backbone of an organic molecule.

carbonyl group (kar'-buh-nēl') A chemical group consisting of a carbon atom linked by a double bond to an oxygen atom.

carboxyl group (kar'-bok-sil) A chemical group consisting of a carbon atom double-bonded to an oxygen atom and also bonded to a hydroxyl group.

carcinogen (kar-sin'-uh-jin) A cancer-causing agent, either high-energy radiation (such as X-rays or UV light) or a chemical.

carcinoma (kar'-sih-nō'-muh) Cancer that originates in the coverings of the body, such as skin or the lining of the intestinal tract.

cardiac cycle (kar'-dē-ak) The alternating contractions and relaxations of the heart.

cardiac muscle A type of striated muscle that forms the contractile wall of the heart.

cardiac output The volume of blood pumped per minute by each ventricle of the heart.

cardiovascular disease (kar'-dē-ō-vas'-kyū-ler) Disorders of the heart and blood vessels.

cardiovascular system A closed circulatory system with a heart and a branching network of arteries, capillaries, and veins.

carnivore An animal that mainly eats other animals.

carpel (kar'-pul) The female part of a flower, consisting of a stalk with an ovary at the base and a stigma, which traps pollen, at the tip.

carrier An individual who is heterozygous for a recessively inherited disorder and who therefore does not show symptoms of that disorder but who may pass on the recessive allele to offspring.

carrying capacity In a population, the number of individuals that an environment can sustain.

cartilage (kar'-ti-lij) A flexible connective tissue consisting of living cells and collagenous fibers embedded in a rubbery matrix.

Casparian strip (kas-par'-ē-un) A waxy barrier in the walls of endodermal cells in a plant root that prevents water and ions from entering the xylem without crossing one or more cell membranes.

cation exchange A process in which positively charged minerals are made available to a plant when hydrogen ions in the soil displace mineral ions from the clay particles.

cecum (sē'-kum) (plural, **ceca**) A blind outpocket at the beginning of the large intestine.

cell A basic unit of living matter separated from its environment by a plasma membrane; the fundamental structural unit of life.

cell body The part of a cell, such as a neuron, that houses the nucleus.

cell cycle An ordered sequence of events (including interphase and the mitotic phase) that extends from the time a eukaryotic cell is first formed from a dividing parent cell until its own division into two cells.

cell cycle control system A cyclically operating set of proteins that triggers and coordinates events in the eukaryotic cell cycle.

cell division The reproduction of a cell through duplication of the genome and division of the cytoplasm.

cell plate A double membrane across the midline of a dividing plant cell, between which the new cell wall forms during cytokinesis.

cell theory The theory that all living things are composed of cells and that all cells come from other cells.

cell wall A protective layer external to the plasma membrane in plant cells, bacteria, fungi, and some protists; protects the cell and helps maintain its shape.

cell-mediated immune response The type of specific immunity brought about by T cells. The cell-mediated immune response fights body cells infected with pathogens. *See also* humoral immune response.

cellular metabolism (muh-tab'-uh-lizm) All the chemical activities of a cell.

cellular respiration The aerobic harvesting of energy from food molecules; the energy-releasing chemical breakdown of food molecules, such as glucose, and the storage of potential energy in a form that cells can use to perform work; involves glycolysis, the citric acid cycle, and oxidative phosphorylation (the electron transport chain and chemiosmosis).

cellular slime mold A type of protist that has unicellular amoeboid cells and aggregated reproductive bodies in its life cycle; a member of the amoebozoan clade.

cellulose (sel'-yū-lōs) A structural polysaccharide of plant cell walls composed of glucose monomers. Cellulose molecules are linked into cable-like fibrils.

centipede A carnivorous terrestrial arthropod that has one pair of long legs for each of its numerous body segments, with the front pair modified as poison claws.

central canal The narrow cavity in the center of the spinal cord that is continuous with the fluid-filled ventricles of the brain.

central nervous system (CNS) The integration and command center of the nervous system; the brain and, in vertebrates, the spinal cord.

central vacuole In a plant cell, a large membranous sac with diverse roles in growth and the storage of chemicals and wastes.

centralization The presence of a central nervous system (CNS) distinct from a peripheral nervous system.

centriole (sen'-trē-ōl) A structure in an animal cell composed of cylinders of microtubule triplets arranged in a 9 + 0 pattern. An animal usually has a centrosome with a pair of centrioles involved in cell division.

centromere (sen'-trō-mēr) The region of a duplicated chromosome where two sister chromatids are joined (often appearing as a narrow "waist") and where spindle microtubules attach during mitosis and meiosis. The centromere divides at the onset of anaphase during mitosis and anaphase II during meiosis.

centrosome (sen'-trō-sōm) Material in the cytoplasm of a eukaryotic cell that gives rise to microtubules; important in mitosis and meiosis; also called the microtubule-organizing center.

cephalization (sef'-uh-luh-zā'-shun) An evolutionary trend toward concentration of the nervous system at the head end.

cephalopod A member of a group of molluscs that includes squids, cuttlefish, octopuses, and nautiluses.

cerebellum (sār'-ruh-bel'-um) Part of the vertebrate hindbrain; mainly a planning center that interacts closely with the cerebrum in coordinating body movement.

cerebral cortex (suh-rē'-brul kor'-teks) A folded sheet of gray matter forming the surface of the cerebrum. In humans, it contains integrating centers for higher brain functions such as reasoning, speech, language, and imagination.

cerebral hemisphere The right or left half of the vertebrate cerebrum.

cerebrospinal fluid (suh-rē'-brō-spī'-nul) Blood-derived fluid that surrounds, nourishes, and cushions the brain and spinal cord.

cerebrum (suh-rē'-brum) The largest, most sophisticated, and most dominant part of the vertebrate forebrain, made up of right and left cerebral hemispheres.

cervix (ser'-viks) The neck of the uterus, which opens into the vagina.

chaparral (shap'-uh-ral') A biome dominated by spiny evergreen shrubs adapted to periodic drought and fires; found where cold ocean currents circulate offshore, creating mild, rainy winters and long, hot, dry summers.

character A heritable feature that varies among individuals within a population, such as flower color in pea plants or eye color in humans.

chelicerate (kē-lih-suh'-rāte) A lineage of arthropods that includes horseshoe crabs, scorpions, ticks, and spiders.

chemical bond An attraction between two atoms resulting from a sharing of outer-shell electrons or the presence of opposite charges on the atoms. The bonded atoms gain complete outer electron shells.

chemical cycling The use and reuse of a chemical element, such as carbon, within an ecosystem.

chemical energy Energy available in molecules for release in a chemical reaction; a form of potential energy.

chemical reaction The making and breaking of chemical bonds, leading to changes in the composition of matter.

chemiosmosis (kem'-ē-oz-mō'-sis) Energy-coupling mechanism that uses the energy of hydrogen ion (H^+) gradients across membranes to drive cellular work, such as the phosphorylation of ADP; powers most ATP synthesis in cells.

chemoautotroph An organism that obtains both energy and carbon from inorganic chemicals. A chemoautotroph makes its own organic compounds from CO_2 without using light energy.

chemoheterotroph An organism that obtains both energy and carbon from organic compounds.

chemoreceptor (kē'-mō-rē-sep'-ter) A sensory receptor that detects chemical changes within the body or a specific kind of molecule in the external environment.

chiasma (kī-az'-muh) (plural, **chiasmata**) The microscopically visible site where crossing over has occurred between chromatids of homologous chromosomes during prophase I of meiosis.

chitin (kī-tin) A structural polysaccharide found in many fungal cell walls and in the exoskeletons of arthropods.

chlamydia A member of a group of bacteria that live inside eukaryotic host cells. Chlamydias include human pathogens that cause blindness and nongonococcal urethritis, a common sexually transmitted disease.

chlorophyll A green pigment located within the chloroplasts of plants, algae, and certain prokaryotes. Chlorophyll a can participate directly in the light reactions, which convert solar energy to chemical energy.

chloroplast (klō'-rō-plast) An organelle found in plants and photosynthetic protists that absorbs sunlight and uses it to drive the synthesis of organic molecules (sugars) from carbon dioxide and water.

choanocyte (kō-an'-uh-sīt) A flagellated feeding cell found in sponges. Also called a collar cell, it has a collar-like ring that traps food particles around the base of its flagellum.

cholesterol (kō-les′-tuh-rol) A steroid that is an important component of animal cell membranes and that acts as a precursor molecule for the synthesis of other steroids, such as hormones.

chondrichthyan (kon-drik′-thē-an) Cartilaginous fish; member of a clade of jawed vertebrates with skeletons made mostly of cartilage, such as sharks and rays.

chorion (kō′r-ē-on) In animals, the outermost extraembryonic membrane, which becomes the mammalian embryo's part of the placenta.

chorionic villi (kōr′-ē-on′-ik vil′-us) Outgrowths of the chorion, containing embryonic blood vessels. As part of the placenta, chorionic villi absorb nutrients and oxygen from, and pass wastes into, the mother's bloodstream.

chorionic villus sampling (CVS) A technique for diagnosing genetic defects while the fetus is in an early development stage within the uterus. A small sample of the fetal portion of the placenta is removed and analyzed.

choroid (kōr′-oyd) A thin, pigmented layer in the vertebrate eye, surrounded by the sclera. The iris is part of the choroid.

Chromalveolata One of five supergroups proposed in a current hypothesis of the evolutionary history of eukaryotes. The other four supergroups are Rhizaria, Excavata, Unikonta, and Archaeplastida.

chromatin (krō′-muh-tin) The combination of DNA and proteins that constitutes eukaryotic chromosomes; often used to refer to the diffuse, very extended form taken by chromosomes when a cell is not dividing.

chromosome (krō′-muh-sōm) A threadlike, gene-carrying structure found in the nucleus of a eukaryotic cell and most visible during mitosis and meiosis; also, the main gene-carrying structure of a prokaryotic cell. A chromosomes consists of one very long piece of chromatin, a combination of DNA and protein.

chromosome theory of inheritance A basic principle in biology stating that genes are located on chromosomes and that the behavior of chromosomes during meiosis accounts for inheritance patterns.

chyme (kīm) The mixture of partially digested food and digestive juices formed in the stomach.

chytrid (kī-trid) Member of a group of fungi that are mostly aquatic and have flagellated spores. They probably represent the most primitive fungal lineage.

ciliate (sil′-ē-it) A type of protist that moves and feeds by means of cilia. Ciliates belong to the supergroup Chromalveolata.

cilium (plural, **cilia**) A short cellular appendage specialized for locomotion, formed from a core of nine outer doublet microtubules and two single microtubules (the 9 + 2 pattern) covered by the cell's plasma membrane.

circadian rhythm (ser-kā′-dē-un) In an organism, a biological cycle of about 24 hours that is controlled by a biological clock, usually under the influence of environmental cues; a pattern of activity that is repeated daily. *See also* biological clock.

circulatory system The organ system that transports materials such as nutrients, O_2, and hormones to body cells and transports CO_2 and other wastes from body cells.

citric acid cycle The chemical cycle that completes the metabolic breakdown of glucose molecules begun in glycolysis by oxidizing acetyl CoA (derived from pyruvate) to carbon dioxide. The cycle occurs in the matrix of mitochondria and supplies most of the NADH molecules that carry energy to the electron transport chains. Together with pyruvate oxidation, the second major stage of cellular respiration.

clade A group of species that includes an ancestral species and all its descendants.

cladistics (kluh-dis′-tiks) An approach to systematics in which common descent is the primary criterion used to classify organisms by placing them into groups called clades.

class In Linnaean classification, the taxonomic category above order.

cleavage (klē′-vij) (1) Cytokinesis in animal cells and in some protists, characterized by pinching in of the plasma membrane. (2) In animal development, the first major phase of embryonic development, in which rapid cell divisions without cell growth transforms the animal zygote into a ball of cells.

cleavage furrow The first sign of cytokinesis during cell division in an animal cell; a shallow groove in the cell surface near the old metaphase plate.

clitoris An organ in the female that engorges with blood and becomes erect during sexual arousal.

clonal selection (klōn′-ul) The production of a lineage of genetically identical cells that recognize and attack the specific antigen that stimulated their proliferation. Clonal selection is the mechanism that underlies the immune system's specificity and memory of antigens.

clone As a verb, to produce genetically identical copies of a cell, organism, or DNA molecule. As a noun, the collection of cells, organisms, or molecules resulting from cloning; colloquially, a single organism that is genetically identical to another because it arose from the cloning of a somatic cell.

closed circulatory system A circulatory system in which blood is confined to vessels and is kept separate from the interstitial fluid.

club fungus *See* basidiomycete.

clumped dispersion pattern A pattern in which the individuals of a population are aggregated in patches.

cnidarian (nī-dār′-ē-un) An animal characterized by cnidocytes, radial symmetry, a gastrovascular cavity, and a polyp and medusa body form. Cnidarians include the hydras, jellies, sea anemones, corals, and related animals.

cnidocyte (nī′-duh-sīt) A specialized cell for which the phylum Cnidaria is named; consists of a capsule containing a fine coiled thread, which, when discharged, functions in defense and prey capture.

coccus (kok′-us) (plural, **cocci**) A spherical prokaryotic cell.

cochlea (kok′-lē-uh) A coiled tube in the inner ear of birds and mammals that contains the hearing organ, the organ of Corti.

codominant Inheritance pattern in which a heterozygote expresses the distinct trait of both alleles.

codon (kō′-don) A three-nucleotide sequence in mRNA that specifies a particular amino acid or polypeptide termination signal; the basic unit of the genetic code.

coelom (sē′-lom) A body cavity completely lined with mesoderm.

coenzyme An organic molecule serving as a cofactor. Most vitamins function as coenzymes in important metabolic reactions.

coevolution Evolutionary change in which adaptations in one species act as a selective force on a second species, inducing adaptations that in turn act as a selective force on the first species; mutual influence on the evolution of two different interacting species.

cofactor A nonprotein molecule or ion that is required for the proper functioning of an enzyme. *See also* coenzyme.

cognition The process carried out by an animal's nervous system that includes perceiving, storing, integrating, and using the information obtained by the animal's sensory receptors.

cognitive map A representation, within an animal's nervous system, of spatial relations among objects in the animal's environment.

cohesion (kō-hē′-zhun) The sticking together of molecules of the same kind, often by hydrogen bonds.

collecting duct A tube in the vertebrate kidney that concentrates urine while conveying it to the renal pelvis.

collenchyma cell (kō-len′-kim-uh) In plants, a cell with a thick primary wall and no secondary wall, functioning mainly in supporting growing parts.

colon (kō′-lun) Large intestine; the portion of the vertebrate alimentary canal between the small intestine and the anus; functions mainly in water absorption and the formation of feces.

communication Animal behavior including transmission of, reception of, and response to signals.

community An assemblage of all the organisms living together and potentially interacting in a particular area.

companion cell In a plant, a cell connected to a sieve-tube element whose nucleus and ribosomes provide proteins for the sieve-tube element.

competitive inhibitor A substance that reduces the activity of an enzyme by binding to the enzyme's active site in place of the substrate. A competitive inhibitor's structure mimics that of the enzyme's substrate.

complement system A family of innate defensive blood proteins that cooperate with other components of the vertebrate defense system to protect against microbes; can enhance phagocytosis, directly lyse pathogens, and amplify the inflammatory response.

complementary DNA (cDNA) A DNA molecule made *in vitro* using mRNA as a template and the enzyme reverse transcriptase. A cDNA molecule therefore corresponds to a gene but lacks the introns present in the DNA of the genome.

complete digestive tract A digestive tube with two openings, a mouth and an anus.

complete dominance A type of inheritance in which the phenotypes of the heterozygote and dominant homozygote are indistinguishable.

complete metamorphosis (met′-uh-mōr′-fuh-sis) A type of development in certain insects in which development from larva to adult is achieved by multiple molts that are followed by a pupal stage. While encased in its pupa, the body rebuilds from clusters of embryonic cells that have been held in reserve. The adult emerges from the pupa.

compost Decomposing organic material that can be used to add nutrients to soil.

compound A substance containing two or more elements in a fixed ratio. For example, table salt (NaCl) consists of one atom of the element sodium (Na) for every atom of chlorine (Cl).

compound eye The photoreceptor in many invertebrates; made up of many tiny light detectors, each of which detects light from a tiny portion of the field of view.

concentration gradient A region along which the density of a chemical substance increases or decreases. Cells often maintain concentration gradients of ions across their membranes. When a gradient exists, substances tend to move from where they are more concentrated to where they are less concentrated.

conception The fertilization of the egg by a sperm cell in humans.

cone (1) In vertebrates, a photoreceptor cell in the retina stimulated by bright light and enabling color vision. (2) In conifers, a reproductive structure bearing pollen or ovules.

coniferous forest A biome characterized by conifers, cone-bearing evergreen trees.

conjugation The union (mating) of two bacterial cells or protist cells and the transfer of DNA between the two cells.

conjunctiva A thin mucous membrane that lines the inner surface of vertebrate eyelids.

connective tissue Animal tissue that functions mainly to bind and support other tissues, having a sparse population of cells scattered through an extracellular matrix, which they produce.

conservation biology A goal-oriented science that endeavors to sustain biological diversity.

continental shelf The submerged part of a continent.

contraception The deliberate prevention of pregnancy.

controlled experiment An experiment in which an experimental group is compared with a control group that varies only in the factor being tested.

convergent evolution The evolution of similar features in different evolutionary lineages, which can result from living in very similar environments.

copulation Sexual intercourse, usually necessary for internal fertilization to occur.

cork The outermost protective layer of a plant's bark, produced by the cork cambium.

cork cambium Meristematic tissue that produces cork cells during secondary growth of a plant.

cornea (kor′-nē-uh) The transparent frontal portion of the sclera, which admits light into the vertebrate eye.

corpus callosum (kor′-pus kuh-lō′-sum) The thick band of nerve fibers that connect the right and left cerebral hemispheres in placental mammals, enabling the hemispheres to process information together.

corpus luteum (kor′-pus lū′-tē-um) A small body of endocrine tissue that develops from an ovarian follicle after ovulation and secretes progesterone and estrogen during pregnancy.

cortex In plants, the ground tissue system of a root, made up mostly of parenchyma cells, which store food and absorb minerals that have passed through the epidermis.

corticosteroid A hormone synthesized and secreted by the adrenal cortex. The corticosteroids include the mineralocorticoids and glucocorticoids.

cotyledon (kot′-uh-lē′-don) The first leaf that appears on an embryo of a flowering plant; a seed leaf. Monocot embryos have one cotyledon; dicot embryos have two.

countercurrent exchange The transfer of a substance or heat between two fluids flowing in opposite directions.

countercurrent heat exchange A circulatory adaptation in which parallel blood vessels convey warm and cold blood in opposite directions, maximizing heat transfer to the cold blood.

covalent bond (ko-vā′-lent) A strong chemical bond in which two atoms share one or more pairs of outer-shell electrons.

craniate A chordate with a head.

crista (kris′tuh) (plural, **cristae**) An infolding of the inner mitochondrial membrane.

crop A pouch-like organ in a digestive tract where food is softened and may be stored temporarily.

cross A mating of two sexually reproducing individuals; often used to describe a genetics experiment involving a controlled mating (a "genetic cross").

cross-fertilization The fusion of sperm and egg derived from two different individuals.

crossing over The exchange of segments between chromatids of homologous chromosomes during synapsis in prophase I of meiosis; also, the exchange of segments between DNA molecules in prokaryotes.

crustacean A member of a major arthropod group that includes lobsters, crayfish, crabs, shrimps, and barnacles.

cuticle (kyū′-tuh-kul) (1) In animals, a tough, nonliving outer layer of the skin. (2) In plants, a waxy coating on the surface of stems and leaves that helps retain water.

cyanobacteria (sī-an′-ō-bak-tēr′-ē-uh) Photoautotrophic prokaryotes with plantlike, oxygen-generating photosynthesis.

cystic fibrosis (sis′-tik fī-brō′-sis) A genetic disease that occurs in people with two copies of a certain recessive allele; characterized by an excessive secretion of mucus and vulnerability to infection; fatal if untreated.

cytokinesis (sī-tō-kuh-nē-sis) The division of the cytoplasm to form two separate daughter cells. Cytokinesis usually occurs in conjunction with telophase of mitosis. Mitosis and cytokinesis make up the mitotic (M) phase of the cell cycle.

cytokinin (sī′-tō-kī′-nin) One of a family of plant hormones that promotes cell division, retards aging in flowers and fruits, and may interact antagonistically with auxins in regulating plant growth and development.

cytoplasm (sī′-tō-plaz′-um) The contents of a eukaryotic cell between the plasma membrane and the nucleus; consists of a semifluid medium and organelles; can also refer to the interior of a prokaryotic cell.

cytosine (C) (sī′-tuh-sin) A single-ring nitrogenous base found in DNA and RNA.

cytoskeleton A network of protein fibers in the cytoplasm of a eukaryotic cell; includes microfilaments, intermediate filaments, and microtubules.

cytotoxic T cell (sī′-tō-tok′-sik) A type of lymphocyte that attacks body cells infected with pathogens.

D

decomposer Prokaryotes and fungi that secrete enzymes that digest nutrients from organic material and convert them to inorganic forms.

decomposition The breakdown of organic materials into inorganic ones.

deductive reasoning A type of logic in which specific results are predicted from a general premise.

dehydration reaction (dē-hī-drā´-shun) A chemical reaction in which two molecules become covalently bonded to each other with the removal of a water molecule.

deletion The loss of one or more nucleotides from a gene by mutation; the loss of a fragment of a chromosome.

demographic transition A shift from zero population growth in which birth rates and death rates are high to zero population growth characterized by low birth and death rates.

denaturation (dē-nā´-chur-ā´-shun) A process in which a protein unravels, losing its specific structure and hence function; can be caused by changes in pH or salt concentration or by high temperature; also refers to the separation of the two strands of the DNA double helix, caused by similar factors.

dendrite (den´-drīt) A neuron fiber that conveys signals from its tip inward, toward the rest of the neuron. A neuron typically has many short dendrites.

density-dependent factor A population-limiting factor whose intensity is linked to population density. For example, there may be a decline in birth rates or a rise in death rates in response to an increase in the number of individuals living in a designated area.

density-dependent inhibition The ceasing of cell division that occurs when cells touch one another.

density-independent factor A population-limiting factor whose intensity is unrelated to population density.

deoxyribonucleic acid (DNA) (dē-ok´-sē-rī´-bō-nū-klā´-ik) A double-stranded helical nucleic acid molecule consisting of nucleotide monomers with deoxyribose sugar and the nitrogenous bases adenine (A), cytosine (C), guanine (G), and thymine (T). Capable of replicating, DNA is an organism's genetic material. *See also* gene.

dermal tissue system The outer protective covering of plants.

desert A biome characterized by organisms adapted to sparse rainfall (less than 30 cm per year) and rapid evaporation.

desertification The conversion of semi-arid regions to desert.

determinate growth Termination of growth after reaching a certain size, as in most animals. *See also* indeterminate growth.

detritivore (duh-trī´-tuh-vor) An organism that consumes organic wastes and dead organisms.

detritus (duh-trī´-tus) Dead organic matter.

deuterostome (dū-ter´-ō-stōm) A mode of animal development in which the opening formed during gastrulation becomes the anus. Animals with the deuterostome pattern of development include the echinoderms and the chordates.

diabetes mellitus (dī-uh-bē´-tis me-lī´-tis) A human hormonal disease in which body cells cannot absorb enough glucose from the blood and become energy starved; body fats and proteins are then consumed for their energy. Type 1 (insulin-dependent) diabetes results when the pancreas does not produce insulin; type 2 (non-insulin-dependent) diabetes results when body cells fail to respond to insulin.

dialysis (dī-al´-uh-sis) Separation and disposal of metabolic wastes from the blood by mechanical means; an artificial method of performing the functions of the kidneys that can be life sustaining in the event of kidney failure.

diaphragm (dī´-uh-fram) The sheet of muscle separating the chest cavity from the abdominal cavity in mammals. Its contraction expands the chest cavity, and its relaxation reduces it.

diastole (dȳ´-as´-tō-lē) The stage of the heart cycle in which the heart muscle is relaxed, allowing the chambers to fill with blood. *See also* systole.

diatom (dī´-uh-tom) A unicellular, autotrophic protist that belongs to the supergroup Chromalveolata. Diatoms possess a unique glassy cell wall containing silica.

dicot (dī´-kot) A term traditionally used to refer to flowering plants that have two embryonic seed leaves, or cotyledons.

differentiation The specialization in the structure and function of cells that occurs during the development of an organism; results from selective activation and deactivation of the cells' genes.

diffusion The spontaneous movement of a substance down its concentration gradient from where it is more concentrated to where it is less concentrated.

digestion The mechanical and chemical breakdown of food into molecules small enough for the body to absorb; the second stage of food processing in animals.

digestive system The organ system involved in ingestion and digestion of food, absorption of nutrients, and elimination of wastes.

dihybrid cross (dī´-hī´-brid) An experimental mating of individuals differing in two characters.

dinoflagellate (dī´-nō-flaj´-uh-let) A member of a group of protists belonging to the supergroup Chromalveolata. Dinoflagellates are common components of marine and freshwater phytoplankton.

diploid In an organism that reproduces sexually, a cell containing two homologous sets of chromosomes, one set inherited from each parent; a 2*n* cell.

directional selection Natural selection in which individuals at one end of the phenotypic range survive and reproduce more successfully than do other individuals.

disaccharide (dī-sak´-uh-rīd) A sugar molecule consisting of two monosaccharides linked by a dehydration reaction.

dispersion pattern The manner in which individuals in a population are spaced within their area. Three types of dispersion patterns are clumped (individuals are aggregated in patches), uniform (individuals are evenly distributed), and random (unpredictable distribution).

disruptive selection Natural selection in which individuals on both extremes of a phenotypic range are favored over intermediate phenotypes.

distal tubule In the vertebrate kidney, the portion of a nephron that helps refine filtrate and empties it into a collecting duct.

disturbance In ecology, a force that changes a biological community and usually removes organisms from it.

DNA *See* deoxyribonucleic acid (DNA).

DNA ligase (lī´-gās) An enzyme, essential for DNA replication, that catalyzes the covalent bonding of adjacent DNA polynucleotide strands. DNA ligase is used in genetic engineering to paste a specific piece of DNA containing a gene of interest into a bacterial plasmid or other vector.

DNA microarray A glass slide carrying thousands of different kinds of single-stranded DNA fragments arranged in an array (grid). A DNA microarray is used to detect and measure the expression of thousands of genes at one time. Tiny amounts of a large number of single-stranded DNA fragments representing different genes are fixed to the glass slide. These fragments, ideally representing all the genes of an organism, are tested for hybridization with various samples of cDNA molecules.

DNA polymerase (puh-lim´-er-ās) A large molecular complex that assembles DNA nucleotides into polynucleotides using a preexisting strand of DNA as a template.

DNA profiling A procedure that analyzes DNA samples to determine if they came from the same individual.

DNA technology Methods used to study and/or manipulate DNA, including recombinant DNA technology.

doldrums (dol´-drums) An area of calm or very light winds near the equator, caused by rising warm air.

domain A taxonomic category above the kingdom level. The three domains of life are Archaea, Bacteria, and Eukarya.

dominance hierarchy The ranking of individuals within a group, based on social interactions and usually maintained by agonistic behavior.

dominant allele The allele that determines the phenotype of a gene when the individual is heterozygous for that gene.

dorsal Pertaining to the back of a bilaterally symmetric animal.

dorsal, hollow nerve cord One of the four hallmarks of chordates, a tube that forms on the dorsal side of the body, above the notochord.

double circulation A circulatory system with separate pulmonary and systemic circuits, in which blood passes through the heart after completing each circuit; ensures vigorous blood flow to all organs.

double fertilization In flowering plants, the formation of both a zygote and a cell with a triploid nucleus, which develops into the endosperm.

double helix The form of native DNA, referring to its two adjacent polynucleotide strands interwound into a spiral shape.

Down syndrome A human genetic disorder resulting from the presence of an extra chromosome 21; characterized by heart and respiratory defects and varying degrees of mental retardation.

Duchenne muscular dystrophy (duh-shen′ dis′-truh-fē) A human genetic disease caused by a sex-linked recessive allele; characterized by progressive weakening and a loss of muscle tissue.

duodenum (dū-ō-dē′-num) The first portion of the vertebrate small intestine after the stomach, where chyme from the stomach mixes with bile and digestive enzymes.

duplication Repetition of part of a chromosome resulting from fusion with a fragment from a homologous chromosome; can result from an error in meiosis or from mutagenesis.

E

eardrum A sheet of connective tissue separating the outer ear from the middle ear that vibrates when stimulated by sound waves and passes the waves to the middle ear.

echinoderm (uh-kī′-nō-derm) Member of a phylum of slow-moving or sessile marine animals characterized by a rough or spiny skin, a water vascular system, an endoskeleton, and radial symmetry in adults. Echinoderms include sea stars, sea urchins, and sand dollars.

ecological footprint An estimate of the amount of land required to provide the raw materials an individual or nation consumes, including food, fuel, water, housing, and waste disposal.

ecological niche (nich) The role of a species in its community; the sum total of a species' use of the biotic and abiotic resources of its environment.

ecological species concept A definition of species in terms of ecological niche, the sum of how members of the species interact with the nonliving and living parts of their environment.

ecological succession The process of biological community change resulting from disturbance; transition in the species composition of a biological community, often following a flood, fire, or volcanic eruption. *See also* primary succession; secondary succession.

ecology The scientific study of how organisms interact with their environment.

ecosystem (ē′-kō-sis-tem) All the organisms in a given area, along with the nonliving (abiotic) factors with which they interact; a biological community and its physical environment.

ecotourism Travel to natural areas for tourism and recreation.

ectoderm (ek′-tō-derm) The outer layer of three embryonic cell layers in a gastrula. The ectoderm forms the skin of the gastrula and gives rise to the epidermis and nervous system in the adult.

ectopic pregnancy (ek-top′-ik) The implantation and development of an embryo outside the uterus.

ectotherm (ek′-tō-therm) An animal that warms itself mainly by absorbing heat from its surroundings. Examples include most amphibians, lizards, and invertebrates.

ectothermic Referring to organisms that do not produce enough metabolic heat to have much effect on body temperature. *See also* ectotherm.

effector cell (1) A muscle cell or gland cell that performs the body's response to stimuli, responding to signals from the brain or other processing center of the nervous system. (2) A lymphocyte that has undergone clonal selection and is capable of mediating an acquired immune response.

egg A female gamete.

ejaculation (ih-jak′-yū-lā′-shun) Expulsion of semen from the penis.

ejaculatory duct The short section of the ejaculatory route in mammals formed by the convergence of the vas deferens and a duct from the seminal vesicle. The ejaculatory duct transports sperm from the vas deferens to the urethra.

electromagnetic receptor A sensory receptor that detects energy of different wavelengths, such as electricity, magnetism, and light.

electromagnetic spectrum The entire spectrum of radiation ranging in wavelength from less than a nanometer to more than a kilometer.

electron A subatomic particle with a single negative electrical charge. One or more electrons move around the nucleus of an atom.

electron microscope (EM) A microscope that uses magnets to focus an electron beam through, or onto the surface of, a specimen. An electron microscope achieves a hundredfold greater resolution than a light microscope.

electron shell An energy level representing the distance of an electron from the nucleus of an atom.

electron transport chain A series of electron carrier molecules that shuttle electrons during the redox reactions that release energy used to make ATP; located in the inner membrane of mitochondria, the thylakoid membranes of chloroplasts, and the plasma membranes of prokaryotes.

electronegativity The attraction of a given atom for the electrons of a covalent bond.

element A substance that cannot be broken down to other substances by chemical means.

elimination The passing of undigested material out of the digestive compartment; the fourth and final stage of food processing in animals.

embryo (em′-brē-ō) A developing stage of a multicellular organism. In humans, the stage in the development of offspring from the first division of the zygote until body structures begin to appear, about the 9th week of gestation.

embryo sac The female gametophyte contained in the ovule of a flowering plant.

embryonic stem cell (ES cell) Cell in the early animal embryo that differentiates during development to give rise to all the different kinds of specialized cells in the body.

embryophyte Another name for land plants, recognizing that land plants share the common derived trait of multicellular, dependent embryos.

emergent properties New properties that arise with each step upward in the hierarchy of life, owing to the arrangement and interactions of parts as complexity increases.

emerging virus A virus that has appeared suddenly or has recently come to the attention of medical scientists.

endemic species A species whose distribution is limited to a specific geographic area.

endergonic reaction (en′-der-gon′-ik) An energy-requiring chemical reaction, which yields products with more potential energy than the reactants. The amount of energy stored in the products equals the difference between the potential energy in the reactants and that in the products.

endocrine gland (en′-dō-krin) A ductless gland that synthesizes hormone molecules and secretes them directly into the bloodstream.

endocrine system (en′-dō-krin) The organ system consisting of ductless glands that secrete hormones and the molecular receptors on or in target cells that respond to the hormones. The endocrine system cooperates with the nervous system in regulating body functions and maintaining homeostasis.

endocytosis (en′-dō-sī-tō′-sis) Cellular uptake of molecules or particles via formation of new vesicles from the plasma membrane.

endoderm (en′-dō-derm) The innermost of three embryonic cell layers in a gastrula; forms the archenteron in the gastrula and gives rise to the innermost linings of the digestive tract and other hollow organs in the adult.

endodermis The innermost layer (a one-cell-thick cylinder) of the cortex of a plant root; forms a selective barrier determining which substances pass from the cortex into the vascular tissue.

endomembrane system A network of membranes inside and around a eukaryotic cell, related either through direct physical contact or by the transfer of membranous vesicles.

endometrium (en'-dō-mē'-trē-um) The inner lining of the uterus in mammals, richly supplied with blood vessels that provide the maternal part of the placenta and nourish the developing embryo.

endoplasmic reticulum (ER) An extensive membranous network in a eukaryotic cell, continuous with the outer nuclear membrane and composed of ribosome-studded (rough) and ribosome-free (smooth) regions. *See also* rough ER; smooth ER.

endorphin (en-dōr'-fin) A pain-inhibiting hormone produced by the brain and anterior pituitary; also serves as a neurotransmitter.

endoskeleton A hard skeleton located within the soft tissues of an animal; includes spicules of sponges, the hard plates of echinoderms, and the cartilage and bony skeletons of vertebrates.

endosperm In flowering plants, a nutrient-rich mass formed by the union of a sperm cell with two polar nuclei during double fertilization; provides nourishment to the developing embryo in the seed.

endospore A thick-coated, protective cell produced within a bacterial cell. Endospore becomes dormant and is able to survive harsh environmental conditions.

endosymbiont theory (en'-dō-sim'-bī-ont) A theory that mitochondria and chloroplasts originated as prokaryotic cells engulfed by an ancestral eukaryotic cell. The engulfed cell and its host cell then evolved into a single organism.

endotherm An animal that derives most of its body heat from its own metabolism. Examples include most mammals and birds.

endothermic Referring to animals that use heat generated by metabolism to maintain a warm, steady body temperature. *See also* endotherm.

endotoxin A poisonous component of the outer membrane of gram-negative bacteria that is released only when the bacteria die.

energy The capacity to cause change, especially to perform work.

energy coupling In cellular metabolism, the use of energy released from an exergonic reaction to drive an endergonic reaction.

energy flow The passage of energy through the components of an ecosystem.

enhancer A eukaryotic DNA sequence that helps stimulate the transcription of a gene at some distance from it. An enhancer functions by means of a transcription factor called an activator, which binds to it and then to the rest of the transcription apparatus. *See also* silencer.

enteric division Part of the autonomic nervous system consisting of complex networks of neurons in the digestive tract, pancreas, and gallbladder.

entropy (en'-truh-pē) A measure of disorder. One form of disorder is heat, which is random molecular motion.

enzyme (en'-zīm) A macromolecule, usually a protein, that serves as a biological catalyst, changing the rate of a chemical reaction without being consumed by the reaction.

epidermis (ep'-uh-der'-mis) (1) In animals, one or more living layers of cells forming the protective covering, or outer skin. (2) In plants, the tissue system forming the protective outer covering of leaves, young stems, and young roots.

epididymis (ep'-uh-did'-uh-mus) A long coiled tube into which sperm pass from the testis and are stored until mature and ejaculated.

epigenetic inheritance The inheritance of traits transmitted by mechanisms not directly involving the nucleotide sequence of a genome, such as the chemical modification of histone proteins or DNA bases.

epinephrine (ep'-uh-nef'-rin) An amine hormone (also called adrenaline) secreted by the adrenal medulla that prepares body organs for action (fight or flight); also serves as a neurotransmitter.

epithelial tissue (ep'-uh-thē'-lē-ul) A sheet of tightly packed cells lining organs, body cavities, and external surfaces; also called epithelium.

erythrocyte (eh-rith'-rō-sȳt) A blood cell containing hemoglobin, which transports oxygen; also called a red blood cell.

erythropoietin (EPO) (eh-rith'rō-poy'uh-tin) A hormone that stimulates the production of erythrocytes. It is secreted by the kidney when tissues of the body do not receive enough oxygen.

esophagus (eh-sof'-uh-gus) A muscular tube that conducts food by peristalsis, usually from the pharynx to the stomach.

essential amino acid An amino acid that an animal cannot synthesize itself and must obtain from food. Eight amino acids are essential for the human adult.

essential element In plants, a chemical element required for the plant to complete its life cycle (to grow from a seed and produce another generation of seeds).

essential fatty acid An unsaturated fatty acid that an animal needs but cannot make.

essential nutrient A substance that an organism must absorb in preassembled form because it cannot synthesize it from any other material. In humans, there are essential vitamins, minerals, amino acids, and fatty acids.

estrogen (es'-trō-jen) One of several chemically similar steroid hormones secreted by the gonads; maintains the female reproductive system and promotes the development of female body features.

estuary (es'-chū-ār-ē) The area where a freshwater stream or river merges with the ocean.

ethylene A gas that functions as a hormone in plants, triggering aging responses such as fruit ripening and leaf drop.

eudicot (yū-dē-kot) Member of a group that consists of the vast majority of flowering plants that have two embryonic seed leaves, or cotyledons.

Eukarya (yū-kar'-ē-uh) Domain of life that includes all eukaryotes.

eukaryotic cell (yū-kar-ē-ot'-ik) A type of cell that has a membrane-enclosed nucleus and other membrane-enclosed organelles. All organisms except bacteria and archaea are composed of eukaryotic cells.

eumetazoan (yū-met-uh-zō'-un) Member of the clade of "true animals," the animals with true tissues (all animals except sponges).

Eustachian tube (yū-stā'-shun) An air passage between the middle ear and throat of vertebrates that equalizes air pressure on either side of the eardrum.

eutherian (yū-thēr'-ē-un) Placental mammal; mammal whose young complete their embryonic development within the uterus, joined to the mother by the placenta.

evaporative cooling The process in which the surface of an object becomes cooler during evaporation.

"evo-devo" Evolutionary developmental biology; the field of biology that combines evolutionary biology with developmental biology.

evolution Descent with modification; the idea that living species are descendants of ancestral species that were different from present-day ones; also, the genetic changes in a population from generation to generation.

evolutionary tree A branching diagram that reflects a hypothesis about evolutionary relationships among groups of organisms.

Excavata One of five supergroups proposed in a current hypothesis of the evolutionary history of eukaryotes. The other four supergroups are Chromalveolata, Rhizaria, Unikonta, and Archaeplastida.

excretion (ek-skrē'-shun) The disposal of nitrogen-containing metabolic wastes.

exergonic reaction (ek'-ser-gon'-ik) An energy-releasing chemical reaction in which the reactants contain more potential energy than the products. The reaction releases an amount of energy equal to the difference in potential energy between the reactants and the products.

exocytosis (ek'-sō-sī-tō'-sis) The movement of materials out of the cytoplasm of a cell by the fusion of vesicles with the plasma membrane.

exoskeleton A hard external skeleton that protects an animal and provides points of attachment for muscles.

exotoxin A poisonous protein secreted by certain bacteria.

exponential growth model A mathematical description of idealized, unregulated population growth.

external fertilization The fusion of gametes that parents have discharged into the environment.

extinction The irrevocable loss of a species.

extirpation The loss of a single population of a species.

extracellular matrix (ECM) The meshwork surrounding animal cells; consists of glycoproteins and polysaccharides.

extraembryonic membranes Four membranes (the yolk sac, amnion, chorion, and allantois) that form a life-support system for the developing embryo of a reptile, bird, or mammal.

extreme halophile A microorganism that lives in a highly saline environment, such as the Great Salt Lake or the Dead Sea.

extreme thermophile A microorganism that thrives in a hot environment (often 60–80°C).

eyecup The simplest type of photoreceptor, a cluster of photoreceptor cells shaded by a cuplike cluster of pigmented cells; detects light intensity and direction.

F

F factor A piece of DNA that can exist as a bacterial plasmid. The F factor carries genes for making sex pili and other structures needed for conjugation, as well as a site where DNA replication can start. F stands for fertility.

F₁ generation The offspring of two parental (P generation) individuals; F_1 stands for first filial.

F₂ generation The offspring of the F_1 generation; F_2 stands for second filial.

facilitated diffusion The passage of a substance through a specific transport protein across a biological membrane down its concentration gradient.

family In Linnaean classification, the taxonomic category above genus.

farsightedness An inability to focus on close objects; occurs when the eyeball is shorter than normal and the focal point of the lens is behind the retina; also called hyperopia.

fat A lipid composed of three fatty acids linked to one glycerol molecule; a triglyceride. Most fats function as energy-storage molecules.

feces The wastes of the digestive tract.

feedback inhibition A method of metabolic control in which a product of a metabolic pathway acts as an inhibitor of an enzyme within that pathway.

fertilization The union of the nucleus of a sperm cell with the nucleus of an egg cell, producing a zygote.

fertilizer A compound given to plants to promote their growth.

fetus (fē′-tus) A developing human from the 9th week of gestation until birth. The fetus has all the major structures of an adult.

fiber (1) In animals, an elongate, supportive thread in the matrix of connective tissue; an extension of a neuron; a muscle cell. (2) In plants, a long, slender sclerenchyma cell that usually occurs in a bundle.

fibrin (fȳ′-brin) The activated form of the blood-clotting protein fibrinogen, which aggregates into threads that form the fabric of a blood clot.

fibrinogen (fȳ′-brin′-uh-jen) The plasma protein that is activated to form a clot when a blood vessel is injured.

fibrous connective tissue A dense tissue with large numbers of collagenous fibers organized into parallel bundles. This is the dominant tissue in tendons and ligaments.

filtrate Fluid extracted by the excretory system from the blood or body cavity. The excretory system produces urine from the filtrate after removing valuable solutes from it and concentrating it.

filtration In the vertebrate kidney, the extraction of water and small solutes, including metabolic wastes, from the blood by the nephrons.

fimbria (plural, **fimbriae**) One of the short, hairlike projections on some prokaryotic cells that help attach the cells to their substrate or to other cells.

first law of thermodynamics The principle of conservation of energy. Energy can be transferred and transformed, but it cannot be created or destroyed.

fission A means of asexual reproduction whereby a parent separates into two or more genetically identical individuals of about equal size.

fixed action pattern (FAP) A genetically programmed, virtually unchangeable behavioral sequence performed in response to a certain stimulus.

flagellum (fluh-jel′-um) (plural, **flagella**) A long cellular appendage specialized for locomotion. The flagella of prokaryotes and eukaryotes differ in both structure and function. Like cilia, eukaryotic flagella have a 9 + 2 arrangement of microtubules covered by the cell's plasma membrane.

flatworm A member of the phylum Platyhelminthes.

fluid feeder An animal that lives by sucking nutrient-rich fluids from another living organism.

fluid mosaic A description of membrane structure, depicting a cellular membrane as a mosaic of diverse protein molecules embedded in a fluid bilayer of phospholipid molecules.

fluke One of a group of parasitic flatworms.

follicle (fol′-uh-kul) A cluster of cells that surround, protect, and nourish a developing egg cell in the ovary. Follicles secrete the hormone estrogen.

food chain A sequence of food transfers from producers through one to four levels of consumers in an ecosystem.

food web A network of interconnecting food chains.

foot In an invertebrate animal, a structure used for locomotion or attachment, such as the muscular organ extending from the ventral side of a mollusc.

foraging Behavior used in recognizing, searching for, capturing, and consuming food.

foraminiferan A protist that moves and feeds by means of thread-like pseudopodia and has porous shells composed of calcium carbonate.

forebrain One of three ancestral and embryonic regions of the vertebrate brain; develops into the thalamus, hypothalamus, and cerebrum.

forensics The scientific analysis of evidence for crime scene and other legal proceedings. Also referred to as forensic science.

fossil A preserved remnant or impression of an organism that lived in the past.

fossil fuel An energy-containing deposit of organic material formed from the remains of ancient organisms.

fossil record The chronicle of evolution over millions of years of geologic time engraved in the order in which fossils appear in rock strata.

founder effect Genetic drift that occurs when a few individuals become isolated from a larger population and form a new population whose gene pool is not reflective of that of the original population.

fovea (fō′-vē-uh) An eye's center of focus and the place on the retina where photoreceptors are highly concentrated.

fragmentation A means of asexual reproduction whereby a single parent breaks into parts that regenerate into whole new individuals.

free-living flatworm A nonparasitic flatworm.

frequency-dependent selection Selection in which the fitness of a phenotype depends on how common the phenotype is in a population.

fruit A ripened, thickened ovary of a flower, which protects developing seeds and aids in their dispersal.

functional group A specific configuration of atoms commonly attached to the carbon skeletons of organic molecules and involved in chemical reactions.

Fungi (fun′-ji) The kingdom that contains the fungi.

G

gallbladder An organ that stores bile and releases it as needed into the small intestine.

gametangium (gam′-uh-tan′-jē-um) (plural, **gametangia**) A reproductive organ that houses and protects the gametes of a plant.

gamete (gam′-ēt) A sex cell; a haploid egg or sperm. The union of two gametes of opposite sex (fertilization) produces a zygote.

gametogenesis The creation of gametes within the gonads.

gametophyte (guh-mē′-tō-fīt) The multicellular haploid form in the life cycle of organisms undergoing alternation of generations; mitotically produces haploid gametes that unite and grow into the sporophyte generation.

ganglion (gang′-glē-un) (plural, **ganglia**) A cluster of neuron cell bodies in a peripheral nervous system.

gas exchange The exchange of O_2 and CO_2 between an organism and its environment.

gastric juice The collection of fluids (mucus, enzymes, and acid) secreted by the stomach.

gastrin A digestive hormone that stimulates the secretion of gastric juice.

gastropod A member of the largest group of molluscs, including snails and slugs.

gastrovascular cavity A central compartment with a single opening, the mouth; functions in both digestion and nutrient distribution and may also function in circulation, body support, waste disposal, and gas exchange.

gastrula (gas'-trū-luh) The embryonic stage resulting from gastrulation in animal development. Most animals have a gastrula made up of three layers of cells: ectoderm, endoderm, and mesoderm.

gastrulation (gas'-trū-lā'-shun) The second major phase of embryonic development, which transforms the blastula into a gastrula. Gastrulation adds more cells to the embryo and sorts the cells into distinct cell layers.

gel electrophoresis (jel' ē-lek'-trō-fōr-ē'-sis) A technique for separating and purifying macromolecules, either DNAs or proteins. A mixture of the macromolecules is placed on a gel between a positively charged electrode and a negatively charged one. Negative charges on the molecules are attracted to the positive electrode, and the molecules migrate toward that electrode. The molecules separate in the gel according to their rates of migration, which is mostly determined by their size: Smaller molecules generally move faster through the gel, while larger molecules generally move more slowly.

gene A discrete unit of hereditary information consisting of a specific nucleotide sequence in DNA (or RNA, in some viruses). Most of the genes of a eukaryote are located in its chromosomal DNA; a few are carried by the DNA of mitochondria and chloroplasts.

gene cloning The production of multiple copies of a gene.

gene expression The process whereby genetic information flows from genes to proteins; the flow of genetic information from the genotype to the phenotype.

gene flow The transfer of alleles from one population to another as a result of the movement of individuals or their gametes.

gene pool All the alleles for all the genes in a population.

gene regulation The turning on and off of genes within a cell in response to environmental stimuli or other factors (such as developmental stage).

gene therapy A treatment for a disease in which the patient's defective gene is supplemented or altered.

genetic code The set of rules that dictates the correspondence between RNA codons in an mRNA molecule and amino acids in protein.

genetic drift A change in the gene pool of a population due to chance. Effects of genetic drift are most pronounced in small populations.

genetic engineering The direct manipulation of genes for practical purposes.

genetic recombination The production, by crossing over and/or independent assortment of chromosomes during meiosis, of offspring with allele combinations different from those in the parents. The term may also be used more specifically to mean the production by crossing over of eukaryotic or prokaryotic chromosomes with gene combinations different from those in the original chromosomes.

genetically modified (GM) organism An organism that has acquired one or more genes by artificial means. If the gene is from another species, the organism is also known as a transgenic organism.

genetics The scientific study of heredity. Modern genetics began with the work of Gregor Mendel in the 19th century.

genital herpes A sexually transmitted disease caused by the herpes simplex virus type 2.

genomic library (juh-nō'-mik) A set of DNA fragments representing an organism's entire genome. Each segment is usually carried by a plasmid or phage.

genomics The study of whole sets of genes and their interactions.

genotype (jē'-nō-tīp) The genetic makeup of an organism.

genus (jē'-nus) (plural, **genera**) In classification, the taxonomic category above species; the first part of a species' binomial; for example, *Homo.*

geologic record A time scale established by geologists that divides Earth's history into three eons—Archaean, Proterozoic, and Phanerozoic—and further subdivides it into eras, periods, and epochs.

germinate To start developing or growing.

gestation (jes-tā'-shun) Pregnancy; the state of carrying developing young within the female reproductive tract.

gibberellin (jib'-uh-rel'-in) One of a family of plant hormones that triggers the germination of seeds and interacts with auxins in regulating growth and fruit development.

gill An extension of the body surface of an aquatic animal, specialized for gas exchange and/or suspension feeding.

gizzard A pouch-like organ in a digestive tract where food is mechanically ground.

glans The rounded, highly sensitive head of the clitoris in females and penis in males.

glia A network of supporting cells that is essential for the structural integrity and normal functioning of the nervous system.

global climate change Increase in temperature and change in weather patterns all around the planet, due mostly to increasing atmospheric CO_2 levels from the burning of fossil fuels. The increase in temperature, called global warming, is a major aspect of global climate change.

glomeromycete Member of a group of fungi characterized by a distinct branching form of mycorrhizae (symbiotic relationships with plant roots) called arbuscules.

glomerulus (glō-mer'-ū-lus) (plural, **glomeruli**) In the vertebrate kidney, the part of a nephron consisting of the capillaries that are surrounded by Bowman's capsule; together, a glomerulus and Bowman's capsule produce the filtrate from the blood.

glucagon (glū'-kuh-gon) A peptide hormone, secreted by the islets of Langerhaus in the pancreas, that raises the level of glucose in the blood. It is antagonistic with insulin.

glucocorticoid (glū'-kuh-kor'-tih-koyd) A corticosteroid hormone secreted by the adrenal cortex that increases the blood glucose level and helps maintain the body's response to long-term stress.

glycogen (glī'-kō-jen) An extensively branched glucose storage polysaccharide found in liver and muscle cells; the animal equivalent of starch.

glycolysis (glī-kol'-uh-sis) The multistep chemical breakdown of a molecule of glucose into two molecules of pyruvate; the first stage of cellular respiration in all organisms; occurs in the cytoplasmic fluid.

glycoprotein (glī'-kō-prō'-tēn) A protein with one of more short chains of sugars attached to it.

goiter An enlargement of the thyroid gland resulting from a dietary iodine deficiency.

Golgi apparatus (gol'-jē) An organelle in eukaryotic cells consisting of stacks of membranous sacs that modify, store, and ship products of the endoplasmic reticulum.

gonad A sex organ in an animal; an ovary or testis.

Gram stain Microbiological technique to identify the cell wall composition of bacteria. Results categorize bacteria as gram-positive or gram-negative.

gram-positive bacteria Diverse group of bacteria with a cell wall that is structurally less complex and contains more peptidoglycan than that of gram-negative bacteria. Gram-positive bacteria are usually less toxic than gram-negative bacteria.

granum (gran'-um) (plural, **grana**) A stack of membrane-bounded thylakoids in a chloroplast. Grana are the sites where light energy is trapped by chlorophyll and converted to chemical energy during the light reactions of photosynthesis.

gravitropism (grav'-uh-trō'-pizm) A plant's directional growth in response to gravity.

gray matter Regions within the central nervous system composed mainly of nerve cell bodies and dendrites.

green alga A member of a group of photosynthetic protists that includes chlorophytes and charophyceans, the closest living relatives of land plants. Green algae include unicellular, colonial, and multicellular species and belong to the supergroup Archaeplastida.

greenhouse effect The warming of Earth due to the atmospheric accumulation of CO_2 and certain other gases, which absorb infrared radiation and reradiate some of it back toward Earth.

ground tissue system A tissue of mostly parenchyma cells that makes up the bulk of a young plant and is continuous throughout its body. The ground tissue system fills the space between the epidermis and the vascular tissue system.

growth factor A protein secreted by certain body cells that stimulates other cells to divide.

growth hormone (GH) A protein hormone secreted by the anterior pituitary that promotes development and growth and stimulates metabolism.

guanine (G) (gwa′-nēn) A double-ring nitrogenous base found in DNA and RNA.

guard cell A specialized epidermal cell in plants that regulates the size of a stoma, allowing gas exchange between the surrounding air and the photosynthetic cells in the leaf.

gymnosperm (jim′-nō-sperm) A naked-seed plant. Its seed is said to be naked because it is not enclosed in an ovary.

H

habitat A place where an organism lives; the environment in which an organism lives.

habituation Learning not to respond to a repeated stimulus that conveys little or no information.

hair cell A type of mechanoreceptor that detects sound waves and other forms of movement in air or water.

haploid In the life cycle of an organism that reproduces sexually, a cell containing a single set of chromosomes; an *n* cell.

Hardy-Weinberg principle The principle that frequencies of alleles and genotypes in a population remain constant from generation to generation, provided that only Mendelian segregation and recombination of alleles are at work.

heart A muscular pump that propels a circulatory fluid (blood) through vessels to the body.

heart attack The damage or death of cardiac muscle cells and the resulting failure of the heart to deliver enough blood to the body.

heart murmur A hissing sound that most often results from blood squirting backward through a leaky valve in the heart.

heart rate The frequency of heart contraction, usually expressed in number of beats per minute.

heartwood In the center of trees, the darkened, older layers of secondary xylem made up of cells that no longer transport water and are clogged with resins. *See also* sapwood.

heat Thermal energy; the amount of energy associated with the movement of the atoms and molecules in a body of matter. Heat is energy in its most random form.

helper T cell A type of lymphocyte that helps activate other types of T cells and may help stimulate B cells to produce antibodies.

hemoglobin (hē′-mō-glō-bin) An iron-containing protein in red blood cells that reversibly binds O_2.

hemophilia (hē′-mō-fil′-ē-uh) A human genetic disease caused by a sex-linked recessive allele; characterized by excessive bleeding following injury.

hepatic portal vein A blood vessel that conveys nutrient-laden blood from capillaries surrounding the intestine directly to the liver.

herbivore An animal that mainly eats plants or algae. *See also* carnivore; omnivore.

herbivory Consumption of plant parts or algae by an animal.

heredity The transmission of traits (inherited features) from one generation to the next.

hermaphroditism (her-maf′-rō-dī-tizm) A condition in which an individual has both female and male gonads and functions as both a male and female in sexual reproduction by producing both sperm and eggs.

heterokaryotic stage (het′-er-ō-ker-ē-ot′-ik) A fungal life cycle stage that contains two genetically different haploid nuclei in the same cell.

heterotroph (het′-er-ō-trōf) An organism that cannot make its own organic food molecules and must obtain them by consuming other organisms or their organic products; a consumer or a decomposer in a food chain.

heterozygote advantage Greater reproductive success of heterozygous individuals compared to homozygotes; tends to preserve variation in gene pools.

heterozygous (het′-er-ō-zī′-gus) Having two different alleles for a given gene.

high-density lipoprotein (HDL) A cholesterol-carrying particle in the blood, made up of thousands of cholesterol molecules and other lipids bound to a protein. HDL scavenges excess cholesterol.

hindbrain One of three ancestral and embryonic regions of the vertebrate brain; develops into the medulla oblongata, pons, and cerebellum.

hinge joint A joint that allows movement in only one plane. In humans, examples include the elbow and knee.

hippocampus (hip′-uh-kam′-pus) An integrative center of the cerebrum; functionally, the part of the limbic system that plays a central role in the formation of memories and their recall.

histamine (his′-tuh-mēn) A chemical alarm signal released by injured cells of vertebrates that causes blood vessels to dilate during an inflammatory response.

histone (his′-tōn) A small protein molecule associated with DNA and important in DNA packing in the eukaryotic chromosome. Eukaryotic chromatin consists of roughly equal parts of DNA and histone protein.

HIV (human immunodeficiency virus) The retrovirus that attacks the human immune system and causes AIDS.

homeobox (hō′-mē-ō-boks′) A 180-nucleotide sequence within a homeotic gene and some other developmental genes.

homeostasis (hō′-mē-ō-stā′-sis) The steady state of body functioning; a state of equilibrium characterized by a dynamic interplay between outside forces that tend to change an organism's internal environment and the internal control mechanisms that oppose such changes.

homeotic gene (hō′-mē-ot′-ik) A master control gene that determines the identity of a body structure of a developing organism, presumably by controlling the developmental fate of groups of cells.

hominin (hah′-mi-nid) Member of a species on the human branch of the evolutionary tree; a species more closely related to humans than to chimpanzees.

homologous chromosomes (hō-mol′-uh-gus) The two chromosomes that make up a matched pair in a diploid cell. Homologous chromosomes are of the same length, centromere position, and staining pattern and possess genes for the same characteristics at corresponding loci. One homologous chromosome is inherited from the organism's father, the other from the mother.

homologous structures Structures in different species that are similar because of common ancestry.

homology Similarity in characteristics resulting from a shared ancestry.

homozygous (hō′-mō-zī′-gus) Having two identical alleles for a given gene.

horizontal gene transfer The transfer of genes from one genome to another through mechanisms such as transposable elements, plasmid exchange, viral activity, and perhaps fusions of different organisms.

hormone (1) In animals, a regulatory chemical that travels in the blood from its production site, usually an endocrine gland, to other sites, where target cells respond to the regulatory signal. (2) In plants, a chemical that is produced in one part of the plant and travels to another part, where it acts on target cells to change their functioning.

horseshoe crab A bottom-dwelling marine chelicerate, a member of the phylum Arthropoda.

human chorionic gonadotropin (hCG) (kōr′-ē-on′-ik gon′-uh-dō-trō′-pin) A hormone secreted by the chorion that maintains the production of estrogen and progesterone by the corpus luteum of the ovary during the first few months of pregnancy. hCG secreted in the urine is the target of many home pregnancy tests.

Human Genome Project (hGP) An international collaborative effort to map and sequence the DNA of the entire human genome. The project was begun in 1990 and completed in 2004.

humoral immune response The type of specific immunity brought about by antibody-producing B cells. The humoral immune response fights bacteria and viruses in body fluids. *See also* cell-mediated immune response.

humus (hyū´-mus) Decomposing organic material found in topsoil.

Huntington's disease A human genetic disease caused by a single dominant allele; characterized by uncontrollable body movements and degeneration of the nervous system; usually fatal 10 to 20 years after the onset of symptoms.

hybrid An offspring of parents of two different species or of two different varieties of one species; an offspring of two parents that differ in one or more inherited traits; an individual that is heterozygous for one or more pairs of genes.

hybrid zone A geographic region in which members of different species meet and mate, producing at least some hybrid offspring.

hydrocarbon An organic compound composed only of the elements carbon and hydrogen.

hydrogen bond A type of weak chemical bond formed when the partially positive hydrogen atom participating in a polar covalent bond in one molecule is attracted to the partially negative atom participating in a polar covalent bond in another molecule (or in another region of the same molecule).

hydrolysis (hī-drol´-uh-sis) A chemical reaction that breaks bonds between two molecules by the addition of water; process by which polymers are broken down and an essential part of digestion.

hydrophilic (hī´-drō-fil´-ik) "Water-loving"; pertaining to polar or charged molecules (or parts of molecules) that are soluble in water.

hydrophobic (hī´-drō-fō´-bik) "Water-fearing"; pertaining to nonpolar molecules (or parts of molecules) that do not dissolve in water.

hydrostatic skeleton A skeletal system composed of fluid held under pressure in a closed body compartment; the main skeleton of most cnidarians, flatworms, nematodes, and annelids.

hydroxyl group (hī-drok´-sil) A chemical group consisting of an oxygen atom bonded to a hydrogen atom.

hypertension A disorder in which blood pressure remains abnormally high.

hypertonic Referring to a solution that, when surrounding a cell, will cause the cell to lose water.

hypha (hī´-fuh) (plural, **hyphae**) One of many filaments making up the body of a fungus.

hypoglycemia (hī´-pō-glī-sē´-mē-uh) An abnormally low level of glucose in the blood that results when the pancreas secretes too much insulin into the blood.

hypothalamus (hī-pō-thal´-uh-mus) The master control center of the endocrine system, located in the ventral portion of the vertebrate forebrain. The hypothalamus functions in maintaining homeostasis, especially in coordinating the endocrine and nervous systems; secretes hormones of the posterior pituitary and releasing hormones that regulate the anterior pituitary.

hypothesis (hī-poth´-uh-sis) (plural, **hypotheses**) A testable explanation for a set of observations based on the available data and guided by inductive reasoning.

hypotonic Referring to a solution that, when surrounding a cell, will cause the cell to take up water.

I

immune system An animal body's system of defenses against agents that cause disease.

immunodeficiency disease An immunological disorder in which the immune system lacks one or more components, making the body susceptible to infectious agents that would ordinarily not be pathogenic.

imperfect fungus A fungus with no known sexual stage.

impotence The inability to maintain an erection; also called erectile dysfunction.

imprinting Learning that is limited to a specific critical period in an animal's life and that is generally irreversible.

***in vitro* fertilization (IVF)** (vē´-tro) Uniting sperm and egg in a laboratory container, followed by the placement of a resulting early embryo in the mother's uterus.

inbreeding Mating between close blood relatives.

inclusive fitness An individual's success at perpetuating its genes by producing its own offspring and by helping close relatives to produce offspring.

incomplete dominance A type of inheritance in which the phenotype of a heterozygote (*Aa*) is intermediate between the phenotypes of the two types of homozygotes (*AA* and *aa*).

incomplete metamorphosis A type of development in certain insects in which development from larva to adult is achieved by multiple molts, but without forming a pupa.

indeterminate growth Growth that continues throughout life, as in most plants. *See also* determinate growth.

induced fit The change in shape of the active site of an enzyme, caused by entry of the substrate, so that it binds more snugly to the substrate.

induction During embryonic development, the influence of one group of cells on an adjacent group of cells.

inductive reasoning A type of logic in which generalizations are based on a large number of specific observations.

inferior vena cava (vē´-nuh kā´-vuh) A large vein that returns oxygen-poor blood to the heart from the lower, or posterior, part of the body. *See also* superior vena cava.

infertility The inability to conceive after one year of regular, unprotected intercourse.

inflammatory response An innate body defense in vertebrates caused by a release of histamine and other chemical alarm signals that trigger increased blood flow, a local increase in white blood cells, and fluid leakage from the blood. The resulting inflammatory response includes redness, heat, and swelling in the affected tissues.

ingestion The act of eating; the first main stage of food processing in animals.

ingroup In a cladistic study of evolutionary relationships, the group of taxa whose evolutionary relationships are being determined. *See also* outgroup.

inhibiting hormone A kind of hormone released from the hypothalamus that prompts the anterior pituitary to stop secreting hormone.

innate behavior Behavior that is under strong genetic control and is performed in virtually the same way by all members of a species.

innate immunity The kind of immunity that is present in an animal before exposure to pathogens and is effective from birth. Innate immune defenses include barriers, phagocytic cells, antimicrobial proteins, the inflammatory response, and natural killer cells.

inner ear One of three main regions of the vertebrate ear; includes the cochlea, organ of Corti, and semicircular canals.

insulin A protein hormone, secreted by the islets of Langerhans in the pancreas, that lowers the level of glucose in the blood. It is antagonistic with glucagon.

integration The analysis and interpretation of sensory signals within neural processing centers of the central nervous system.

integrins A transmembrane protein that interconnects the extracellular matrix and the cytoskeleton.

integumentary system (in-teg´-yū-ment-ter-ē) The organ system consisting of the skin and its derivatives, such as hair and nails in mammals. The integumentary system helps protect the body from drying out, mechanical injury, and infection.

interferon (in´-ter-fer´-on) An innate defensive protein produced by virus-infected vertebrate cells and capable of helping other cells resist viruses.

intermediate One of the compounds that form between the initial reactant and the final product in a metabolic pathway, such as between glucose and pyruvate in glycolysis.

intermediate filament An intermediate-sized protein fiber that is one of the three main kinds of fibers making up the cytoskeleton of eukaryotic cells. Intermediate filaments are ropelike, made of fibrous proteins.

internal fertilization Reproduction in which sperm are typically deposited in or near the female reproductive tract and fertilization occurs within the tract.

interneuron (in′-ter-nūr′-on) A nerve cell, located entirely within the central nervous system, that integrates sensory signals and relays signals to other interneurons and to motor neurons.

internode The portion of a plant stem between two nodes.

interphase The period in the eukaryotic cell cycle when the cell is not actually dividing. Interphase constitutes the majority of the time spent in the cell cycle. *See also* mitotic phase (M phase).

interspecific competition Competition between individuals or populations of two or more species requiring a limited resource.

interspecific interactions Relationships between individuals of different species in a community.

interstitial fluid (in′-ter-stish′-ul) An aqueous solution that surrounds body cells and through which materials pass back and forth between the blood and the body tissues.

intertidal zone (in′-ter-tīd′-ul) A shallow zone where the waters of an estuary or ocean meet land.

intestine The region of a digestive tract located between the gizzard or stomach and the anus and where chemical digestion and nutrient absorption usually occur.

intraspecific competition Competition between members of a population for a limited resource.

invasive species A non-native species that spreads beyond its original point of introduction and causes environmental or economic damage.

inversion A change in a chromosome resulting from reattachment of a chromosome fragment to the original chromosome, but in a reverse direction. Mutagens and errors during meiosis can cause inversions.

invertebrate An animal that lacks a backbone.

ion (ī-on) An atom or group of atoms that has gained or lost one or more electrons, thus acquiring a charge.

ionic bond (ī-on′-ik) A chemical bond resulting from the attraction between oppositely charged ions.

iris The colored part of the vertebrate eye, formed by the anterior portion of the choroid.

isomers (ī′-sō-mers) Organic compounds with the same molecular formula but different structures and, therefore, different properties.

isotonic (ī-sō-ton′-ik) Referring to a solution that, when surrounding a cell, has no effect on the passage of water into or out of the cell.

isotope (ī′-sō-tōp) One of several atomic forms of an element, each with the same number of protons but a different number of neutrons.

K

karyotype (kār′-ē-ō-tīp) A display of micrographs of the metaphase chromosomes of a cell, arranged by size and centromere position. Karyotypes may be used to identify certain chromosomal abnormalities.

kelp Large, multicellular brown algae that form undersea "forests."

keystone species A species that is not usually abundant in a community yet exerts strong control on community structure by the nature of its ecological role, or niche.

kilocalorie (kcal) A quantity of heat equal to 1,000 calories. Used to measure the energy content of food, it is usually called a "Calorie."

kin selection The natural selection that favors altruistic behavior by enhancing reproductive success of relatives.

kinesis (kuh-nē′-sis) (plural, **kineses**) Random movement in response to a stimulus.

kinetic energy (kuh-net′-ik) The energy of motion; the energy of a mass of matter that is moving. Moving matter does work by imparting motion to other matter.

kingdom In classification, the broad taxonomic category above phylum.

K-selection The concept that in certain (*K*-selected) populations, life history is centered around producing relatively few offspring that have a good chance of survival.

L

labia majora (lā′-bē-uh muh-jor′-uh) A pair of outer thickened folds of skin that protect the female genital region.

labia minora (lā′-bē-uh mi-nor′-uh) A pair of inner folds of skin, bordering and protecting the female genital region.

labor The series of events that expel the infant from the uterus.

lactic acid fermentation Glycolysis followed by the reduction of pyruvate to lactate, regenerating NAD^+.

lancelet One of a group of small, bladelike, invertebrate chordates.

landscape Several different ecosystems linked by exchanges of energy, materials, and organisms.

landscape ecology The application of ecological principles to the study of the structure and dynamics of a collection of ecosystems; the scientific study of the biodiversity of interacting ecosystems.

large intestine *See* colon.

larva (lar′-vuh) (plural, **larvae**) A free-living, sexually immature form in some animal life cycles that may differ from the adult in morphology, nutrition, and habitat.

larynx (lār′-inks) The upper portion of the respiratory tract containing the vocal cords; also called the voice box.

lateral line system A row of sensory organs along each side of a fish's body that is sensitive to changes in water pressure. It enables a fish to detect minor vibrations in the water.

lateral meristem Plant tissue made up of undifferentiated cells that enable roots and shoots of woody plants to thicken. The vascular cambium and cork cambium are lateral meristems.

lateralization The phenomenon in which the two hemispheres of the brain become specialized for different functions during infant and child brain development.

law of independent assortment A general rule in inheritance (originally formulated by Gregor Mendel) that when gametes form during meiosis, each pair of alleles for a particular characteristic segregate independently of other pairs; also known as Mendel's second law of inheritance.

law of segregation A general rule in inheritance (originally formulated by Gregor Mendel) that individuals have two alleles for each gene and that when gametes form by meiosis, the two alleles separate, each resulting gamete ending up with only one allele of each gene; also known as Mendel's first law of inheritance.

leaf The main site of photosynthesis in a plant; typically consists of a flattened blade and a stalk (petiole) that joins the leaf to the stem.

learning Modification of behavior as a result of specific experiences.

leech A member of one of the three large groups of annelids, known for its bloodsucking ability. *See* annelid.

lens The structure in an eye that focuses light rays onto the retina.

leukemia (lū-kē′-mē-ah) A type of cancer of the blood-forming tissues, characterized by an excessive production of white blood cells and an abnormally high number of them in the blood; cancer of the bone marrow cells that produce leukocytes.

leukocyte (lū′-kō-sȳt) A blood cell that functions in fighting infections; also called a white blood cell.

lichen (lī′-ken) A close association between a fungus and an alga or between a fungus and a cyanobacterium, some of which are known to be beneficial to both partners.

life cycle The entire sequence of stages in the life of an organism, from the adults of one generation to the adults of the next.

life history The series of events from birth through reproduction to death.

life table A listing of survivals and deaths in a population in a particular time period and predictions of how long, on average, an individual of a given age will live.

ligament A type of fibrous connective tissue that joins bones together at joints.

light microscope (LM) An optical instrument with lenses that refract (bend) visible light to magnify images and project them into a viewer's eye or onto photographic film.

light reactions The first of two stages in photosynthesis; the steps in which solar energy is absorbed and converted to chemical energy in the form of ATP and NADPH. The light reactions power the sugar-producing Calvin cycle but produce no sugar themselves.

lignin A chemical that hardens the cell walls of plants.

limbic system (lim'-bik) A functional unit of several integrating and relay centers located deep in the human forebrain; interacts with the cerebral cortex in creating emotions and storing memories.

limiting factor An environmental factor that restricts population growth.

linkage map A listing of the relative locations of genes along a chromosome, as determined by recombination frequencies.

linked genes Genes located near each other on the same chromosome that tend to be inherited together.

lipid An organic compound consisting mainly of carbon and hydrogen atoms linked by nonpolar convalent bonds, making the compound mostly hydrophobic. Lipids include fats, phospholipids, and steroids and are insoluble in water.

liver The largest organ in the vertebrate body. The liver performs diverse functions, such as producing bile, preparing nitrogenous wastes for disposal, and detoxifying poisonous chemicals in the blood.

lobe-fin A bony fish with strong, muscular bonus supported by bones.

locomotion Active movement from place to place.

locus (plural, **loci**) The particular site where a gene is found on a chromosome. Homologous chromosomes have corresponding gene loci.

logistic growth model A mathematical description of idealized population growth that is restricted by limiting factors.

long-day plant A plant that flowers in late spring or early summer, when day length is long. Long-day plants actually flower in response to short nights.

long-term memory The ability to hold, associate, and recall information over one's lifetime.

loop of Henle (hen'-lē) In the vertebrate kidney, the portion of a nephron that helps concentrate the filtrate while conveying it between a proximal tubule and a distal tubule.

loose connective tissue The most widespread connective tissue in the vertebrate body. It binds epithelia to underlying tissues and functions as packing material, holding organs in place.

low-density lipoprotein (LDL) A cholesterol-carrying particle in the blood, made up of thousands of cholesterol molecules and other lipids bound to a protein. An LDL particle transports cholesterol from the liver for incorporation into cell membranes.

lung An infolded respiratory surface of terrestrial vertebrates that connects to the atmosphere by narrow tubes.

lymph A colorless fluid, derived from interstitial fluid, that circulates in the lymphatic sytem.

lymph node An organ of the immune system located along a lymph vessel. Lymph nodes filter lymph and contain cells that attack viruses and bacteria.

lymphatic system (lim-fat'-ik) The vertebrate organ system through which lymph circulates; includes lymph vessels, lymph nodes, and the spleen. The lymphatic system helps remove toxins and pathogens from the blood and interstitial fluid and returns fluid and solutes from the interstitial fluid to the circulatory system.

lymphocyte (lim'-fuh-sīt) A type of white blood cell that is chiefly responsible for the acquired immune response and is found mostly in the lymphatic system. *See* B cell; T cell.

lymphoma (lim-fō'-muh) Cancer of the tissues that form white blood cells.

lysogenic cycle (lī'-sō-jen'-ik) A type of bacteriophage replication cycle in which the viral genome is incorporated into the bacterial host chromosome as a prophage. New phages are not produced, and the host cell is not killed or lysed unless the viral genome leaves the host chromosome.

lysosome (lī-sō-sōm) A digestive organelle in eukaryotic cells; contains hydrolytic enzymes that digest engulfed food or damaged organelles.

lytic cycle (lit'-ik) A type of viral replication cycle resulting in the release of new viruses by lysis (breaking open) of the host cell.

M

macroevolution Evolutionary change above the species level, encompassing the origin of new taxonomic groups, adaptive radiation, and mass extinction.

macromolecule A giant molecule formed by the joining of smaller molecules, usually by a dehydration reaction: a protein, carbohydrate, or nucleic acid.

macronutrient A chemical substance that an organism must obtain in relatively large amounts. *See also* micronutrient.

macrophage (mak'-rō-fāj) A large, amoeboid, phagocytic white blood cell that functions in innate immunity by destroying microbes and in acquired immunity as an antigen-presenting cell.

major depression Depressive mental illness characterized by a low mood most of the time.

major histocompatibility complex (MHC) molecule *See* self protein.

malignant tumor An abnormal tissue mass that can spread into neighboring tissue and to other parts of the body; a cancerous tumor.

malnutrition A failure to obtain adequate nutrition.

mammal Member of a clade of amniotes that possess mammary glands and hair.

mantle In a mollusc, the outgrowth of the body surface that drapes over the animal. The mantle produces the shell and forms the mantle cavity.

marsupial (mar-sū'-pē-ul) A pouched mammal, such as a kangaroo, opossum, or koala. Marsupials give birth to embryonic offspring that complete development while housed in a pouch and attached to nipples on the mother's abdomen.

mass number The sum of the number of protons and neutrons in an atom's nucleus.

matter Anything that occupies space and has mass.

mechanoreceptor (mek'-uh-nō-ri-sep'-ter) A sensory receptor that detects changes in the environment associated with pressure, touch, stretch, motion, or sound.

medulla oblongata (meh-duh'-luh ob'-long-got'-uh) Part of the vertebrate hindbrain, continuous with the spinal cord; passes data between the spinal cord and forebrain and controls autonomic, homeostatic functions, including breathing, heart rate, swallowing, and digestion.

medusa (med-ū'-suh) (plural, **medusae**) One of two types of cnidarian body forms; an umbrella-like body form.

meiosis (mī-ō'-sis) In a sexually reproducing organism, the division of a single diploid nucleus into four haploid daughter nuclei. Meiosis and cytokinesis produce haploid gametes from diploid cells in the reproductive organs of the parents.

membrane potential The charge difference between a cell's cytoplasm and extracellular fluid due to the differential distribution of ions.

memory The ability to store and retrieve information. *See also* long-term memory; short-term memory.

memory cell A clone of long-lived lymphocytes formed during the primary immune response. Memory cells remain in a lymph nodes until activated by exposure to the same antigen that triggered its formation. When activated, a memory cell forms a large clone that mounts the secondary immune response.

meninges (muh-nin'-jēz) Layers of connective tissue that enwrap and protect the brain and spinal cord.

menstrual cycle (men'-strū-ul) The hormonally synchronized cyclic buildup and breakdown of the endometrium of some primates, including humans.

menstruation (men'-strū-ā'-shun) Uterine bleeding resulting from shedding of the endometrium during a menstrual cycle.

meristem (mer'-eh-stem) Plant tissue consisting of undifferentiated cells that divide and generate new cells and tissues.

mesoderm (mez'-ō-derm) The middle layer of the three embryonic cell layers in a gastrula. The mesoderm gives rise to muscles, bones, the dermis of the skin, and most other organs in the adult.

mesophyll (mes'-ō-fil) The green tissue in the interior of a leaf; a leaf's ground tissue system; the main site of photosynthesis.

messenger RNA (mRNA) The type of ribonucleic acid that encodes genetic information from DNA and conveys it to ribosomes, where the information is translated into amino acid sequences.

metabolic pathway A series of chemical reactions that either builds a complex molecule or breaks down a complex molecule into simpler compounds.

metabolic rate The total amount of energy an animal uses in a unit of time.

metabolism The totality of an organism's chemical reactions.

metamorphosis (met'-uh-môr'-fuh-sis) The transformation of a larva into an adult. *See* complete metamorphosis; incomplete metamorphosis.

metaphase (met'-eh-fāz) The third stage of mitosis, during which all the cell's duplicated chromosomes are lined up at an imaginary plane equidistant between the poles of the mitotic spindle.

metastasis (muh-tas'-tuh-sis) The spread of cancer cells beyond their original site.

methanogen (meth-an'-ō-jen) An archaean that produces methane as a metabolic waste product.

methyl group A chemical group consisting of a carbon atom bonded to three hydrogen atoms.

microevolution A change in a population's gene pool over generations.

microfilament The thinnest of the three main kinds of protein fibers making up the cytoskeleton of a eukaryotic cell; a solid, helical rod composed of the globular protein actin.

micrograph A photograph taken through a microscope.

micronutrient An element that an organism needs in very small amounts and that functions as a component or cofactor of enzymes. *See also* macronutrient.

microRNA (miRNA) A small, single-stranded RNA molecule that associates with one or more proteins in a complex that can degrade or prevent translation of an mRNA with a complementary sequence.

microtubule The thickest of the three main kinds of fibers making up the cytoskeleton of a eukaryotic cell; a hollow tube made of globular proteins called tubulins; found in cilia and flagella.

microvillus (plural, **microvilli**) One of many microscopic projections on the epithelial cells in the lumen of the small intestine. Microvilli increase the surface area of the small intestine.

midbrain One of three ancestral and embryonic regions of the vertebrate brain; develops into sensory integrating and relay centers that send sensory information to the cerebrum.

middle ear One of three main regions of the vertebrate ear; a chamber containing three small bones (the hammer, anvil, and stirrup) that convey vibrations from the eardrum to the oval window.

migration The regular back-and-forth movement of animals between two geographic areas at particular times of the year.

millipede A terrestrial arthropod that has two pairs of short legs for each of its numerous body segments and that eats decaying plant matter.

mineral In nutrition, a simple inorganic nutrient that an organism requires in small amounts for proper body functioning.

mineralocorticoid (min'-er-uh-lō-kort'-uh-koyd) A corticosteroid hormone secreted by the adrenal cortex that helps maintain salt and water homeostasis and may increase blood pressure in response to long-term stress.

missense mutation A change in the nucleotide sequence of a gene that alters the amino acid sequence of the resulting polypeptide. In a missense mutation, a codon is changed from encoding one amino acid to encoding a different amino acid.

mitochondrial matrix The compartment of the mitochondrion enclosed by the inner membrane and containing enzymes and substrates for the citric acid cycle.

mitochondrion (mī'-tō-kon'-drē-on) (plural, **mitochondria**) An organelle in eukaryotic cells where cellular respiration occurs. Enclosed by two membranes, it is where most of the cell's ATP is made.

mitosis (mī'-tō-sis) The division of a single nucleus into two genetically identical nuclei. Mitosis and cytokinesis make up the mitotic (M) phase of the cell cycle.

mitotic phase (M phase) The part of the cell cycle when the nucleus divides (via mitosis), its chromosomes are distributed to the daughter nuclei, and the cytoplasm divides (via cytokinesis), producing two daughter cells.

mitotic spindle A football-shaped structure formed of microtubules and associated proteins that is involved in the movement of chromosomes during mitosis and meiosis.

mixotroph A protist that is capable of both autotrophy and heterotrophy.

mold A rapidly growing fungus that reproduces asexually by producing spores.

molecular biology The study of the molecular basis of genes and gene expression; molecular genetics.

molecular clock Evolutionary timing method based on the observation that at least some regions of genomes evolve at constant rates.

molecular systematics A scientific discipline that uses nucleic acids or other molecules in different species to infer evolutionary relationships.

molecule Two or more atoms held together by covalent bonds.

mollusc (mol'-lusk) A soft-bodied animal characterized by a muscular foot, mantle, mantle cavity, and visceral mass. Molluscs include gastropods (snails and slugs), bivalves (clams, oysters, and scallops), and cephalopods (squids and octopuses).

molting The process of shedding an old exoskeleton or cuticle and secreting a new, larger one.

monoclonal antibody (mAb) (mon'-ō-klōn'-ul) An antibody secreted by a clone of cells and therefore specific for the one antigen that triggered the development of the clone.

monocot (mon'-ō-kot) A flowering plant whose embryos have a single seed leaf, or cotyledon.

monogamous Referring to a type of relationship in which one male mates with just one female, and both parents care for the children.

monohybrid cross An experimental mating of individuals differing in a single character.

monomer (mon'-uh-mer) The subunit that serves as a building block of a polymer.

monophyletic (mon'-ō-fī-let'-ik) Pertaining to a group of taxa that consists of a common ancestor and all its descendants, equivalent to a clade.

monosaccharide (mon'-ō-sak'-uh-rīd) The simplest carbohydrate; a simple sugar with a molecular formula that is generally some multiple of CH_2O. Monosaccharides are the monomers of disaccharides and polysaccharides.

monotreme (mon'-uh-trēm) An egg-laying mammal, such as the duck-billed platypus.

morning after pill (MAP) A birth control pill taken within three days of unprotected intercourse to prevent fertilization or implantation.

morphological species concept A definition of species in terms of measurable anatomical criteria.

motor neuron A nerve cell that conveys command signals from the central nervous system to effector cells, such as muscle cells or gland cells.

motor output The conduction of signals from a processing center in the central nervous system to effector cells.

motor system The component of the vertebrate peripheral nervous system that carries signals to and from skeletal muscles, mainly in response to external stimuli. Most actions of the motor system are voluntary.

motor unit A motor neuron and all the muscle fibers it controls.

mouth An opening through which food is taken into an animal's body, synonymous with oral cavity.

movement corridor A series of small clumps or a narrow strip of quality habitat (usable by organisms) that connects otherwise isolated patches of quality habitat.

multipotent stem cell An unspecialized cell that can divide to produce one identical daughter cell and a more specialized daughter cell, which undergoes differentiation. A multipotent stem cell can form multiple types of cells, but not all types of cells in the body.

muscle fiber Muscle cell.

muscle tissue Tissue consisting of long muscle cells that can contract, either on its own or when stimulated by nerve impulses; the most abundant tissue in a typical animal. *See* skeletal muscle; cardiac muscle; smooth muscle.

muscular system The organ system that includes all the skeletal muscles in the body. (Cardiac muscle and smooth muscle are components of other organ systems.)

mutagen (myū′-tuh-jen) A chemical or physical agent that interacts with DNA and causes a mutation.

mutagenesis (myū′-tuh-jen′-uh-sis) The creation of a change in the nucleotide sequence of an organism's DNA.

mutation A change in the nucleotide sequence of an organism's DNA; the ultimate source of genetic diversity. A mutation also can occur in the DNA or RNA of a virus.

mutualism An interspecific relationship in which both partners benefit.

mycelium (mī-sē′-lē-um) (plural, **mycelia**) The densely branched network of hyphae in a fungus.

mycorrhiza (mī′-kō-rī′-zuh) (plural, **mycorrhizae**) A close association of plant roots and fungi that is beneficial to both partners.

mycosis A general term for a fungal infection.

myelin sheath (mī′-uh-lin) A series of cells, each wound around, and thus insulating, the axon of a nerve cell in vertebrates. Each pair of cells in the sheath is separated by a space called a node of Ranvier.

myofibril (mī′-ō-fī′-bril) A contractile strand in a muscle cell (fiber), made up of many sarcomeres. Longitudinal bundles of myofibrils make up a muscle fiber.

myosin A type of protein filament that interacts with actin filaments to cause cell contraction.

N

NAD⁺ Nicotinamide adenine dinucleotide; a coenzyme that can accept electrons during the redox reactions of cellular metabolism. The plus sign indicates that the molecule is oxidized and ready to pick up hydrogens; the reduced, hydrogen (electron)-carrying form is NADH.

NADP⁺ Nicotinamide adenine dinucleotide phosphate, an electron acceptor that, as NADPH, temporarily stores energized electrons produced during the light reactions.

natural family planning A form of contraception that relies on refraining from sexual intercourse when conception is most likely to occur; also called the rhythm method.

natural killer (NK) cell A cell type that provides an innate immune response by attacking cancer cells and infected body cells, especially those harboring viruses.

natural selection A process in which individuals with certain inherited traits are more likely to survive and reproduce than are individuals that do not have those traits.

nearsightedness An inability to focus on distant objects; occurs when the eyeball is longer than normal and the lens focuses distant objects in front of the retina; also called myopia.

negative feedback A primary mechanism of homeostasis, whereby a change in a physiological variable triggers a response that counteracts the initial change. Negative feedback is a common control mechanism in which a chemical reaction, metabolic pathway, or hormone-secreting gland is inhibited by the products of the reaction, pathway, or gland. As the concentration of the products builds up, the product molecules themselves inhibit the process that produced them.

negative pressure breathing A breathing system in which air is pulled into the lungs.

nematode (nem′-uh-tōd) A roundworm, characterized by a pseudocoelom, a cylindrical, wormlike body form, and a tough cuticle that is molted to permit growth.

nephron The tubular excretory unit and associated blood vessels of the vertebrate kidney; extracts filtrate from the blood and refines it into urine. The nephron is the functional unit of the urinary system.

nerve A cable-like bundle of neurons tightly wrapped in connective tissue.

nerve cord An elongated bundle of neurons, usually extending longitudinally from the brain or anterior ganglia. One or more nerve cords and the brain make up the central nervous system in many animals.

nerve net A weblike system of interconnected neurons, characteristic of radially symmetric animals such as a hydra.

nervous system The organ system that forms a communication and coordination network between all parts of an animal's body.

nervous tissue Tissue made up of neurons and supportive cells.

neural tube (nyūr′-ul) An embryonic cylinder that develops from the ectoderm after gastrulation and gives rise to the brain and spinal cord.

neuron (nyūr′-on) A nerve cell; the fundamental structural and functional unit of the nervous system, specialized for carrying signals from one location in the body to another.

neurosecretory cell A nerve cell that synthesizes hormones and secretes them into the blood and also conducts nerve signals.

neurotransmitter A chemical messenger that carries information from a transmitting neuron to a receiving cell, either another neuron or an effector cell.

neutron A subatomic particle having no electrical charge, found in the nucleus of an atom.

neutrophil (nyū′-truh-fil) An innate, defensive, phagocytic white blood cell that can engulf bacteria and viruses in infected tissue.

nitrogen fixation The conversion of atmospheric nitrogen (N_2) to nitrogen compounds (NH_4^+, NO_3^-) that plants can absorb and use.

node The point of attachment of a leaf on a stem.

node of Ranvier (ron′-vē-ā) An unmyelinated region on a myelinated axon of a nerve cell, where nerve signals are regenerated.

noncompetitive inhibitor A substance that reduces the activity of an enzyme without entering an active site. By binding elsewhere on the enzyme, a noncompetitive inhibitor changes the shape of the enzyme so that the active site no longer effectively catalyzes the conversion of substrate to product.

nondisjunction An accident of meiosis or mitosis in which a pair of homologous chromosomes or a pair of sister chromatids fail to separate at anaphase.

nonpolar covalent bond A covalent bond in which electrons are shared equally between two atoms of similar electronegativity.

nonself molecule A foreign antigen; a protein or other macromolecule that is not part of an organism's body. *See also* self protein.

nonsense mutation A change in the nucleotide sequence of a gene that converts an amino-acid-encoding codon to a stop codon. A nonsense mutation results in a shortened polypeptide.

norepinephrine (nor′-ep-uh-nef′-rin) An amine hormone (also called noradrenaline) secreted by the adrenal medulla that prepares body organs for action (fight or flight); also serves as a neurotransmitter.

notochord (nō′-tuh-kord) A flexible, cartilage-like, longitudinal rod located between the digestive tract and nerve cord in chordate animals; present only in embryos in many species.

nuclear envelope A double membrane that encloses the nucleus, perforated with pores that regulate traffic with the cytoplasm.

nuclear transplantation A technique in which the nucleus of one cell is placed into another cell that already has a nucleus or in which the nucleus has been previously destroyed.

nucleic acid (nū-klā′-ik) A polymer consisting of many nucleotide monomers; serves as a blueprint for proteins and, through the actions of proteins, for all cellular structures and activities. The two types of nucleic acids are DNA and RNA.

nucleic acid probe In DNA technology, a radioactively or fluorescently labeled single-stranded nucleic acid molecule used to find a specific gene or other nucleotide sequence within a mass of DNA. The probe hydrogen-bonds to the complementary sequence in the targeted DNA.

nucleoid (nū′-klē-oyd) A dense region of DNA in a prokaryotic cell.

nucleolus (nū-klē´-ō-lus) A structure within the nucleus where ribosomal RNA is made and assembled with proteins imported from the cytoplasm to make ribosomal subunits.

nucleosome (nū´-klē-ō-sōm) The bead-like unit of DNA packing in a eukaryotic cell; consists of DNA wound around a protein core made up of eight histone molecules.

nucleotide (nū´-klē-ō-tīd) A building block of nucleic acids, consisting of a five-carbon sugar covalently bonded to a nitrogenous base and one or more phosphate groups.

nucleus (plural, **nuclei**) (1) An atom's central core, containing protons and neutrons. (2) The genetic control center of a eukaryotic cell.

O

obesity The excessive accumulation of fat in the body.

ocean acidification Decreasing pH of ocean waters due to absorption of excess atmospheric CO_2 from the burning of fossil fuels.

ocean current One of the river-like flow patterns in the oceans.

omnivore An animal that eats animals as well as plants or algae.

oncogene (on´-kō-jēn) A cancer-causing gene; usually contributes to malignancy by abnormally enhancing the amount or activity of a growth factor made by the cell.

oogenesis (ō´-uh-jen´-uh-sis) The development of mature egg cells.

open circulatory system A circulatory system in which blood is pumped through open-ended vessels and bathes the tissues and organs directly. In an animal with an open circulatory system, blood and interstitial fluid are one and the same.

operator In prokaryotic DNA, a sequence of nucleotides near the start of an operon to which an active repressor protein can attach. The binding of a repressor prevents RNA polymerase from attaching to the promoter and transcribing the genes of the operon. The operator sequence thereby acts as a "genetic switch" that can turn all the genes in an operon on or off as a single functional unit.

operculum (ō-per´-kyuh-lum) (plural, **opercula**) A protective flap on each side of a fish's head that covers a chamber housing the gills. Movement of the operculum increases the flow of oxygen-bearing water over the gills.

operon (op´-er-on) A unit of genetic regulation common in prokaryotes; a cluster of genes with related functions, along with the promoter and operator that control their transcription.

opportunistic infection An infection that can be controlled by a normally functioning immune system but that causes illness in a person with an immunodeficiency.

opposable thumb An arrangement of the fingers such that the thumb can touch the ventral surface of the fingertips of all four fingers.

optimal foraging theory The basis for analyzing behavior as a compromise between feeding costs and feeding benefits.

oral cavity The mouth of an animal.

oral contraceptive *See* birth control pill.

order In Linnaean classification, the taxonomic category above family.

organ A specialized structure composed of several different types of tissues that together perform specific funstions.

organ of Corti (kor´-tē) The hearing organ in birds and mammals, located within the cochlea.

organ system A group of organs that work together in performing vital body functions.

organelle (ōr-guh-nel´) A membrane-enclosed structure with a specialized function within a cell.

organic compound A chemical compound containing the element carbon and usually the element hydrogen.

organism An individual living thing, such as a bacterium, fungus, protist, plant, or animal.

orgasm A series of rhythmic, involuntary contractions of the reproductive structures.

osmoconformer (oz´-mō-con-form´-er) An organism whose body fluids have a solute concentration equal to that of its surroundings. Osmoconformers do not have a net gain or loss of water by osmosis. Examples include most marine invertebrates.

osmoregulation The homeostatic maintenance of solute concentrations and the balance of water gain and loss.

osmoregulator An organism whose body fluids have a solute concentration different from that of its environment and that must use energy in controlling water loss or gain. Examples include most land-dwelling and freshwater animals.

osmosis (oz-mō´-sis) The diffusion of water across a selectively permeable membrane.

osteoporosis (os´-tē-ō-puh-rō´-sis) A skeletal disorder characterized by thinning, porous, and easily broken bones.

outer ear One of three main regions of the ear in reptiles (including birds) and mammals; made up of the auditory canal and, in many birds and mammals, the pinna.

outgroup In a cladistic study, a taxon or group of taxa known to have diverged before the lineage that contains the group of species being studied. *See also* ingroup.

ovarian cycle (ō-vār´-ē-un) Hormonally synchronized cyclic events in the mammalian ovary, culminating in ovulation.

ovary (1) In animals, the female gonad, which produces egg cells and reproductive hormones. (2) In flowering plants, the basal portion of a carpel in which the egg-containing ovules develop.

oviduct (ō´-vuh-dukt) The tube that conveys egg cells away from an ovary; also called a fallopian tube. In humans, the oviduct is the normal site of fertilization.

ovulation (ah´-vyū-lā´-shun) The release of an egg cell from an ovarian follicle.

ovule (ō-vyūl) In plants, a structure that develops within the ovary of a seed plant and contains the female gametophyte.

oxidation The loss of electrons from a substance involved in a redox reaction; always accompanies reduction.

oxidative phosphorylation (fos´-fōr-uh-lā´-shun) The production of ATP using energy derived from the redox reactions of an electron transport chain; the third major stage of cellular respiration.

ozone layer The layer of ozone (O_3) in the upper atmosphere that protects life on Earth from the harmful ultraviolet rays in sunlight.

P

P generation The parent individuals from which offspring are derived in studies of inheritance; P stands for parental.

P site One of two of a ribosome's binding sites for tRNA during translation. The P site holds the tRNA carrying the growing polypeptide chain. (P stands for peptidyl tRNA.)

paedomorphosis (pē´-duh-mōr´-fuh-sis) The retention in an adult of juvenile features of its evolutionary ancestors.

pain receptor A sensory receptor that detects pain.

paleoanthropology (pā´-lē-ō-an´-thruh-pol´-uh-jē) The study of human origins and evolution.

paleontologist (pa´-lē-on-tol´-uh-jist) A scientist who studies fossils.

pancreas (pan´-krē-us) A gland with dual functions: The digestive portion secretes digestive enzymes and an alkaline solution into the small intestine via a duct. The endocrine portion secretes the hormones insulin and glucagon into the blood.

Pangaea (pan-jē´-uh) The supercontinent that formed near the end of the Paleozoic era, when plate movements brought all the landmasses of Earth together.

parasite Organism that derives its nutrition from a living host, which is harmed by the interaction.

parasympathetic division The component of the autonomic nervous system that generally promotes body activities that gain and conserve energy, such as digestion and reduced heart rate. *See also* sympathetic division.

parathyroid gland (pār´-uh-thī´-royd) One of four endocrine glands that are embedded in the surface of the thyroid gland and that secrete parathyroid hormone.

parathyroid hormone (PTH) A peptide hormone secreted by the parathyroid glands that raises blood calcium level.

parenchyma cell (puh-ren´-kim-uh) In plants, a relatively unspecialized cell with a thin primary wall and no secondary wall; functions in photosynthesis, food storage, and aerobic respiration and may differentiate into other cell types.

Parkinson's disease A motor disorder caused by a progressive brain disease and characterized by difficulty in initiating movements, slowness of movement, and rigidity.

parsimony (par'-suh-mō'-nē) In scientific studies, the search for the least complex explanation for an observed phenomenon.

partial pressure The pressure exerted by a particular gas in a mixture of gases; a measure of the relative amount of a gas.

passive immunity Temporary immunity obtained by acquiring ready-made antibodies. Passive immunity lasts only a few weeks or months.

passive transport The diffusion of a substance across a biological membrane, with no expenditure of energy.

pathogen An agent, such as a virus, bacteria, or fungus, that causes disease.

pattern formation During embryonic development, the emergence of a body form with specialized organs and tissues in the right places.

PCR *See* polymerase chain reaction (PCR).

pedigree A family genetic tree representing the occurrence of heritable traits in parents and offspring across a number of generations. A pedigree can be used to determine genotypes of matings that have already occurred.

pelagic realm (puh-laj'-ik) The region of an ocean occupied by seawater.

penis The copulatory structure of male mammals.

peptide bond The covalent bond between two amino acid units in a polypeptide, formed by a dehydration reaction.

peptidoglycan (pep'-tid-ō-glī'-kan) A polymer of complex sugars cross-linked by short polypeptides; a material unique to bacterial cell walls.

per capita rate of increase The average contribution of each individual in a population to population growth.

perennial (puh-ren'-ē-ul) A plant that lives for many years.

peripheral nervous system (PNS) The network of nerves and ganglia carrying signals into and out of the central nervous system.

peristalsis (per'-uh-stal'-sis) Rhythmic waves of contraction of smooth muscles. Peristalsis propels food through a digestive tract and also enables many animals, such as earthworms, to crawl.

permafrost Continuously frozen ground found in the tundra.

peroxisome An organelle containing enzymes that transfer hydrogen atoms from various substrates to oxygen, producing and then degrading hydrogen peroxide.

petal A modified leaf of a flowering plant. Petals are the often colorful parts of a flower that advertise it to pollinators.

pH scale A measure of the relative acidity of a solution, ranging in value from 0 (most acidic) to 14 (most basic). The letters pH stand for potential hydrogen and refer to the concentration of hydrogen ions (H^+).

phage (fāj) *See* bacteriophage.

phagocyte (fag'-ō-sȳ't) A white blood cell (for example, a neutrophil or monocyte) that engulfs bacteria, foreign proteins, and the remains of dead body cells.

phagocytosis (fag'-ō-sī-tō'-sis) Cellular "eating"; a type of endocytosis in which a cell engulfs macromolecules, other cells, or particles into its cytoplasm.

pharyngeal slit (fā-rin'-jē-ul) A gill structure in the pharynx; found in chordate embryos and some adult chordates.

pharynx (fār'-inks) The organ in a digestive tract that receives food from the oral cavity; in terrestrial vertebrates, the throat region where the air and food passages cross.

phenotype (fē'-nō-tīp) The expressed traits of an organism.

phenotypic plasticity An individual's ability to change phenotype in response to local environmental conditions.

phloem (flō'-um) The portion of a plant's vascular tissue system that transports sugars and other organic nutrients from leaves or storage tissues to other parts of the plant.

phloem sap The solution of sugars, other nutrients, and hormones conveyed throughout a plant via phloem tissue.

phosphate group (fos'-fāt) A chemical group consisting of a phosphorus atom bonded to four oxygen atoms.

phospholipid (fos'-fō-lip'-id) A lipid made up of glycerol joined to two fatty acids and a phosphate group, giving the molecule two nonpolar hydrophobic tails and a polar hydrophilic head. Phospholipids form bilayers that function as biological membranes.

phosphorylation (fos'-fōr-uh-lā'-shun) The transfer of a phosphate group, usually from ATP, to a molecule. Nearly all cellular work depends on ATP energizing other molecules by phosphorylation.

photic zone (fō'-tik) The region of an aquatic ecosystem into which light penetrates and where photosynthesis occurs.

photoautotroph An organism that obtains energy from sunlight and carbon from CO_2 by photosynthesis.

photoheterotroph An organism that obtains energy from sunlight and carbon from organic sources.

photon (fō'-ton) A fixed quantity of light energy. The shorter the wavelength of light, the greater the energy of a photon.

photoperiod The relative lengths of day and night; an environmental stimulus that plants use to detect the time of year.

photophosphorylation (fō'-tō-fos'-fōr-uh-lā'-shun) The production of ATP by chemiosmosis during the light reactions of photosynthesis.

photopsin (fō-top'-sin) One of a family of visual pigments in the cones of the vertebrate eye that absorb bright, colored light.

photoreceptor A type of electromagnetic sensory receptor that detects light.

photorespiration In a plant cell, a metabolic pathway that consumes oxygen, releases CO_2, and decreases photosynthetic output. Photorespiration generally occurs on hot, dry days, when stomata close, O_2 accumulates in the leaf, and rubisco fixes O_2 rather than CO_2. Photorespiration produces no sugar molecules or ATP.

photosynthesis (fō'-tō-sin'-thuh-sis) The process by which plants, autotrophic protists, and some bacteria use light energy to make sugars and other organic food molecules from carbon dioxide and water.

photosystem A light-capturing unit of a chloroplast's thylakoid membrane, consisting of a reaction-center complex surrounded by numerous light-harvesting complexes.

phototropism (fō'-tō-trō'-pizm) The growth of a plant shoot toward light (positive phototropism) or away from light (negative phototropism).

phylogenetic species concept A definition of species as the smallest group of individuals that shares a common ancestor, forming one branch on the tree of life.

phylogenetic tree (fī'-lō-juh-net'-ik) A branching diagram that represents a hypothesis about the evolutionary history of a group of organisms.

phylogeny (fī-loj'-uh-nē) The evolutionary history of a species or group of related species.

phylum (fī'-lum) (plural, **phyla**) In Linnaean classification, the taxonomic category above class.

physiology (fī'-zē-ol'-uh-ji) The study of the functions of an organism's structures.

phytochrome (fī'-tuh-krōm) A plant protein that has a light-absorbing component.

phytoplankton (fī'-tō-plank'-ton) Algae and photosynthetic bacteria that drift passively in aquatic environments.

pineal gland (pin'-ē-ul) An outgrowth of the vertebrate brain that secretes the hormone melatonin, which coordinates daily and seasonal body activities such as the sleep/wake circadian rhythm with environmental light conditions.

pinna (pin'-uh) The flap-like part of the outer ear, projecting from the body surface of many birds and mammals; collects sound waves and channels them to the auditory canal.

pinocytosis (pē'-nō-sī-tō'-sis) Cellular "drinking"; a type of endocytosis in which the cell takes fluid and dissolved solutes into small membranous vesicles.

pistil Part of the reproductive organ of an angiosperm, a single carpel or a group of fused carpels.

pith Part of the ground tissue system of a dicot plant. Pith fills the center of a stem and may store food.

pituitary gland An endocrine gland at the base of the hypothalamus; consists of a posterior lobe, which stores and releases two hormones produced by the hypothalamus, and an anterior lobe, which produces and secretes many hormones that regulate diverse body functions.

pivot joint A joint that allows precise rotations in multiple planes. An example in humans is the joint that rotates the forearm at the elbow.

placenta (pluh-sen′-tuh) In most mammals, the organ that provides nutrients and oxygen to the embryo and helps dispose of its metabolic wastes; formed of the embryo's chorion and the mother's endometrial blood vessels.

placental mammal (pluh-sen′-tul) Mammal whose young complete their embryonic development in the uterus, nourished via the mother's blood vessels in the placenta; also called a eutherian.

plasma The liquid matrix of the blood in which the blood cells are suspended.

plasma cell An antibody-secreting B cell.

plasma membrane The membrane at the boundary of every cell that acts as a selective barrier to the passage of ions and molecules into and out of the cell; consists of a phospholipid bilayer with embedded proteins.

plasmid A small ring of independently replicating DNA separate from the main chromosome(s). Plasmids are found in prokaryotes and yeasts.

plasmodesma (plaz′-mō-dez′-muh) (plural, **plasmodesmata**) An open channel in a plant cell wall through which strands of cytoplasm connect from adjacent cells.

plasmodial slime mold (plaz-mō′-dē-ul) A type of protist that has amoeboid cells, flagellated cells, and an amoeboid plasmodial feeding stage in its life cycle.

plasmodium (1) A single mass of cytoplasm containing many nuclei. (2) The amoeboid feeding stage in the life cycle of a plasmodial slime mold.

plate tectonics (tek-tän′-iks) The theory that the continents are part of great plates of Earth's crust that float on the hot, underlying portion of the mantle. Movements in the mantle cause the continents to move slowly over time.

platelet A pinched-off cytoplasmic fragment of a bone marrow cell. Platelets circulate in the blood and are important in blood clotting.

pleiotropy (plī′-uh-trō-pē) The control of more than one phenotypic characteristic by a single gene.

polar covalent bond A covalent bond between atoms that differ in electronegativity. The shared electrons are pulled closer to the more electronegative atom, making it slightly negative and the other atom slightly positive.

polar ice A terrestrial biome that includes regions of extremely cold temperature and low precipitation located at high latitudes north of the arctic tundra and in Antarctica.

polar molecule A molecule containing polar covalent bonds and having an unequal distribution of charges.

pollen grain The structure that will produce the sperm in seed plants; the male gametophyte.

pollination In seed plants, the delivery by wind or animals of pollen from the pollen-producing parts of a plant to the stigma of a carpel.

polychaete (pol′-ē-kēt) A member of the largest group of annelids. *See* annelid.

polygamous Referring to a type of relationship in which an individual of one sex mates with several of the other.

polygenic inheritance (pol′-ē-jen′-ik) The additive effects of two or more gene loci on a single phenotypic characteristic.

polymer (pol′-uh-mer) A large molecule consisting of many identical or similar monomers linked together by covalent bonds.

polymerase chain reaction (PCR) (puh-lim′-uh-rās) A technique used to obtain many copies of a DNA molecule or a specific part of a DNA molecule. In the procedure, the starting DNA is mixed with a heat-resistant DNA polymerase, DNA nucleotides, and a few other ingredients. Specific nucleotide primers flanking the region to be copied ensure that it, and not other regions of the DNA, is replicated during the PCR procedure.

polynucleotide (pol′-ē-nū′-klē-ō-tīd) A polymer made up of many nucleotide monomers covalently bonded together.

polyp (pol′-ip) One of two types of cnidarian body forms; a columnar, hydra-like body.

polypeptide A polymer (chain) of amino acids linked by peptide bonds.

polyploid An organism that has more than two complete sets of chromosomes as a result of an accident of cell division.

polysaccharide (pol′-ē-sak′-uh-rīd) A carbohydrate polymer of many monosaccharides (sugars) linked by dehydration reactions.

pons (pahnz) Part of the vertebrate hindbrain that functions with the medulla oblongata in passing data between the spinal cord and forebrain and in controlling autonomic, homeostatic functions.

population A group of individuals belonging to one species and living in the same geographic area.

population density The number of individuals of a species per unit area or volume.

population ecology The study of how members of a population interact with their environment, focusing on factors that influence population density and growth.

population momentum In a population in which $r = 0$, the continuation of population growth as girls in the prereproductive age group reach their reproductive years.

positive feedback A type of control in which a change triggers mechanisms that amplify that change.

post-anal tail A tail posterior to the anus; found in chordate embryos and most adult chordates.

posterior Pertaining to the rear, or tail, of a bilaterally symmetric animal.

posterior pituitary An extension of the hypothalamus composed of nervous tissue that secretes hormones made in the hypothalamus; a temporary storage site for hypothalamic hormones.

postzygotic barrier A reproductive barrier that prevents hybrid zygotes produced by two different species from developing into viable, fertile adults. Includes reduced hybrid viability, reduced hybrid fertility, and hybrid breakdown.

potential energy The energy that matter possesses because of its location or arrangement. Water behind a dam possesses potential energy, and so do chemical bonds.

predation An interaction between species in which one species, the predator, eats the other, the prey.

prepuce (prē′-pyūs) A fold of skin covering the head of the clitoris or penis.

pressure flow mechanism The method by which phloem sap is transported through a plant from a sugar source, where sugars are produced, to a sugar sink, where sugars are used.

prevailing winds Winds that result from the combined effects of Earth's rotation and the rising and falling of air masses.

prezygotic barrier A reproductive barrier that impedes mating between species or hinders fertilization if mating between two species is attempted. Includes temporal, habitat, behavioral, mechanical, and gametic isolation.

primary consumer In the trophic structure of an ecosystem, an organism that eats plants or algae.

primary growth Growth in the length of a plant root or shoot, produced by an apical meristem.

primary immune response The initial immune response to an antigen, which appears after a lag of several days.

primary oocyte (ō′-uh-sīt) A diploid cell, in prophase I of meiosis, that can be hormonally triggered to develop into an egg.

primary phloem *See* phloem.

primary production The amount of solar energy converted to chemical energy (in organic compounds) by autotrophs in an ecosystem during a given time period.

primary spermatocyte (sper-mat′-eh-sīt′) A diploid cell in the testis that undergoes meiosis I.

primary structure The first level of protein structure; the specific sequence of amino acids making up a polypeptide chain.

primary succession A type of ecological succession in which a biological community arises in an area without soil. *See also* secondary succession.

primary xylem *See* xylem.

primers Short, artificially created, single-stranded DNA molecules that bind to each end of a target sequence during a PCR procedure.

prion An infectious form of protein that may multiply by converting related proteins to more prions. Prions cause several related diseases in different animals, including scrapie in sheep and mad cow disease.

problem solving Applying past experiences to overcome obstacles in novel situations.

producer An organism that makes organic food molecules from CO_2, H_2O, and other inorganic raw materials: a plant, alga, or autotrophic prokaryote.

product An ending material in a chemical reaction.

progestin (prō-jes′-tin) One of a family of steroid hormones, including progesterone, produced by the mammalian ovary. Progestins prepare the uterus for pregnancy.

programmed cell death The timely and tidy suicide (and disposal of the remains) of certain cells, triggered by certain genes; an essential process in normal development; also called apoptosis.

prokaryotic cell (prō-kār′-ē-ot′-ik) A type of cell lacking a membrane-enclosed nucleus and other membrane-enclosed organelles; found only in the domains Bacteria and Archaea.

prolactin (PRL) (prō-lak′-tin) A protein hormone secreted by the anterior pituitary that stimulates human mammary glands to produce and release milk and produces other responses in different animals.

prometaphase The second stage of mitosis, during which the nuclear envelope fragments and the spindle microtubules attach to the kinetochores of the sister chromatids.

promiscuous Referring to a type of relationship in which mating occurs with no strong pair-bonds or lasting relationships.

promoter A specific nucleotide sequence in DNA located near the start of a gene that is the binding site for RNA polymerase and the place where transcription begins.

prophage (prō′-fāj) Phage DNA that has inserted by genetic recombination into the DNA of a bacterial chromosome.

prophase The first stage of mitosis, during which the chromatin condenses to form structures (sister chromatids) visible with a light microscope and the mitotic spindle begins to form, but the nucleus is still intact.

prostate gland (pros′-tāt) A gland in human males that secretes a thin fluid that nourishes the sperm.

protein A functional biological molecule consisting of one or more polypeptides folded into a specific three-dimensional structure.

proteobacteria A clade of gram-negative bacteria that encompasses enormous diversity, including all four modes of nutrition.

proteomics The study of whole sets of proteins and their interactions.

protist A member of the kingdom Protista. Most protists are unicellular, though some are colonial or multicellular.

proton A subatomic particle with a single positive electrical charge, found in the nucleus of an atom.

proto-oncogene (prō′-tō-on′-kō-jēn) A normal gene that, through mutation, can be converted to a cancer-causing gene.

protostome A mode of animal development in which the opening formed during gastrulation becomes the mouth. Animals with the protostome pattern of development include the flatworms, molluscs, annelids, nematodes, and arthropods.

protozoan (prō′-tō-zō′-un) (plural, **protozoans**) A protist that lives primarily by ingesting food; a heterotrophic, "animal-like" protist.

proximal tubule In the vertebrate kidney, the portion of a nephron immediately downstream from Bowman's capsule that conveys and helps refine filtrate.

proximate cause In animal behavior, a condition in an animal's internal or external environment that is the immediate reason or mechanism for a behavior.

proximate question In animal behavior, a question that concerns the immediate reason for a behavior.

pseudocoelom (sū′-dō-sē′-lōm) A body cavity that is not lined with mesoderm and is in direct contact with the wall of the digestive tract.

pseudopodium (sū′-dō-pō′-dē-um) (plural, **pseudopodia**) A temporary extension of an amoeboid cell. Pseudopodia function in moving cells and engulfing food.

pulmonary artery A large blood vessel that conveys blood from the heart to a lung.

pulmonary circuit The branch of the circulatory system that supplies the lungs. *See also* systemic circuit.

pulmonary vein A blood vessel that conveys blood from a lung to the heart.

pulse The rhythmic stretching of the arteries caused by the pressure of blood during contraction of ventricles in systole.

punctuated equilibria In the fossil record, long periods of apparent stasis, in which a species undergoes little or no morphological change, interrupted by relatively brief periods of sudden change.

Punnett square A diagram used in the study of inheritance to show the results of random fertilization.

pupil The opening in the iris that admits light into the interior of the vertebrate eye. Muscles in the iris regulate the pupil's size.

Q

quaternary consumer (kwot′-er-ner-ē) An organism that eats tertiary consumers.

quaternary structure The fourth level of protein structure; the shape resulting from the association of two or more polypeptide subunits.

R

R plasmid A bacterial plasmid that carries genes for enzymes that destroy particular antibiotics, thus making the bacterium resistant to the antibiotics.

radial symmetry An arrangement of the body parts of an organism like pieces of a pie around an imaginary central axis. Any slice passing longitudinally through a radially symmetric organism's central axis divides it into mirror-image halves.

radioactive isotope An isotope whose nucleus decays spontaneously, giving off particles and energy.

radiolarian A protist that moves and feeds by means of threadlike pseudopodia and has a mineralized support structure composed of silica.

radiometric dating A method for determining the absolute ages of fossils and rocks, based on the half-life of radioactive isotopes.

radula (rad′-yū-luh) A toothed, rasping organ used to scrape up or shred food; found in many molluscs.

random dispersion pattern A pattern in which the individuals of a population are spaced in an unpredictable way.

ray-finned fish Bony fish; member of a clade of jawed vertebrates having fins supported by thin, flexible skeletal rays.

reabsorption In the vertebrate kidney, the reclaiming of water and valuable solutes from the filtrate.

reactant A starting material in a chemical reaction.

reading frame The way a cell's mRNA-translating machinery groups the mRNA nucleotides into codons.

receptor potential The electrical signal produced by sensory transduction.

receptor-mediated endocytosis (en′-dō-sī-tō′-sis) The movement of specific molecules into a cell by the inward budding of membranous vesicles, which contain proteins with receptor sites specific to the molecules being taken in.

recessive allele An allele that has no noticeable effect on the phenotype of a gene when the individual is heterozygous for that gene.

recombinant DNA A DNA molecule carrying nucleotide sequences derived from two or more sources.

recombination frequency With respect to two given genes, the number of recombinant progeny from a mating divided by the total number of progeny. Recombinant progeny carry combinations of alleles different from those in either of the parents as a result of crossing over during meiosis.

Recommended Dietary Allowance (RDA) A recommendation for daily nutrient intake established by a national scientific panel.

rectum The terminal portion of the large intestine where the feces are stored until they are eliminated.

red alga A member of a group of marine, mostly multicellular, autotrophic protists, which includes the reef-building coralline algae. Red algae belong to the supergroup Archaeplastida.

red blood cell *See* erythrocyte.

red bone marrow A specialized tissue that is found in the cavities at the ends of bones and that produces blood cells.

red-green colorblindness A category of common, sex-linked human disorders involving several genes on the X chromosome; characterized by a malfunction of light-sensitive cells in the eyes; affects mostly males but also homozygous females.

redox reaction Short for **red**uction-**oxi**dation reaction; a chemical reaction in which electrons are lost from one substance (oxidation) and added to another (reduction).

reduction The gain of electrons by a substance involved in a redox reaction; always accompanies oxidation.

reflex An automatic reaction to a stimulus, mediated by the spinal cord or lower brain.

regeneration The regrowth of body parts from pieces of an organism.

regulatory gene A gene that codes for a protein, such as a repressor, that controls the transcription of another gene or group of genes.

relative fitness The contribution an individual makes to the gene pool of the next generation, relative to the contributions of other individuals in the population.

releasing hormone A kind of hormone secreted by the hypothalamus that promotes the release of hormones from the anterior pituitary.

renal cortex The outer portion of the vertebrate kidney, above the renal medulla.

renal medulla The inner portion of the vertebrate kidney, beneath the renal cortex.

repetitive DNA Nucleotide sequences that are present in many copies in the DNA of a genome. The repeated sequences may be long or short and may be located next to each other (tandomly) or dispersed in the DNA.

repressor A protein that blocks the transcription of a gene or operon.

reproduction The creation of new individuals from existing ones.

reproductive cloning Using a somatic cell from a multicellular organism to make one or more genetically identical individuals.

reproductive cycle A recurring sequence of events that produces eggs, makes them available for fertilization, and prepares the female body for pregnancy.

reproductive isolation The existence of biological factors (barriers) that impede members of two species from producing viable, fertile hybrids.

reproductive system The organ system responsible for reproduction.

reptile Member of the clade of amniotes that includes snakes, lizards, turtles, crocodilians, and birds, along with a number of extinct groups, such as dinosaurs.

respiratory system The organ system that functions in exchanging gases with the environment. It supplies the blood with O_2 and disposes of CO_2.

resting potential The voltage across the plasma membrane of a resting neuron. The resting potential in a vertebrate neuron is typically around -70 millivolts, with the inside of the cell negatively charged relative to the outside.

restoration ecology The use of ecological principles to develop ways to return degraded ecosystems to conditions as similar as possible to their natural, predegraded state.

restriction enzyme A bacterial enzyme that cuts up foreign DNA (at specific DNA sequences called *restriction sites*), thus protecting bacteria against intruding DNA from phages and other organisms. Restriction enzymes are used in DNA technology to cut DNA molecules in reproducible ways. The pieces of cut DNA are called restriction fragments.

restriction fragment length polymorphism (RFLP) (rif′-lip) Variation in the length of a restriction fragment. RFLPs are produced when homologous DNA sequences containing SNPs are cut up with restriction enzymes.

restriction fragments Molecules of DNA produced from a longer DNA molecule cut up by a restriction enzyme. Restriction fragments are used in genome mapping and other applications.

restriction site A specific sequence on a DNA strand that is recognized as a "cut site" by a restriction enzyme.

retina (ret′-uh-nuh) The light-sensitive layer in an eye, made up of photoreceptor cells and sensory neurons.

retrovirus An RNA virus that reproduces by means of a DNA molecule. It reverse-transcribes its RNA into DNA, inserts the DNA into a cellular chromosome, and then transcribes more copies of the RNA from the viral DNA. HIV and a number of cancer-causing viruses are retroviruses.

reverse transcriptase (tran-skrip′-tās) An enzyme used by retroviruses that catalyzes the synthesis of DNA on an RNA template.

RFLP *See* restriction fragment length polymorphism (RFLP).

Rhizaria One of five supergroups proposed in a current hypothesis of the evolutionary history of eukaryotes. The other four supergroups are Chromalveolata, Excavata, Unikonta, and Archaeplastida.

rhizome (rī′-zōm) A horizontal stem that grows below the ground.

rhodopsin (ro-dop′-sin) A visual pigment that is located in the rods of the vertebrate eye and that absorbs dim light.

rhythm method A form of contraception that relies on refraining from sexual intercourse when conception is most likely to occur; also called natural family planning.

ribonucleic acid (RNA) (rī-bō-nū-klā′-ik) A type of nucleic acid consisting of nucleotide monomers with a ribose sugar and the nitrogenous bases adenine (A), cytosine (C), guanine (G), and uracil (U); usually single-stranded; functions in protein synthesis, gene regulation, and as the genome of some viruses.

ribosomal RNA (rRNA) (rī′-buh-sōm′-ul) The type of ribonucleic acid that, together with proteins, makes up ribosomes; the most abundant type of RNA in most cells.

ribosome (rī′-buh-sōm) A cell structure consisting of RNA and protein organized into two subunits and functioning as the site of protein synthesis in the cytoplasm. In eukaryotic cells, the ribosomal subunits are constructed in the nucleolus.

ribozyme (rī′-bō-zīm) An RNA molecule that functions as an enzyme.

RNA interference (RNAi) A biotechnology technique used to silence the expression of specific genes. Synthetic RNA molecules with sequences that correspond to particular genes trigger the breakdown of the gene's mRNA.

RNA polymerase (puh-lim′-uh-rās) A large molecular complex that links together the growing chain of RNA nucleotides during transcription, using a DNA strand as a template.

RNA splicing The removal of introns and joining of exons in eukaryotic RNA, forming an mRNA molecule with a continuous coding sequence; occurs before mRNA leaves the nucleus.

rod A photoreceptor cell in the vertebrate retina enabling vision in dim light.

root cap A cone of cells at the tip of a plant root that protects the root's apical meristem.

root hair An outgrowth of an epidermal cell on a root, which increases the root's absorptive surface area.

root pressure The upward push of xylem sap in a vascular plant, caused by the active pumping of minerals into the xylem by root cells.

root system All of a plant's roots, which anchor it in the soil, absorb and transport minerals and water, and store food.

rough endoplasmic reticulum (reh-tik′-yuh-lum) That portion of the endoplasmic reticulum with ribosomes attached that make membrane proteins and secretory proteins.

***r*-selection** The concept that in certain (*r*-selected) populations, a high reproductive rate is the chief determinant of life history.

rule of addition A rule stating that the probability that an event can occur in two or more alternative ways is the sum of the separate probabilities of the different ways.

rule of multiplication A rule stating that the probability of a compound event is the product of the separate probabilities of the independent events.

ruminant (rū´-min-ent) An animal, such as a cow or sheep, with multiple stomach compartments housing microorganisms that can digest cellulose.

S

SA (sinoatrial) node (sỹ´-nō´-ā´-trē-ul) The pacemaker of the heart, located in the wall of the right atrium, that sets the rate and timing at which all cardiac muscle cells contract.

sac fungus *See* ascomycete.

salivary glands Glands associated with the oral cavity that secrete substances to lubricate food and begin the process of chemical digestion.

salt A compound resulting from the formation of ionic bonds; also called an ionic compound.

sapwood Light-colored, water-conducting secondary xylem in a tree. *See also* heartwood.

sarcoma (sar-kō´-muh) Cancer of the supportive tissues, such as bone, cartilage, and muscle.

sarcomere (sar´-kō-mēr) The fundamental unit of muscle contraction, composed of thin filaments of actin and thick filaments of myosin; in electron micrographs, the region between two narrow, dark lines, called Z lines, in a myofibril.

saturated fatty acid A fatty acid in which all carbons in the hydrocarbon tail are connected by single bonds and the maximum number of hydrogen atoms are attached to the carbon skeleton. Saturated fats and fatty acids solidify at room temperature.

savanna A biome dominated by grasses and scattered trees.

scanning electron microscope (SEM) A microscope that uses an electron beam to study the fine details of cell surfaces or other specimens.

scavenger An animal that feeds on the carcasses of dead animals.

schizophrenia Severe mental disturbance characterized by psychotic episodes in which patients have a distorted perception of reality.

sclera (sklār´-uh) A layer of connective tissue forming the outer surface of the vertebrate eye. The cornea is the frontal part of the sclera.

sclereid (sklār´-ē-id) In plants, a very hard sclerenchyma cell found in nutshells and seed coats.

sclerenchyma cell (skluh-ren´-kē-muh) In plants, a supportive cell with rigid secondary walls hardened with lignin.

scrotum A pouch of skin outside the abdomen that houses a testis and functions in cooling sperm, keeping them viable.

search image The mechanism that enables an animal to find a particular kind of food efficiently.

second law of thermodynamics The principle stating that every energy conversion reduces the order of the universe, increasing its entropy. Ordered forms of energy are at least partly converted to heat.

secondary consumer An organism that eats primary consumers.

secondary endosymbiosis A theory that explains the evolution of protist diversity as the product of a symbiotic association that arose when an autotrophic eukaryotic protist (a product of primary endosymbiosis) was engulfed by a heterotrophic eukaryotic protist.

secondary growth An increase in a plant's diameter, involving cell division in the vascular cambium and cork cambium.

secondary immune response The immune response elicited when an animal encounters the same antigen at some later time. The secondary immune response is more rapid, of greater magnitude, and of longer duration than the primary immune response.

secondary oocyte (ō´-uh-sīt´) A haploid cell resulting from meiosis I in oogenesis, which will become an egg after meiosis II.

secondary phloem *See* phloem.

secondary spermatocyte (sper-mat´-uh-sīt´) A haploid cell that results from meiosis I in spermatogenesis and becomes a sperm cell after meiosis II.

secondary structure The second level of protein structure; the regular local patterns of coils or folds of a polypeptide chain.

secondary succession A type of ecological succession that occurs where a disturbance has destroyed an existing biological community but left the soil intact. *See also* primary succession.

secondary xylem *See* xylem.

secretion (1) The discharge of molecules synthesized by a cell. (2) In the vertebrate kidney, the discharge of wastes from the blood into the filtrate from the nephron tubules.

seed A plant embryo packaged with a food supply within a protective covering.

seed coat A tough outer covering of a seed, formed from the outer coat (integuments) of an ovule. In a flowering plant, the seed coat encloses and protects the embryo and endosperm.

seedless vascular plants The informal collective name for lycophytes (club mosses and their relatives) and pterophytes (ferns and their relatives).

segmentation Subdivision along the length of an animal body into a series of repeated parts called segments; allows for greater flexibility and mobility.

selective permeability (per´-mē-uh-bil´-uh-tē) A property of biological membranes that allows some substances to cross more easily than others and blocks the passage of other substances altogether.

self protein A protein on the surface of an antigen-presenting cell that can hold a foreign antigen and display it to helper T cells. Each individual has a unique set of self proteins that serve as molecular markers for the body. Lymphocytes do not attack self proteins unless the proteins are displaying foreign antigens; therefore, self proteins mark normal body cells as off-limits to the immune system. The technical name for self proteins is *major histocompatibility complex (MHC) proteins. See also* nonself molecule.

self-fertilize A form of reproduction that involves fusion of sperm and egg produced by the same individual organism.

semen (sē´-mun) The sperm-containing fluid that is ejaculated by the male during orgasm.

semicircular canals Fluid-filled channels in the inner ear that detect changes in the head's rate of rotation or angular movement.

semiconservative model Type of DNA replication in which the replicated double helix consists of one old strand, derived from the old molecule, and one newly made strand.

seminal vesicle (sem´-uh-nul ves´-uh-kul) A gland in males that secretes a thick fluid that contains fructose, which provides most of the sperm's energy.

seminiferous tubule (sem´-uh-nif´-uh-rus) A coiled sperm-producing tube in a testis.

sensitive period A limited phase in an individual animal's development when learning of particular behaviors can take place.

sensory adaptation The tendency of sensory neurons to become less sensitive when they are stimulated repeatedly. For example, a prominent smell becomes unnoticeable over time.

sensory input The conduction of signals from sensory receptors to processing centers in the central nervous system.

sensory neuron A nerve cell that receives information from sensory receptors and conveys signals into the central nervous system.

sensory receptor A specialized cell or neuron that detects stimuli and sends information to the central nervous system.

sensory transduction The conversion of a stimulus signal to an electrical signal by a sensory receptor.

sepal (sē´-pul) A modified leaf of a flowering plant. A whorl of sepals encloses and protects the flower bud before it opens.

sessile An organism that is anchored to its substrate.

sex chromosome A chromosome that determines whether an individual is male or female.

sex-linked gene A gene located on a sex chromosome. In humans, the vast majority of sex-linked genes are located on the X chromosome.

sexual dimorphism (dī-mōr´-fizm) Marked differences between the secondary sex characteristics of males and females.

sexual reproduction The creation of genetically unique offspring by the fusion of two haploid sex cells (gametes), forming a diploid zygote.

sexual selection A form of natural selection in which individuals with certain inherited traits are more likely than other individuals to obtain mates.

sexually transmitted disease (STD) A contagious disease spread by sexual contact.

shared ancestral characters A character shared by members of a particular clade that originated in an ancestor that is not a member of that clade.

shared derived characters An evolutionary novelty that is unique to a particular clade.

shoot system All of a plant's stems, leaves, and reproductive structures.

short tandem repeat (STR) A series of short DNA sequences that are repeated many times in a row in the genome.

short-day plant A plant that flowers in late summer, fall, or winter, when day length is short. Short-day plants actually flower in response to long nights.

short-term memory The ability to hold information, anticipations, or goals for a time and then release them if they become irrelevant.

sickle-cell disease A genetic condition caused by a mutation in the gene for hemoglobin. The mutation causes the protein to crystallize, which deforms red blood cells into a curved shape. Such blood cells produce a cascade of symptoms that can be life-threatening.

sieve plate An end wall in a sieve-tube element that facilitates the flow of phloem sap.

sieve-tube element A food-conducting cell in a plant; also called a sieve-tube member. Chains of sieve-tube elements make up phloem tissue.

signal In behavioral ecology, a stimulus transmitted by one animal to another animal.

signal transduction pathway In cell biology, a series of molecular changes that converts a signal on a target cell's surface to a specific response inside the cell.

silencer A eukaryotic DNA sequence that functions to inhibit the start of gene transcription; may act analogously to an enhancer by binding a repressor. *See also* enhancer.

silent mutation A mutation in a gene that changes a codon to one that encodes for the same amino acid as the original codon. The amino acid sequence of the resulting polypeptide is thus unchanged.

single circulation A circulatory system with a single pump and circuit, in which blood passes from the sites of gas exchange to the rest of the body before returning to the heart.

single nucleotide polymorphism (SNP) A one-nucleotide variation in DNA sequence found within the genomes of at least 1% of a population.

single-lens eye The camera-like eye found in some jellies, polychaetes, spiders, many molluscs, and vertebrates.

sister chromatid (krō'-muh-tid) One of the two identical parts of a duplicated chromosome in a eukaryotic cell. Prior to mitosis, sister chromatids remain attached to each another at the centromere.

skeletal muscle A type of striated muscle attached to the skeleton; generally responsible for voluntary movements of the body.

skeletal system The organ system that provides body support and protects body organs, such as the brain, heart, and lungs.

small intestine The longest section of the alimentary canal. It is the principal site of the enzymatic hydrolysis of food macromolecules and the absorption of nutrients.

smooth endoplasmic reticulum That portion of the endoplasmic reticulum that lacks ribosomes.

smooth muscle A type of muscle lacking striations; responsible for involuntary body activities.

SNP *See* single nucleotide polymorphism (SNP).

social behavior Any kind of interaction between two or more animals, usually of the same species.

social learning Modification of behavior through the observation of other individuals.

sociobiology The study of the evolutionary basis of social behavior.

sodium-potassium (Na-K) pump A membrane protein that transports sodium ions out of, and potassium ions into, a cell against their concentration gradients. The process is powered by ATP.

solute (sol'-yūt) A substance that is dissolved in a solution.

solution A liquid that is a homogeneous mixture of two or more substances.

solvent The dissolving agent of a solution. Water is the most versatile solvent known.

somatic cell (sō-mat'-ik) Any cell in a multicellular organism except a sperm or egg cell or a cell that develops into a sperm or egg.

spatial learning Modification of behavior based on experience of the spatial structure of the environment.

speciation The evolution of a new species.

species diversity The variety of species that make up a community. Species diversity includes both species richness (the total number of different species) and the relative abundance of the different species in the community.

sperm A male gamete.

spermatogenesis (sper-mat'-ō-jen'-uh-sis) The formation of sperm cells.

spermicide A sperm-killing chemical (cream, jelly, or foam) that works with a barrier device as a method of contraception.

sphincter (sfink'-ter) A ringlike band of muscle fibers that regulates passage between some compartments of the alimentary canal.

spinal cord A jellylike bundle of nerve fibers that runs lengthwise inside the spine in vertebrates and integrates simple responses to certain stimuli.

spirochete A member of a group of helical bacteria that spiral through the environment by means of rotating, internal filaments.

sponge An aquatic animal characterized by a highly porous body.

sporangium (spuh-ranj'-ē-um') (plural, **sporangia**) A structure in fungi and plants in which meiosis occurs and haploid spores develop.

spore (1) In plants and algae, a haploid cell that can develop into a multicellular individual without fusing with another cell. (2) In prokaryotes, protists, and fungi, any of a variety of thick-walled life cycle stages capable of surviving unfavorable environmental conditions.

sporophyte (spōr'-uh-fīt) The multicellular diploid form in the life cycle of organisms undergoing alternation of generations; results from a union of gametes and meiotically produces haploid spores that grow into the gametophyte generation.

stabilizing selection Natural selection that favors intermediate variants by acting against extreme phenotypes.

stamen (stā'-men) A pollen-producing male reproductive part of a flower, consisting of a filament and an anther.

starch A storage polysaccharide in plants; a polymer of glucose.

start codon (kō'-don) On mRNA, the specific three-nucleotide sequence (AUG) to which an initiator tRNA molecule binds, starting translation of genetic information.

stem The part of a plant's shoot system that supports the leaves and reproductive structures.

stem cell An unspecialized cell that can divide to produce an identical daughter cell and a more specialized daughter cell, which undergoes differentiation.

steroid (ster'-oyd) A type of lipid whose carbon skeleton is in the form of four fused rings with various chemical groups attached. Examples are cholesterol, testosterone, and estrogen.

steroid hormone A lipid made from cholesterol that acts as a regulatory chemical, entering a target cell and activating the transcription of specific genes.

stigma (stig'-muh) (plural, **stigmata**) The sticky tip of a flower's carpel, which traps pollen grains.

stimulus (plural, **stimuli**) (1) In the context of a nervous system, any factor that causes a nerve signal to be generated. (2) In behavioral biology, an environmental cue that triggers a specific response.

stoma (stō'-muh) (plural, **stomata**) A pore surrounded by guard cells in the epidermis of a leaf. When stomata are open, CO_2 enters a leaf, and water and O_2 exit. A plant conserves water when its stomata are closed.

stomach An organ in a digestive tract that stores food and performs preliminary steps of digestion.

stop codon In mRNA, one of three triplets (UAG, UAA, UGA) that signal gene translation to stop.

STR *See* short tandem repeat (STR).

STR analysis Short tandem repeat analysis; a method of DNA profiling that compares the lengths of short tandem repeats (STRs) selected from specific sites within the genome.

strata (singular, **stratum**) Rock layers formed when new layers of sediment cover older ones and compress them.

stretch receptor A type of mechanoreceptor sensitive to changes in muscle length; detects the position of body parts.

stroke The death of nervous tissue in the brain, usually resulting from rupture or blockage of arteries in the head.

stroma (strō′-muh) The dense fluid within the chloroplast that surrounds the thylakoid membrane and is involved in the synthesis of organic molecules from carbon dioxide and water. Sugars are made in the stroma by the enzymes of the Calvin cycle.

stromatolite (strō-mat′-uh-līt) Layered rock that results from the activities of prokaryotes that bind thin films of sediment together.

substrate (1) A specific substance (reactant) on which an enzyme acts. Each enzyme recognizes only the specific substrate or substrates of the reaction it catalyzes. (2) A surface in or on which an organism lives.

substrate feeder An organism that lives in or on its food source, eating its way through the food.

substrate-level phosphorylation The formation of ATP by an enzyme directly transferring a phosphate group to ADP from an organic molecule (for example, one of the intermediates in glycolysis or the citric acid cycle).

sugar sink A plant organ that is a net consumer or storer of sugar. Growing roots, shoot tips, stems, and fruits are sugar sinks supplied by phloem.

sugar source A plant organ in which sugar is being produced by either photosynthesis or the breakdown of starch. Mature leaves are the primary sugar sources of plants.

sugar-phosphate backbone In a polynucleotide (DNA or RNA strand), the alternating chain of sugar and phosphate to which nitrogenous bases are attached.

superior vena cava (vē′-nuh kā′-vuh) A large vein that returns oxygen-poor blood to the heart from the upper body and head. *See also* inferior vena cava.

surface tension A measure of how difficult it is to stretch or break the surface of a liquid. Water has a high surface tension because of the hydrogen bonding of surface molecules.

surfactant A substance secreted by alveoli that decreases surface tension in the fluid that coats the alveoli.

survivorship curve A plot of the number of members of a cohort that are still alive at each age; one way to represent age-specific mortality.

suspension feeder An aquatic animal that sifts small food particles from the water; sometimes called a filter feeder.

sustainability The goal of developing, managing, and conserving Earth's resources in ways that meet the needs of people today without compromising the ability of future generations to meet theirs.

sustainable agriculture Long-term productive farming methods that are environmentally safe.

sustainable resource management Management of a natural resource so as not to damage the resource.

swim bladder A gas-filled internal sac that helps bony fishes maintain buoyancy.

symbiosis (sim′-bē-ō-sis) A physically close association between organisms of two or more species.

sympathetic division A set of neurons in the autonomic nervous system that generally prepares the body for energy-consuming activities, such as fleeing or fighting. *See also* parasympathetic division.

sympatric speciation The formation of new species in populations that live in the same geographic area.

synapse (sin′-aps) A junction between two neurons, or between a neuron and an effector cell. Electrical or chemical signals are relayed from one cell to another at a synapse.

synaptic cleft (sin-ap′-tik) In a chemical synapse, a narrow gap separating the synaptic terminal of a transmitting neuron from a receiving neuron or an effector cell.

synaptic terminal The tip of a transmitting neuron's axon, where signals are sent to another neuron or to an effector cell.

synaptic vesicle A membrane-enclosed sac containing neurotransmitter molecules at the tip of the presynaptic axon.

systematics A scientific discipline focused on classifying organisms and determining their evolutionary relationships.

systemic acquired resistance A defensive response in plants infected with a pathogenic microbe; helps protect healthy tissue from the microbe.

systemic circuit The branch of the circulatory system that supplies oxygen-rich blood to, and carries oxygen-poor blood away from, organs and tissues in the body. *See also* pulmonary circuit.

systems biology An approach to studying biology that aims to model the dynamic behavior of whole biological systems based on a study of the interactions among the system's parts.

systole (sis′-tō-lē) The contraction stage of the heart cycle, when the heart chambers actively pump blood. *See also* diastole.

T

T cell A type of lymphocyte that matures in the thymus and is responsible for the cell-mediated immune response. T cells are also involved in humoral immunity.

taiga The northern coniferous forest, characterized by long, snowy winters and short, wet summers, extending across North America and Eurasia to the southern border of the arctic tundra; also found just below alpine tundra on mountainsides in temperate zones.

tapeworm A parasitic flatworm characterized by the absence of a digestive tract.

target cell A cell that responds to a regulatory signal, such as a hormone.

taxis (tak′-sis) (plural, **taxes**) Virtually automatic orientation toward or away from a stimulus.

taxon A named taxonomic unit at any given level of classification.

taxonomy The scientific discipline concerned with naming and classifying the diverse forms of life.

technology The application of scientific knowledge for a specific purpose, often involving industry or commerce but also including uses in basic research.

telomere (tel′-uh-mēr) The repetitive DNA at each end of a eukaryotic chromosome.

telophase The fifth and final stage of mitosis, during which daughter nuclei form at the two poles of a cell. Telophase usually occurs together with cytokinesis.

temperate broadleaf forest A biome located throughout midlatitude regions, where there is sufficient moisture to support the growth of large, broadleaf deciduous trees.

temperate grassland A grassland region maintained by seasonal drought, occasional fires, and grazing by large mammals.

temperate rain forest Coniferous forests of coastal North America (from Alaska to Oregon) supported by warm, moist air from the Pacific Ocean.

temperate zones Latitudes between the tropics and the Arctic Circle in the north and the Antarctic Circle in the south; regions with milder climates than the tropics or polar regions.

temperature A measure of the intensity of heat in degrees, reflecting the average kinetic energy or speed of molecules.

tendon Fibrous connective tissue connecting a muscle to a bone.

tendril A modified leaf used by some plants to climb around a fixed structure.

terminal bud Embryonic tissue at the tip of a shoot, made up of developing leaves and a compact series of nodes and internodes.

terminator A special sequence of nucleotides in DNA that marks the end of a gene. It signals RNA polymerase to release the newly made RNA molecule and then to depart from the gene.

territory An area that one or more individuals defend and from which other members of the same species are usually excluded.

tertiary consumer (ter´-shē-ār-ē) An organism that eats secondary consumers.

tertiary structure The third level of protein structure; the overall three-dimensional shape of a polypeptide due to interactions of the R groups of the amino acids making up the chain.

testcross The mating between an individual of unknown genotype for a particular characteristic and an individual that is homozygous recessive for that same characteristic. The testcross can be used to determine the unknown genotype (homozygous dominant versus heterozygous).

testicle A testis and scrotum together.

testis (plural, **testes**) The male gonad in an animal. The testis produces sperm and, in many species, reproductive hormones.

testosterone (tes-tos´-tuh-rōn) An androgen hormone that stimulates an embryo to develop into a male and promotes male body features.

tetrad A paired set of homologous chromosomes, each composed of two sister chromatids. Tetrads form during prophase I of meiosis, when crossing over may occur.

tetrapod A vertebrate with two pairs of limbs. Tetrapods include mammals, amphibians, and birds and other reptiles.

thalamus (thal´-uh-mus) An integrating and relay center of the vertebrate forebrain; sorts and relays selected information to specific areas in the cerebral cortex.

theory A widely accepted explanatory idea that is broader in scope than a hypothesis, generates new hypotheses, and is supported by a large body of evidence.

therapeutic cloning The cloning of human cells by nuclear transplantation for therapeutic purposes, such as the generation of embryonic stem cells. See nuclear transplantation; reproductive cloning.

thermodynamics The study of energy transformation that occurs in a collection of matter. See first law of thermodynamics; second law of thermodynamics.

thermoreceptor A sensory receptor that detects heat or cold.

thermoregulation The homeostatic maintenance of internal temperature within a range that allows cells to function efficiently.

thick filament The thicker of the two protein filaments in muscle fibers, consisting of staggered arrays of myosin molecules.

thigmotropism (thig´-mō-trō´-pizm) A plant's directional growth movement in response to touch.

thin filament The thinner of the two protein filaments in muscle fibers, consisting of two strands of actin and two strands of regulatory protein coiled around each other.

three-domain system A system of taxonomic classification based on three basic groups: Bacteria, Archaea, and Eukarya.

threshold The minimum change in a membrane's voltage that must occur to generate an action potential (nerve signal).

thylakoid (thī´-luh-koyd) A flattened membranous sac inside a chloroplast. Thylakoid membranes contain chlorophyll and the molecular complexes of the light reactions of photosynthesis. A stack of thylakoids is called a granum.

thymine (T) (thī´-min) A single-ring nitrogenous base found in DNA.

thymus gland (thī´-mus) An endocrine gland in the neck region of mammals that is active in establishing the immune system; secretes several hormones that promote the development and differentiation of T cells.

thyroid gland (thī´-royd) An endocrine gland located in the neck that secretes thyroxine (T_4), triiodothyronine (T_3), and calcitonin.

thyroid-stimulating hormone (TSH) A protein hormone secreted by the anterior pituitary that stimulates the thyroid gland to secrete its hormones.

thyroxine (T_4) (thī-rok´-sin) An amine hormone secreted by the thyroid gland that stimulates metabolism in virtually all body tissues. Each molecule of this hormone contains four atoms of iodine.

Ti plasmid A bacterial plasmid that induces tumors in plant cells that the bacterium infects. Ti plasmids are often used as vectors to introduce new genes into plant cells. Ti stands for "tumor inducing."

tissue An integrated group of cells with a common function, structure, or both.

tissue system One or more tissues organized into a functional unit within a plant or animal.

tonicity The ability of a solution surrounding a cell to cause that cell to gain or lose water.

topsoil The uppermost soil layer, consisting of a mixture of particles derived from rock, living organisms, and humus.

trace element An element that is essential for life but required in extremely minute amounts.

trachea (trā´-kē-uh) (plural, **tracheae**) The windpipe; the portion of the respiratory tube that passes from the larynx to the two bronchi.

tracheal system A system of branched, air-filled tubes in insects that extends throughout the body and carries oxygen directly to cells.

tracheid (trā´-kē-id) A tapered, porous, water-conducting and supportive cell in plants. Chains of tracheids or vessel elements make up the water-conducting, supportive tubes in xylem.

trade winds The movement of air in the tropics (those regions that lie between 23.5° north latitude and 23.5° south latitude).

trait A variant of a character found within a population, such as purple or white flowers in pea plants.

trans fat An unsaturated fat, formed artificially during hydrogenation of vegetable oils, which is linked to health risks.

transcription The synthesis of RNA on a DNA template.

transcription factor In the eukaryotic cell, a protein that functions in initiating or regulating transcription. Transcription factors bind to DNA or to other proteins that bind to DNA.

transduction (1) The transfer of bacterial genes from one bacterial cell to another by a phage. (2) See sensory transduction. (3) See signal transduction pathway.

transfer RNA (tRNA) A type of ribonucleic acid that functions as an interpreter in translation. Each tRNA molecule has a specific anticodon, picks up a specific amino acid, and conveys the amino acid to the appropriate codon on mRNA.

transformation The incorporation of new genes into a cell from DNA that the cell takes up from the surrounding environment.

transgenic organism An organism that contains genes from another species.

translation The synthesis of a polypeptide using the genetic information encoded in an mRNA molecule. There is a change of "language" from nucleotides to amino acids.

translocation (1) During protein synthesis, the movement of a tRNA molecule carrying a growing polypeptide chain from the A site to the P site on a ribosome. (The mRNA travels with it.) (2) A change in a chromosome resulting from a chromosomal fragment attaching to a nonhomologous chromosome; can occur as a result of an error in meiosis or from mutagenesis.

transmission electron microscope (TEM) A microscope that uses an electron beam to study the internal structure of thinly sectioned specimens.

transpiration The evaporative loss of water from a plant.

transpiration-cohesion-tension mechanism A transport mechanism that drives the upward movement of water in plants. Transpiration exerts a pull that is relayed downward along a string of molecules held together by cohesion and helped upward by adhesion.

transport vesicle A small membranous sac in a eukaryotic cell's cytoplasm carrying molecules produced by the cell. The vesicle buds from the endoplasmic reticulum or Golgi and eventually fuses with another organelle or the plasma membrane, releasing its contents.

transposable element A transposable genetic element, or "jumping gene"; a segment of DNA that can move from one site to another within a cell and serve as an agent of genetic change.

TRH (TSH-releasing hormone) A peptide hormone that triggers the release of TSH (thyroid-stimulating hormone), which in turn stimulates the thyroid gland.

trial-and-error learning Learning to associate a particular behavior with a positive or negative effect.

triiodothyronine (T_3) (trī´-ī-ō-dō-thī´-rō-nīn) An amine hormone secreted by the thyroid gland that stimulates metabolism in virtually all body tissues. Each molecule of this hormone contains four atoms of iodine.

trimester In human development, one of three 3-month-long periods of pregnancy.

triplet code A set of three-nucleotide-long "words" that specify the amino acids for polypeptide chains. *See* genetic code.

trisomy 21 *See* Down syndrome.

trophoblast (trŏf′-ō-blast) In mammalian development, the outer portion of a blastocyst. Cells of the trophoblast secrete enzymes that enable the blastocyst to implant in the endometrium of the mother's uterus.

tropical forest A terrestrial biome characterized by high levels of precipitation and warm temperatures year-round.

tropics Latitudes between 23.5° north and south.

tropism (trō′-pizm) A growth response that makes a plant grow toward or away from a stimulus.

true coelom A body cavity completely lined with tissue derived from mesoderm.

true-breeding Referring to organisms for which sexual reproduction produces offspring with inherited traits identical to those of the parents. The organisms are homozygous for the characteristics under consideration.

tubal ligation A means of sterilization in which a segment of each of a woman's two oviducts (fallopian tubes) is removed. The ends of the tubes are then tied closed to prevent eggs from reaching the uterus (commonly referred to as having the "tubes tied").

tuber An enlargement at the end of a rhizome in which food is stored.

tumor An abnormal mass of rapidly growing cells that forms within otherwise normal tissue.

tumor-suppressor gene A gene whose product inhibits cell division, thereby preventing uncontrolled cell growth. A mutation that deactivates a tumor-suppressor gene may lead to cancer.

tundra A biome at the northernmost limits of plant growth and at high altitudes, characterized by dwarf woody shrubs, grasses, mosses, and lichens.

tunicate One of a group of invertebrate chordates, also known as sea squirts.

U

ultimate cause In animal behavior, the evolutionary reason for a behavior.

ultimate question In animal behavior, a question that addresses the evolutionary basis for behavior.

ultrasound imaging A technique for examining a fetus in the uterus. High-frequency sound waves echoing off the fetus are used to produce an image of the fetus.

uniform dispersion pattern A pattern in which the individuals of a population are evenly distributed over an area.

Unikonta One of five supergroups proposed in a current hypothesis of the evolutionary history of eukaryotes. The other four supergroups are Chromalveolata, Rhizaria, Excavata, and Archaeplastida.

unsaturated fatty acid A fatty acid that has one or more double bonds between carbons in the hydrocarbon tail and thus lacks the maximum number of hydrogen atoms. Unsaturated fats and fatty acids do not solidify at room temperature.

uracil (U) (yū′-ruh-sil) A single-ring nitrogenous base found in RNA.

urea (yū-rē′-ah) A soluble form of nitrogenous waste excreted by mammals and most adult amphibians.

ureter (yū-rē′-ter or yū′-reh-ter) A duct that conveys urine from the kidney to the urinary bladder.

urethra (yū-rē′-thruh) A duct that conveys urine from the urinary bladder to the outside. In the male, the urethra also conveys semen out of the body during ejaculation.

uric acid (yū′-rik) An insoluble precipitate of nitrogenous waste excreted by land snails, insects, birds, and some reptiles.

urinary bladder The pouch where urine is stored prior to elimination.

urinary system The organ system that forms and excretes urine while regulating the amount of water and ions in the body fluids.

urine Concentrated filtrate produced by the kidneys and excreted by the bladder.

uterus (yū′-ter-us) In the reproductive system of a mammalian female, the organ where the development of young occurs; the womb.

V

vaccination (vak′-suh-nā′-shun) A procedure that presents the immune system with a harmless variant or derivative of a pathogen, thereby stimulating the immune system to mount a long-term defense against the pathogen.

vaccine (vak-sēn′) A harmless variant or derivative of a pathogen used to stimulate a host organism's immune system to mount a long-term defense against the pathogen.

vacuole (vak′-ū-ōl) A membrane-enclosed sac that is part of the endomembrane system of a eukaryotic cell and has diverse functions.

vagina (vuh-jī′-nuh) Part of the female reproductive system between the uterus and the outside opening; the birth canal in mammals; also accommodates the male's penis and receives sperm during copulation.

vas deferens (vas def′-er-enz) (plural, **vasa deferentia**) Part of the male reproductive system that conveys sperm away from the testis; the sperm duct; in humans, the tube that conveys sperm between the epididymis and the common duct that leads to the urethra.

vascular bundle (vas′-kyū-ler) A strand of vascular tissues (both xylem and phloem) in a plant stem.

vascular cambium (vas′-kyū-ler kam′-bē-um) During secondary growth of a plant, the cylinder of meristematic cells, surrounding the xylem and pith, that produces secondary xylem and phloem.

vascular cylinder The central cylinder of vascular tissue in a plant root.

vascular plant A plant with xylem and phloem, including club mosses, ferns, gymnosperms, and angiosperms.

vascular tissue Plant tissue consisting of cells joined into tubes that transport water and nutrients throughout the plant body.

vascular tissue system A transport system formed by xylem and phloem throughout the plant. Xylem transports water and minerals, while phloem transports sugars and other organic nutrients.

vasectomy (vuh-sek′-tuh-mē) Surgical removal of a section of the two sperm ducts (vasa deferentia) to prevent sperm from reaching the urethra; a means of sterilization in males.

vector In molecular biology, a piece of DNA, usually a plasmid or a viral genome, that is used to move genes from one cell to another.

vein (1) In animals, a vessel that returns blood to the heart. (2) In plants, a vascular bundle in a leaf, composed of xylem and phloem.

ventilation A mechanism that provides for the flow of air or water over a respiratory surface.

ventral Pertaining to the underside, or bottom, of a bilaterally symmetric animal.

ventricle (ven′-truh-kul) (1) A heart chamber that pumps blood out of the heart. (2) A space in the vertebrate brain filled with cerebrospinal fluid.

venule (ven′-yūl) A vessel that conveys blood between a capillary bed and a vein.

vertebra (ver′-tuh-bruh) (plural, **vertebrae**) One of a series of segmented skeletal units that enclose the nerve cord, making up the backbone of a vertebrate animal.

vertebral column Backbone, composed of a series of segmented units called vertebrae.

vertebrate (ver′-tuh-brāt) A chordate animal with a backbone. Vertebrates include lampreys, chondrichthyans, ray-finned fishes, lobe-finned fishes, amphibians, reptiles (including birds), and mammals.

vesicle (ves′-i-kul) A sac made of membrane in the cytoplasm of a eukaryotic cell.

vessel element A short, open-ended, water-conducting and supportive cell in plants. Chains of vessel elements or tracheids make up the water-conducting, supportive tubes in xylem.

vestigial structure A feature of an organism that is a historical remnant of a structure that served a function in the organism's ancestors.

GLOSSARY

villus (vil′-us) (plural, **villi**) (1) A finger-like projection of the inner surface of the small intestine. (2) A finger-like projection of the chorion of the mammalian placenta. Large numbers of villi increase the surface areas of these organs.

viroid (vī′-royd) A plant pathogen composed of molecules of naked, circular RNA several hundred nucleotides long.

virus A microscopic particle capable of infecting cells of living organisms and inserting its genetic material. Viruses are generally not considered to be alive because they do not display all of the characteristics associated with life.

visceral mass (vis′-uh-rul) One of the three main parts of a mollusc, containing most of the internal organs.

visual acuity The ability of the eyes to distinguish fine detail. Normal visual acuity in humans is usually reported as "20/20 vision."

vital capacity The maximum volume of air that a mammal can inhale and exhale with each breath.

vitamin An organic nutrient that an organism requires in very small quantities. Many vitamins serve as coenzymes or parts of coenzymes.

vitreous humor (vit′-rē-us hyū′-mer) A jellylike substance filling the space behind the lens in the vertebrate eye; helps maintain the shape of the eye.

vocal cord One of a pair of bands of elastic tissue in the larynx. Air rushing past the tensed vocal cords makes them vibrate, producing sounds.

vulva The collective term for the external female genitalia.

W

water mold A fungus-like protist in the supergroup Chromalveolata.

water vascular system In echinoderms, a radially arranged system of water-filled canals that branch into extensions called tube feet. The system provides movement and circulates water, facilitating gas exchange and waste disposal.

wavelength The distance between crests of adjacent waves, such as those of the electromagnetic spectrum.

westerlies Winds that blow from west to east.

wetland An ecosystem intermediate between an aquatic ecosystem and a terrestrial ecosystem. Wetland soil is saturated with water permanently or periodically.

white blood cell *See* leukocyte.

white matter Regions within the central nervous system composed mainly of axons, with their whitish myelin sheaths.

whole-genome shotgun method A method for determining the DNA sequence of an entire genome. After a genome is cut into small fragments, each fragment is sequenced and then placed in the proper order.

wild-type trait The version of a character that most commonly occurs in nature.

wood Secondary xylem of a plant. *See also* heartwood; sapwood.

wood ray A column of parenchyma cells that radiates from the center of a log and transports water to its outer living tissues.

X

X chromosome inactivation In female mammals, the inactivation of one X chromosome in each somatic cell.

xylem (zī′-lum) The nonliving portion of a plant's vascular system that provides support and conveys xylem sap from the roots to the rest of the plant. Xylem is made up of vessel elements and/or tracheids, water-conducting cells. Primary xylem is derived from the procambium. Secondary xylem is derived from the vascular cambium in plants exhibiting secondary growth.

xylem sap The solution of inorganic nutrients conveyed in xylem tissue from a plant's roots to its shoots.

Y

yeast A single-celled fungus that inhabits liquid or moist habitats and reproduces asexually by simple cell division or by the pinching of small buds off a parent cell.

yellow bone marrow A tissue found within the central cavities of long bones, consisting mostly of stored fat.

yolk sac An extraembryonic membrane that develops from the endoderm. The yolk sac produces the embryo's first blood cells and germ cells and gives rise to the allantois.

Z

zoned reserve An extensive region of land that includes one or more areas that are undisturbed by humans. The undisturbed areas are surrounded by lands that have been altered by human activity.

zooplankton (zō′-ō-plank′-tun) Animals that drift in aquatic environments.

zygomycete (zī′-guh-mī-sēt) Member of a group of fungi characterized by a sturdy structure called a zygosporangium, in which meiosis produces haploid spores.

zygote (zī′-gōt) The diploid fertilized egg, which results from the union of a sperm cell nucleus and an egg cell nucleus.

zygote fungus *See* zygomycete.

Index

Page numbers with *f* indicate figure, *t* indicate table, and those in bold indicate page where listed as a key term.

2, 4-D herbicide, 669
3' end, DNA, 189
3-phosphoglyceric acid (3-PGA), 116
5' end, DNA, 189

A

Abdomen, 378, 380
Abiotic factors, **680**, 683, 688
Abiotic reservoirs, **752**–53
Abiotic synthesis, 294–96
Abnormal behavior, 714
ABO blood groups, **167**
Abortion, 545
Abscisic acid (ABA), 664*t*, **667**
Abscission, leaf, 667–69
Absorption, **355**, **431**, 439. *See also* Digestion
Abstinence, 545
Abundance, relative, 746
Acanthostega, 395
Accommodation, visual, 596*f*
Acetylcholine, **570**, 574–75, 614
Acetyl CoA, **96**–97, 102
Achondroplasia, 162*t*, **163**
Acidic solutions, 28
Acid precipitation, **29**, 695, 755
Acid reflux, 437
Acids, **28**
    acid precipitation, ocean acidification, and, 29
    DNA and RNA as nucleic, 184–85 (*see also* Nucleic acids)
    sensitivity of life to, 28
    stomach, 433, 436–37
Acquired characters, 258
Acquired immunity. *See* Adaptive immunity
Acquired immunodeficiency syndrome. *See* AIDS (acquired immunodeficiency syndrome)
Acromegaly, 522
Acrosome, **546**
Actin, 65, 132, **612**–13
Actinomycetes, 327
Action potentials, **567**
    conversion of air pressure waves to, perceived as sound by ears, 592–93
    conversion of stimulus energy to, by sensory receptors, 588–89
    nerve signals as, 567–68
    in sensory reception, 588–89
Activation energy (E_A), **83**
Activators, **211**, 214
Active immunity, **489**
Active sites, **84**
Active transport, **78**, 512, 566–68
Adam's apple, 434
Adaptations, **257**. *See also* Evolution; Natural selection
    allowing long lives for some trees, 640
    behavioral (*see* Behavior)
    birds as feathered reptiles with flight, 398
    camouflage, 259
    circulatory system, 467
    as compromises, 273
    correlation of structure and function in, 413
    of gills for gas exchange in aquatic environments, 456–57
    to global climate change, 769
    human skin colors as, to sunlight, 407
    natural selection, adaptive evolution, and, 269
    of organisms by natural selection to abiotic and biotic factors, 683
    of plants to herbivory, 742–43

plant terrestrial, 342–43
of prey species to predation, 742
prokaryotic capacities for rapid, to environmental changes, 322
as property of life, 2
structural, for external exchange between organ systems and environment, 424–25
of thermoregulation to balance heat gain and loss, 506–7
of vertebrate digestive systems as related to diet, 441
Adaptive evolution, 269. *See also* Adaptations; Evolution
Adaptive immunity, **489**. *See also* Immune systems
    as acquired immunity to specific invaders, 489
    antibodies as weapons of humoral immune response of, 494
    antibody marking of antigens for elimination and, 495
    dependence of, on molecular fingerprints of self proteins, 500
    destruction of infected body cells by cytotoxic T cells of, 498
    dual defense by lymphocytes of, 490–91
    increased susceptibility to opportunistic infections from HIV destruction of helper T cells of, 498–99
    innate immunity vs., 485 (*see also* Innate immunity)
    monoclonal antibodies of, as powerful tools in laboratories and clinics, 496
    mustering of defensive forces against specific antigens by clonal selection of, 492–93
    rapid evolution of HIV and, 499
    specific regions of antigens for antibody binding in, 491
    stimulation of humoral and cell-mediated immune responses by helper T cells of, 497
Adaptive radiations, **286**, 304, 399
Adderall, 571
Addiction, 577
Addition, rule of, 160
Adelie penguins, 768
Adenine (A), 46–47, 184, **185**
Adenoid, 488*f*
Adhesion, **26**, **646**
Adipose tissue, **417**, 423, 447, 506–7
ADP (adenosine diphosphate), 82, 94–97
Adrenal cortex, **528**
Adrenal glands, 501, 520–21*t*, **528**–29
Adrenaline (epinephrine). *See* Epinephrine (adrenaline)
Adrenal medulla, **528**
Adrenocorticotropic hormone (ACTH), 521*t*, 522, **528**–29
Adult stem cells, **223**, 481
Aerobic denitrification, 755
Aerobic exercise, 615
Aerobic respiration, 297, 615–16. *See also* Cellular respiration
Aerosols, 120
Africa, 405–6
African Americans, 168
African plums, 354*f*
Agar, 336
Agarose, 243
Agent Orange, 665
Age structures, **733**–34

Agglutination, antigen, 495
Aggression, 715
Aging, plant, 630, 640, 668–69
Agonistic behavior, **716**, 718
Agre, Peter, 78
Agriculture
    abnormal behaviors caused by chemicals of, 714
    animal cloning in, 223
    artificial selection in, 258
    beginnings of, 622
    C_3 crop plants in, 117
    degradation of aquatic ecosystems by, 756
    ecosystem services and, 757
    fungal parasites and pathogens in, 359
    genetically modified and transgenic organisms in, 239
    greenhouse gases from, 767
    habitat loss and, 764
    integrated pest management in, 731
    monocultures in, 639, 746
    in nitrogen cycle, 755
    organic farming and sustainable, 654
    phosphorus cycle and, 754
    plant cloning in, 221
    plant diversity and, 354
    products of recombinant DNA technology for, 236–37
    research in, to improve yields and nutritional value of crops, 654–55
    secondary succession and, 748
    soil degradation by, 653
    uses of plant hormones in, 669
Agrobacterium tumefaciens, 239
AIDS (acquired immunodeficiency syndrome), 199, **203**, **498**–99. *See also* HIV (human immunodeficiency virus)
Air
    breathing of, 395, 457
    nitrogen in, 754
    plant adaptations for obtaining nutrients from, 342–43, 644
    pollution of, 361, 459, 695, 764–65
Air pressure waves, hearing and, 592–93
Alarm calls
    kin selection and, 717
    social learning and, 708–9
Albatrosses, 398
Albinism, 162*t*
Albumen, 397
Alcohol consumption, 440, 477, 555, 571
Alcohol fermentation, **101**
Alcohols, 35, 37
Aldehydes, 35
Aldoses, 37
Aldosterone, 529
Algae, **330**
    biofuel production from, 107, 119, 333
    eutrophication and blooms of, 756
    in freshwater biomes, 688
    land plants vs., 342–43*f*
    lichens as symbiotic associations of fungi and, 361
    red and green, as archaeplastids, 336
    secondary endosymbiosis of, 331
Ali, Muhammad, 583*f*
Alimentary canals, **432**–33
Alkaline solutions, 28
Alkaptonuria, 190
Allantois, 397, 399, 554, **555**

INDEX

INDEX

Communication, **711**
  between animals, 711
  eukaryotic cell, 56–57, 69
  nervous system, 418
Communities, 3, 680, **740–49**
  adaptations of plants to herbivory in, 742–43
  adaptations of prey species to predation in, 742
  benefits of mutualism to organisms in, 741
  community ecology as study of organisms and populations of, 740
  devastation of, by invasive species, 749
  disproportionate impact of keystone species on diversity of, 747
  disturbance and ecological succession in, 748
  ecosystems as including, 750
  effects of global climate change on, 768–69
  effects of parasites and pathogens on composition of, 743
  influences of regional climate on distribution of terrestrial, 684–85
  interconnection of food chains and formation of food webs in, 745
  interspecific competition for limited shared resources in, 741
  interspecific interactions of, 740
  in life's hierarchy of organization, 3, 680, 740
  species richness and relative abundance in species diversity of, 746
  of terrestrial biomes, 689
  trophic structure of, as key factor in dynamics of, 744
Community ecology, 740. *See also* Communities
Compact bone, 609
Companion cells, **629**
Comparative anatomy, 262
Competition
  agonistic behavior and, 716
  interspecific, 740–41
  intraspecific, 728
Competitive inhibitors, **85**
Complementary base pairing, DNA, 47
Complementary DNA (cDNA), 219, **235**
Complement systems, **486**, 495
Complete digestive tracts, **373**
Complete dominance, **166–67**
Complete metamorphosis, **380**
Compost, **651**, 653
Compound eyes, **595**
Compounds, **18**, 24. *See also* Molecules; Organic compounds
Computed tomography (CT), 422
Computer models, 187*f*
Concentration gradient, **75**
Conception, **554**. *See also* Fertilization
Condoms, 499, 545
Conduction, 506
Cones, pine tree, 348–49
Cones, retinal, **598**
Congenital disorders, human, 148
Coniferous forests, **693**
Conifers, 345, 348–49, 621. *See also* Gymnosperms
Conjugation, **204–5**
Conjunctiva, **596**
Conjunctivitis, 596
Connective tissue, 44, **417**
Conservation
  organizations for, 408
  problems and opportunities posed by imprinting for programs in, 705
  soil, 653
Conservation biology, 760–69, **770–79**
  establishing protected areas to slow biodiversity loss in, 772
  loss of biodiversity and, 761–69 (*see also* Biodiversity)
  loss of tiger species and, 761

protection of endangered populations as one goal of, 770
  restoration of degraded habitats by restoration ecology as developing science in, 776–77
  sustainable development as ultimate goal of, 777
  sustaining ecosystems and landscapes as priority for, 771
  Yellowstone to Yukon Conservation Initiative to preserve biodiversity by connecting protected areas in, 774–75
  zoned reserves as attempts by, to reverse ecosystem disruption, 773
Constipation, 441
Constriction, blood vessel, 507
Consumers
  in biogeochemical cycles, 752–53
  in ecosystems, 5
  in energy flow, 750
  in trophic structures, 744
Continental drift, macroevolution and, 300–301
Continental shelves, **686**
Contraband animal products, 245
Contraception, **545**, 732–33
Contractile proteins, 43, 418
Contractile vacuoles, 62
Contraction, muscle, 612–15
Contrast, 52–53
Control. *See* Regulation
Control groups, 11
Controlled experiments, **11**
Control points, gene regulation, 216, 217
Convection, 506
Convergent evolution, **308**, 415, 689
Cooling, evaporative, 26
Cooperation, 715, 717
Copulation, **535**, 545. *See also* Fertilization; Mating
Copying, DNA. *See* DNA replication
Coquerel's sifaka, 401*f*
Coral reefs
  algae on, 336
  cnidarians and, 371
  global climate change and bleaching of, 768
  keystone species of, 747
  loss of biodiversity of, 762
  marine organisms of, 686–87
  microbes and, 319
  mutualisms of, 741
  ocean acidification and, 29
  pollution of, 695
  protists of, 332
Coral snakes, 10–11
Cork, **632–33**
Cork cambium, **633**
Cormorants, 277–78, 282
Corn, 636, 638, 651, 670
Corn leaf blight, 746
Cornea, **596**
Corn smut, 359
Coronary arteries, 470
Corpus callosum, **577**, 579
Corpus luteum, **536**, 541–43
Corridors, movement, 771, 774–75
Cortex, **626**
Corticosteroids, **529**
Cortisone, 529
Costa Rica, 773
Cost-benefit analysis, foraging, 710
Cotton, 285
Cotyledons, **623**, 638
Coughing, 460
Countercurrent exchange, **456–57**
Countercurrent heat exchange, **507**
Courtship rituals, 280–81, 398, 535, 699, 702, 712–13. *See also* Mating

Covalent bonds, **22–23**
Cowbirds, 771
Coyotes, 441
Crabs, 379
Cranial nerves, 573
Craniates, **390–91**. *See also* Vertebrates
Crawling, 604–5
Crayfish, 379
C-reactive protein (CRP), 473
Creatine phosphate, 615
Creosote bushes, 639
Cretaceous mass extinction, 302–3
Creutzfeldt-Jakob disease, 203
Crick, Francis, 186–87, 190
Cri du chat (cry of the cat) syndrome, 148
Crime scene investigations. *See* Forensics
Cristae, **63**
Crocodiles, 311, 397
Crohn's disease, 500
Crop, digestive, **432**
Crops, agricultural. *See also* Agriculture
  angiosperms as, 352
  evolution of, 285
  genetically modified and transgenic organisms for, 240
  human breeding of, 258, 622
  importance of plant diversity to, 354
  improvement of yields and nutritional value of, 654–55
  root crops, 625
Cross-bridges, muscle contraction and, 613, 615, 616
Crosses, genetic, **155–59**
Cross-fertilization, **155–59**
Cross-fostering experiments, 703
Crossing over, **142**
  bacterial DNA transfer in, 204–5
  genetic variability from, 142–43, 265
  mapping genes using data from, 174
  production of new combinations of alleles by, 172–73
Cross-pollination, 622
Crust, 300
Crustaceans, **379**
C soil horizon, 652
CT (computed tomography), 422
CT-PET scanners, 422
Cuboidal epithelium, 416
Cubozoans, 371
Culex pipiens, 380
Culture, science and, 11
Cupula, 594
Currents
  freshwater, 688
  ocean, 685
Cuticle, 342, **373, 626**
Cuttings, 221, 639
Cuttlefish, 375, 712
Cyanide, 99
Cyanobacteria, 323, **327**, 361, 756
Cycling, nutrient, 5, 750, 752–56
Cystic fibrosis (CF), **162–63**, 164, 239, 324
Cytokinesis, **129**, 131*f*, 132, 139*f*
Cytokinins, 664*t*, **666**
Cytoplasm, **55**, 194
Cytosine (C), 46–47, 184, **185**, 213
Cytoskeleton, **65**
  human sperm motility problems and, 67
  movement of cilia and flagella of, 66
  organization of cell structure and function by, 57, 65, 69*t*
  plant cell wall functions and, 68
  support and regulation functions of extracellular matrix and, 67
  types of cell junctions in animal tissue and, 68
Cytotoxic T cells, **497**, 498

INDEX

hypothalamus and pituitary gland as
connections between nervous
systems and, 522–23
vertebrate, 520–23
Endocytosis, **79**, 478
Endoderm, 366, 368, **549**, 554
Endodermis, **626**
Endomembrane system, **59–63**
cell maintenance by vacuoles in, 62
cell products and Golgi apparatus in, 61
connection of organelles of, 59, 69
endoplasmic reticulum as biosynthetic factory
in, 60–61
lysosomes as digestive compartments in, 62
peroxisomes and connection of organelles
of, 63
Endometrium, **537**
Endoplasmic reticulum (ER), 58, **59**–61, 69*t*, 614
Endorphins, **523**, 571
Endoskeletons, **382**, 390, **607**
Endosperm, **635**
Endospores, **322**, 329
Endosymbiont theory, **64**, 108, 331
Endosymbiosis, 64, 327, 330–31
Endothermic organisms, **398**
Endotherms, 469, **506**
Endotoxins, **328**
Energy, **80**
as animal diet requirement, 442
as capacity to perform work, 80
chemical reactions and release or storage of, 81
detection of mechanical, by mechanoreceptors,
590–91*f*
eukaryotic cell processing of, 56–57, 63–64, 69
(*see also* Cellular respiration;
Fermentation; Photosynthesis)
expense of, in active transport of solutes across
plasma membranes, 78
fats as lipids for storing, 40
flow of, in ecosystems, 5
glycolysis energy investment phase, 94–95*f*
glycolysis energy payoff phase, 94–95*f*
processing of, as property of life, 2
prokaryotic sources of, 323
renewable sources of (*see* Biofuels)
as requirement of animal diet, 442
sources of, as abiotic factor for life in
biosphere, 682
stimuli as, 588 (*see also* Stimuli (stimulus))
thermodynamics and transformations
of, 80–81
Energy barriers, enzymatic lowering of, 83
Energy budgets, ecosystem, 750–51
Energy coupling, **81**–82
Energy flow, **750**–52
Enhancers, **214**
Enteric division, autonomic nervous system,
574–**75**
Entomologists, 380
Entropy, **80**–81
Environmental issues. *See also* Environments
acid precipitation and ocean acidification, 29,
695, 755
amphibian decline, 396
bioremediation of pollution using prokaryotes,
324–25
carcinogens, 227
chemical pollutants causing abnormal animal
behaviors, 714
degradation of aquatic ecosystems by nutrient
inflow, 756
ecological footprints of overconsumption,
734–35
genetically modified organisms, 240
global climate change (*see* Global climate
change)
human sperm motility problems, 67

insights of ecology into, 681
mass extinctions, 302–3
oil spills, 325, 360, 739, 764
ozone layer depletion, 120, 303
pollution (*see* Pollution)
sustainable resource management, 731
Environmental Protection Agency
(EPA), 714
Environments. *See also*
Environmental issues
allergies as overreactions to allergens of, 501
animal behavior as result of genetics and,
702–3
behavioral adaptations to (*see* Behavior)
of biosphere, 679 (*see also* Biosphere)
diabetes and, 527
ecology as study of interactions of organisms
with, 680
effects of, on human characters, 170
exchanges of matter and energy between organisms and, 5
extreme, of archaea, 326
gene regulation in response to changes in, 210
gills as adapted for gas exchange in
aquatic, 456–57
homeostatic regulation of internal,
by animals, 425
human behavior as result of genetics and, 719
human impacts on, 12
natural selection and, 273
plant responses to, 670–75
prokaryotic capacities for rapid adaptations to
changes in, 322
prokaryotic gene regulation in response to,
210–11
reproductive cloning and, 222–23
response to, as property of life, 2
sex determination by, 175
structural adaptations for external exchange
between organ systems and, 424–25
Enzymes, **36**, **83**–85
acceleration of chemical reactions by lowering
of energy barriers by, 83
in cellular respiration of organic
compounds, 102–3
cutting and pasting DNA using restriction, 234
digestive, 438–39
in DNA replication, 188–89
drugs, pesticides, and poisons as
inhibitors of, 85
in formation of polymers, 296
gene regulation and, 210–11
Golgi apparatus, 61
lysosomal, 62
membrane proteins as, 74
one gene–one enzyme hypothesis and, 190
optimal conditions, cofactors, and catalytic
cycle of, 84
as proteins, 43
ribosomes and synthesis of, 59
ribozymes as, 296
R plasmids, antibiotic resistance, and, 205
rubisco as, 116, 118
selectivity of catalysis by, 84
smooth ER and, 60
storage and breakdown of food in stomachs
with, 433, 436–37
tRNA in transcription and, 195
Eosinophils, 479
Epidemiology, 446
Epidermis, 423, **626**
Epididymis, **538**
Epigenetic inheritance, 212–**13**
Epiglottis, 434
Epileptic seizures, 566, 579
Epinephrine (adrenaline), 472, 501, 518, 521*t*,
528, 570–71

Epiphytes, 657
Epithelial tissue, **416**, 423
Epitopes. *See* Antigens
EPO. *See* Erythropoietin (EPO)
Equations, photosynthesis, 110
Equatorial tropical forests, 690
Equilibrium
diffusion and, 75
equilibrium receptors and, 594
genetic, 266–67
punctuated, 289
Erectile dysfunction, 559, 571
Erection, 539, 571
Ergots, 359
Erosion, soil, 653, 757
Erythrocytes (red blood cells), 76, 162*t*, 168, 216,
417, 474, **479**–81
Erythropoietin (EPO), **480**
Escherichia coli, 127, 182–83, 210, 232, 236–37*t*,
247, 321, 326, 441
Esophagus, **432**, 434–35
Essential amino acids, **443**
Essential elements, 18, **650**
Essential fatty acids, **443**
Essential inorganic plant nutrients, 650.
See also Nutrients, plant
Essential minerals, 444–45
Essential nutrients, 442–**43**
Essential vitamins, 444–45
Estradiol, 35*f*
Estrogens, 521*t*, **529**, 536, 542–43, 555,
558–59, 610
Estuaries, **687**
Ethanol, 101, 107
Ethical issues
on gene therapies, 241
on genetic testing technologies, 165
on human cloning, 222–23
on synthetic chemicals in agriculture, 669
Ethyl alcohol, 101, 107
Ethylene, 664*t*, **668**–69
Eucalyptus trees, 656
Eudicots, **623**, 626–27*f*, 636, 638
Euglena, 330
Eukarya domain, **7**, 313, 325.
See also Eukaryotes
Eukaryote (term), 55
Eukaryotes
alternative RNA splicing in, 214–15
cells of (*see* Eukaryotic cells)
differences between bacteria, archaea,
and, 325
diversity of protists as, 330–31
Eukarya domain of, 7, 313, 325
evolution of multicellularity in, 337
multiple gene expression regulation mechanisms in, 217
origin of, 297
protein regulation of transcription in, 214
Eukaryotic cell cycle, 128–36. *See also* Cell
division
anchorage, cell density, and chemical
growth factors affecting cell division
in, 133
cancer cell production of malignant
tumors in, 135
chromosome duplication in, 128
cytokinesis differences for plant and
animal cells in, 132
growth, cell replacement, and asexual
reproduction by mitosis in, 136
growth factor signals of cell cycle control
system of, 134
stages of cell division and multiplication
of cells in, 129
stages of cell division by mitosis in,
130–31

INDEX

INDEX

osmoregulation by, 508
stress response and, 529
Killer whales, 9
Killifish, 730–31
Kilocalories (kcals), **91**, 442, **442**
Kinesis, **706**
Kinetic energy, **80**, 89
Kingdoms, 7, **309**, 313, 344–45
King penguins, 701
King snakes, 10–11
Kin selection, **717**
Kissimmee River Restoration Project, 776–77
Klamath-Siskiyou Wilderness, 762
Klinefelter syndrome, 147
Knee-jerk replex, 564*f*
Knuckle walkers, 402
Koala bears, 441, 710
Koch, Robert, 328
Koch's postulates, 328–29
Krebs, Hans, 96
Krebs cycle. *See* Citric acid cycle
K-selection, **730–31**

L

Labels, food, 240, 446
Labia majora, **537**
Labia minora, **537**
Labor, **558**
Laboratories, monoclonal antibodies in, 496
Labrador retrievers, 153, 158–59
lac operon, 210–11
Lactase, 33, 36, 43, 47, 250, 438*t*–39
Lactate, 101
Lactation, 559
Lactic acid fermentation, **101**, 615
Lactose, 210–11, 439
Lactose intolerance, 33, 36, 47, 250, 439
Lakes, 688
Lamarck, Jean Baptiste, 256
Lambda phage, 200
Lamellae, 456–57
Lampreys, 391
Lancelets, **383**, 390
Land
    colonization of, 297 (*see also* Terrestrial biomes)
    facilitation of tetrapod movement onto, by evolution of lungs, 458
    plant adaptations to life on, 342–43
Landforms, local climate and, 685
Landmarks, spatial learning and, 706
Landscape ecology, **771**
Landscapes, **680**, **771**
Language, 578
Lap band surgery, 448
Large intestines, **440**–41
Larvae (larva), **366**
Larynx, 434, **458**
Laser-assisted in situ keratomileusis (LASIK), 597
Lateralization, **578**–79
Lateral line system, **392**
Lateral meristems, **632**
Latitudes, polar ice at high, 694
Laurasia, 300–301
Law enforcement. *See* Forensics
Law of energy conservation, 80
Law of independent assortment, 157, **158–60**, 171–72
Law of segregation, **156–57**, 160, 171
LDLs (low-density lipoproteins).
    See Low-density lipoproteins (LDLs)
Leaf molds, 647
Leakey, Louis, 718
Learning, **703–9**
    animal associative, as associating stimuli or behaviors with responses, 708

animal movement as depending on cognitive maps of, 707
animal movement as simple response to stimuli or requiring spatial, 706
habituation as, 703
imprinting as, posing problems and opportunities for conservation programs, 705
imprinting as, requiring innate behaviors and experience, 704
limbic system and, 581
problem-solving behavior and cognition in, 709
social, employing observation and imitation of others, 708–9
Leaves (leaf), **624**. *See also* Shoots
    abscission of, 667, 668–69
    modified, 625
    of monocots and eudicots, 623*f*
    photosynthesis by, 109 (*see also* Photosynthesis)
    as plant organs, 342, 624
Leber's congenital amaursis (LCA), 241
Lederberg, Joshua, 232
Leeches, **377**, 572
Left cerebral hemisphere, 578
Legumes, 656, 754–55
Lemba people, 177
Lemmings, 729
Lemurs, 1, 9, 89, 400, 408, 414, 711, 772, 777
Lenses, **595**–97
Leopard gecko, 408
Leptin, 447
Lethal autosomal disorders, 163
Leucine, 42, 191
Leukemias, **135**, 148, 241, **481**
Leukocytes (white blood cells), **479**
    diabetes mellitus and, 527
    five types of, 479
    functions of, 417
    HIV and, 203
    as innate immune cells, 486 (*see also* Innate immunity)
    karyotypes and, 144
    leukemias of, 135, 148, 241, 481
    lysosomal enzymes and, 62
    stem cells and, 481
Lewinsky, Monica, 245
Libraries
    cDNA, 235
    genomic, 235–36
Lichens, 357, **361**, 748
Life
    abiotic synthesis of organic molecules and origin of, 295
    acid precipitation, ocean acidification, and threats to, 29
    biology, evolution, and everyday, 12
    biology as scientific study of, 2 (*see also* Biology; Science)
    carbon and molecular diversity of, 34
    cells as structural and functional units of, 4 (*see also* Cells)
    chemical basis of (*see* Chemistry)
    common properties of all forms of, 2
    conditions on early Earth and origin of, 294, 296
    constructing phylogenetic tree of, as work in progress, 314
    diversity of (*see* Biodiversity)
    emergent properties in hierarchy of organization of, 3, 414
    evolution as explanation of unity and diversity of, 1, 8–9 (*see also* Evolution)
    forms of, as biotic factors (*see* Biotic factors)
    fossil record as history of, 8
    history of, as evolutionary tree, 263

hypothesis testing in everyday, 10
interactions of organisms with environments, 5
macroevolution as history of, 297 (*see also* Macroevolution)
microbial (*see* Microbes; Microbial genetics; Prokaryotes; Protists; Viruses)
physical and chemical factors influencing, in biosphere, 682
sensitivity of, to acidic and basic conditions, 28
spontaneous formation of plasma membranes in origin of, 75
themes in study of, 2–5
three-domain system of classifying, 6–7
unity of, based on DNA and genetic code, 6
water and search for extraterrestrial, 29
water as requirement for, 17 (*see also* Water)
water as solvent of, 27
Life cycles, **137**
    fungal, 356, 358
    human, 137*f*
Life cycles, plant, 346–54
    alternation of generations in, 343, 346, 635
    angiosperm, 634*f*, 635
    angiosperms as sporophytes with gametophytes in flowers, 350–54
    gametophyte domination in moss, 346–47
    origin of fossil fuels in ancient forests of seedless vascular plants, 348
    pine trees as sporophytes with gametophytes in cones, 348–49
    sporophyte domination in fern and other, 347
Life histories, **730–31**
Lifestyle choices, cancer and, 227
Life tables, **725**
Lifetime immunity, 492–93
Ligaments, 417, **611**
Light. *See also* Solar energy; Sunlight
    detection of, by electromagnetic receptors, 591
    plant guard cells and, 647
    plant phototropism, auxins, and, 662–63, 670
    prokaryote nutrition and, 323
    setting of plant biological clocks by phytochromes as detectors of, 673
    vision and, 595–98
Light-harvesting complexes, 113
Light microscope (LM), **52–53**
Lightning, 295
Light reactions, **111–15**. *See also* Photosynthesis
    absorption of visible radiation by pigments in, 112
    ATP and NADPH synthesis by photosystems in, 114
    ATP synthesis by chemiosmosis in, 115
    capture of solar energy by, 113
    overview of links between Calvin cycle and, 111, 118
Lignin, 68, **343**, 357, 628
Lignum vitae, 633
Limb buds, 556
Limbic system, 579, **581**
Limbs, tetrapod, 390, 396, 553, 603
Limiting factors, **726**–27, 728
Linkage maps, **174**, 249
Linked genes, **172**
Linkers, DNA, 212
Linnaeus, Carolus, 308–9
Linoleic acid, 443
Lions, 517, 529
Lipase, 438*t*–39
Lipids, 36, **40–41**, 74. *See also* Fats
Liquid matter, 18
Liquid water, 26–27. *See also* Water
Liver, 433, **438**, 440, 445, 615
Liver cancer, 498
Liverworts, 344
Living fossil, 378
Lizards, 397

in HIV strains, 499
humans as agents of, 12
for human skin color, 407
life histories and, 730–31
limitations of, 273
as mechanism for microevolution, 268
as only mechanism for adaptive
evolution, 269
scientific observations of, 259
Nature reserves, 772
Nature vs. nurture issue, 719
Neanderthals, 250, 405–6
Nearsightedness, **597**
Near vision, 596*f*
Nectar, 353
Negative feedback, **426**, 436–37, 480. *See also*
Feedback regulation; Homeostasis
Negative ions, 652
Negative pressure breathing, **460**–61
Neisseria gonorrheae, 321, 485
Neisseria meningitides, 328
Nematodes (Nematoda), **373**, 743
Nephrons, **511**–13
Nerve cells. *See* Neurons
Nerve cords, 383, **572**
Nerve gases, 85
Nerve nets, **572**
Nerves, **564**, 573
Nerve signals, 566–71
as charge differences across neuron
membranes, 566
chemical synapses and, 570
drugs acting at chemical synapses and, 571
electrical signals as, 518
neuron communication at synapses and, 569
neurotransmitters as variety of small
molecules, 570–71
propagation of action potentials along
axons as, 568
transmission process of, as change in
membrane potential and generation
of action potentials, 566–67
Nervous systems, **421**, 562–63, **564**–85
coupling of stimulus and response by central
nervous system, 600
electrical signals of, 518
evolution of, and changes in body
symmetry, 572
human brain in human, 576–83
hypothalamus and pituitary gland as
connections between endocrine
systems and, 522–23
nerve signals and signal transmission in,
566–71
overview of, 572–76
spinal cord and spinal cord injuries of
human, 563
structure and function of, 564–65
vertebrate, as highly centralized, 573
vertebrate brain development from three
anterior bulges of neural tube in, 576
vertebrate peripheral, as functional
hierarchy in, 574–75
Nervous tissue, **418**
Nests, 311
Net primary production, 750–51
Networks, nervous tissue, 418
Neural plate and neural folds, 550
Neural tubes, 165, 446, **550**–51, 576
Neurofibrillary tangles, 583
Neurological disorders, human, 582–83
Neurons, **418**, **564**
communication of, at synapses, 569
as functional units of nervous systems, 565
nerve signals as charge differences across
membranes of, 566
neurotransmitters and, 518

sensory receptors as specialized, 588–91
stimulation of muscle contraction by
motor, 614–15
Neurophysiologists, 579
Neurosecretory cells, **518**, 522–23
Neurospora crassa, 190
Neurosurgery, 579
Neurotransmitters, **569**
as chemical signals, 518, 569–70
small molecules functioning as,
570–71
stress and, 501
Neutralization, antigen, 495
Neutral solutions, 28
Neutrons, **20**
Neutrophils, 479, 485–**86**
Newborn screening, 165
New Orleans, 643
New World monkeys, 401, 408
New York City, 762
Niacin, 445
Niall of the Nine Hostages, 177
Nicotine, 62, 571, 742
Night blindness, 598
Night length, plant photoperiods and, 672
Nirenberg, Marshall, 192
Nitrate ions, 651, 655
Nitric acid precipitation, 755
Nitric oxide, 571
Nitrifying bacteria, 655–56
Nitrogen, 320, 651, 653, 756
Nitrogen cycle, 754–55
Nitrogen fixation, 327, **655**–56, **754**–55
Nitrogenous bases, 46–47, 184
Nitrogenous waste disposal, animal, 509.
See also Excretion; Urinary systems
Nitrogen oxides, 29, 695, 755
Nitrosomonas, 327
Nitrous oxide, 755, 766, 767
Nodes, 311, **624**
Nodes of Ranvier, **565**
Noncoding DNA, 194, 248
Noncompetitive inhibitors, **85**
Nondisjunctions, **146**
Nongonococcol urethritis, 327
Non-native species, 749
Nonpolar covalent bonds, **23**
Non-protein-coding RNAs, 215. *See also* RNA
(ribonucleic acid)
Nonself molecules, **497**
Nonsense mutations, **199**
Nonvascular plants, 344
Norepinephrine (noradrenaline), 521*t*, **528**,
571, 575
Nori, 336
North American prairie, 692
North Star, migration and, 707
Norway rats, 702–3
Nostrils, 458
Notochords, **383**, **550**
Novelties, evolutionary, 306
N-P-K ratio, fertilizer, 651
Nuclear envelope, **58**
Nucleariids, 337
Nuclear transplantation, **222**
Nucleases, 438*t*–39
Nucleic acid probes, **236**
Nucleic acids, **46**–47. *See also* DNA
(deoxyribonucleic acid); RNA
(ribonucleic acid)
DNA and RNA as, 46, 184–85
enzymatic digestion of, 438–39
in food processing, 431
life and, 36
as polymers of nucleotides, 46–47

recent human evolution of lactose tolerance
and, 47
Nucleoid, **55**
Nucleolus, **58**
Nucleosomes, **212**
Nucleotides, **46**, **184**
DNA and RNA as polymers of, 36, 184–85
in food processing, 431
molecular clocks and, 313
nucleic acids as polymers of, 46–47
triplet genetic code of codons of, 191–92
Nucleus (nuclei), **20**, **58**
in atomic composition, 20
as characteristic of eukaryotic cells, 4, 55, 56
DNA and RNA in, 46
as eukaryotic cell genetic control center,
58, 69*t*
Nurture vs. nature issue, 719
Nuthatches, 709
Nutrient runoff, 756–57
Nutrients
as abiotic factor for life in biosphere, 682
cycling of, in ecosystems, 5, 750, 752–56
degradation of aquatic ecosystems by
inflow of, 756
essential, for animal diet, 442–43 (*see also*
Absorption; Diet; Food; Nutrition,
animal)
food labels for human, 446 (*see also* Nutrition,
human)
as important abiotic factor in freshwater
biomes, 688
Nutrients, plant, 650–55. *See also* Nutrition, plant
acquisition of, from air, water, and soil,
342–43, 644
agricultural research on, to improve yields and
nutritional value of crops, 654–55
fertilizers to prevent deficiencies in, 651
organic farming, sustainable agriculture,
and, 654
plant health and complete diet of essential
inorganic, 650
soil and, 650–55 (*see also* Soil)
soil conservation as essential for, and essential
to human life, 653
support of plant growth by, in fertile soil, 652
symbiosis and, 655–57
Nutrition, animal, 428–51. *See also* Nutrition,
human
digestion in specialized compartments
for, 432
essential nutrients in diets in, 443
four stages of food processing for, 431
modes for obtaining and ingesting food
for, 430
powering of bodies by chemical energy
from, 442
three requirements of diets in, 442
Nutrition, human. *See also* Nutrition, animal
agricultural research to improve value of
crops for, 654–55
dietary risk factors for cardiovascular disease
and cancer in, 449
effects of, on phenotypic characters, 170
genetically modified and transgenic
organisms and, 239
health risks and benefits of weight loss
plans in, 448
human digestive system and, 433–41
(*see also* Digestive systems)
nutritional information on food labels
for, 446
obesity crisis and, 429, 447
scientific observations and experiments
to determine needs of, 446
vitamins and essential minerals in healthy diets
in, 444–45

Sexual selection, **271**, 284
Shape
    animal, as result of natural selection, 415
    antigen and antibody, 491
    enzyme, 84
    focusing of human eyes by changing position
        and, 596
    prokaryotic cell, 320–21
    protein, 43–45*f*
Shared ancestral characters, **310**
Shared derived characters, **310**
Shared resources, interspecific competition
    for, 741
Sharks, 392, 415, 507, 588, 607
Sheep, 209, 222
Shivering, 506
Shock, 501
Shoots. *See also* Flowers; Leaves; Stems
    modified, 625
    phototropism and, 662–63
    primary growth of, 631
    shoot systems and, 624
    stimulation of elongation of cells in young, by
        auxins, 664–65
Shoot systems, **624**
Short-day plants, **672**
Shortgrass prairies, 692
Short tandem repeats (STRs), **244**
Short-term memory, **581**
Shotgun cloning, 234
Shrimp, 282, 365, 379
Shrubs, chaparral and spiny, 692
Siamese fighting fish, 716
Siberian tigers, 761, 770
Sickle-cell disease, 162*t*, 164, **168**,
    199, 272–73
Side chains, protein, 42
Sieve plate, **629**
Sieve-tube elements, **629**, 648–49
Signaling mechanisms, hormonal, 519
Signal proteins, 43
Signals, communication, **711**
Signals, nerve. *See* Nerve signals
Signal transduction pathways, **220**
    in cell cycle control systems, 134
    in cell-to-cell signaling and gene
        regulation, 220
    in hormonal signaling, 519
    interference with, by faulty proteins
        in cancer, 226
    in plant growth and development, 664
    plasma membranes and, 74
    in sensory reception, 588–89
Silencers, **214**
Silent mutations, **199**
Silent Spring (book), 681
Silt, 695
Silverswords, 770
Simple epithelium, 416
Simpson, O. J., 245
Single bonds, 23
Single-celled organisms, origin of, 297
Single circulation, **469**
Single-gene human disorders, 162–63
Single-gene human traits, 161
Single-lens eyes, **595**
Single nucleotide polymorphisms
    (SNPs), **246**
Sinoatrial (SA) node. *See* SA
    (sinoatrial) node
Sister chromatids, **128**, 137–39
Sixth mass extinction, 303
Size
    animal, as result of natural selection, 415
    cell, 4, 52, 54–55, 320
    sorting DNA by, using gel electrophoresis in
        DNA profiling, 243

Skeletal muscle, **418**, 611–16
    contractile apparatus of each cell of, 612
    contraction of, when thin filaments slide across
        thick filaments, 612–13
    effects on athletic performance of
        characteristics of fibers of, 616
    horse movement and, 603
    interaction of skeletons and, in movement, 611
    motor neuron stimulation of contraction of,
        614–15
    motor system and, 574
    muscle tissue of, 418
    skeletal systems and, 420
    supply to, of energy for exercise by aerobic
        respiration, 615
Skeletal systems, **420**. *See also* Skeletal muscle;
    Skeletons
Skeletons, 606–11
    bones as complex living organs of, 609
    evolution of, as variations on ancient theme,
        608–9
    horse movement and, 603
    interaction of muscles and, in movement, 611
    resistance to stress and healing from injuries of
        bones of, 610
    skeletal systems and, 420
    types of, 606–7
    types of joints of, for different types of
        movement, 611
    vertebrate, 608–11*f*
Skeletons, carbon, 34*f*
Skill memories, 581
Skin
    amphibian, 396
    artificial, 419
    as barrier to pathogens, 486
    colors of human, as adaptations to sunlight,
        170, 407
    epithelium tissue in animal, 416
    integumentary systems and, 423
    reptilian, 397
    as respiratory organ, 454–55
    sensory receptors in human, 590*f*
    spiny, of echinoderms, 382
    structure and functions of, 423
    thermoregulation and blood flow to, 507
Skin cancer, 120, 227, 499, 764
Skulls, 304–5, 390, 403–5, 608
Skunks, 280
Sleep, 571, 580
Sleeping sickness, 335
Sleep-wake circadian rhythms, 520–21*t*
Sliding-filament model of muscle
    contraction, 612–13
Slime molds, 335
Slow-twitch muscle fibers, 616
Sludge, 324
Slugs, 374
Small intestines, 419, 433, **438–39**
Smallpox, 238, 489
Small RNAs, 215
Smart plants, 653
Smell, 599
Smithells, Richard, 446
Smith's litter frog, 408*f*
Smoking
    as cancer risk factor, 227
    as cardiovascular disease risk factor, 473
    effects of, on DNA, 189
    effects of, on fetuses during pregnancy, 463, 555
    effects of, on lungs, 459–60
    effects of, on windpipe cilia, 66
    as hypertension risk factor, 477
    as osteoporosis risk factor, 610
Smooth endoplasmic reticulum (ER), 59, **60**, 69*t*
Smooth muscle, **418**, 477
Smuts, 357, 359

Snails, 281, 374
Snakes, 397, 591, 608–9, 763
Snapping shrimp, 282
Snowshoe hare populations, 729
Snowy owls, 682*f*
SNPs. *See* Single nucleotide polymorphisms
    (SNPs)
Social behavior, **715–19**
    concept of inclusive fitness as explanation
        of altruistic, 717
    human, as result of genetic and environmental
        factors, 719
    insights into chimpanzee, by Jane Goodall, 718
    maintenance of dominance hierarchies by
        agonistic, 716
    parceling out of space and resources by
        territorial, 715
    resolution of confrontations between
        competitors by agonistic, 716
    sociobiology as study of, in evolutionary
        context, 715
Social learning, 703*t*, **708–9**
Society
    age structures and trends of, 734
    biology, technology and, 12
    science and, 11
Sociobiology, **715**, 719. *See also* Social behavior
Sodium, 445
Sodium chloride, 18*f*, 24, 512
Sodium hydroxide, 28
Sodium-potassium (Na-K) pumps, 78, 512,
    566–68
Soil
    agriculture and degradation of, 757
    bioremediation of contaminated, by
        sunflowers, 643
    conservation of, as essential to human life, 653
    nitrogen cycle and, 754–55
    plant acquisition of nutrients from, 342–43,
        644 (*see also* Nutrients, plant)
    secondary succession and, 748
    support of plant growth by fertile topsoil, 652
Solar energy. *See also* Sunlight
    as biosphere energy source, 682
    capture of, by photosystems in photosynthesis,
        113
    climate and seasons from uneven distribution
        of, 684–85
    conversion of, to chemical energy by
        photosynthesis, 64, 111, 118 (*see also*
        Photosynthesis)
    ecosystem energy flow and, 750
    sunlight as electromagnetic, 112
Solid matter, 18
Solid water. *See* Ice
Solomon, Susan, 120
Solutes, **27**, 75–78, 645. *See also* Osmoregulation
Solutions, **27–28**, 76–77
Solvents, **27**, 76. *See also* Water
Somatic cells, **136**, 148. *See also* Bodies, animal
Somatosensory cortex, 578
Somites, 551, 556, 608–9
Songbirds, 286, 704. *See also* Birds
Sound
    detection of, by hair cells as
        mechanoreceptors, 590–91*f*
    hearing as conversion of air pressure waves to
        action potentials by ears and perceived
        as, 592–93
    as signals, 711
Sour tastes, 599
Southeast Asia, 408
Sow bugs, 706
Soybeans, 661
Space, territorial behavior and, 715
Space-filling models, 23
Spatial learning, 703*t*, **706**